Pre-Algebra

Sixth Edition

Supplemented with:

- Multimedia Electronic Lecture Notes for Teachers.
- Multimedia Tutorial for Students
- On-line Testing and Practice Testing
- Several Technology Tools to support instructions including:
  - ✓ On-line grade book for faculty and progress reports for students
  - ✓ On-line student survey and reports
  - ✓ Student activity reports
  - ✓ Solution manuals

Man M. Sharma
Clark Atlanta University

Roxann King
Prince George Community College

Asha Mittal
Kirori Mal College

Educo International Inc.
1-800-963-3826

ACKNOWLEDGEMENTS

Managing Editor

Madan G. Chopra, Educo International Inc.

Editors

Brenda Teal, Prince George's Community College, MD

Regina Bentley, Prince George's Community College, MD

Peter Speier, Prince George's Community College, MD

Trudy Meyer, El Camino College, CA

Production Services

Educo International, Inc.

Desktop Publishing

Sunita Verma and Ramesh Thomas

Educo International, Inc.

Evaluators

The following persons have made significant contributions to this edition of the book. The authors express their sincerest thanks for suggestions, evaluation, and preparation of support materials to:

Steven Castillo	Los Angeles Valley College, CA
Diana Moore	El Centro College, Dallas, TX
Lynda Little	Antelope Valley College, CA
Raymond Badalian	Los Angeles City College, CA
Angel Rivera	University of Turabo, PR
Rudy Johnson	Central State University, OH
Sayku Waritay	Livingston College, NC
Mary Bradley	South Western Community College, NC
Howard Speier	Chandler Gilbert College, AZ

The production of this book and support materials would not have been possible without the encouragement and contributions of faculty members from institutions in the United States, and Puerto Rico.

Partial funding for developing some of the technology supplements was provided by a grant from the **U.S. Department of Education (Grant #P120A020110)**.

ISBN: 978-1-888469-91-2

Printed at: Replika Press Pvt. Ltd.

PREFACE

This textbook is written for college students who need to review the prerequisite for any beginning algebra course. It is written with students in mind, using simple language, highlighted key words, and a step-by-step approach. Each chapter section is divided into logically arranged objectives. Each objective has:

- **discussion** leading to the statement of rules and procedures.
- **examples** showing step-by-step procedures. Each example, in the electronic version of this book, has several randomly generated versions.
- **margin exercises**, found in the margin near each example, to be used as warm up exercises.

Each **section ends** with a set of exercises for each of the objectives. Each **chapter ends** with the **chapter summary, review exercise,** and a **self test.** The chapter summary provides definitions of key words or phrases, rules and procedures, and worked-out margin examples in the margin for each rule or procedure.

This book is supplemented with an electronic version, that can be accessed from the web by faculty as lecture notes and by students as tutorials. The electronic version of the book is 100% compatible with this printed textbook and has the advantage of dynamic graphics, pedagogically sound animations, and visually appealing screen designs with attractive color combinations. As a tutorial for students, the electronic version provides an effective tool that is highly interactive and engaging. The electronic version can also be used for online teaching.

Highlights of Contents:

The textbook contains eleven chapters. The chapter topics are listed in the Table of Contents.

TECHNOLOGY SUPPORT

One of the **most useful features** of this book is the technology support to students in the form of tutorials, practice tests, instructor-created online quizzes and tests, and instant progress reports. These features are described below in more detail. **All technology components are provided through Macromedia Flash and HTML, delivered through the web and requiring no special installations**. These features are described below in more detail.

A. Multimedia Electronic Lecture Notes (ELN) for Instructors and Tutorials for Students

- Tutorials with examples are embedded with dynamic graphics, animations, and step by step solutions.

- Vivid screen designs and animations make the presentation of topics clearer, as documented by students and instructors in several pilot studies.

- The ELN for instructors are designed to enhance interactivity with students, affording instructors minimal writing and drawing and more emphasis on class discussion.

- The ELN, which can be used in class to supplement conventional teaching, are available to students as tutorials from the web for self study, from anywhere at anytime. Each example in the tutorial has several versions generated by randomized parameters. The student can see the solution to the first version, and then click the 'Next Version' to attempt similar exercises.

- The Tutorials feature has built-in diagnostics and several other learning activities to help in learning the concepts.

B. Practice tests

- These pre-created tests, one for each section of all chapters, are available to reinforce the concepts learned in the Tutorials.

- Each practice test has several sets of questions with step-by-step solutions. Students may choose one set with solutions, and another set without solutions.

- All practice tests contain only Free Response questions.

C. Homework on the Internet with Embedded Tutorial

- Different types of free response questions, with several variations for each question, are used to create online homework. Instructors can create the homework using a large question bank of free response questions, provided by the system, or just assign the pre-created homework.

- Each student gets a different set of questions, with tutorial type assistance, a solution to the first variation, and feedback for other variations, with the option to change the answer. Students can complete the assignment in multiple sessions.

- Homework is instantly graded by the system and scores are transferred automatically to the grade book.

- Students can print the graded homework report.

D. Quizzes/Tests on Internet (Free-Response, or Multiple-Choice or Mixed)

- Responses to test questions may be entered from the keyboard, or through a **small online keypad using the mouse**.

- The keypad contains mathematical symbols needed for the responses to enter the item being attempted. After every quiz, students get instant feedback on their score. They can see step-by-step solutions, go to practice mode with an embedded tutorial, or take the quiz over again, if allowed by the instructor.

- There will be no loss of work done by the students if during a test or homework sessions the power goes off, the web connection is lost, or the student closes Test/Assignment window improperly.

- The work completed at the time of disconnect will be considered work submitted and the rest of the work can be completed in a new login session.

- A large question bank of , both Multiple Choice and Free Response, is available for each objective of the content for web based testing and practice testing.

- A browser based math editor is available to instructors to add their own questions to the quizzes or tests.

- An easy-to-use online test generator, is available to instructors to create online quizzes/tests, to print multiple versions of class test with answer keys, or to generate and administer online tests.

- The test generator provides several options to instructors to deliver tests and homework to students in several test modes: with or without feedback, with or without solutions, single or multiple sessions, graded or just for practice, and several more.

- Instructors may allow students to take quizzes more than once, from anywhere at any time, and every time the quiz is different, covering similar types of items.

- For every graded test created by the instructors, the system generates online practice tests for students. Items for these practice tests are selected by the system and cover the objectives selected by the instructor for the graded test. The system provides different sets of items for every practice test session.

- Instructors may print multiple versions of quizzes or tests along with answer keys.

- Instructors may conduct proctored major tests, password-protected, in local computer labs, or print the tests and transfer the scores to the online graded book

E. Test Your Skill Activity (TYS)

- This activity, one for each section of all chapters is available to test the speed and accuracy with which a student can complete a set of questions.

- Students can set their own time limit, and select their own attempt mode (with or without feedback).

- Each TYS activity contains several sets of 10 to 30 questions. Students can attempt various sets with different time limits to increase their speed, or develop quick reflexes for completing the problems.

F. Activity Reports

- Instructors can view/print student activity reports at any time. These provide detailed information on time spent by students on each activity.

- There is an enhanced electronic grade book (online) with several unique features including; direct transfer of scores to the grade book, and **individualized progress reports for students**.

G. Internal E-mail

- Instructors can compile e-mails using the system's full function e-mail editor: bolding, underlining, bulleting, and attachment. There are multiple target audiences:

  - Students to instructor or classmates.
  - Instructor to students (of a section, a course, or all courses).
  - Campus coordinator to instructors, students, Educo.

H. Several other Communication Tools

- **Announcements**

  - Faculty to his/her students.
  - Campus coordinator to Instructors, students of a section/course or to all.
  - Educo to different groups of users.

- **Chat, threaded discussion, group discussions**

To the students:

We sincerely hope that the approaches followed in this book with several options of technology support will help you better prepare for your next course in mathematics.

To the instructors:

The authors would appreciate any suggestion for improvement in any component of this package, either for the presentation of the textbook or its support materials on the web. Suggestions can be forwarded through **Contact us** link on the login page.

Man M. Sharma

Roxmann King

TABLE OF CONTENTS

Sample Screens

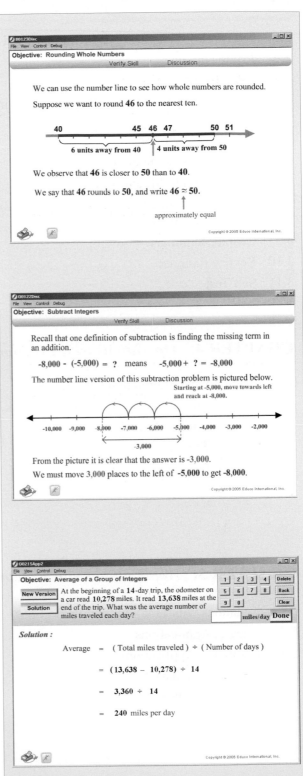

TABLE OF CONTENTS

Sample Screens

CHAPTER 3: *Introduction to Rational Numbers*

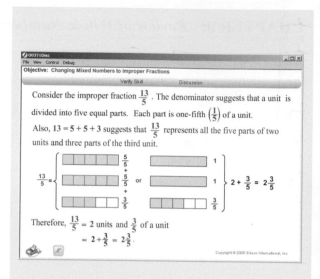

CHAPTER 4: *Operations with Fractions*

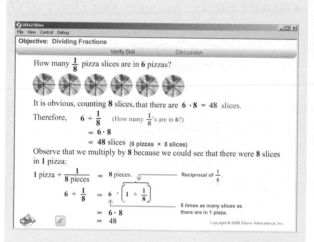

CHAPTER 5: *Applications with Fractions*

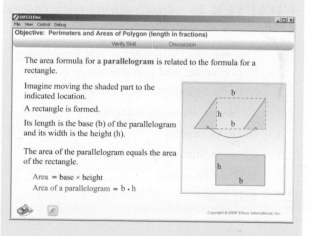

TABLE OF CONTENTS

Sample Screens

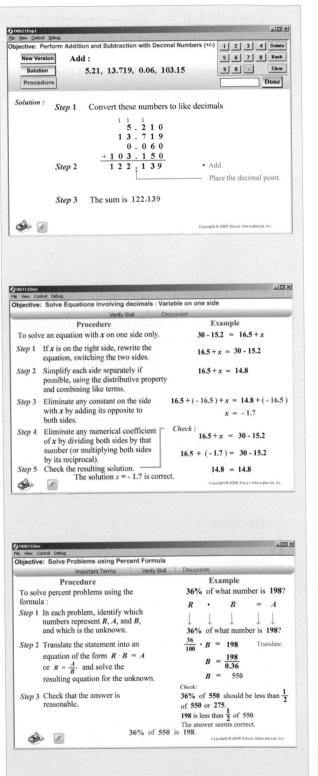

TABLE OF CONTENTS

CHAPTER 9: *Basic Statistics, Plotting Points and Lines*

CHAPTER 10: *Measurements*

Sample Screens

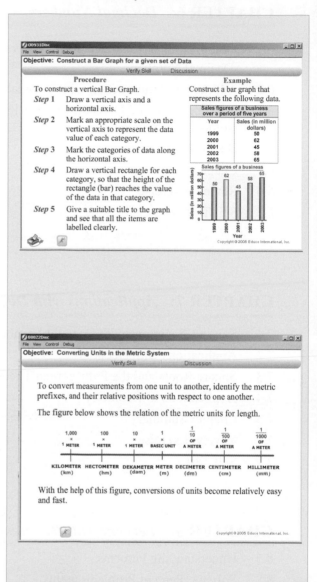

Review of Whole Numbers

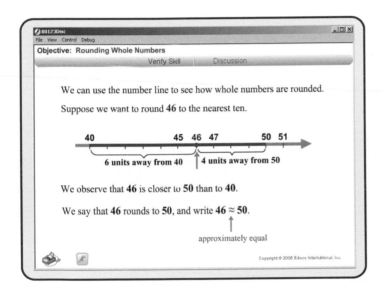

Review of Whole Numbers

REVIEW OF WHOLE NUMBERS

Introduction

In this chapter, we will review the place value system for whole numbers, review the basic operations (addition, subtraction, multiplication, and division), and discuss other concepts such as the number line, and rounding off numbers.

This chapter is divided into three sections:

0.1   *Place Value System: A Quick Review;*

0.2   *Number Lines, Inequality Symbols, and Rounding Whole Numbers; and*

0.3   *Fundamental Operations with Whole Numbers.*

0.1   PLACE VALUE SYSTEM: A QUICK REVIEW

IMPORTANT VOCABULARY

1. A **set** is a collection of objects. The objects belonging to a set are its **members** or **elements.**

2. The **natural numbers** or **counting numbers** are the set {1, 2, 3, 4, ...}. There are as many natural numbers as we need. There is no **last** natural number. The smallest natural number is 1.

3. The **whole numbers** include all the natural numbers and the number *zero* (0). The set {**0**, 1, 2, 3, 4, ...} is the set of whole numbers. The number 0 is the smallest whole number. The only whole number which is not a natural number is 0.

4. Numbers of the type 0, 1, 2, 45, and 117 are called **numerals.**

5. The ten numerals 0, 1, 2, 3, 4, 5, 6, 7, 8, and 9 are called **digits.**

6. **Word names** are the spoken or written words used when reading numbers.
    The word name for 45 is forty-five; and for 345, three hundred forty-five.

> Objectives
>
> After completing this section you will be able to:
>
> A. Find the place value of a digit or identify a digit with a given place value; and
>
> B. Write a whole number in words or write the word name of a number as a numeral.

0.1 A.   Place value of a digit

•   Each digit in a numeral has a **place value** determined by its position.

   For the number 347:   **7** is in the position having the place value **ones,**

                             4 is in the position having the place value **tens,**

                 and   **3** is in the position having the place value **hundreds.**

•   When reading or writing *large* numbers, the digits are grouped (from right to left) into groups of three, which are separated by a comma. For example, the number 725931680 is written as 725,931,680.

- From right to left, the first five groups are called **ones**, **thousands**, **millions**, **billions**, and **trillions**. Each digit within a group contains the *place values* ones, tens, and hundreds.

Trillions Group			Billions Group			Millions Group			Thousands Group			Ones Group		
HUNDREDS	TENS	ONES	HUNDREDS	TENS	ONES	HUNDREDS	TENS	ONES	HUNDREDS	TENS	ONES	HUNDREDS	TENS	ONES

Figure 0.1 7 000500

The group on the extreme left, *may* have one, two, or three digits, but all the other groups *must* have three digits.

For example,

in	**7**,251,394	the group on the left has *one* digit;
in	**54**,389	the group on the left has *two* digits; and
in	**131**,702	the group on the left has *three* digits.

- The place value of a digit in the *ones group* is ones, tens, or hundreds.

- The place value of a digit in any *other* group is ones, tens, or hundreds, followed by the group name.

Consider the numeral 39,625,173,480 =   3 9 ,   6 2 5 ,   1 7 3 ,   4 8 0

Group Names →   **Billions   Millions   Thousands   Ones**

The digit **2** in the millions group has a place value of two ten millions (20,000,000).

The digit in the hundred thousands place is 1. It has a place value of 1 hundred thousand (100,000).

> ◁ Note ▷ We often refer to a number such as 1,500 as 15 hundred rather than by individual place values 1 thousand 5 hundred. Grouping place values is an alternative way to understand numbers. 1,500 can also be expressed as 150 tens or 1500 ones.

Warm-Up

1. Determine the place value of the indicated digits in 18,705,243.

   (a) 7

   (b) 4

Example 1 Determine the place value of the following digits in 57,932.

(a) 5   (b) 9

Solutions

(a)

Thousands Ones ← Group Names

5 7, 9 3 2

↑

Ten thousands ← Position followed by group name

The place value of the digit 5 is **ten thousand.**

(b)

Thousands Ones ← Group Names

5 7, 9 3 2 ← 9 is in the hundreds place in the ones group.

↑

Hundreds   The group name ones is not stated.

The place value of the digit 9 is **hundred.**

Example 2 Identify the digit in the:

  (a) thousands place in 378,925; and

  (b) ten millions place in 92,456,821.

Solutions

  (a)   Thousands place in 378,925

  (Note that thousands place means one thousands place.)

Group names ⟶ Thousands   Ones

$$\overbrace{3\ 7\ 8},\ \overbrace{9\ 2\ 5}$$

↑

One thousands place

The digit in the thousands place is **8**.

  (b)   Ten millions place in 92,456,821

Millions Thousands   Ones

$$\overbrace{9\ 2},\ \overbrace{4\ 5\ 6},\ \overbrace{8\ 2\ 1}$$

The millions group is the third group.

92,456,821

↑

ten millions place ⟵·············· Position followed by group name.

The digit in the ten millions place is **9**.

0.1 B.   Word Name for a Numeral

• Word names can be spoken or written to indicate the actual numbers.

  The word names of some 2-digit and 3-digit numbers are written below:

The Number	Word Name
85	Eighty-five
40	Forty
19	Nineteen
43	Forty-three
275	Two hundred seventy-five
308	Three hundred eight
999	Nine hundred ninety-nine

• It is **not** correct to read 275 as two hundred **and** seventy-five.

  ⚠ **Caution:** | Do not use "**and**" when reading or writing a whole number.
  The word **and** is used for a decimal point in a decimal number.

• To write the word name for a number with more than three digits, we begin with the *left-most* group and write the word name followed by its group name. Repeat the same step for all the groups (from left to right), separating them by commas. Do not write the group name "ones".

3

For example, to write the word name of the number 27,502,375, we proceed as in the following table:

Place value name for group (from left to right)	27	502	375
Word name for group	twenty-seven	five hundred two	three hundred seventy-five
Group name	↓ Millions	↓ Thousands	↓

The word name of 27,502,375 is:

Twenty-seven million, five hundred two thousand, three hundred seventy-five.

- To write the numeral for the word name, write the numeral for each group from left to right inserting a comma before beginning the next group. For example, the numeral for:

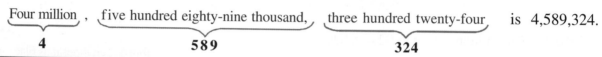

Four million , five hundred eighty-nine thousand, three hundred twenty-four is 4,589,324.

4   5 8 9   3 2 4

Warm-Up

3. (a) Write the word name for:

(i) 67,799

(ii) 351,006

(b) Write the numeral for the word name:

One million, forty-five thousand, eighty-two.

Answers:

3. (a) (i) Sixty-seven thousand, seven hundred ninety-nine.

(ii) Three hundred fifty-one thousand, six.

(b) 1,045,082

Example 3   **(a)** Write the word name for 73,458,695.

           (b) Write the numeral for the word name:

Three million, sixty-seven thousand, nine hundred thirty-two.

Solutions

(a)   The steps of the procedure are demonstrated below:

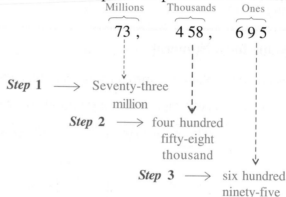

Millions   Thousands   Ones

73 ,   4 5 8 ,   6 9 5

Step 1 ⟶ Seventy-three million

Step 2 ⟶ four hundred fifty-eight thousand

Step 3 ⟶ six hundred ninety-five

The word name is:

Seventy-three million, four hundred fifty-eight thousand, six hundred ninety-five.

(b) Three million, sixty-seven thousand, nine hundred thirty-two.

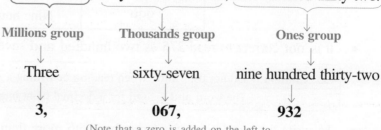

Millions group	Thousands group	Ones group
↓	↓	↓
Three	sixty-seven	nine hundred thirty-two
↓	↓	↓
3,	**067,**	**932**

(Note that a zero is added on the left to fill out the third place in the group.)

The numeral is **3,067,932**.

Exercise 0.1

A. In exercises 1-10, determine the place value of 7.

1. 3,670
2. 85,742
3. 9,472
4. 70,936
5. 400,700
6. 7,000,500
7. 57,932
8. 5,982,763,210
9. 87,052,100,455,000
10. 56,789,002,331,345

In exercises 11-20, identify the digit in the hundreds place.

11. 4,792
12. 1,029
13. 4,938
14. 6,812
15. 763,210
16. 60,039
17. 27,531
18. 25,105
19. 87,396
20. 111,220

In exercises 21-32, identify the digit in the ten millions place.

21. 14,668,394,250
22. 561,072,001
23. 45,900,130
24. 187,325,004
25. 106,218,987
26. 39,444,150
27. 735,008,126
28. 56,789,002,331
29. 6,580,256,000
30. 947,385,178
31. 56,892,430
32. 5,187,143,000

B. In exercises 33-46, write the word name.

33. 538
34. 530
35. 5,622
36. 13,084
37. 10,815
38. 72,039
39. 8,888
40. 2,229
41. 46,208
42. 15,872
43. 703,109
44. 6,597
45. 1,235,956
46. 4,580,000,250

In exercises 47-53, write the numeral for the word name.

47. Seventy thousand, five hundred ninety-nine.
48. Fifty-two thousand, six hundred fifty-two.
49. Nine hundred twenty-five.
50. One hundred fifty million, forty thousand, thirty-one.
51. Thirty-four thousand, nine hundred ten.
52. Thirty-two million, twenty-seven thousand, nine hundred ten.
53. One hundred fifteen billion, three hundred million, four hundred thousand, sixty-five.
54. Rewrite the numeral 27,531 interchanging the digits in the thousands and the ones places.
55. Rewrite the numeral 8,956,200 interchanging the digits in the tens and the hundred thousands places.

Applications

56. Elena buys a new dress for $575. What word name should she write on the check?

57. The author of a book on mathematics received $12,750 as royalties from the publisher for the year 2003. Write the word name for the amount received.

58. Red Lion Inns earned ten million, six hundred fifty-eight thousand, five hundred dollars during the first quarter of 2004. Write the numeral representing the earnings of Red Lion Inns.

59. The officials for Power Ball, an interstate lottery game, estimate the prize money for the next drawing to be thirty-one million, six hundred fifty thousand dollars. Write the numeral for the prize.

60. The total land area of the earth is approximately 52,425,000 square miles. Write the word name for the area.

0.2 NUMBER LINE, INEQUALITY SYMBOLS, AND ROUNDING WHOLE NUMBERS

Objectives

After completing this section, you will be able to:

A. Draw and use a number line;

B. Compare two whole numbers; and

C. Round a whole number to a given place.

IMPORTANT VOCABULARY

1. A **number line** is a line on which the numbers are represented by points.

2. The **graph** of a number is the point on a number line that corresponds to that number.

3. The symbol for equality "**=**" is read "is equal to".

4. **Inequality symbols** are symbols that are used to express a relationship between two numbers.

   The symbol $\neq$ is read "is not equal to".

   The symbol $<$ is read "is less than"; the symbol $>$ is read "is greater than".

   The symbol $\leq$ is read "is less than or equal to".

   The symbol $\geq$ is read "is greater than or equal to".

5. To **round** a whole number means to give an approximate value to a given rounding place. The number 457,249 rounded to the nearest tens place is 457,250. We write

   $$457,249 \approx 457,250 \quad \text{to the nearest ten.}$$

   The symbol $\approx$ is read *approximately equal to*.

0.2 A.   Drawing and Using a Number Line

A **Number Line** is a line on which numbers are represented by points. The whole numbers can be represented by points on a number line as follows:

Draw a line and mark a point on it. Label this point with the number 0 (Figure 0.2).

Figure 0.2

Beginning with 0, make marks to the right of 0, at equal intervals and label them by the numbers 1, 2, 3, 4, ... as shown in Figure 0.3. The arrow means that the numbers continue forever.

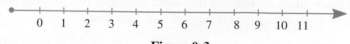

Figure 0.3

- We generally use horizontal and vertical lines for number lines. Figure 0.3 shows a horizontal number line and Figure 0.4 demonstrates a vertical number line. Note that on a vertical number line, the points for 1, 2, 3, ... are marked *above* the point for zero.

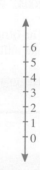

Figure 0.4

- The graph of a number is the point on a number line that corresponds to that number. The graphs of numbers from the set {1, 3, 7, 8, 11} are indicated by dots, as shown in Figure 0.5.

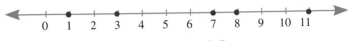

Figure 0.5

 Note It will be seen in later chapters that there are many types of numbers, besides whole numbers (such as integers, fractions, decimal numbers), that can be graphed on number lines.

Example 1   (a) Graph the set X = {2, 6, 10, 7, 4}.

(b) Graph all whole numbers less than 5.

Solutions

(a) Draw a number line and show the points corresponding to the numbers 2, 6, 10, 7, 4 by dots.

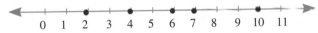

This represents the graph of X = {2, 6, 10, 7, 4}.

(b) Draw a number line. Numbers less than 5 all lie to the left of 5. Show these by dots.

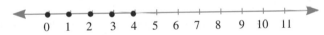

This represents the graph of all whole numbers less than 5.

Warm-Up

1. (a) Graph the set A = {2, 0, 5, 9, 1}

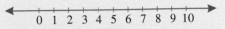

(b) Graph all whole numbers that are greater than 2 but less than 7.

(*Hint:* Graph all numbers between 2 and 7.)

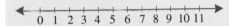

Answers:

1. (a)
(b)

0.2 B.   Comparing Two Whole Numbers

If two whole numbers are not equal, then one is *greater than* the other. Numbers can be compared with the help of a *number line*.

For any two numbers graphed on a number line, **the number farther to the right is greater than any number to the left** or, equivalently, **the number on the left is smaller than any number to its right**.

This relation can be expressed using **inequality symbols.**

The symbol < is read "is less than" and the symbol > is read "is greater than".

The symbols < and > always point to the smaller number.

For example, 11 is to the right of 8, so 11 is greater than 8, or 11 > 8.

5 is to the left of 8, so 5 is less than 8, or 5 < 8.

The inequality 5 < 8 means the same as 8 > 5, although it is read differently.

 Note There are other symbols used for inequalities.

≤ is read "is less than or equal to".

≥ is read "is greater than or equal to".

≠ is read "is not equal to".

Procedure to compare large whole numbers:

Step **1**   Count the number of digits in both the numbers.

Step **2**   The number having **more** digits is **greater**. If the number of digits in both numbers is the same then compare the digits in the corresponding places one by one, starting from the left most digit. In the first place that the digits are different, the number having the greater digit is greater.

Warm-Up

2. Compare the given pairs of numbers and write a true inequality statement in each case.

(a) 6,798 ; 935

(b) 257,399 ; 258,399

Answers:

2. (a) 6,798 > 935 **or** 935 < 6,798

(b) 257,399 < 258,399 **or**
258,399 > 257,399

Example 2   Compare the following pairs of numbers. Write a true inequality statement in each case.

(a) 21,752 and 9,580

(b) 2,178,456 and 2,178,546

Solutions

(a)   The number 21,752 is greater than the number 9,580 since it has more digits.

$$21,752 > 9,580$$

(b)   Both numbers have the same number of digits. Write the numbers one below the other as shown:

2,178,**4**56   (First number)

2,178,**5**46   (Second number)

Compare the corresponding digits one by one starting from the left most digit. The first four digits of both numbers are the same. The fifth digit in the second number is greater than the fifth digit in the first number.

The second number, 2,178,546, is greater than 2,178,456; so we write

$$2,178,\mathbf{5}46 > 2,178,\mathbf{4}56.$$

0.2 C.   Rounding Whole Numbers

Some numbers state exact values; others give only approximate values. For example, if the monthly income of a person is $4,752, he may say that his monthly income is approximately $4,750, or he may even claim that his monthly income is about $4,800, or $5,000. In this case, the income has been rounded respectively to the nearest ten ($4,750), hundred ($4,800), or thousand ($5,000).

- To **round** a given number means to find another number close to the given number. The desired place of accuracy must be stated. A number can be rounded to the nearest ten, hundred, or any other desired place value.

- We can use the number line to understand how whole numbers are rounded. Suppose we want to round 46 to the nearest ten. Look at the number line.

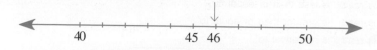

Since 46 is closer to 50 than to 40, we say that 46 rounds to 50, and write $46 \approx 50$ (read : 46 is approximately equal to 50). In this case we say that the number has been **rounded up**.

- To round 548 to the *nearest hundred*, we look at the numbers between 500 and 600 on the number line:

We observe that 548 is closer to 500 than to 600; thus, 548 rounds to 500, and we write $548 \approx 500$ to the nearest hundred. In this case we say that the number has been **rounded down**.

- Numbers can be rounded without using a number line but by using the following rules.

RULES FOR ROUNDING WHOLE NUMBERS
Rule 1   If the digit to the right of the rounding place is 5 or greater, **round up** by adding 1 to the *digit* at the rounding place, and changing the remaining digits to the right of it to zeros.
Rule 2   If the digit to the right of the rounding place is less than 5, **round down** by leaving the digit in the rounding place as it is and changing the digits to the right of the rounding place to zeros.

Let us round 578,623 to the nearest *thousand* without using a number line. Place an arrow under the digit in the rounding place:

$$578{,}623$$

Since the digit to the right of arrow is 6 (greater than 5), *round up* by Rule 1. That is, add 1 to the digit in the rounding place, and replace each digit to the right of it with zeros. Now, 578 thousands become 579 thousands.

Thus, $578{,}623 \approx 579{,}000$ to the nearest thousand.

If we want to round 578,623 to the nearest *hundred*, we place an arrow under 6, the digit in the hundreds place:

$$578{,}623$$

Since the digit to the right of the arrow is 2 (less than 5), *round down* by Rule 2. That is, leave the digit in the rounding place as it is, and replace each digit to the right of it with zeros.

Thus, $578{,}623 \approx 578{,}600$ to the nearest hundred.

Procedure to round a whole number to a desired place of accuracy:

     Step 1   Identify the digit in the rounding place by drawing an arrow under it.

     Step 2   Round up or down according to the applicable rule.

Warm-Up

3. Round the following numbers as indicated:

(a) (i) 2,987 to the nearest hundred;

(ii) 8,945 to the nearest hundred.

Example 3 (When the digit at the rounding place is 9)

Round the following numbers as indicated:

(a) 3,496 ; to the nearest ten

(b) 15,932 ; to the nearest hundred

(c) 9,540 ; to the nearest thousand.

Solutions

(a) 3,4**9**6   3,4**9**6   3,**5**00
     ↑   ↑   ↑

The rounding place is tens, and the digit at the rounding place is 9.

The digit to the right of the arrow is 6. 6 is greater than 5, we *round up*.

Add 1 to 9. This affects two digits, both 4 and 9: 49 becomes 50. Also replace the digit to the right to the arrow with zero.

$3,496 \approx 3,500$ to the nearest ten.

(b) (i) 794 to the nearest ten;

(ii) 19,568 to the nearest thousand.

(b) 15,**9**32   15,**9**32   15,**9**00
     ↑   ↑   ↑

The rounding place is hundreds, and the digit at the rounding place is 9.

The digit to the right of the arrow is 3; 3 is *less* than 5, so *round down*.

Leave 9 as it is, and change all the digits to its right to zeros.

$15,932 \approx 15,900$ to the nearest hundred.

(c) (i) 96 to the nearest ten;

(ii) 2,980 to the nearest hundred.

(c) **9**,540   **9**,540   **10**,000
     ↑   ↑   ↑

The rounding place is the left-most place, and the digit at the rounding place is 9.

The digit to the right of the arrow is 5, so *round up*.

Add 1 to 9, which means change 9 to 10. This converts the given 4-digit number to a 5-digit number.

$9,540 \approx 10,000$ to the nearest thousand.

4. The annual budget of a household is $35,740. What is the budget rounded to the nearest thousand.

Example 4 The annual budget of a community college is $23,567,850. It is reported to the newspaper to the nearest hundred thousand dollars. What amount is reported?

Solution

23,**5**67,850   Identify the digit in the hundred thousands place.
   ↑

23,**6**00,000   Since the digit to the right is 6, round up.

To the nearest hundred thousand, the reported amount is $23,600,000.

Answers:

3. (a) (i) 3,000   (ii) 8,900
   (b) (i) 790   (ii) 20,000
   (c) (i) 100   (ii) 3,000

4. $ 36,000

Exercise 0.2

A. In exercises 1-10, graph the given set of numbers on a number line.

1. {0, 3, 6, 7}   2. {4, 2, 1, 8, 9}   3. {0, 5, 6, 7, 1}   4. {3, 5, 7, 9, 11}

5. {21, 24, 27, 32}   6. {15, 17, 21, 23, 25}   7. {35, 36, 40, 44}   8. All whole numbers between 4 and 12.

9. All whole numbers between 2 and 8.   10. All whole numbers less than 8.

B. In exercises 11-24, insert the appropriate symbol in the box that will make the statement true: >, <, or =.

11. 5 ☐ 7   12. 10 ☐ 0   13. 8 ☐ 8   14. 0 ☐ 6   15. 9 ☐ 13

16. 2 ☐ 1   17. 20 ☐ 20   18. 41 ☐ 14   19. 24 ☐ 18   20. 27 ☐ 19

21. 1 ☐ 0   22. 13 ☐ 15   23. 78 ☐ 69   24. 40 ☐ 38

In exercises 25-34, compare the pair of numbers using an inequality symbol (< or >).

25. 15 and 22   26. 18 and 7   27. 28 and 24   28. 4 and 9   29. 12 and 14

30. 13 and 9   31. 0 and 1   32. 6 and 5   33. 11 and 15   34. 3 and 0

In exercises 35-56, determine whether the given statement is True or False. Rewrite every false statement to make it true.

35. 4 > 12   36. 8 < 5   37. 15 > 9   38. 0 < 6   39. 4 > 2   40. 13 > 11

41. 7 < 0   42. 0 > 3   43. 14 > 19   44. 8 > 6   45. 15 > 12   46. 10 < 8

47. 25 > 18   48. 13 < 11   49. 19 > 26   50. 1 > 0   51. 12 > 9   52. 6 < 13

53. 4 = 4   54. 14 < 12   55. 8 > 3   56. 16 > 21

In exercises 57-70, identify which number is greater.

57. 235 ; 68   58. 2,568 ; 2,590   59. 462 ; 527   60. 89 ; 110   61. 2,349 ; 2,680

62. 715 ; 698   63. 5,730 ; 4,985   64. 4,329 ; 4,587   65. 690 ; 700   66. 35,789 ; 46,120

67. 10,429 ; 9,987   68. 82,574 ; 2,890   69. 375 ; 357   70. 2,985 ; 2,890

In exercises 71-81, write a true inequality statement using an inequality symbol (< or >).

71. 15 and 22   72. 7 and 18   73. 758 and 749   74. 384 and 348

75. 25,140 and 24,952   76. 80,701 and 81,000   77. 4,320,008 and 29,100,000   78. 543,290,100 and 543,293,100

79. 99,990 and 99,909   80. 73,993,705 and 73,983,705   81. 3,056,919 and 3,056,915

C. In exercises 82-108, round the number to the given place.

82. 78 ; tens   83. 743 ; hundreds   84. 4,175 ; tens   85. 563 ; hundreds

86. 536 ; hundreds   87. 5,484 ; tens   88. 9,348 ; tens   89. 5,484 ; thousands

90. 6,844 ; thousands   91. 1,751,100 ; thousands   92. 1,751,900 ; thousands   93. 5,837 ; tens

94. 5,837 ; hundreds   95. 52,425,000 ; ten thousands   96. 456,172,978; millions

97. 82,579,090 ; hundred thousands   98. 2,951 ; hundreds   99. 1,619 ; tens

100. 935,700 ; hundred thousands   101. 72,238 ; thousands   102. 597 ; tens

103. 972 ; hundreds   104. 14,498 ; tens   105. 89,762 ; thousands

106. 78,000 ; ten thousands   107. 43,987 ; ten thousands   108. 284,960 ; thousands

Applications

109. A publishing company sold 258,630 books of mathematics during the years 2002 and 2003. Write the number of volumes sold to the nearest thousand.

110. Tom Peterson's Appliances buys five television sets for a total of $1,375. What is the price to the nearest hundred?

111. An office space in downtown San Francisco is listed for $4,689,250. Give the list price of the space to the nearest ten thousand dollars.

112. Linda, Kevin, and Jesse went on vacation. They spent $1,250, $890, and $1,275, respectively. Who spent the most? Who spent the least?

113. Which is larger, 50 billion or 5 ten billion?

114. What is the largest value of y that makes $38y4 > 3,864$ false?

115. For what value(s) of y is the inequality $4y39 > 4,562$ true? What is the smallest such value of y?

116. A community college receives two bids for the construction of its new library: bid A for $6,874,500 and bid B for $6,456,950. It wants to award the contract to the lower bidder. To which bidder should the contract be awarded?

0.3 FUNDAMENTAL OPERATIONS WITH WHOLE NUMBERS

Objectives

After completing this section, you will be able to:

A. Add and subtract whole numbers;

B. Multiply and divide whole numbers.

IMPORTANT VOCABULARY

1. **Variable:** A variable is a letter that is used to represent an unknown number.

2. **Addition:** The symbol to indicate addition is "**+**" and is read "plus". The result of an addition is called the **sum**. The numbers being added are called **terms**.

$8 + 3 = 11$ is read "8 plus 3 equals 11." 8 and 3 are the *terms*, and 11 is the *sum*.

3. **Subtraction:** The symbol for subtraction is "**–**" (read: "minus"). When one number is subtracted from the other, the result is called the **difference**. The numbers involved in this subtraction are called **terms**.

$12 - 3 = 9$ is read as "12 minus 3 equals 9".
      12 and 3 are the **terms.**

- Subtraction can be thought of as finding the missing term in an addition exercise. To find the difference in $19 - 12$, we may ask: "What should be added to 12 to get 19?" We can represent the problem in the following format:

$$12 \quad + \quad \underline{\quad ? \quad} \quad = \quad 19$$

  term   missing term   sum

This kind of 'addition' problem is called subtraction and can be written as

$$19 \quad - \quad 12 \quad = \quad \underline{\quad ? \quad}$$

  sum   minus   term   missing term
                        (or difference)

In this case, we know that the missing term is 7.   (12 + 7 = 19),
so we have 19 − 12 = 7.

Thus, we observe that **addition and subtraction** represent *inverse operations*. For each addition fact, we can write two related subtraction facts. For instance, 5 + 4 = 9 represents two subtraction facts:

$$9 - 4 = 5 \quad \text{and} \quad 9 - 5 = 4.$$

4. Multiplication: The usual symbol which indicates multiplication is "$\times$" and is read "multiplied by" or "times". The numbers being multiplied are called the **factors** and the result obtained is called the **product**.

$3 \times 5 = 15$ is read as "3 times 5 equals 15". 3 and 5 are *factors* and 15 is the *product*.

The product 3×5 is also written as $3 \cdot 5$ or $3(5)$ or $(3)5$ or $(3)(5)$.

5. Division: The symbol to indicate division is "$\div$" and is read "divided by".

Therefore, the division problem $36 \div 4$ can also be written as $\dfrac{36}{4}$ **or** $4\overline{)36}$.

The division problem $47 \div 5$ does not have a whole number quotient.

$$\begin{array}{r} 9 \\ 5\overline{)47} \\ 45 \\ \hline 2 \end{array}$$ It can be written as $47 \div 5 = 9 \text{ R } 2.$

In this case 9 is called the **quotient** and 2 is called the **remainder**.

• These four operations: addition, subtraction, multiplication, and division are called the **fundamental operations.**

0.3 A.   Addition and Subtraction of Whole Numbers

• **To add two or more whole numbers with more than one digit,** we write the numbers in columns, so that the corresponding place values are lined up vertically, and then add in each column as illustrated below:

(a) *Addition without carrying*:   Let us find the sum of 405, 72, and 612.

Write the numbers in columns, lining up the places, and add the digits in each column.

	4	0	5
		7	2
+	6	1	2
The desired sum →	10	8	9

(b) *Addition with carrying* : In the addition process, if the sum of digits in a column is a two-digit number, then we write the ones digit in that column, and **carry** the other digit to the next column to the left. (This is done since each place can contain only one digit.)

As an illustration, let us add the numbers 256 and 379. Write the numbers in columns lining up the places:

	1 ←	1 ←	
	2	5	6
+	3	7	9
6	1 3	1 5	

It is usual to show the above addition as:

1	1	
2	5	6
+ 3	7	9
6	3	5

← Carry over digits

Carrying is done mentally.

Warm-Up

1. (a) Find the sum of 7,629, 1,682, and 4,491. Round it to the nearest thousand.

(b) Find the sum 973 + 32 + 156 + 4,678 rounded to the nearest thousand.

Example 1 Add and round the sum as indicated:

(a) 1,691; 9,441; and 6,785. Round the sum to the nearest hundred.

(b) 4,678 ; 345 ; 76,458 ; and 69. Round the sum to the nearest thousand.

Solutions Write the numbers in columns, lining up the places, then add the numbers in each column starting from the ones and moving left.

(a)

	1 ←	2 ←		
	1	6	9	1
+	9	4	4	1
+	6	7	8	5
1 7	1 9	2 1	7	

1,691 + 9,441 + 6,785 = 17,917 (the sum)

The sum 17,917 rounded to the nearest hundred is 17,900.

(b)

	1	1	2	3		← Carry-over digits
		4	6	7	8	The numbers are to be written in columns, lining up the places.
			3	4	5	
	7	6	4	5	8	
		+	6	9		
Sum =	8	1	5	5	0	

⚠ **Caution:** The digit which is carried to the next column should always be written on the top of the whole column of numbers.

The sum 81,550 rounded to the nearest thousand is 82,000.

- Finding the difference in 987 − 234 is more difficult because we do not easily recognize what to add to 234 to get 987. To find the difference between large numbers, we write them in columns so that the corresponding place values are aligned, and then subtract in each column as explained below.

(a) *Subtraction without borrowing*: Consider the difference in 987 − 234.

First Term → 987
Second Term → − 234
Difference → 753 ;

so, 987 − 234 = 753.

We can check by adding:

	2	3	4
+	7	5	3
	9	8	7

(b) *Subtraction with borrowing*:

When using the column format, it may not be possible sometimes to subtract without borrowing as explained in the following example:

$$892 - 365$$

We cannot subtract 5 ones from 2 ones, so from 9 tens, we borrow 1 ten or 10 ones and add this to the 2 ones, leaving behind 8 tens. Then we cross out 9 and write 8 for it; cross out 2 and write 12 for it.

	8	12
8	9	2
− 3	6	5
5	2	7

difference → 5 2 7

- Subtract the ones column: 12 − 5 = 7
- Subtract the tens column: 8 − 6 = 2
- Subtract the hundreds column: 8 − 3 = 5

Example 2 Subtract and round the difference to the nearest ten.

(a) 365 from 734   (b) 395 from 3,803

Solutions

(a)

	6	12	
		2	14
	7	3	4
−	3	6	5
difference →	3	6	9

The difference 369 rounded to the nearest ten is 370.

(b) Subtract 395 from 3,803.

			9	13
		7	10	
3	8	0	3	
−		3	9	5
3	4	0	8	

3,803 − 395 = 3,408

The difference of 3,803 and 395 rounded to the nearest ten is 3,410.

Warm-Up

2. Subtract and round the difference as indicated:

(a) 267 from 569 to the nearest ten.

(b) 449 from 2,364 to the nearest hundred.

15

- In a subtraction problem (first term – the second term) if the first term has digits with a zero place value then we can use an alternative method for subtraction. Place values are given to groupings, rather than single digits.

<table>
<tr><td>

Warm-Up

3. Subtract:

(a)
$$\begin{array}{r} 6032 \\ -1476 \\ \hline \end{array}$$

(b)
$$\begin{array}{r} 50300 \\ -2489 \\ \hline \end{array}$$

(c)
$$\begin{array}{r} 50000 \\ -29422 \\ \hline \end{array}$$

Answer:

1. (a) 13,802 ; 14,000   **(b)** 5,839 ; 6,000

2. (a) 302 ; 300   **(b)** 1,915 ; 1,900

3. (a) 4,556   **(b)** 47,811

   (c) 20,578

</td><td>

Example 3   Subtract:

(a) 395   from   2,604   (b) 8,976   from   100,205

(c) 555   from   9,000

Solutions

(a)   Subtract 395 from 2,604

$$\begin{array}{r} {\scriptstyle 5\ 9\ 14} \\ 2\,6\,0\,4 \\ -\quad 3\,9\,5 \\ \hline 2\,2\,0\,9 \end{array}$$

Start on the right.
- 5 cannot be subtracted from 4. Go to the next column. Borrow 1 from 60, 60 becomes 59, and 4 becomes 14. No more borrowing is necessary.
- Subtract each column.

2,604 – 395 = 2,209

(b)   Subtract 8,976   from   100,205

$$\begin{array}{r} {\scriptstyle 11} \\ {\scriptstyle 0\ 9\ 9\ 9\ 15} \\ 1\,0\,0\,2\,0\,5 \\ -\quad 8\,9\,7\,6 \\ \hline 9\,1\,2\,2\,9 \end{array}$$

- 6 cannot be subtracted from 5. Borrow 1 from 20, 20 becomes 19, and 5 becomes 15. 7 is okay ; 9 is not. Borrow 1 from 100, 100 becomes 099, and 1 becomes 11. 8 is okay.
- Subtract each column.

(c)   Subtract 555   from   9,000

$$\begin{array}{r} {\scriptstyle 8\ 9\ 9\ 10} \\ 9\,0\,0\,0 \\ -\quad 5\,5\,5 \\ \hline 8\,4\,4\,5 \end{array}$$

- 5 cannot be subtracted from 0. Borrow 1 from 900, 900 becomes 899, and 0 becomes 10. No more borrowing is needed.
- Subtract each column.

</td></tr>
</table>

0.3 B.   Multiplication and Division with Whole Numbers

a.   Multiplication with Whole Numbers

- Multiplication is basically a shorter form of repeated addition.

$\underbrace{4 + 4}_{2 \text{ fours}} =$ 2×4 or $2 \cdot 4$ or $2(4)$ is read as "2 times 4" or "2 multiplied by 4".

$\underbrace{4 + 4 + 4}_{3 \text{ fours}} =$ 3×4 or $3 \cdot 4$ or $3(4)$ is read as "3 multiplied by 4" or "3 times 4".

The signs $\times$ or a raised dot $\cdot$ (as in $2 \cdot 4$) are called **multiplication signs**. The use of parentheses ( ), as in $3(4)$, also indicates multiplication.

- We call $2 \times 4 = 8$ a **multiplication fact.**

   In $2 \times 4 = 8$, the numbers 2 and 4 are called **factors** and 8 is called the **product**.

Important Observation

- To quickly multiply a number by 10, 20, 30, ... , 90, we multiply the given number by 1, 2, 3, ..., 9, respectively, and write one zero to the right of the product. Similarly, to multiply a given number by 100, 200, 300, ..., 900, we multiply the given number by 1, 2, 3, ... 9, respectively, and write two zeros to the right of the product.

Examples:

$$52 \times 30 = 52 \times 3 \text{ tens}$$
$$= 156 \text{ tens}$$
$$= 1,560$$

$$214 \times 200 = 214 \times 2 \text{ hundreds}$$
$$= 428 \text{ hundreds}$$
$$= 42,800$$

- To multiply a given number by a two-digit number, study the following example carefully to understand the process. To multiply 184 by 42:

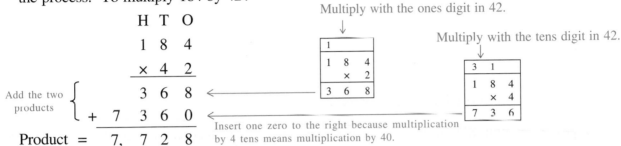

Insert one zero to the right because multiplication by 4 tens means multiplication by 40.

Study the following example carefully.

Example 4   Multiply:

(a) 371(58)   (b) 1,872 × 405

Solutions

(a)

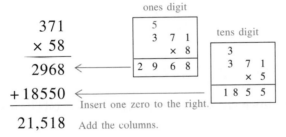

$$371(58) = 21,518.$$

Warm-Up

4. Multiply:

(a) 847 (75)

(b) 9321 × 807

(b)

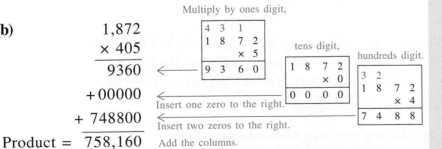

Showing a row of zeros can be omitted since the product of any number and zero is zero, and adding zero does not change the sum.

b. Division with Whole Numbers

- Division is a short form of repeated subtraction. Recall that multiplication is the same as repeated addition.

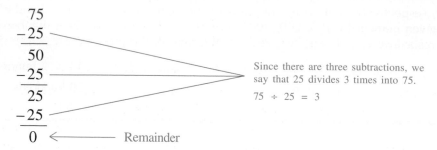

Since there are three subtractions, we say that 25 divides 3 times into 75.

$75 \div 25 = 3$

Thus, we say $75 \div 25 = 3$.

- The division $75 \div 25$ can also be written as:

$$\frac{75}{25}, \quad \text{or} \quad 25\overline{)75}$$

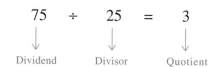

- ## Multiplication and Division are Inverse Operations

For each multiplication fact involving two non-zero numbers there are two related division facts. For example,

Multiplication Fact	Corresponding division facts		
$9 \times 5 = 45$	$45 \div 5 = 9$	and	$45 \div 9 = 5$
$3 \times 7 = 21$	$21 \div 7 = 3$	and	$21 \div 3 = 7$

Dividend   Divisor   Quotient   Dividend   Divisor   Quotient

Observe that $\boxed{\text{Divisor} \times \text{Quotient} = \text{Dividend}}$

- Multiplication facts, such as $8 \times 0 = 0$, in which one factor is zero and the other is non-zero, give rise to only one division fact.

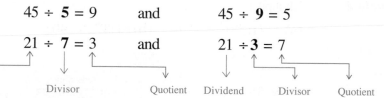

$8 \times 0 = 0$ gives $0 \div 8 = 0$ It is not true to say $0 \div 0 = 8$

$0 \times 12 = 0$ gives $0 \div 12 = 0$ It is not true to say $0 \div 0 = 12$

If such division facts are permitted, we would get $8 = 12$, which certainly makes no sense.

We cannot divide 0 by 0.

- It is important to note that we cannot divide any non-zero whole number by zero. For example, let us try to divide 7 by 0. Dividing 7 by 0 is the same as finding the missing factor in the product $0 \times ? = 7$. $0 \times$ any number $= 0$. No whole number can be found to meet the requirement $0 \times ? = 7$.

  $\boxed{\text{We say that division by zero is } \textbf{undefined}.}$

- However, we can divide zero by any non-zero whole number. Since

  $11 \times 0 = \mathbf{0}$,   we can say $\mathbf{0} \div 11 = 0$;

  $0 \times 9 = \mathbf{0}$,   we can say $\mathbf{0} \div 9 = 0$.

Observe that the quotient in each case is zero.

$\boxed{\text{When zero is divided by any non-zero number, the quotient is always zero.}}$

- Multiplication facts, such as $3 \times 1 = 3$ and $12 \times 1 = 12$, give rise to very special types of division facts.

  $3 \times 1 = \mathbf{3}$ gives $3 \div 1 = \mathbf{3}$ and $\mathbf{3} \div 3 = 1$

  $12 \times 1 = \mathbf{12}$ gives $12 \div 1 = \mathbf{12}$ and $\mathbf{12} \div 12 = 1$

  > When any number is divided by 1, the quotient is the number itself: $8 \div 1 = 8$.
  > When a non-zero number is divided by itself, the quotient is always 1: $4 \div 4 = 1$.

- The division facts considered so far involved small numbers so the quotient could be obtained either by inspection or by the method of repeated subtraction. But these methods are not very convenient to apply in every problem of division, such as finding the quotient $9,360 \div 45$. Moreover, division does not always involve factors (or *exact divisors*). A more general method of performing division is commonly called the method of **long division** or the **division algorithm** and is illustrated below.

  Let us divide 69 by 3.

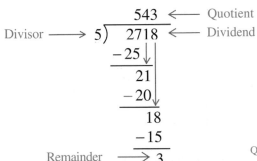

- Divide the left-most place (tens place in this case).

- Divide in the next place (ones place in this case): 9 ones ÷ 3 = 3 ones.

- Continue the process until all the digits in the dividend have been used.

  So, $69 \div 3 = 23$.

- Not all division problems have a zero remainder.

  Divide 2,718 by 5.

$$
\begin{array}{r}
543 \quad \longleftarrow \text{Quotient} \\
\text{Divisor} \longrightarrow 5{\overline{\smash{)}\,2718}} \quad \longleftarrow \text{Dividend} \\
-25 \\
\hline
21 \\
-20 \\
\hline
18 \\
-15 \\
\hline
\text{Remainder} \longrightarrow 3
\end{array}
$$

- 2 (the left-most digit in the dividend) cannot be divided by 5; so, we consider the group 27, the first two digits from the left.

- 5 can go into 27 only 5 times.

- Bring down the next digit from the dividend, and write it next to the remainder 2 to get the number 21.

- Now, divide 21 by 5. Continue the process until all the digits in the dividend have been used.

Symbolically, we write $2{,}718 \div 5 = \underset{\uparrow}{543} \;\; R \;\; \underset{\uparrow}{3}$

Quotient Remainder

 Note   In the above problem, the remainder 3 is less than the divisor 5.

The **remainder** is always **smaller** than the divisor.

$$\text{Divisor} \times \text{Quotient} + \text{Remainder} = \text{Dividend}$$

$$5 \times 543 + 3 = 2{,}718$$

- *If the remainder is 0, then both the divisor and the quotient are* **factors** *of the dividend.*
  For instance, in $69 \div 3 = 23$, both 3 and 23 are factors of 69.

Important Observation

• When we divide a number by 10, 100, 1000, ... the quotient is obtained by removing one, two, three, ... digits, respectively, starting from the right most digit and moving towards the left. The digits removed, taken in order, constitute the remainder. The remaining digits on the left form the quotient.

Notice: The number of digits removed is the same as the number of 0's in the divisor.

Example: Find the quotient and remainder, if any, without using long division.

$$4{,}589 \div 100 \quad = \quad 45 \ R \ 89$$
$$89{,}742 \div 1{,}000 = \quad 89 \ R \ 742$$

Warm-Up

5. Divide by the 'long division' method and check your answers:

(a) $9{,}385 \div 45$

(b) $16\overline{)8{,}073}$

Example 5 Divide $9{,}860 \div 47$, using the division algorithm (long division method) and check the answer.

Solution

```
              Th  H T O  ←——— Place values have been indicated.
Quotient ——→         2 0 9      Step 1  Multiply 47 · 2 = 94 (which is < 98);
              47 ) 9 8 6 0              so, write 2 for the quotient in the
                                        hundreds column.
Step 1 ——→       9 4↓|
                   4 6          Step 2  47 will not divide into 46; so, write
Step 2 ——→           0↓                 0 in the next place in the quotient,
                                        and multiply 47 · 0 = 0.
                   4 6 0
Step 3 ——→         4 2 3        Step 3  We find 47 goes 9 times into 460:
                                        47 × 9 = 423, which is less than
                     3 7  R             460; so, write 9 in the right-most
                                        place of the quotient.
```

$$9{,}860 \div 47 = 209 \ R \ 37.$$

Check: We must get:
Divisor × Quotient + R = Dividend

```
         6  3
    2  0  9 ←— Quotient ——→  9, 8 2 3
   ×  4  7 ←— Divisor         +   3 7 ←— Remainder
    1  4  6  3                9, 8 6 0 ←— Dividend
  + 8  3  6  0
    9, 8  2  3
```

Remark: The most difficult step in the division algorithm is determining the digits in the quotient. This can be easily accomplished if a table of multiples is created for the divisor with repeated addition or with a calculator.

We can solve Example 5 using the table for the multiples of 47.

If you don't have a calculator, write 47 on the bottom edge of a scrap paper.

47 + 47	Add the same number to itself to get the next multiple.
94 + 47	Keep adding the number successively.
141	

Keep adding 47 successively to get the next multiple and complete the list as shown in the table. The tenth multiple of 47, 10 · 47, should be 470. This checks your list of multiples.

List of multiples of the divisor 47
47 · 1 = 47
47 · 2 = 94
47 · 3 = 141
47 · 4 = 188
47 · 5 = 235
47 · 6 = 282
47 · 7 = 329
47 · 8 = 376
47 · 9 = 423

Neatness is essential. In dividing 9,860 by 47 it is very important to place the digits of the quotient precisely in place.

$$47 \overline{)9860} \quad \overset{2}{}$$

47 goes into 9860 more than 200 times.

The first digit 2 must be *directly* above the 8 because it represents 200. Then there must be a digit above the 6 and also above the 0. Be especially careful in placing a 0 when the divisor does not divide, before going on to the next place. Try Example 5 again with the table available. See how easy it becomes.

Example 6   Show that 25 and 37 are factors (or divisors) of 925.

Solution   We divide: Either $925 \div 25$ or $925 \div 37$

$$
\begin{array}{r}
37 \quad \longleftarrow \text{Quotient} \\
\text{Divisor} \longrightarrow 25\overline{)\,925\,} \longleftarrow \text{Dividend} \\
75 \\
\hline
175 \\
175 \\
\hline
\text{Remainder} \longrightarrow 0
\end{array}
$$

Since the remainder is zero, both *the divisor* and the *quotient* are factors of the dividend.

25 and 37 are indeed factors of 925.
$925 = 25 \cdot 37$.

Example 7   Divide using a calculator. Find the remainder, if any.
   (a) $70{,}577 \div 89$ **(b)** $59{,}602 \div 103$

Solutions

(a)   ENTER $\boxed{70577}$ $\boxed{\div}$ $\boxed{89}$ $\boxed{=}$ 793 ←—Final Display

The quotient is 793 and the remainder is 0.
(We may say that 89 is a factor of 70,577.)

(b)   ENTER $\boxed{59602}$ $\boxed{\div}$ $\boxed{103}$ $\boxed{=}$ 578.66019

The quotient is 578. We need to find the remainder.

$$
\begin{array}{r}
578\,\text{R}\,? \\
103\overline{)\,59{,}602}
\end{array}
$$

To find the remainder, first find the product of 103 and 578.

ENTER $\boxed{103}$ $\boxed{\times}$ $\boxed{578}$ $\boxed{=}$ 59534

Now, subtract this product from the dividend to get the remainder.

$$
\begin{array}{r}
578 \\
103\overline{)\,59{,}602} \\
-59{,}534 \\
\hline
?
\end{array}
$$

ENTER $\boxed{59602}$ $\boxed{-}$ $\boxed{59534}$ $\boxed{=}$ 68.

So, $59{,}602 \div 103 = 578\,\text{R}\,68$ (Since the remainder is non-zero, 103 is not a factor of 59,602.)

Warm-Up

6. (a)   Show that 18 and 16 are factors of 288.

(b)   Show that 13 is a factor (divisor) of 1,105.

   Hint : Divide $1{,}105 \div 13$ and find that the remainder is zero.

7. Divide using a calculator and find the remainder, if any.

(a) $59{,}704 \div 73$

(b) $123{,}474 \div 124$

Answers:

4. (a) 63,525   **(b)** 7,522,047

5. (a) 208 R 25   **(b)** 504 R 9

6. (a) 288 = 18 · 16   **(b)** 1,105 = 13 · 85

7. (a) 817 R 63   **(b)** 995 R 94

> **Note** Some calculators will calculate the quotient and the remainder. The above process provides good understanding of the divisor, the dividend, and the quotient.

Exercise **0.3**

A. In exercises 1-30, find the sum or the difference as indicated. Round each answer to the nearest hundred.

1.
```
   5,437
     209
      88
 + 1,879
```

2.
```
   3,693
     209
   3,147
 +    33
```

3.
```
   1,592
   2,601
      55
 +   592
```

4.
```
  34,675
   3,201
  57,832
 +    72
```

5.
```
      17
   1,859
   5,937
 + 32,164
```

6. 4,083 + 16,756

7. 245 + 380 + 79

8. 39 + 836 + 6,289

9. 4,392 + 945 + 6,110 + 7,515 + 5,785

10. 546 + 39 + 52 + 185

11. 12 + 46 + 39 + 62

12. 10 + 68 + 87 + 34

13. 1,682 + 4,491 + 7,629

14. 72 + 495 + 11 + 7,963

15. 34 + 549 + 1,008 + 1,456

16.
```
   3,783
 -   569
```

17.
```
  73,913
 - 31,397
```

18.
```
  19,039
 -  7,450
```

19.
```
   4,002
 -  1,271
```

20.
```
   5,070
 -  4,375
```

21.
```
  76,532
 - 20,496
```

22.
```
   1,947
 -   785
```

23.
```
  72,987
 - 40,189
```

24.
```
   8,652
 -  1,076
```

25.
```
     438
 -   283
```

26.
```
   3,875
 -  3,257
```

27.
```
  74,503
 - 33,086
```

28.
```
   9,863
 -  6,893
```

29.
```
  15,830
 -  9,750
```

30.
```
  16,245
 -  8,250
```

31. Subtract the sum of 4,805 and 2,967 from the sum of 3,835 and 4,990.

32. Add the sum of 239 and 450 to the difference of 785 and 325.

33. Add the difference of 2,756 and 2,342 to the sum of 4,589 and 311.

34. Subtract the difference of 5,305 and 4,839 from the sum of 3,525 and 4,839.

35. Subtract the difference of 7,803 and 6,816 from the difference of 4,011 and 879.

36. Find the two sums: 578 + 1,693 and 1,693 + 578. Observe that the sum of two numbers does not change even when we change the order of the numbers.

B. In exercises 37-85, find the product.

37. 41 × 5

38. 232 × 3

39. 879 × 0

40. 0 × 37

41. 706 × 6

42. 46 × 2

43. 38 × 9

44. 25 × 4

45. 56 × 7

46. 0 × 18

47. 335 × 2

48. 40 × 30

49. 8,250 × 1

50. 1 × 358

51. 5 × 19

52. 235 × 0

53. 30 × 15

54. 20 × 40

55. 251 × 1

56. 700 × 50

57. (400)(19)

58. (0) 999   **59.** 800×30 **60.** 78×456 **61.** 414×23 **62.** 235×31 **63.** 82×98 **64.** $1,372 \times 208$

65. $1,790 \times 230$ **66.** $2,140 \times 350$ **67.** 687×34 **68.** 346×276 **69.** $633 \times 2,361$ **70.** (32) (71) (82)   **71.** (25) (37)

72. (42) (85)   **73.** (53) (69)   **74.** (836) (48)   **75.** (693) (56)   **76.** (261) (345)   **77.** (428) (378)   **78.** (15) (36) (72)

79. $64 \times 52 \times 47$ **80.** 37×56 **81.** 412×593 **82.** 89×19 **83.** $3,941 \times 587$ **84.** $3,947 \times 594$ **85.** $4,977 \times 5,124$

In exercises 86-110, divide and find the remainder, if any.

86. $235 \div 4$ **87.** $2,512 \div 7$ **88.** $5,313 \div 5$ **89.** $538 \div 3$ **90.** $43,758 \div 6$

91. $456 \div 1$ **92.** $5029 \div 2$ **93.** $397 \div 7$ **94.** $78 \div 1$ **95.** $729 \div 21$

96. $1,397 \div 18$ **97.** $7,380 \div 47$ **98.** $1,728 \div 12$ **99.** $11,376 \div 237$ **100.** $492 \div 15$

101. $857 \div 12$ **102.** $3,025 \div 5$ **103.** $975 \div 25$ **104.** $1,356 \div 20$ **105.** $3462 \div 34$

106. $613\overline{)1,245,648}$ **107.** $215\overline{)153,874}$ **108.** $\dfrac{10,172,486}{206}$ **109.** $\dfrac{12,345}{975}$ **110.** $\dfrac{46,087}{356}$

In exercises 111-117, use division properties to find the quotient and remainder, if any, without long division.

111. $2,356 \div 100$ **112.** $9,073 \div 10$ **113.** $9,073 \div 1000$ **114.** $8,923,104 \div 1000$

115. $573 \div 573$ **116.** $0 \div 47$ **117.** $0 \div 1$

In exercises 118-137, divide using a calculator to find the quotient and remainder.

118. $825 \div 23$ **119.** $29,742 \div 31$ **120.** $8,324 \div 39$ **121.** $1,504 \div 47$ **122.** $85,607 \div 28$

123. $7,529 \div 36$ **124.** $4,029 \div 187$ **125.** $5,312 \div 191$ **126.** $6,395 \div 268$ **127.** $45,729 \div 396$

128. $49,862 \div 510$ **129.** $456 \div 49$ **130.** $\dfrac{78,555}{416}$ **131.** $8,721 \div 291$ **132.** $\dfrac{6,199}{207}$

133. $35,279 \div 148$ **134.** $42,111 \div 253$ **135.** $52,002 \div 285$ **136.** $11,376 \div 237$ **137.** $89,721 \div 307$

138. Can we divide 0 by 9 ?   **139.** Can we divide 5 by 0 ?   **140.** Can we divide 35 by 1 ?

141. Can we divide 0 by 0 ?   **142.** Can we multiply 0 by 0 ?   **143.** Can we multiply 0 by 4 ?

144. Can we divide 0 by 4 ?   **145.** Can we divide 26 by 0 ?   **146.** Can we divide 1 by 1 ?

147. Can we divide 24 by 0 ?   **148.** Show that 12 and 17 are factors or divisors of 204.

149. Show that 35 and 59 are factors or divisors of 2,065.

150. Show that 48 and 26 are factors or divisors of 1,248.   **151.** Show that 18 and 35 are factors or divisors of 630.

0.4 CHAPTER SUMMARY

Part I Definitions, Important Vocabulary, and Symbols

1. The **natural numbers** are: 1, 2, 3, 4, ...

2. The **whole numbers** are: **0**, 1, 2, 3, 4, ...

3. The **numeral** for "forty-five" is 45.

4. The ten numerals 0, 1, 2, 3, 4, 5, 6, 7, 8, and 9 are called **digits**.

5. The **word name** for the number 345 is " three hundred forty-five".

6. A **number line** is a line on which the numbers are represented by points. The point A, in the figure, is the **graph** of the number 5.

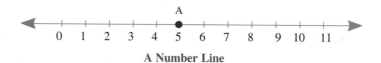

A Number Line

7. The symbol for **equality** is = (read: is equal to). The symbol ≠ is read: "is not equal to".

8. **Inequality symbols** are used to express a relationship between two numbers that are not equal.

The symbol < is read "**is less than**".   45 < 57 is read "45 is less than 57".

The symbol > is read "**is greater than**".   57 > 45 is read "57 is greater than 45".

The symbol ≤ is read "**is less than or equal to**".   5 ≤ 5 is read "5 is less than or equal to 5".

The symbol ≥ is read "**is greater than or equal to**".   15 ≥ 10 is read "15 is greater than or equal to 10".

9. A **set** is a well-defined collection of objects, called **elements** or **members**. The set whose members are 2, 3, 9, 14 is written as {2, 3, 9, 14}.

10. To **round** a whole number means to give an approximate value to a given rounding place. The symbol ≈ is read as "is approximately equal to".

$$457{,}249 \approx 457{,}250 \text{ to the nearest ten.}$$

11. **Fundamental Operations of Algebra:**

(i) Addition: The symbol to indicate addition is + (read: "plus").

$$\underbrace{243 \ + \ 102}_{\text{Terms}} = 345 \longleftarrow \text{Sum}$$

5 + 3 is read as "5 plus 3".

(ii) Subtraction: The symbol to indicate subtraction is – (read: "minus").

7 – 4 is read as "7 minus 4".

$$\underbrace{12 \ - \ 3}_{\text{Terms}} = 9 \longleftarrow \text{Difference}$$

(iii) Multiplication: The multiplication symbol × or a dot "·" are read as "multiplied by" or "times". 5 × 7 or 5 · 7 is read as 5 multiplied by 7 or 5 times 7.

$$\underset{\underset{\text{Factor}}{\uparrow}}{5} \ \times \ \underset{\underset{\text{Factor}}{\uparrow}}{7} = 35 \longleftarrow \text{Product}$$

(iv) Division: The division symbol "÷" is read "divided by".

$12 \div 4$ may also be written as $\dfrac{12}{4}$ or $4\overline{)12}$.

$$12 \div 4 = 3 \leftarrow \text{Quotient}$$

Dividend   Divisor

Each is read twelve divided by 4.

$$15 \div 6 = 2 \text{ R } 3 \leftarrow \text{Remainder}$$

Dividend   Divisor   Quotient

> **FORMULA**
> Quotient × Divisor + Remainder = Dividend

Part II   Procedures and Rules

WHOLE NUMBERS

1. Place value chart :

Trillions Group			Billions Group			Millions Group			Thousands Group			Ones Group		
HUNDREDS	TENS	ONES	HUNDREDS	TENS	ONES	HUNDREDS	TENS	ONES	HUNDREDS	TENS	ONES	HUNDREDS	TENS	ONES

Examples

2. To identify the place within the group.

Step **1** Identify the group using the place value chart.

Step **2** Identify the position within the group.

2. Identify the digit in the ten thousands place in 23,725,914. The thousands group is 725. The tens place is in the middle of the group. The digit is 2.

3. To write the word name of a number :

Step **1** Start with the left-most group. Write the word name for the group followed by the group name.

Step **2** Repeat step 1 for the remaining groups until all groups are named.

> ⚠ **Caution:** The group name "ones" is not written.

3. Write the word name of 42,357.

Left-most group: 42,
Word name for the group: **Forty-two**
Group name: **thousands**.

Next (last) group: 357
Word name for the group is
"three hundred fifty-seven"
Group name: Ones (not written)

The word name is: Forty-two thousand, three hundred fifty-seven.

4. To **graph** a set of numbers : Draw a number line, and show the numbers in the given set by dots.

4.

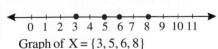

Graph of X = {3, 5, 6, 8}

Examples

5. Write True or False for the following inequality statements:

    (a) $7 > 4$ **(b)** $1 < 5$ **(c)** $6 < 2$

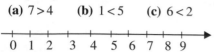

    0 1 2 3 4 5 6 7 8 9

(a)   **True:** 4 is to the left of 7, and the symbol is pointing to 4.

(b)   **True:** 1 is to the left of 5, and the symbol is pointing to 1.

(c)   **False:** 2 is to the left of 6, but the symbol is pointing to 6.

6. Addition:

  a) *Without carrying:*

```
    2 0 3
      7 4
  + 1 1 2
sum → 3 8 9
```

  b) *With carrying:*

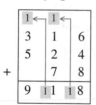

Subtraction:

  c) *Without borrowing:*

```
    5 4 4
      3 2
  - 5 1 4
```

  d) *With borrowing:*

7. a)

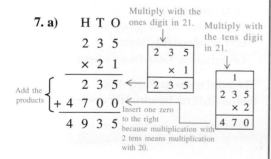

Multiply with the ones digit in 21.

Multiply with the tens digit in 21.

Add the products

Insert one zero to the right because multiplication with 2 tens means multiplication with 20.

COMPARING WHOLE NUMBERS

5. To write True or False for an inequality statement involving small numbers:

Graph or visualize the two numbers on a number line and see if the inequality symbol is pointing towards the smaller number, the left-most on the number line. If so, the statement is True, otherwise it is False.

ADDITION AND SUBTRACTION WITH WHOLE NUMBERS

6. a)   *Addition without carrying :*   **To add two or more whole numbers with more than one digit,** we write the numbers in columns, so that the corresponding place values are lined up vertically, and then add in each column.

b)   *Addition with carrying :*   In the addition process, if the sum of digits in a column is a two-digit number, we write the ones digit in that column, and **carry** the other digit to the next column to the left.

c)   *Subtraction without borrowing :*   To find the difference of whole numbers, we write them in columns so that the corresponding place values are aligned, and then subtract in each column. We can check the difference by adding.

d)   *Subtraction with borrowing :*   Find the difference of the digits in the right-most column (ones). If subtraction in this column cannot be done, borrow one from the next column to the left and rename the upper digits in both the columns, by adding 10 to the digit in the current column, and subtracting 1 from the digit in the left column.

MULTIPLICATION AND DIVISION WITH WHOLE NUMBERS

7. a)   *Multiplication without carrying :*

   Step 1   Write the numbers in columns, lining up the places.

   Step 2   Multiply the first number by the ones digit in the second number, and write the product below the second number, lining up the places.

   Step 3   Repeat for each digit to the left of the one's digits.

   Step 4   When the multiplication is complete, add all the results to find the product.

Examples

7. b) *Multiplication with carrying*:

Step **1** Write the numbers in columns, lining up the places.

Step **2** Start multiplying with the ones digit. If the product is ten or more, carry the tens digit to the next column and add it to the product in that column.

Step **3** When the multiplication is complete, add all the results to find the product.

7. b)

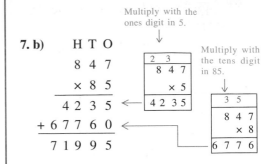

$$
\begin{array}{r}
\text{H T O} \\
8\ 4\ 7 \\
\times\ 8\ 5 \\
\hline
4\ 2\ 3\ 5 \\
+\ 6\ 7\ 7\ 6\ 0 \\
\hline
7\ 1\ 9\ 9\ 5
\end{array}
$$

8. *Long division*:

Step **1** Starting from the left most digit in the dividend (and moving towards the right), identify the first 'group' of digits in which division can be performed.

Step **2** Divide the group by the divisor, and place the partial quotient above the right most digit in the group. Write the product of this partial quotient and the divisor under the digits of the group, lining up the places.

Step **3** Subtract and bring down the next digit in the dividend and append it to the right of the difference obtained to get the next group of digits.

Step **4** Perform division in this group. Continue the process until all the digits have been used.

Step **5** Write the answer as :

Quotient R remainder, if the remainder in the final subtraction is not zero, otherwise, write only the quotient.

8. Divide 59,602 by 103.

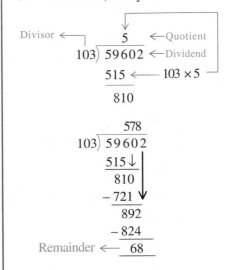

$$
\begin{array}{r}
578 \\
103)\overline{59602} \\
515\downarrow \\
\hline
810 \\
-\ 721\ \downarrow \\
\hline
892 \\
-\ 824 \\
\hline
68
\end{array}
$$

Remainder ← 68

$59{,}602 \div 103 = 578\,\text{R}\,68.$

Some Important Multiplication and Division Facts

$9 \times 5 = 45 \qquad 45 \div 5 = 9 \qquad \text{and} \qquad 45 \div 9 = 5$

Divisor × Quotient = Dividend

It is very important to know that we **cannot** divide any whole number by zero. But we **can** divide zero by any non-zero whole number.

i) We cannot divide any whole number by zero.

$$12 \div 0 \quad \text{or} \quad \frac{12}{0} \quad \text{is undefined.}$$

ii) When zero is divided by any non-zero number, the quotient is always zero.

$$0 \div 11 = 0$$

iii) When any number is divided by 1, the quotient is the number itself: $8 \div 1 = 8.$

i) $\dfrac{15}{0}$ or $15 \div 0$ is undefined.

ii) $\dfrac{0}{5} = 0$

iii) $\dfrac{7}{1} = 7$

iv) $\dfrac{13}{13} = 1$

iv) When a non-zero number is divided by itself, the quotient is always 1: $4 \div 4 = 1$.

v) $\dfrac{17}{3} = 5$ R 2 ; 2 is smaller than 5.

v) The **remainder** is always **smaller** than the divisor.

vi) $\dfrac{30}{5} = 6$ R 0

5 and 6 are factors of 30.

vi) *If the remainder is 0, then both the divisor and the quotient are* **factors** *of the dividend.*

$69 \div 3 = 23$ R 0. Both 3 and 23 are factors of 69.

0.5 REVIEW EXERCISE

In exercises 1-8, determine the place value of the given digit.

1. 524,310 ; 4
2. 70,529 ; 0
3. 97, 435 ; 3
4. 384,975 ; 7

5. 20,158 ; 8
6. 586,019 ; 6
7. 1,256, 790 ; 2
8. 78,539 ; 9

In exercises 9-14, identify the digit for the given place value.

9. 2,730,205 ; hundred thousands
10. 215,738 ; hundreds
11. 799,102 ; ones

12. 45,300 ; thousands
13. 75,987 ; tens
14. 23,490,148 ; millions

In exercises 15-16, write the word name for the numeral.

15. 82,143
16. 3,456,000,351

In exercises 17-18, write the numeral for the word name.

17. Two hundred fifty-three million, sixty thousand, forty-seven.

18. One hundred twenty-two billion, fifty thousand, ninety-two.

In exercises 19-20, graph the set of whole numbers on a number line.

19. $X = \{0, 3, 4, 5, 7, 9\}$
20. Set of whole numbers between 25 and 32.

In exercises 21-29, round the number to the given place value.

21. 496 ; tens
22. 325,740 ; thousands
23. 172,978 ; hundreds

24. 4,528 ; thousands
25. 25,243 ; ten thousands
26. 423,270 ; ten thousands

27. 265,540 ; thousands
28. 69,325 ; hundreds
29. 476,209 ; hundred thousands

In exercises 30-39, find the sum or the difference as indicated. Round the answer to the nearest hundred.

30.	31.	32.	33.	34.
865	3,874	678	21,211	25,234
734	4,469	6,789	11,923	21,387
572	+ 932	6,027	74,486	16,512
+ 321		+ 67	+ 30,871	+ 1,234

35.	36.	37.	38.	39.
3,426	86,549	43,278	2,951,320	4,512,123
− 1,642	− 73,840	− 8,524	− 2,478,204	− 1,634,345

In exercises 40-42, subtract and check using addition.

40. 278 from 582   **41.** 25,743 from 56,258   **42.** 6,789 from 9,876

In exercises 43-50, find the product and verify your answer using a calculator.

43. 75×34 **44.** 432×35 **45.** 85×96 **46.** $1,892 \times 250$

47. $\begin{array}{r} 2,376 \\ \times\ 569 \\ \hline \end{array}$ **48.** $\begin{array}{r} 784 \\ \times\ 345 \\ \hline \end{array}$ **49.** $\begin{array}{r} 468 \\ \times\ 73 \\ \hline \end{array}$ **50.** $\begin{array}{r} 5,544 \\ \times\ 664 \\ \hline \end{array}$

In exercises 51-54, divide and find the remainder, if any.

51. $1,296 \div 15$ **52.** $3,125 \div 25$ **53.** $6,380 \div 49$ **54.** $51\overline{)1729}$

In exercises 55-58, find the quotient and remainder, if any, using a calculator.

55. $49,346 \div 654$ **56.** $6,387 \div 48$ **57.** $846 \div 52$ **58.** $9,123 \div 351$

0.6 SELF TEST

In exercises 1-3, determine the place value of the given digit.

1. 31,456 ; 3   **2.** 596,023 ; 6   **3.** 4,211,567 ; 4

In exercises 4-6, identify the digit for the given place value.

4. 23,456 ; thousands   **5.** 64,321 ; ten thousands   **6.** 54,320,123 ; millions

7. Rewrite the numeral 54,321 interchanging the digits in the ten thousands and tens place value.

8. Graph the set A = {0, 4, 5, 6, 9, 11} on a number line.

In problems 9-10, round the given number as indicated.

9. 7,254 to the nearest ten.   **10.** 1,257,650 to the nearest thousand.

In problems 11-16, perform the indicated operations.

11. $2,752 + 14,972$ **12.** $17,274 - 4,792$ **13.** 37×200

14. 275×28 **15.** $2,472 \div 200$ **16.** $435 \div 87$

17. In the following exercises, find the exact sum or the difference as indicated. Then round the answer to the nearest hundred.

     (a) $\begin{array}{r} 1,345 \\ 255 \\ +\ 802 \\ \hline \end{array}$ **(b)** $\begin{array}{r} 2,543 \\ 1,213 \\ +\ 4,567 \\ \hline \end{array}$ **(c)** $\begin{array}{r} 98,325 \\ -\ 4,241 \\ \hline \end{array}$ **(d)** $\begin{array}{r} 785,432 \\ -\ 53,765 \\ \hline \end{array}$

18. Find the product of 623×4921, and verify your answer on a calculator.

19. Find the remainder, if any. Verify your answer.

     (a) $1,982 \div 25$ **(b)** $2,671 \div 32$

Integers and Order of Operations

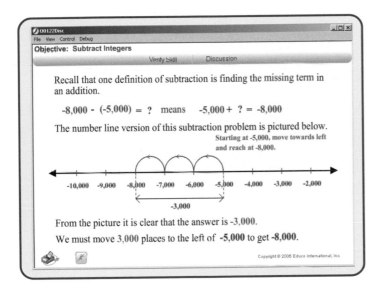

-4 -3 -2 -1 0 1 2 3 4

INTEGERS AND ORDER OF OPERATIONS 1

Introduction

In this chapter, we will introduce the set of Integers. We shall learn to perform the basic operations of addition, subtraction, multiplication, and division with integers; introduce the concept of 'opposite'; and discuss how to simplify expressions involving integers.

This chapter is divided into the following four sections:

1.1 *Definition of Integers; Opposites and Absolute Values;*

1.2 *Addition and Subtraction with Integers;*

1.3 *Multiplication and Division with Integers; and*

1.4 *Exponents; Order of Operations; Evaluating Numerical Expressions.*

1.1 DEFINITION OF INTEGERS; OPPOSITES; ABSOLUTE VALUES

IMPORTANT VOCABULARY

1. The set of **integers** is the set of all whole numbers and their opposites.
   Integers: $\{\ldots-3, -2, -1, 0, 1, 2, 3, \ldots\}$

2. The **positive integers** are the integers that are greater than zero.
   $\{1, 2, 3, \ldots\}$

3. The **negative integers** are the integers that are less than zero.
   $\{\ldots-3, -2, -1\}$
   The number zero is neither positive nor negative.

4. The **absolute value** of an integer a is its distance from 0 on the number line, and is symbolically written as $|a|$ (read: **'absolute value** of a'.)
   $$|2| = 2 ; \quad |-3| = 3$$

5. The **opposite** of an integer 'a' is denoted by '$-a$', and is read as "**opposite of a**".
   The opposite of   4   is -4.
   The opposite of -5 is $-(-5) = 5.$ 5

> **Objectives**
>
> After completing this section, you will be able to:
>
> A. Identify and graph integers; identify the opposite of an integer; compare any two integers; and
>
> B. Find the absolute value of an integer.

1.1 A. Graphing Integers; Finding the Opposite of an Integer; and Comparing Two Integers

- In Chapter 0 we discussed the operations of addition, subtraction, multiplication, and division on whole numbers. Observe that in subtractions like:

$$2 - 5, \qquad 7 - 11, \qquad 1 - 124$$

where the second term is larger than the first, there is no answer in whole numbers. We shall now try to find these answers by introducing *negative* numbers.

Consider a number line, with all the whole numbers graphed on it. All the whole numbers other than zero are to the right of zero. The number 1 is *one* unit from 0; the number 3 is *three* units from 0; and so on (see Figure 1.1).

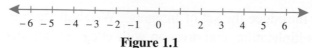

Figure 1.1

Let us subtract five from two, "$2 - 5$", on this number line.

For $2 - 5$, move two positive units to the right starting at zero, and reach the point labelled '2'; then move 5 units to the left of the point 2 (see Figure 1.2).

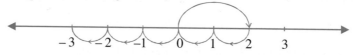

Figure 1.2

We reach a point which lies to the left of 0 at a distance of 3 units from 0. We label this point as '-3', read: "negative 3"; so, we have

$$2 - 5 = -3.$$

'-3' is also read as "the opposite of 3." The opposite of 3 *means* 3 units on the *opposite side* of 0.

Similarly, to compute $7 - 11$, we first reach the point 7, and then we move 11 units to the left (Figure 1.3). We reach a point which lies to the left of 0, at a distance of 4 units from 0.

Figure 1.3

We label this point as "-4", read: "negative 4" or "the opposite of 4", and we have

$$7 - 11 = -4;$$

thus, by introducing such numbers, that is, the opposites of whole numbers, we can find answers to all subtractions of the type '$a - b$' where a and b are any two whole numbers.

The **opposite of 1** is *one* unit to the *left of* 0; it is symbolized as **–1** and is called **negative 1**.

The **opposite of 2** is *two* units to the *left of* 0; it is symbolized as **–2** and is called **negative 2**.

The **opposite of 7** is *seven* units to the *left of* 0; it is symbolized as **–7** and is called **negative 7**; and so on (see Figure 1.4).

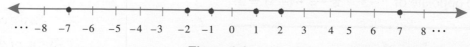

Figure 1.4

All whole numbers and their opposites taken together constitute the **set of integers**.

Set of Integers: $\{\ldots, -3, -2, -1, 0, 1, 2, 3, \ldots\}$

Figure 1.4 shows all the integers on a number line.

- **Positive and Negative Integers:** Integers are classified into three types: the *positive integers*, the *negative integers*, and *zero* (Figure 1.5). The numbers to the *right* of 0, that is, all the whole numbers except 0, are called the **positive integers**.

The numbers to the *left* of 0, that is, the opposites of all the whole numbers except 0, are called **negative integers**.

The number 0 is neither positive nor negative.

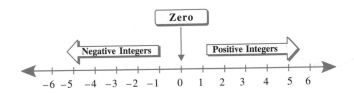

Figure 1.5

A positive integer may be indicated by a '**+**' sign before it.

For example, 15 may be written as   +15.   (read "positive 15")

A negative integer is written with a '**−**' sign (for example, −3).   (read "negative 3")

If no sign is written before the number, it is understood to be +. For example, 7 means +7.

> **Note** that the set of all the positive integers along with the number 0 is the set of whole numbers. It is common to call the set of **whole numbers** the **set of all non-negative integers**. Thus,
>
> Positive integers are: 1, 2, 3, 4, ...
>
> Negative integers are: −1, −2, −3, −4, ...
>
> Non-negative integers are: 0, 1, 2, 3, 4, ...
>
> Non-positive integers are: 0, −1, −2, −3, −4, ...
>
> (0 is the only non-negative integer which is not a positive integer.)

Example 1   Graph the set of integers A = {−4, −1, 3, 5, −2}.

Solution

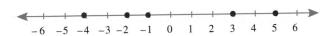

The graph is shown by dots.

Warm-Up

1. Graph the set of integers
   P = {−6, −2, −1, 0, 2, 4}.

- In daily life situations, positive and negative integers, are commonly used to represent quantities with opposite characteristics, as in the following examples:

Negative	*Zero*	*Positive*
Left of zero		**Right of zero**
(−7)	(0)	(8)
Loss	**Break even**	**Profit**
(−$74)	($0)	($250)

	Negative	*Zero*	*Positive*
	Below sea level	**At sea level**	**Above sea level**
	−572 feet	0 ft	3,200 feet
	Fall in price	**No change**	**Rise in price**
	− $1.25	$0	$2.5
	Temperature below zero	**At zero temp**	**Temperature above zero**
	− 4° F	0° F	32° F

Most quantities can be measured with integers. Some values, however, are expressed with non-negative numbers only. Cost and measurement are two such quantities where the negatives do not make any sense.

For example: The area of the lake is 4 square miles. The cost of the table was $390.

- **Find the opposite of an Integer:**

Refer to the number line in Figure 1.6. Observe that the numbers 2 and −2 are located at the same distance from 0 on opposite sides. The same is true for 7 and –7. We say that 2 and –2 are **opposites of each other**; also, 7 and –7 are **opposites of each other**. To be more specific,

$$-(3) \quad = \quad -3 \qquad \text{and} \qquad -(-3) \quad = \quad 3$$
↑   ↑
opposite of 3   is   −3   opposite of −3   is   3
(or +3)

$$- (+7) \quad = \quad -7 \qquad \text{and} \qquad -(-7) \quad = \quad 7$$
↑   ↑
opposite of +7   is   −7   opposite of −7   is   7
(or 7)

The opposite of 0 is 0 ; that is, $-(0) = 0$.

- The symbol "−" before a number is used in two different ways:

         27 − 12   means: Subtract 12 from 27.

    − 12 or − (12) means: The opposite of 12, or negative 12.

To find the 'opposite' of a number, we refer to the number line in Figure 1.6.

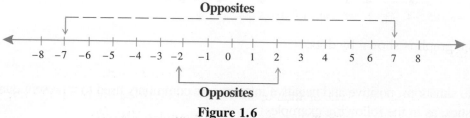

Figure 1.6

We find that:

        The opposite of a *positive* integer is a *negative* integer;

        The opposite of a *negative* integer is a *positive* integer ; and

        The opposite of 0 is 0 itself.

Example 2   Find the opposites of the following integers:

   (a) -3 **(b)** 4 **(c)** -8 **(d)** $+6$ **(e)** 0

Solutions

(a)   Opposite of $-3 = \underset{\underset{\text{symbol for opposite}}{\uparrow}}{-}(-3)$

Since -3 is 3 units on the left of 0, its opposite is 3 units on the right of 0.

$= 3$

(b)   Opposite of $4 = \underset{\underset{\text{opposite}}{\uparrow}}{-}(4)$

As 4 is 4 units to the right of 0, its opposite is 4 units to the left of 0.

$= -4$

(c)   Opposite of $-8 = -(-8)$

The opposite of a negative number is the corresponding positive number.

$= 8$

(d)   Opposite of $+6 = -(+6)$

The opposite of a positive number is the corresponding negative number.

$= -6$

(e)   Opposite of $0 = -(0)$

The opposite of 0 is 0 itself.

$= 0$

> **Remark:**   To find the opposite of a non-zero integer, we simply change its sign.

• **Comparing Integers** (Inequality Relationships):

Integers can be compared in the same way as we compare whole numbers with the help of a number line. To compare two integers, we graph them on a number line. The number on the right is *greater* than the number on the left; equivalently, the number on the left is *smaller* than the number on the right. The following inequality relationships can be observed on the number line in Figure 1.7. (The numbers being compared have been graphed using identical marks.)

Using the symbol '<'	*Using the symbol '>'*
$4 < 7$	$7 > 4$
$-5 < 2$	$2 > -5$
$-4 < -1$	$-1 > -4$

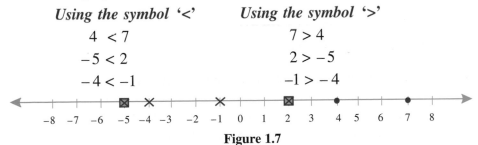

Figure 1.7

Observe that:

1. All positive numbers are *larger* than 0, since they all lie to the right of zero on the number line.

2. All negative numbers are *smaller* than 0, since they all lie to the left of zero on the number line.

3. Each negative number is smaller than every positive number. (Why?)

> **Observation:**
>
> A quick look at the number line shows that if m and n are two positive numbers, and
>
> $$m > n \quad \text{then} \quad -m < -n.$$
>
> $-m \quad -n \quad 0 \quad n \quad m$
>
> That is, if we replace the integers with their opposite the inequality is reversed.

Warm-Up

3. Determine whether each statement is true or false.

(a) $-5 > -8$

(b) $7 < 3$

(c) $4 > -5$

(d) $0 < 6$

Answers:

1.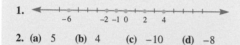

2. (a) 5   (b) 4   (c) −10   (d) −8

3. (a) True (b) False (c) True   (d) True

Example 3   Determine whether each statement is true or false.

(a) $-6 < -9$ (b) $-5 < 7$

(c) $-2 > 0$ (d) $-4 > -8$

Solutions   Visualize or draw a number line

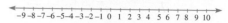

(a)   By locating the numbers −6 and −9 on the number line, we find that −6 is on the right of −9; therefore, $-6 > -9$.

    Hence, $-6 < -9$ is **False.**

(b) $-5 < 7$ is **True,**   because a negative number is less than every positive number.

(c) $-2 > 0$ is **False,**   because every negative number is less than 0.

(d) $-4 > -8$ is **True,**   because on the number line, the point labeled −4 is to the right of the point labeled −8.

1.1 B.   Finding the Absolute Value of an Integer

> *Definition:*   The **absolute value** of an integer is the distance between the number and zero on the number line.

Distances, which are measurements, **cannot be negative.**

We use vertical bars $|\ \ |$ to indicate the absolute value.

The absolute value of 7 is written as $|7|$.

The absolute value of −5 is written as $|-5|$.

Let's use the number line in Figure 1.8 to find the absolute values of some numbers.

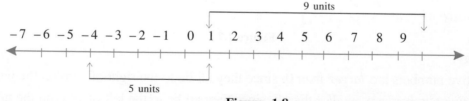

Figure 1.8

The absolute value of $9 = |9|$
$= 9.$

The distance between the numbers 9 and 0 is 9 units.
(Note that the absolute value of positive 9 is 9.)

The absolute value of $-5 = |-5|$
$= 5.$

The distance between the numbers −5 and 0 is 5 units.
(Note that the absolute value of negative 5 is 5.)

Since the distance between 0 and 0 is zero,

the absolute value of 0 $= |0| = 0.$

Observe the following characteristics of absolute value:

1. **The absolute value of a number measures the distance from 0 and distance is never negative.** The absolute value of a positive number or of zero is the number itself, and the absolute value of a negative number is its opposite.

2. **The absolute value of a number is the same as the absolute value of the opposite of that number**, since both are the *same* number of units away from zero. For example, $+4$ and -4 are both 4 units from 0 (Figure 1.9); thus, $\left|+4\right| = \left|-4\right| = 4$.

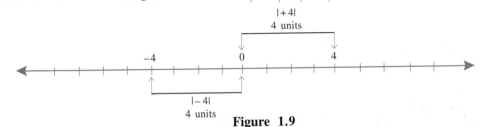

Figure 1.9

> *Rule:*   If the number **a** is zero or positive, $\left|a\right| = a$.
>
> If the number **a** is negative, $\left|-a\right| = a$.   (the opposite of *a*)
>
> The absolute value of an integer is never negative.

Example 4   Find the absolute values of the following numbers:

(a) -27 (b) 14 (c) $-(-9)$ (d) $-(+11)$

Solutions

(a)   Absolute value of $-27 = \left|-27\right|$ The distance to 0 is 27 units.

$\qquad = 27.$

(b)   Absolute value of $14 = \left|14\right|$ The distance to 0 is 14 units.

$\qquad = 14.$

(c)   Absolute value of $-(-9) = \left|-(-9)\right|$ $-(-9) = $ opposite of -9
$\qquad\qquad\qquad\qquad\qquad\qquad = 9.$

$\qquad = \left|9\right| = 9.$ The distance to 0 is 9 units.

(d)   Absolute value of $-(+11) = \left|-(+11)\right|$ $-(+11) = $ opposite of $+11$
$\qquad\qquad\qquad\qquad\qquad\qquad\qquad = -11.$

$\qquad = \left|-11\right|$ The distance to 0 is 11 units.

$\qquad = 11.$

◁ Note   The absolute value of an integer is always a positive number.

Warm-Up

4. Find the absolute value of:

(a) -16

(b) 21

(c) (-3)

(d) (35)

Warm-Up

5. Determine whether the following inequality statements are True or False:

(a) $|-7| > |-6|$

(b) $|-15| > |-7|$

$|-3| > |-2|$

$3 > 2$

(c) $|-9| \le |9|$

$3 > 2$

true?

6. In each of the following statements, find all the possible integer values for the variable that will make the statement True.

(a) $|x| = 8$

(b) $|a| = -1$

(c) $|x| = 0$

7. Find the possible integer values of 'x' for which the statement is true.

(a) $|x| \ge 3$

Example 5 Determine whether the following inequality statements are True or False:

(a) $|-5| < |-4|$ **(b)** $|3| > |-2|$ **(c)** $|-12| \ge 12$

Solutions

$12 \ge 12$

(a) $|-5| < |-4|$

$5 < 4$

Therefore, $|-5| < |-4|$ is **False.**

(b) $|3| > |-2|$

$3 > 2$

Therefore, $|3| > |-2|$ is **True.**

(c) $|-12| \ge 12$

$12 \ge 12$

Therefore, $|-12| \ge 12$ is **True**

Example 6 In each of the following statements, find all the possible integer values for the variable that will make the statement True.

(a) $|a| = 5$ **(b)** $|x| = -4$ **(c)** $|m| = 0$

Solutions

(a) $|a| = 5$: Since $|-5| = 5$ and $|5| = 5$, therefore $a = -5$ or 5.

$|a| = 5$ means those integers 'a' which are at a distance of 5 units from 0 on a number line, on either side of 0.

(b) $|x| = -4$: There is no value of x for which $|x| = -4$ is true. The absolute value of a number is *never negative*.

(c) $|m| = 0$: $|m| = 0$ will be true only when $m = 0$.

Example 7 Find the possible integer values of 'a' for which the following inequality statements are true. Graph these integers on a number line.

(a) $|a| \le 5$ **(b)** $|a| > 6$

Solutions

(a) $|a| \le 5$ means the distance of a from 0 is less than or equal to 5. Therefore, $|a| \le 5$ is true for all those integers which are at a distance of 5 units or less than 5 units from 0, on either side of 0. These integers are:

$$\{-5, -4, -3, -2, -1, 0, 1, 2, 3, 4, 5\}$$

Graph:

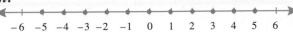

(b) $\left| a \right| > 6$ is true for all those integers '*a*' which are at a distance more than 6 units from 0, on either side of 0. There is an infinite number of such integers. These integers are:

$$\{\ldots, -9, -8, -7, 7, 8, 9, \ldots\}$$

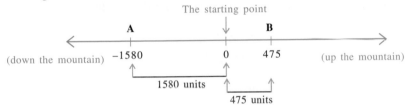

The dashed arrows above the number line indicate that the graph continues without end.

Example 8   Two cyclists start from the same point on a mountain. One travels 1,580 feet down the mountain in 10 minutes, and the other travels 475 feet up the mountain in the same time. Express the distances traveled using signed numbers. How far are they from each other after 10 minutes?

Solution   Let the starting point represent the number 0; "up the mountain" the *positive* direction; and "down the mountain" the *negative* direction.

The starting point

A   B
(down the mountain) −1580   0   475 (up the mountain)

1580 units
475 units

Figure 1.10

Represent 1 foot by 1 unit. Then,

Distance travelled by the first cyclist in 10 minutes
(down the mountain)   = −1,580 feet;

Distance travelled by the second cyclist in 10 minutes
(up the mountain)   = + 475 feet

The positions of the cyclists after 10 minutes is indicated by the points A and B, (Figure 1.10).

The distance between them = distance of A from 0 + distance of B from 0

$$= \left| -1,580 \text{ feet} \right| + \left| 475 \text{ feet} \right|$$

$$= 1,580 \text{ feet} + 475 \text{ feet}$$

$$= 2,055 \text{ feet};$$

hence, after 10 minutes they are 2,055 feet away from each other.

(b) $\left| x \right| < 7$

8. In the year 2002 Tri Com cable showed a loss of $16 million. In 2003 the company showed a profit of $9 million. How much did the profit increase from 2002 to 2003?

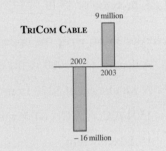

Answers:

4. (a) 16   **(b)** 21   **(c)** 3   **(d)** 35

5. (a) True **(b)** True **(c)** True

6. (a) $x = 8$ or -8 **(b)** No value of a
   (c) $x = 0$

7. (a) $\{\ldots -5, -4, -3, 3, 4, 5, \ldots\}$

-5 -4 -3 -2 -1 0 1 2 3 4 5

   (b) $\{-6, -5, -4, -3, -2, -1, 0, 1, 2, 3, 4, 5, 6\}$

-6 -5 -4 -3 -2 -1 0 1 2 3 4 5 6

8. It increased by $25 million.

Exercise 1.1

A. In exercises 1-10, locate the given number on the number line. Indicate the location by a dot.

1. −5   **2.** 4   **3.** 21   **4.** +16   **5.** −17

6. −9   **7.** 0   **8.** −35   **9.** 11   **10.** −1

In exercises 11-20, write the opposite of the given integer.

11. −5   **12.** 4   **13.** 21   **14.** +16   **15.** −17 *17*

16. −9   **17.** 0 = 0   **18.** −35   **19.** 11   **20.** −1

In exercises 21-30, find the negative (opposite) of the given number.

21. −(−35)   **22.** −(+7)   **23.** −(8 − 3)   **24.** −(−28)   **25.** 14

26. −25   **27.** +19   **28.** −(−10)   **29.** 0   **30.** −26

In exercises 31-35, write the given statement using an integer.

31. 1,700 yd below sea level   **32.** A rise in the price of $2.50   **33.** A deficit of $350

34. A decrease of 35 lb   **35.** A temperature of 17 °C above 0 °C

In exercises 36-44, write the opposite of the given statement.

36. A deposit of $1,000 in the checking account   **37.** A profit of $125

38. A withdrawal of $270 from the checking account.   **39.** 560 yd above sea level   **40.** A loss of $35

41. 1504 A.C. (A.C.: After Christ)   **42.** 8 units to the left of zero on a number line

43. 15° F below zero   **44.** 1360 B.C. (B.C.: Before Christ)

In exercises 45-61, determine whether the given statement is true or false. If the statement is false, change the inequality or equality symbol so that the statement is true.

45. $8 < -5$ **46.** $-5 < 2$ **47.** $4 \leq -4$ **48.** $-10 < -3$ **49.** $0 = -0$

50. $-5 < -8$ **51.** $-5 < 8$ **52.** $-(+12) = -12$ **53.** $4 \leq -7$ **54.** $10 \geq -10$

55. $19 > 20$ **56.** $-(-8) = 8$ **57.** $15 > 17$ **58.** $-15 > -17$ **59.** $-6 < 0$

60. $-20 < -19$ **61.** $9 \leq 19$

B. In exercises 62-73, find the absolute value.

62. $\left|-15\right|$ **63.** $\left|-8\right|$ **64.** $\left|12\right|$ **65.** $\left|-9\right|$

66. $\left|18\right|$ **67.** $\left|0\right|$ 0   **68.** $\left|-45\right|$ **69.** $\left|+45\right|$ *45*

70. $\left|-(-4)\right|$ **71.** $\left|\text{opposite of} +10\right|$ **72.** $\left|-27\right|$ **73.** $\left|\text{opposite of} -16\right|$
−10

In exercises 74-87, determine whether the given inequality statement is True or False. If it is false, change the inequality or equality so that the statement is true.

74. $\left|-8\right| < \left|-3\right|$ **75.** $\left|10\right| < \left|14\right|$ **76.** $\left|-5\right| > \left|4\right|$ **77.** $\left|-9\right| < 5$ **78.** $\left|-4\right| = -4$
−6 < 6

79. $-6 < \left|-6\right|$ *T*   **80.** $\left|-6\right| < -\left|6\right|$ **81.** $\left|-15\right| = -15$ **82.** $\left|27\right| > \left|-27\right|$ **83.** $8 > \left|-8\right|$
15 = −f

84. $\left|-2\right| \leq \left|2\right|$ **85.** $\left|0\right| > \left|-4\right|$ **86.** $\left|-25\right| \geq 25$ **87.** $\left|-16\right| = \left|16\right|$
0 > 4

In exercises 88-92, find the integer values of the variable that satisfy the given equation.

88. $|a| = 7$ 89. $|x| = -5$ 90. $|y| = -1$ 91. $|b| = 0$ 92. $|x| = 35$

In exercises 93-102, find the integers that satisfy the given condition.

93. $|x| < 4$ 94. $|x| \leq 3$ 95. $|a| > 7$ 96. $|y| \geq 9$ 97. $|x| > 0$

98. $|a| > -5$ 99. $|x| \leq 6$ 100. $|x| = -x$ 101. $|y| < -2$ 102. $|b| = 9$

In exercises 103-111, evaluate the given expression.

103. $|+(+26)|$ 104. $11 + |-12|$ 105. $|5| - |0|$ 5   106. $|-|-1||$ 107. $8 - |-3|$

108. $|-20| - 18$ 109. $16 - |-14|$ 110. $|-(-35)|$ 111. $|-23| + |3|$

Applications

112. If 60 miles east of a fire tower is represented by $+60$, how would you represent 75 miles west of the fire tower?

113. On a thermometer, temperatures above zero are written as positive and below zero as negative. How will a reading of 3°C below zero be written?

114. In a bank, the amounts deposited are shown by using positive numbers, and the amounts withdrawn by negative numbers. If a man deposits \$375 on Monday and withdraws \$100 the next day, how will each transaction be shown in his accounts statement?

115. Two friends start from the same point and walk in opposite directions. In 15 minutes, one walks east a distance of 2,590 yd, and the other walks west a distance of 3,400 yd. Find the distance between them after 15 minutes.

1.2 ADDITION AND SUBTRACTION WITH INTEGERS

IMPORTANT VOCABULARY

1. **Additive inverse:** The **opposite** of an integer is called its additive inverse.

    The additive inverse of 4 is -4;

    the additive inverse of -2 is 2.

2. **Inverse property of addition:** The sum of an integer and its additive inverse is 0.

    $4 + (-4) = 0$; $(-2) + 2 = 0$

Objectives

After completing this section, you will be able to:
A. Add integers and recognize the properties of addition;
B. Subtract integers and determine the change between two integer values; and
C. Estimate the sum and the difference of integers.

1.2 A.   Addition with Integers; Properties of Addition

1. Addition with Integers

We already know how to perform the operations of addition and subtraction with whole numbers. Here we will learn to perform these operations with integers.

Finding the Sum of Integers with Like Signs

On a number line, to add 3 + 4, we start with 3. Then, to add 4, we move 4 units to the right. The number corresponding to the end point is the required sum: **3 + 4 = 7**

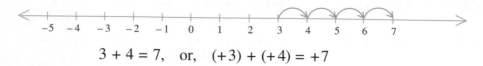

$$3 + 4 = 7, \quad \text{or,} \quad (+3) + (+4) = +7$$

Figure 1.11

In short, to add 4 to 3, we count 4 units to the *right* of 3. The point reached gives us the sum. We shall use this idea to find the sum of positive and negative integers.

- On a number line, *adding a positive number* means to move "**to the right**" or in the positive direction. Adding a negative number means to move "**to the left**" or in a negative direction.

  Adding 3 to a number means 'move 3 units to the right of the number'; adding −4 to a number means 'move 4 units to the left of the number'.

Thus, to find the sum (−3) + (−4), we move 4 units to the left of −3. We end up at the point −7; (See Figure 1.12)

so,   **(−3) + (−4) = −7.**

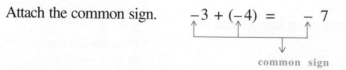

Figure 1.12

- Two negative integers are added exactly the same way as two positive integers but on the left side of 0.

- We can also find the sum of −3 and −4 without using a number line.

To find the sum of −3 and −4:

1. Add their absolute values.

$$\left| -3 \right| = 3 \; ; \quad \left| -4 \right| = 4 \quad \text{and} \quad 3 + 4 = 7$$

2. Attach the common sign. $-3 + (-4) = -7$

common sign

Procedure to add two or more signed numbers with like signs:

　　　Step **1**　　Add the absolute values of the numbers.

　　　Step **2**　　Attach the common sign to the sum obtained in step 1.

Example 1   Add:

    (a) $-15 + (-5)$ **(b)** $125 + 15$

    (c) $-7 + (-13) + (-20)$

Solutions

(a)
    sum of the absolute values

$$-15 + (-5) = -(15 + 5)$$

The common sign

$$= -20$$

Step 1 Add the absolute values of the numbers:

$$|-15| = 15$$
$$+|-5| = 5$$
$$\overline{\quad\quad 20}$$

Step 2 Both numbers are negative; so the sum is negative.

(b)
$$125 + 15 = 140$$

Step 1 Add the absolute values of the numbers:

$$|125| = 125$$
$$+|15| = 15$$
$$\overline{\quad\quad 140}$$

Step 2 Both numbers are positive; so the sum is positive.

(c)
    sum of absolute values

$$-7 + (-13) + (-20) = -(7 + 13 + 20)$$

The common sign

$$= -(40)$$
$$= -40$$

Step 1 $|-7| + |-13| + |-20|$
$= 7 + 13 + 20 = 40$

Step 2 All the numbers are negative; therefore, the sum is negative.

Finding the Sum of Integers with Unlike Signs

Let us find the sum: $(-7) + 4$.

To find the sum $(-7) + 4$, start with -7. Then move 4 units to the right (since 4 is positive). See Figure 1.13.

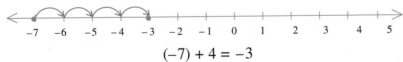

$$(-7) + 4 = -3$$

Figure 1.13

We end up at the point -3; so, $(-7) + 4 = -3$.

Similarly, Figure 1.14 below illustrates the sum $8 + (-3)$. The sum is obtained by moving 3 units to the left of 8. We end up at 5;

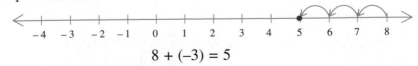

$$8 + (-3) = 5$$

Figure 1.14

so, $8 + (-3) = 5$.   Note that the sum has the sign of 8 (or $+8$) and 8 has a larger absolute value than does -3.

Note

It is obvious from the above discussion that (i) the sum of a number and its own opposite is zero:

$$4 + (-4) = 0 \qquad (-6) + 6 = 0;$$

and (ii) the sum of a signed number and zero is the number itself:

$$5 + 0 = 5 \qquad 0 + (-3) = -3 \qquad 0 + 0 = 0.$$

- We can also find the sum of 8 and -3 without using the number line.

  To find the sum $8 + (-3)$:

  1. Find the difference of the larger absolute value and the smaller absolute value.

$$\left|8\right| - \left|-3\right| = 8 - 3 = 5 \qquad |8| > |-3|$$

  2. Attach the sign of the integer with the larger absolute value.

Procedure to add two signed numbers with unlike signs:

Step **1** Find the absolute values of the two numbers.

Step **2** Subtract the smaller absolute value from the larger one.

Step **3** Prefix the sign of the number that has the larger absolute value.

Warm-Up	**Example 2** Add.

2. Add.

(a) $-85 + 98$

(b) $352 + (-500)$

Example 2 Add.

(a) $-10 + 12$ (b) $8 + (-12)$

Solutions

(a) $\left|-10\right| = 10, \left|12\right| = 12$

$$12 - 10 = 2;$$

thus, $-10 + 12 = \mathbf{2}.$

Step **1** Find the absolute values.

Step **2** Subtract the smaller absolute value (10) from the larger one (12).

Step **3** The positive number has the larger absolute value, so the sum is positive.

The usual shortcut is:

Difference of the absolute values

$$-10 + 12 = +(12 - 10) = 2$$

Sign of the number that has the larger absolute value

$$\begin{array}{r} 12 \\ -\ 10 \\ \hline 2 \end{array}$$

The absolute value of -12

(b) $8 + (-12 = -(12 - 8)$

The absolute value of 8

The sign of the number having larger absolute value (-12)

$$= -(4)$$

$$= \mathbf{-4}.$$

The answer is negative because the number having the larger absolute value is negative.

Answers:

1. (a) -108 (b) 423 (c) -140

2. (a) 13 (b) -148

RULES FOR ADDITION WITH INTEGERS

To summarize the above discussion and to state the rules for addition with integers, we should first note that both the signs + and − are used for two different purposes: as a sign of a number and as an operation symbol.

(i) The sum of two positive integers is positive.

$$(+3) \quad + \quad (+5) \quad = \quad +8$$

positive   plus   positive   positive

[handwritten: + + + = Positive]

(ii) The sum of two negative integers is negative.

$$(-5) \quad + \quad (-7) \quad = \quad -12$$

negative   plus   negative   negative

[handwritten: − + − = Neg]

(iii) The sum of a positive integer and a negative integer may be positive or negative (or zero) depending on which number has the larger absolute value.

$$(+4) \quad + \quad (-9) \quad = \quad -5$$

positive   plus   negative   negative

$|-9| > |4|$, so the sum has the sign of 9.

$$(+8) \quad + \quad (-2) \quad = \quad +6$$

positive   plus   negative   positive

$|+8| > |-2|$, so the sum has the sign of +8.

$$(7) \quad + \quad (-7) \quad = \quad 0$$

positive   plus   negative

Since $|7| = |-7|$, the sum is zero.

(iv) Addition with integers is performed using the following rules:

RULES FOR ADDITION WITH INTEGERS
Rule 1   To add two or more integers with *like* signs, add their absolute values and use the common sign with the sum obtained.
Rule 2   To add two integers with *unlike* signs, subtract their absolute values (the smaller from the larger) and use the sign of the integer that has the larger absolute value.

2. Properties of Addition

Addition of integers has the following properties:

i. Commutative Property: Addition is commutative. That means we can add numbers in any order.

$$8 + (-3) \qquad\qquad (-3) + 8$$

Start from 8 and move 3 units to the left; we end up at 5.

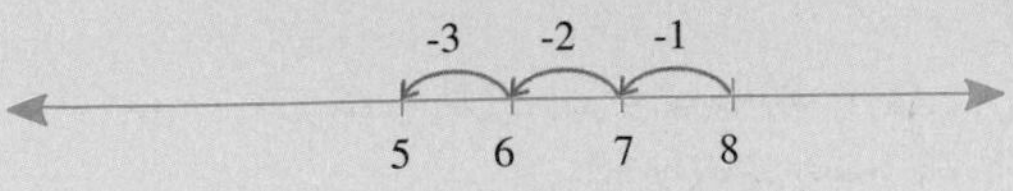

Start from −3 and move 8 units to the right; we end at 5.

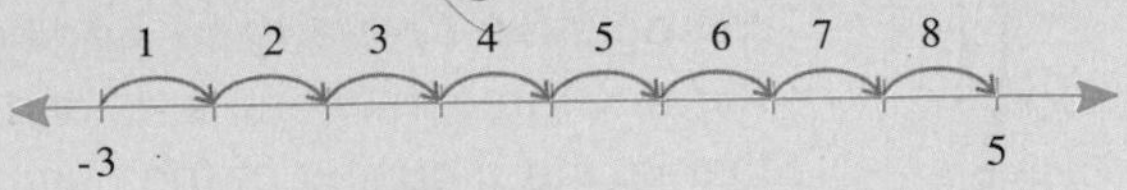

[handwritten number line: −3 −2 −1 0 1 2 3 4 5]

$8 + (-3) = (-3) + 8$;

therefore, the order of addition makes no difference.

> **ii. Associative Property :** Addition is associative; that is, to find the sum of three integers, we can group them in any manner.

For example, $[(-2) + 5] + (-8) = (-2) + [5 + (-8)]$

$[(-2) + 5] + (-8) = 3 + (-8)$	$(-2) + [5 + (-8)] = (-2) + [-3]$
$= -(8 - 3)$	$= -(2 + 3)$
$= -5$	$= -5$

The sum on each side is the same.

We can use both properties to see that even if we first add -2 and -8, and then add 5 to the sum obtained, we will get the same answer:

$$[(-2) + (-8)] + 5 = -(2 + 8) + 5$$
$$= -10 + 5$$
$$= -5$$

We conclude that to find the sum of three (or more) integers, we can group them in any manner.

> **iii. Identity Property :** The number 0 is the additive identity for integers, because the sum of an integer and 0 is the same integer.

Examples: $0 + (-2) = -2$ $3 + 0 = 3$ $0 + (+9) = +9$ $0 + 0 = 0$

> **iv. Inverse Property :** When a number is added to its additive inverse (opposite) the sum is always zero.

Since $3 + (-3) = 0$, we say that 3 is the additive inverse of -3, or that -3 is the additive inverse of 3.

Since 3 and -3 are opposites of each other, we find that the *additive inverse* of an integer is the same as its *opposite*. Thus, we have the following definition:

> *Definition:*
>
> The **opposite** of an integer is called its **additive inverse**.

The sum of an integer and its additive inverse is 0. For example,

additive inverse of 12 is -12; $12 + (-12) = 0$

additive inverse of -4 is 4; $(-4) + 4 = 0$

additive inverse of 0 is 0; $0 + 0 = 0$

We conclude the discussion by stating the above properties in general terms.

> **Properties of Addition**
>
> 1. **Commutative Property of Addition**
>   For any two integers a and b, $a + b = b + a$;
>   that is, the order of numbers in addition can be changed.
>
> 2. **Associative Property of Addition**
>   For any three integers a, b, and c, $(a + b) + c = a + (b + c)$;
>   that is, the grouping of the numbers can be changed.

3. **Identity Property of Addition**
   For any integer a, $a + 0 = a$; $0 + a = a$.
   The number 0 is the **additive identity** for integers.

4. **Inverse Property of Addition**
   For every integer a, there is another integer, namely its opposite $-a$,
   called the **additive inverse** of a such that $a + (-a) = 0$.
   The additive inverse of 0 is 0 itself.

Example 3   Identify the property that is demonstrated.

   (a) $(-2 + 6) + (-8) = -2 + [6 + (-8)]$

   (b) $0 + (-9) = -9$

Solutions

   (a) $(-2 + 6) + (-8) = -2 + [6 + (-8)]$

   Associative Property of Addition.

   (b) $0 + (-9) = -9$

   Identity Property of addition.

Example 4   Fill in the blanks to make the statement true.

   (a) $-3 + 4 = \underline{\hspace{1cm}} + (-3)$

   (b) $-6 + \underline{\hspace{1cm}} = 0$

Solutions:

   (a) $-3 + 4 = \underline{\hspace{1cm}} + (-3)$

   $-3 + 4 = \mathbf{4} + (-3)$

   Commutative Property.

   (b) $-6 + \underline{\hspace{1cm}} = 0$

   $-6 + \mathbf{6} = 0$

   Inverse Property.

Warm-Up

3. Identify the property that is demonstrated.

   (a) $[5 + (-3)] + (-4) = 5 + [-3 + (-4)]$

   (b) $(-8) + 4 = 4 + (-8)$

4. Fill in the blanks to make the statement True.

   (a) $-7 + (-5) = \underline{\hspace{0.5cm}} + (-7)$

   (b) $8 + \underline{\hspace{0.5cm}} = 0$

- **Adding a group of Integers**

The properties of addition discussed above are very useful for adding a large group of integers, as explained in the following procedure

Procedure to add a group of signed numbers:

   Step 1   Using the commutative and associative properties of integers, group together integers of like signs.

   Step 2   Add all the positive numbers and all the negative numbers separately.

   Step 3   Add the two sums obtained in Step 2.

5. Simplify:

(a) $-48 + 15 + (-17) + 26$

(b) $35 + (-46) + 58$

Example 5 Simplify:

(a) $-12 + 9 + (-20) + 15$ (b) $56 + (-72) + 21$

Solutions

(a) Using the Associative property of addition we can re-arrange the numbers in this sum to group together the numbers with like signs.

$$-12 + 9 + (-20) + 15 = -12 + (-20) + 9 + 15$$

First, add the negative numbers:

$$-12 + (-20) = -(12 + 20)$$
$$= -32.$$

Next, add the positive numbers: $9 + 15 = 24.$

Now, add the two sums obtained above:

$$-32 + 24 = -(32 - 24)$$
$$= -8.$$

- $|-32| = 32$, $|24| = 24$
- Difference of the absolute values $= 32 - 24 = 8$.
- Use the sign of -32, since -32 has the larger absolute value.

Hence, $-12 + 9 + (-20) + 15 = -8.$

The usual shortcut is:

$$-12 + 9 + (-20) + 15$$
$$= [-12 + (-20)] + [9 + 15]$$
$$= (-32) + (24)$$
$$= -(32 - 24)$$
$$= -8.$$

- Group the numbers having like signs.
- Add the numbers in each group.
- Add the numbers having unlike signs as explained in Example 2.

(b) $56 + (-72) + 21$

$$= (56 + 21) + (-72)$$
$$= 77 + (-72)$$
$$= +(77 - 72)$$
$$= 5.$$

- Use the Associative property to group the numbers having like signs.
- Add the numbers in each group.
- Add the numbers having unlike signs.

 • **Using Calculator to Compute the Sum**

On a scientific calculator the key marked $\boxed{(-)}$ gives the "opposite". The key marked $\boxed{-}$ is used for subtraction. To find the opposite of 14,

ENTER $\boxed{(-)}$ $\boxed{14}$; thus, -14 is entered as $\boxed{(-)}$ $\boxed{14}$.

DISPLAY -14 → Opposite of 14

and to find the opposite of -7,

ENTER $\boxed{(-)}$ $\boxed{(-)}$ $\boxed{7}$

DISPLAY 7 ← Opposite of -7

Example 6   Compute the sum on a calculator.

$$-45 + 732 + (-126) + (-65)$$

ENTER   [(−)] [45] [+] [732] [+] [(−)] [126] [+] [(−)] [65] [=]

DISPLAY   496
                ↑
            The sum

6. (a) Find the opposites.
   (i) 45   (ii) − 36

(b) Find the sum.
   $26 + (-348) + (-152) + 193$

Answers:

3. (a) Associative property of Addition.
   (b) Commutative property of Addition.
4. (a) −5   **(b)** (−8)
5. (a) − 24   **(b)** 47
6. (a) i. − 45; **ii.** 36 **(b)** − 281

1.2 B.   Subtraction with Integers

a. Subtraction of Integers

Juanita, a college student, currently owes her parents $8,000 for educational loans. On her birthday, her father announces that he has had a wonderful year in his business and that he will celebrate by reducing $5,000, the money that Juanita currently owes her parents. Juanita thinks to herself, "This is just as good as if he had just handed me a check for $5,000!" Juanita now owes her parents only $3,000.

$$-\$8,000 - (-\$5,000) = -\$8,000 + \$5,000 = -\$3,000$$

Recall from Chapter 0 that one definition of subtraction is finding the missing term in an addition.

$$-8,000 - (-5,000) = ?$$ means $$-5,000 + ? = -8,000$$

The number line version of this subtraction problem is pictured below.

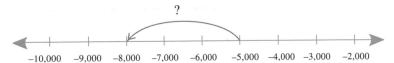

From the picture it is clear that the answer is **−3,000.**

We must move 3,000 places to the left of − 5,000 to get − 8,000.

Examine the addition problem **−8,000 + 5,000 = ?**, which is pictured below. It is a different problem, but it has the same answer, −3,000.

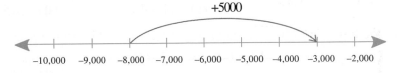

Notice that **−8,000 − (−5,000)** is numerically equivalent to **−8,000 + 5,000.**

Subtracting always gives the same answer as adding the opposite (additive inverse) of the second term.

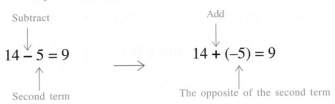

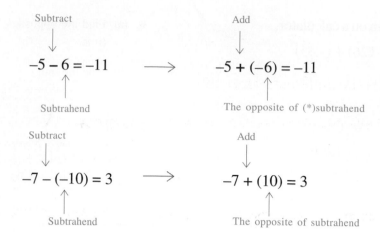

Subtract → $-5 - 6 = -11$ ⟶ Add → $-5 + (-6) = -11$

Subtrahend   The opposite of (*)subtrahend

* **Subtrahend** means the number being subtracted.

Subtract → $-7 - (-10) = 3$ ⟶ Add → $-7 + (10) = 3$

Subtrahend   The opposite of subtrahend

To subtract the second number from the first number, therefore, change the sign of the second number and add to the first number.

For example, $\quad -15 - 4 = -15 + (-4) = -19 ; \qquad 7 - (-8) = 7 + (8) = 15.$

The above rule enables us to define the **difference** of two integers as follows:

> ### Definition:
>
> For any two integers a and b, the difference between a and b is defined as follows:
>
> $$a - b = a + (-b)$$
>
> minus   plus   opposite

Procedure to subtract two signed numbers:

 Step **1** Rewrite each subtraction as an addition of the opposite of the number being subtracted.

 Step **2** Find the sum.

Warm-Up

7. Simplify:

(a) $-278 - (-143)$

(b) $-5 - 19$

Example 7

Simplify:

(a) $-13 - (-5)$ (b) $-48 - 76$

(c) $24 - 45$ (d) $245 - (-36)$

Solutions

(a) $\mathbf{-13 - (-5)} = -13 + (5)$

             $= -(13 - 5)$

             $= \mathbf{-8}$

- Here, -5 is to be subtracted. Rewrite as an addition problem by adding 5, the opposite of -5.
- Since the signs are different, we subtract the absolute values and use the sign of -13, since it has the larger absolute value.

(b) $\mathbf{-48 - 76} = -48 + (-76)$

             $= -(48 + 76)$

             $= \mathbf{-124}$

- The number to be subtracted is 76. Rewrite as an addition problem by adding -76, the opposite of 76.
- Add. Since both numbers have like signs, we add their absolute values, and use the common sign.
- $48 + 76 = 124$

(c) $24 - 45 = 24 + (-45)$

$ = -(45 - 24)$

$ = -21$

- Instead of subtracting 45, add its opposite, -45.
- Add.
- $45 - 24 = 21$.

(d) $245 - (-36) = 245 + (36)$

$ = 245 + 36$

$ = 281$

- Rewrite as addition problem by adding the opposite of -36.
- Add.

Procedure to simplify numerical expressions involving more than two integers:

Step 1 Change each subtraction to addition by adding the opposite of the number to be subtracted.

Step 2 Evaluate the sum.

Example 8 Simplify the following numerical expressions:

(a) $5 - 4 - (-9) - 13$

(b) $-14 - 58 - (-13) - (-16)$

Solutions

(a) $5 - 4 - (-9) - 13$

$= 5 + (-4) + (9) + (-13)$

$= (5 + 9) + [(-4) + (-13)]$

$= 14 + (-17)$

$= -(17 - 14)$

$= -3$.

- Change all subtractions to additions.
- First, add the positive and the negative numbers separately. Then add the two sums.

(b) $-14 - 58 - (-13) - (-16)$

$= -14 + (-58) + (+13) + (+16)$

$= [-14 + (-58)] + [13 + 16]$

$= -72 + 29$

$= -(72 - 29)$

$= -(43)$

$= -43$.

- Change all subtractions to additions.
- Add the negative and positive numbers separately.
- Add the two sums.

 Example 9 Find the difference: $-21,269 - (-19,584)$

Solution

ENTER $(-)$ $\boxed{21269}$ $\boxed{-}$ $(-)$ $\boxed{19,584}$ $\boxed{=}$ $\boxed{-1685}$

$\uparrow$

Final Display

---

8. Evaluate.

(a) $-7 - (-8) - 4 - (-2)$

(b) $23 - 32 - (-5) - (-74)$

9. Find the difference.

$-37,145 - (-4,894)$

(c) $173 - 196$

(d) $387 - (-43)$

b.   Change in Value

Subtraction with integers is often used to find the change in value between two readings of measurements such as temperatures, altitudes, and distances. It is also used to find changes in dollar values such as profit, net worth, or market value.

To calculate the change between two integer values, including directions (positive for up and negative for down), we first identify the 'beginning value' and the 'final value', and then subtract using the following rule:

Change in value = 'the final value' – 'the initial value'.

minus

For example, in the morning of a winter day, within two hours the temperature at a particular place dropped from a high of 22°F above zero to a low of 8°F below zero. The change in the temperature can be obtained as follows:

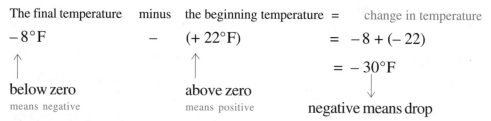

The final temperature	minus	the beginning temperature	=	change in temperature
$-8°F$	$-$	$(+22°F)$		$= -8 + (-22)$
↑		↑		$= -30°F$
below zero		above zero		↓
means negative		means positive		negative means drop

The change was –30°F, which means the temperature dropped by 30 °F.

Example 10   Application

Felicia lives in a city where the altitude is 1,023 feet above sea level. She goes to visit her sister in a city where the altitude is 125 feet below the sea level. How much does her altitude change on the day that she travels to her sister's house?

Solution

The beginning altitude $= +1,023$ ft

The final altitude $= -125$ ft

'Above sea level' is considered the positive direction; 'below sea level', the negative.

$$\begin{aligned} \text{Change} &= \text{Final} - \text{Beginning} \\ &= (-125\text{ ft}) - (1023\text{ ft}) \\ &= -(125 + 1023)\text{ ft} \\ &= -1,148\text{ ft.} \end{aligned}$$

When the word "difference" is used in a subtraction, the first term is the first number mentioned and the second term is the second number mentioned.

Note | Change is the difference between the final and the beginning values.

1.2 C.   Estimating Sums and Differences

We use estimation frequently in our daily routine. When we get money out of an automated teller prior to spending an evening with friends, we estimate the amount needed for the evening. Builders estimate the cost of a building and are awarded a contract based on their estimates. If they are poor estimators, they can lose a lot of money. In mathematics, estimation often refers to predicting an answer before the exact calculation is made.

Adding is a process of putting like amounts together and counting them.

$$\$2981 + \$865 = \$?$$

You might ask: "How much is this altogether?"

If you were estimating you might ask: "Approximately how many hundreds is this altogether?"

To answer this, you would round to hundreds and add.

3,000   +   **9**00 = **3,9**00

30 hundred + 9 hundred = 39 hundred

$$\$3900 \text{ or } \$3,900$$

To estimate is to calculate approximately. An estimate is an approximation.

To estimate a sum or difference, we round all terms to the same place value and then add or subtract. The place value should be large enough to allow simple mental arithmetic. Usually the largest or next-to-largest place value is used.

 Note The more places that we use in estimating, the closer the estimate will be to the actual value. However, we usually want to make the estimate as simple as possible to get a quick approximation of the value of an answer. To keep it quick and simple we usually round only to the largest place value when estimating sums or differences.

Procedure to estimate a sum or difference:

Step **1**   Round all numbers to the largest place value.

Step **2**   Add or subtract to get the estimate.

Example 11   Estimate the sum or difference. Then compare with the actual sum or difference by using a calculator.

(a) $-973 + (-822)$

(b) $973 + 32 + 156 + 46 + 4,678$

(c) $6,349 - 2,950$

Solutions

(a)

-973	$\approx$	-1000	Both have the same largest place value, hundreds.
-822	$\approx$	$-\ 800$	Round to hundreds.
		-1800	The estimate is -1800 or $-1,800$.

(The actual sum is -1795. The estimate is very close.)

(b) $996 - 41 + 167 + 52 + 5500$

(c) $7,519 - 5,840$

Answers:

11. (a) 200; 140   **(b)** 6,800 ; 6,674

    (c) 2,000; 1,679

Rounding to thousands yields the estimate 6,000.
Rounding to hundreds yields the estimate 5,900. The
actual sum is 5,885. Both estimates are close.

Round to **thousands**		or	round to **hundreds**.	
↓			↓	

(b)

0973	→	1000		973	→	1000
0032	→	0000		032	→	000
0156	→	0000	or	156	→	200
0046	→	0000		046	→	000
4678	→	5000		4678	→	4700
		6000				**5900**

All the numbers can be rounded to thousands or they can
all be rounded to hundreds.

(c)

6349	≈	6000
-2950	≈	-3000
		3000

Both numbers have the same largest place value, thousands.
Both are rounded to thousands for estimating.

Exercise 1.2

A.   **In exercises 1-15, add the given numbers using a number line.**

1. $-5 + (-4)$ **2.** $2 + (-7)$ **3.** $-10 + 8$ **4.** $-1 + 7$ **5.** $-3 + (-8)$

6. $-9 + (-2)$ **7.** $10 + (-8)$ **8.** $-7 + 7$ **9.** $-6 + 0$ **10.** $12 + (-15)$

11. $6 - 0$ **12.** $-2 + (-3)$ **13.** $5 + (-5)$ **14.** $4 + (-6)$ **15.** $-5 + 11$

In exercises 16-35, perform addition.

16. $-23 + (-52)$ **17.** $81 + 39$ **18.** $-143 + (-726)$ **19.** $-75 + (-54)$ **20.** $-15 + 8$

21. $-73 + 42$ **22.** $-15 + 11$ **23.** $23 + (-45)$ **24.** $32 + (-43)$ **25.** $27 + (-76)$

26. $-28 + (-32)$ **27.** $45 + (-59)$ **28.** $57 + (-66)$ **29.** $-46 + (-63)$ **30.** $58 + (-79)$

31. $-76 + (-23)$ **32.** $52 + (-114)$ **33.** $-162 + (-814)$ **34.** $173 + (-161)$ **35.** $512 + (-112)$

In exercises 36-51, simplify the numerical expression.

36. $5 + (-9) + 3 + (-4)$ **37.** $-14 + 48 + (-61) + (-63)$ **38.** $-21 + 25 + (-34) + 18$ **39.** $-11 + 26 + (-37) + 19$

40. $-13 + 27 + (-38) + 20$ **41.** $-17 + 16 + (-18) + 21$ **42.** $12 + (-25) + 18 + (-13)$ **43.** $14 + (-17) + 21 + (-19)$

44. $18 + (–2) + 23 + (–25)$ **45.** $19 + (–23) + 41 + (–24)$ **46.** $25 + (–15) + (–17) + 23$ **47.** $–56 + 32 + (–89) + (–23)$

48. $924 + (–535) + (–389)$ **49.** $–955 + 850 + (–145)$ **50.** $789 + (–987) + 345$ **51.** $–765 + (–456) + 975$

In exercises 52-67, compute the expression using a calculator.

52. $–9 – 4 – 7 + (–3)$ **53.** $–21 – 5 – 8 + (–2)$ **54.** $–4 – (–3) + (–5) + 7 – 2$ **55.** $–6 + (+8) + 10 – 3$

56. $35 – 18 – (– 14) + 5$ **57.** $13 – 21 – (– 15) + 7$ **58.** $21 – 18 + (–18) + 6 – (– 20)$

59. $–16 + (– 8) – 6(– 28)$ **60.** $–(–19) – 16 + (– 15) + 4$ **61.** $132 – (–43) + (–152) + 15$

62. $155 – (– 25) – 90 – (–15)$ **63.** $258 + (–43) – 27 – (–145)$ **64.** $–266 – (–165) + 11 + (–21)$

65. $–284 + (–16) + 250 – (–130)$ **66.** $–292 – (–180)$ **67.** $298 + (–85) – (–15) – 115$

In exercises 68-75, name the property of addition that is illustrated.

68. $–15 + 8 = 8 + (–15)$ **69.** $–25 + 0 = –25$ **70.** $[2 + (–3)] + (–7) = 2 + [(–3) + (–7)]$

71. $(–18) + 18 = 0$ **72.** $–7 + (–8) = –8 + (–7)$ **73.** $12 + (–12) = 0$

74. $0 + (– 9) = – 9$ **75.** $– 4 + [6 + (– 10)] = [– 4 + 6] + (– 10)$

In exercises 76-81, use the properties of addition to fill in the blanks to make the given statements true, and name the property that is used.

76. $5 + (\_\_) = 0$ **77.** $– 2 + (– 3) = (– 3) + (\_\_)$ **78.** $(–9) + (+ 9) = (\_\_)$

79. $[–11 + (–4)] + 7 = – 11 + (\_\_ + 7)$ **80.** $– 25 + (\_\_) = –25$ **81.** $13 + (\_\_) = 0$

B. In exercises 82-106, simplify the numerical expression.

82. $–5 – (–6)$ **83.** $–37 – (– 43)$ **84.** $23 – (–59)$ **85.** $– 45 – 0$ **86.** $–27 – (–14)$

87. $35 – (+ 21)$ **88.** $– 89 – (–89)$ **89.** $78 – 34$ **90.** $45 – (– 17)$ **91.** $–95 – 45$

92. $– 32 – 56$ **93.** $– 32 – (–56)$ **94.** $– 32 – (+ 56)$ **95.** $5 – (–8)$ **96.** $45 – (– 35)$

97. $–35 – (+ 60)$ **98.** $– 43 + (–58)$ **99.** $54 – (–56)$ **100.** $–105 – 45$ **101.** $93 – (+ 34)$

102. $98 + (–44)$ **103.** $99 + (–51)$ **104.** $–101 + (–38)$ **105.** $–63 – (+28)$ **106.** $148 + (–88)$

In exercises 107-116, simplify the numerical expression.

107. $–13 – (– 3) – (– 5) – 6$ **108.** $– 12 – 6 – (–19) – (–8)$ **109.** $–5 – 9 – (– 13)$ **110.** $34 – 56 – (– 25)$

111. $28 – (–18) – 5$ **112.** $– 15 – (–25) – |–10|$ **113.** $–5 + |(–11 + 3|) – 2 – (+5)$

114. $[–25 – (–11)] + [–37 – 12]$ **115.** $–18 – [– (– 5)]$ **116.** $26 – 13 + 17 – (–5)$

C. In exercises 117-140, estimate the value of the expression and then find its value using a calculator.

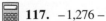

117. $–1,276 – (+486)$ **118.** $–3,758 – (– 2,890)$ **119.** $– 6,825 – 2,340$ **120.** $–3,983 – (– 4,123)$ **121.** $4,234 +1,913$

122. $4,561 – 1,623$ **123.** $5,678 – (–2,567)$ **124.** $–6,457 – (–8,567)$ **125.** $–8,321– (– 2,578)$ **126.** $6,987 – 5,678$

127. 7,123 – (–3,567)   **128.** –7,267 – (–7,654)   **129.** 7,654 – (–3,456)   **130.** 7,831 – (–6,549) **131.** 8,523 – (–4,612)

132. 19,789 – 12567   **133.** 21,123 – 19,001   **134.** 26,504 – 25,012   **135.** 28,001 – 24,001   **136.** 31,543 + (–21,231)

137. 35,240 – (–42,150) **138.** 76,341 + (–45,456) **139.** 235,150 – (+17,385) **140.** 254,100 + (–18,395)

141. What should be added to –5 to get a sum of –18?   **142.** What should be added to –14 to get a sum of –25?

143. What should be subtracted from – 8 to get a difference of 12?

144. What should be subtracted from –15 to get a difference of –10?

Applications

145. Find the change in temperature:
   (a) from 3° below zero to 7° below zero ;   **(b)** from 6° below zero to 5° above zero.

146. Find the change in temperature: **(a)** from 10° below zero to 5° below zero; **(b)** from 15° above zero to 3° below zero.

147. Find the change in direction: **(a)** from 40° W to 20° W;   **(b)** from 20° E to 60° E.
   (*Hint:* E is for East, means positive; W is for West, means negative.)

148. Find the gain or loss of points in a game: **(a)** from 40 to –100; **(b)** from –40 to 180.

149. A new business has a profit of $400 in the first month, a loss of $1,300 in the second month, and a profit of $800 in the third month. Find the net profit or net loss over the first three months using integers.

150. An airplane was flying at an altitude of 25,700 feet. Later, it dropped by 22,800 feet. Find the new altitude.

151. The lowest temperature ever recorded in Little Rock, Arkansas is –5 °F. The highest temperature ever recorded is 117 °F more than the lowest temperature ever recorded. What is the highest temperature recorded?

152. On a particular day the maximum temperature was 43° F. The next day the maximum temperature was –5° F. What was the change in the temperature?

153. On the morning of a winter day the temperature at a particular place was 10° F below zero. By noon, the temperature was 18° F above zero. By how much did the temperature change?

154. The top of Mount Whitney, visible from Death Valley, has an altitude of 14,494 ft above sea level. The bottom of Death Valley is 282 ft below sea level. Using zero as sea level, determine the difference between these two altitudes.

155. Viking II records low and high temperatures of –180° C and –105° C for one day on the surface of Mars. What is the change in temperature for that day?

156. In four days, the stock market showed a gain of 32 points, a gain of 10 points, a loss of 20 points, and a loss of 25 points. What was the net change in the stock market in four days?

1.3 MULTIPLICATION AND DIVISION WITH INTEGERS

1.3 A.   Multiplication with Integers

- **Multiplying Two Integers with Different Signs**

  Two numbers can be multiplied in any order
  (the *commutative* property of multiplication):

  $$4(5) = 5(4); \quad 16 \cdot 8 = 8 \cdot 16; \quad 12 \times 9 = 9 \times 12$$

  We can use the same properties to multiply a positive
  and a negative number. Let us multiply 5 and – 6.

  $$5(-6) = (-6) + (-6) + (-6) + (-6) + (-6) \qquad \text{5 times } -6 \text{ means add } -6 \text{ five times}$$

  $$= -30. \qquad \text{The product is negative.}$$

The same result can be obtained by placing "–" sign before the product: $5(-6) = -(5 \cdot 6)$

$$= -30.$$

With whole numbers, $(4)(5) = 5(4) = 20$.

Similarly,

$$(-4)(5) = 5(-4) = (-4) + (-4) + (-4) + (-4) + (-4)$$

$$\uparrow \qquad = -20 \qquad \text{The product is negative.}$$

Reversing the
order of factors

The same result can be obtained by placing the "–" sign before the product $(-4)5 = -(4 \cdot 5)$

$$= -20$$

Using the above information we get the following rule:

> **The product of a positive and a negative number is the negative of the product of their absolute values.**

This is sometimes stated as: "The product of two numbers with unlike signs is negative." That is,

$$(+)\,(-) = (-) \qquad \text{and} \qquad (-)\,(+) = (-).$$

For example:

$$5\,(-4) = -(5 \cdot 4) \qquad \text{and} \qquad (-7)(4) = -(7 \cdot 4)$$

$$= -20 \qquad\qquad\qquad = -28$$

Procedure to find the product of two integers with unlike signs:

  Step 1   Find the product of their absolute values.

  Step 2   Attach a negative sign to the product.

Example 1   Find the products.

  (a) $4(-5)$ **(b)** $(-45)(3)$

Solutions

  (a) $4(-5) = -(4 \times 5)$ Multiply the absolute values and
  attach the negative sign.

  $$= -20.$$

Objectives 📑

After completing this section, you will be able to:

A. Multiply integers and estimate products; properties of multiplication; and

B. Divide integers and estimate quotients.

Warm-Up

1.   Find the products.

   (a) $-16(4)$

(b) $24\,(-11)$

(b) $(-45)(3) = -[(45)(3)]$

The absolute value of the first factor

The absolute value of the second factor

The product is negative.

$$= -135.$$

- **Multiplying Two Integers with *Like* Signs**

We already know how to multiply two positive numbers, and a positive and a negative number. We use the product of a positive and a negative to develop a procedure for multiplying two negative numbers. Let us study the following pattern carefully:

$$-4(5) = -20$$
$$-4(4) = -16 \qquad -16 = -20 + 4$$
$$-4(3) = -12 \qquad -12 = -16 + 4$$
$$-4(2) = -8 \qquad -8 = -12 + 4$$
$$-4(1) = -4 \qquad -4 = -8 + 4$$
$$-4(0) = 0 \qquad\quad 0 = -4 + 4$$
$$-4(-1) = ?$$
$$-4(-2) = ?$$

We observe that each product is 4 more than the one above it. Continuing this pattern, we have:

$$-4(-1) = 4 \qquad 0 + 4 = 4;\ \text{Also, } 4 = 4(1)$$
$$-4(-2) = 8 \qquad 4 + 4 = 8;\ \text{Also, } 8 = 4(2)$$
$$-4(-3) = 12 \qquad 8 + 4 = 12;\ \text{Also, } 12 = 4(3)$$

and so on.

We observe that in each of the last three cases the product is positive.

The product can be obtained by multiplying the absolute values of the two factors; thus, we get the following rule:

> **The product of two numbers with like signs (that is, both positive or both negative) is positive, and is equal to the product of their absolute values.**

This can be stated as: "The product of two numbers with like signs is positive"; that is,

$$(+)\,(+) = (+) \qquad \text{and} \qquad (-)\,(-) = (+).$$

Examples:

$$(+4)\,(+9) = |+4| \cdot |+9| = 4 \cdot 9 = 36 \ \text{ or } \ (+36);$$
$$(-3)\,(-5) = |-3| \cdot |-5| = 3 \cdot 5 = 15 \ \text{ or } \ (+15).$$

- Note that the additive inverse (the opposite) of an integer a can be treated as -1 times a; that is,

$$-a = (-1) \cdot a.$$

opposite

Procedure to find the product of two (or more) integers:

> *Step* **1** Find the product of their absolute values.
>
> *Step* **2** **a.** The product is positive if there is an *even* number of negative factors or no negative factor.
>
> **b.** The product is negative if there is an *odd* number of negative factors.

Example 2   Multiply.

(a) $(-16)(-5)$ (b) $2(-7)(5)(-3)(-4)$

(c) $-9(-12)(-5)(6)(-1)$

Solutions

(a) $(-16)(-5) = 16 \cdot 5$
- Multiply the absolute values.

$\quad\quad\quad = 80$
- The product of two negative integers is positive.

(b) $2(-7)(5)(-3)(-4)$

There is an odd (3) number of negative factors, therefore, the product is negative.

$\quad = -(2 \cdot 7 \cdot 5 \cdot 3 \cdot 4)$
- Multiply the absolute values.

Numbers can be grouped in any manner.

Grouping the numbers whose product is 10 makes calculations easier.

$\quad = -(2 \cdot 5 \cdot 7 \cdot 3 \cdot 4)$
- The product is negative since there are 3 (an odd number) negative factors.

$\quad = -(10 \cdot 21 \cdot 4)$

$\quad = -(210 \cdot 4)$

$\quad = -840$

(c) $-9(-12)(-5)(6)(-1)$
- Multiply the absolute values.

$\quad = 9 \cdot 12 \cdot 5 \cdot 6 \cdot 1$
- There is an even number (4) of negative factors, therefore, the product is positive.

$\quad = 9 \cdot 60 \cdot 6$

$\quad = 540 \cdot 6$

Note: For fast multiplication, select the appropriate combinations.

$\quad = 3,240$

- **Estimating Products**

To estimate products each number is rounded to its largest place value. The largest place value is always the first value. This is called **front-end rounding.**

To front-end round -382, we round to the nearest hundred, -400.

To estimate the product of $-3,982$ and 43, front-end round each factor. Then multiply.

$$
\begin{array}{rcr}
-3,982 & \approx & -4,000 \\
\times \quad 43 & \approx & \times 40 \\
\hline
 & & -160,000
\end{array}
\quad
\begin{array}{l}
\searrow \rightarrow \ \ 4 \text{ zeros} \\
\\
\leftarrow \ \ 4 \text{ zeros}
\end{array}
$$

The estimate of the product is –160,000. The actual product is –171,226.

(Note the use of the short cut for multiplication involving factors with trailing zeros.)

Procedure for estimating a product:

Step 1   Front-end round each factor.

Step 2   Multiply the rounded factors.

Warm-Up

3. Estimate the product of 6,852 and 594. Then compare with the actual product.

Answers:

1. (a) – 64   (b) –264
2. (a) 45   (b) –4,800   (c) 840
3. 4,200,000; 4,070,088

Example 3 Estimate the product of 472 and 8,593. Then compare with the actual product.

Solution

$$
\begin{array}{rcr}
8{,}593 & \approx & 9{,}000 \\
\times\,472 & \approx & \times\,500 \\
\hline
 & & 4{,}500{,}000
\end{array}
$$

- Front end round factors.
- Multiply using short cut.

The estimate is 4,500,000. The actual product is 4,055,896.

- The properties for multiplication are similar to the properties we stated for addition.

1. Commutative Property of Multiplication

For any two numbers a and b, $a \cdot b = b \cdot a$;

that is, the order of numbers in multiplication can be reversed.

Examples:
- $5(-3) = (-3)(5)$ The product on each side is –15.
- $(-7)(-8) = (-8)(-7)$ The product on each side is 56.

2. Associative Property of Multiplication

For any three numbers a, b, and c, $(a \cdot b) \cdot c = a \cdot (b \cdot c)$;

the grouping of the numbers can be changed.

Example:
- $[4 \cdot (-5)] \cdot (-6) = 4 \cdot [(-5) \cdot (-6)]$
- $(-20)(-6) = 4 \cdot (30)$
- $120 = 120$

3. Identity Property for Multiplication

For any number a $a \cdot 1 = a$; $1 \cdot a = a$.

The product of 1 and the number is the same number.

The number 1 is called the **multiplicative identity.**

Examples:
- $(-2) \cdot 1 = -2$
- $1 \cdot (-3) = -3$
- $4 \cdot 1 = 4$

4. Zero Factor Property

For any integer a $a \cdot 0 = 0$; $0 \cdot a = 0$.

The product of a number and 0 is always 0.

Examples:
- $0(-3) = 0$; $0(+6) = 0$; $8 \cdot 0 = 0$

Note   The inverse property for multiplication will be defined when we discuss division of fractions in Chapter 4.

Example 4   Complete the following statements.

(a) $9(-2) = (-2)\,(\underline{})$ (b) $3(4 \cdot 8) = (3 \cdot 4)\,(\underline{})$

(c) $(-4) \cdot 1 = (\underline{})$ (d) $(-5) \cdot 0 = (\underline{})$

Solutions

(a) $9(-2) = (-2)(\mathbf{9})$ Commutative property for multiplication.

(b) $3(4 \cdot 8) = (3 \cdot 4)(\mathbf{8})$ Associative Property

(c) $(-4) \cdot 1 = (\mathbf{-4})$ Identity Property

(d) $(-5) \cdot 0 = (\mathbf{0})$ Zero Factor Property

Example 5   Identify the property illustrated in the following statements.

(a) $(-9) \cdot 1 = -9$ (b) $7[2(-9)] = [7 \cdot 2]\,(-9)$

(c) $(-7) \cdot 4 = 4 \cdot (-7)$

Solutions

(a)   Identity Property for Multiplication.

(b)   Associative Property for Multiplication.

(c)   Commutative Property for Multiplication.

Warm-Up

4.   Complete the following statements.

(a) $(-9) \cdot 2 = 2 \cdot (\underline{})$

(b) $4(3 \cdot 7) = (4 \cdot 3) \cdot (\underline{})$

(c) $1 \cdot (-9) = (\underline{})$

(d) $0 \cdot (7) = (\underline{})$

5.   Identify the property illustrated in the following statements.

(a) $7 \cdot (-4) = (-4) \cdot 7$

(b) $8 \cdot [(-4) \cdot 9] = [8 \cdot (-4)] \cdot 9$

(c) $(-8) \cdot 1 = -8$

---

5.   Distributive Property of Multiplication over Addition or Subtraction

If *a, b,* and *c* are any three numbers, then

$a \cdot (b + c) = a \cdot b + a \cdot c;$

$(a + b) \cdot c = a \cdot c + b \cdot c;$

that is, multiplication distributes over addition.

$a \cdot (b - c) = a \cdot b - a \cdot c;$

$(a - b) \cdot c = a \cdot c - b \cdot c;$

that is, multiplication distributes over subtraction.

Example:
$$(-3) \cdot (-2 + 5) = \underbrace{(-3) \cdot (-2)} + \underbrace{(-3) \cdot 5}$$
$$(-3) \cdot (3) = \quad 6 \quad + \; -15$$
$$-9 = \quad -9.$$
Both left and right sides are equal.

Warm-Up

6. Complete the following statements.

(a) $9(-3+8)$

$= ?(-3) + ?(8)$

(b) $-5(7-4)$

$= (-5)(?) + (?)(-4)$

7. Simplify the following expressions.

(a) $7 + (-2)(4+8)$

(b) $9 + 6(19-12)$

Answers:

4. (a) -9 (b) 7 (c) -9 (d) 0

5. (a) Commutative Property of Multiplication.
   (b) Associative Property of Multiplication.
   (c) Identity Property of Multiplication.

6. (a) $9, 9$ (b) $7, -5$

7. (a) -17 (b) 51

Example 6   Complete the following statements.

(a) $2(4+5) = 2(?) + 2(?)$

(b) $-2(9+2) = (?)9 + (?)(2)$

Solutions

(a) $2(4+5) = 2(?) + 2(?)$

$2(4+5) = 2(4) + 2(5)$ Using distributive property.

(b) $-2(9+2) = (?)9 + (?)2$ Using distributive property.

$-2(9+2) = (-2)9 + (-2)2$ Using distributive property.

Example 7   Simplify the following expressions.

(a) $4 + 3(4+8)$ (b) $-2 + 4(6-4)$

Solutions

(a) $4 + 3(4+8) = 4 + 3(4) + 3(8)$ Using distributive property.

$= 4 + 12 + 24$

$= 16 + 24$

$= 40$

(b) $-2 + 4(6-4) = -2 + 4(6) - 4(4)$ Using distributive property.

$= -2 + 24 - 16$

$= 22 - 16$

$= 6$

- The commutative and associative properties of multiplication enable us to find the product of more than two integers. We can multiply any two integers and continue to multiply until all the integers have been multiplied. For example, to find the product $(-3)(5)(-6)(-2)$,

$$(-3)(5)(-6)(-2) = (-15)(-6)(-2) = (+90)(-2) = -180.$$

multiply   multiply   multiply

$(-3)(5) = -15$ $(-15)(-6) = +90$

Using the properties, we can multiply in any order and get the same results.

$$(-3) \cdot (5) \cdot (-6) \cdot (-2) = [(-2) \cdot (5)] \cdot [(-6) \cdot (-3)]$$ Observe that this order makes the multiplication simpler.

$$= (-10) \cdot (18)$$

$$= -180.$$

- If we multiply more than two signed numbers, then:
  the product is *positive* if there is an **even number** of negative *factors*; and
  the product is *negative* if there is an **odd number** of negative *factors*.

$2(-3)(-4)(5) = 120$ There are *two* (even number) negative factors.

$2(-3)(-4)(-5) = -120$ There are *three* (odd number) negative factors.

1.3 B.   Division with Integers

- **Dividing Two Integers with Unlike Signs:**

  Recall that division is the *inverse* operation for multiplication.

  To find the quotient $-15 \div 3$ $\left(\text{or } \dfrac{-15}{3} \right)$ means to find the missing factor in $3 \cdot (?) = -15$.

  Since $3(-5) = -15$,   therefore, $\dfrac{-15}{3} = -5.$

  Similarly, $\dfrac{48}{-6} = -8$ because the missing factor in $(-6)(?) = 48$ is -8.

  Observe that the quotient of a positive and a negative number is the negative of the quotient of their absolute values.

- **Dividing Two Integers with Like Signs:**   We already know how to divide two positive numbers. The quotient of two positive numbers is always positive.

  Let us consider the division of two negative numbers, say -12 and -4.

  $$\frac{-12}{-4} = 3 \qquad \text{because the missing factor in } (-4)(?) = -12 \text{ is } 3.$$

  Observe that 3 is positive and this is the quotient of the absolute values of -12 and -4.
  When we divide two numbers with like signs, the quotient is positive, and is the same as the quotient of their absolute values.

Procedure to divide two integers or signed numbers:

Step **1**   Find the quotient of their absolute values.

Step **2**   If the two integers are of the same sign, the quotient is positive; otherwise, the quotient is negative.

Example 8   Find the quotient.

   (a) $-20 \div 5$ **(b)** $-27 \div (-3)$ **(c)** $24 \div (-4)$

Solutions

(a) $-20 \div 5 \quad = \quad \dfrac{-20}{5}$

$= -\left(\dfrac{20}{5} \right)$ • Divide the absolute values: $|-20| \div |5|$
$= 20 \div 5 = 4$
The quotient of two numbers with unlike signs is negative.

$= -4$

(b) $-27 \div (-3) \quad = \quad \dfrac{-27}{-3}$ • Divide $|-27| \div |-3| = 27 \div 3 = 9.$

$= \dfrac{27}{3}$ • The quotient of two negative numbers is positive.

$= 9$

Warm-Up

8. Find the quotient.

   (a) $-36 \div 6$

   (b) $-44 \div (-11)$

(c) $125 \div (-5)$

(c) $24 \div (-4) = \dfrac{24}{-4}$ • Divide the absolute values : $|24| \div |-4|$

$= 24 \div 4 = 6$

$= -\left(\dfrac{24}{4}\right)$ • Use "–" sign because the numbers have *unlike* signs.

$= -6$

We notice that both multiplication and division have the same rules for determining the sign of the answer.

Multiplication and Division of Two Integers

To multiply or divide two numbers, multiply or divide their absolute values.

If the signs of the two numbers are the same, the result is *positive* (+).

If the signs are unlike, the result is *negative* (–).

Examples:

• $(-15)(-3) = +(15 \cdot 3)$ The signs are the same.

$= 45$

$\dfrac{-15}{-3} = \left(\dfrac{15}{3}\right)$

$= 5$

Examples:

• $15(-3) = -(15 \cdot 3)$

$= -45$ The signs are unlike.

$\dfrac{15}{-3} = -\left(\dfrac{15}{3}\right)$

$= -5$

Warm-Up

9. Find the quotient $-954{,}720 \div (-765)$ to the nearest hundred.

Example 9 Compute the quotient and round the quotient to the nearest ten:

$$-146{,}496 \div (-327)$$

Solution

ENTER   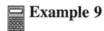 448

$-146{,}496 \div (-327) = 448 \approx 450$ to the nearest ten.

↑

Rounding place

• We conclude the discussion by observing the following facts about division:

(a) The divisor is always a non-zero number. Remember, we cannot divide any number by 0.

Division by 0 is undefined.

Note: Enter $-4 \div 0$ on your calculator and observe what you get.

(b) For any integer a, $\dfrac{a}{1} = a$,   or equivalently , $a = \dfrac{a}{1}$.

(c) For any integer a, $a \neq 0$ $\boxed{\dfrac{0}{a} = 0}$.

Examples: **(a)** $\dfrac{-10}{1} = -10$ **(b)** $\dfrac{0}{-10} = 0$ **(c)** $\dfrac{-10}{0}$ is undefined.

$\longrightarrow$ The estimate of the quotient is 90.

- ## Estimating Quotients

No rounding is needed in order to obtain a good estimate of a quotient.

Carefully locate the position of the first digit in the quotient. Enter that digit or a close guess of its value. Fill in the remaining places with zeros.

$$\begin{array}{r} 90 \\ 43\overline{)3982} \end{array}$$

The actual quotient is very close: 92 R 26.

Example 10 Estimate the quotient. Then compare with the actual quotient. $\quad -35,942 \div 57$

Solution

To estimate the quotient, carefully place the first digit in the quotient. Enter zeros for the remaining places.

$$\begin{array}{r} -600 \\ 57\overline{)-35942} \end{array}$$

The first digit in the quotient is placed above the 9 in the dividend.

The estimate of the quotient is -600. It is close to the actual value.

$$\begin{array}{r} 630 \\ 57\overline{)35942} \\ -35910 \\ \hline 32 \end{array} \quad \longleftarrow 630 \times 57$$

A calculator division yields a quotient of 630 with a remainder of 32.

Example 11 **(Application)**

A certain company loses \$538,875 during a 15-month period. Determine the average monthly loss.

Solution

The company's loss during a 15-month period

$= -\$538,875$;

therefore, the average monthly loss

$= -\$538,875 \div 15 = -35,925.$ Use calculator.

So, the company's average monthly loss

$= -\$35,925.$

Exercise 1.3

Multiplication

A. **In exercises 1-19, find the product.**

1. $3(-9)$ 2. $(-8)5$ 3. $4(-7)$ 4. $(-5)4$ 5. $(-16) \cdot 4$

6. $-27 \cdot 4$ 7. $8 \cdot (-5)$ 8. $-7 \cdot 5$ 9. $9 \cdot (-3)$ 10. $24 \cdot (-15)$

11. $-18 \cdot (-5)$ 12. $(-9)(-8)$ 13. $(16)(8)$ 14. $12 \cdot 30$ 15. $-7 \cdot (-34)$

16. $(-9)(-7)$ 17. $(6)(-15)$ 18. $(-20)(4)$ 19. $(-13)(-8)$

In exercises 20-39, find the product.

20. $-18(-5)(2)$ 21. $15(-10)(-9)(-8)$ 22. $-8(-6)(-5)$ 23. $(-1)(-1)(-3)(-4)(5)$

24. $(-3)(-2)(6)(0)$ 25. $4(-3)(-2)(1)$ 26. $(-1)(-1)(-1)(375)$ 27. $(-2)(-3)(-4)(-1)$

28. $-6(-2)(4)(-1)$ 29. $(-1)(-1)(-1)(-1)(-1)$ 30. $(-2)(-2)(-3)(15)$ 31. $(-2)(-4)(-8)(-16)$

32. $-7(-5)(-6)(-4)$ 33. $-11(-2)(-2)(-2)$ 34. $12(-3)(-3)(-3)$ 35. $-15(-2)(-5)(-8)$

36. $-16(-1)(-3)(-5)$ 37. $18(-1)(-2)(-4)$ 38. $25(-2)(-5)(-6)$ 39. $28(-2)(-2)(-5)(-5)$

In exercises 40-59, estimate the product and compare it with the actual product using a calculator.

40. 340×491 41. -541×356 42. 475×583 43. -491×598

44. -565×621 45. 611×461 46. -632×499 47. -665×55

48. $482 \times 1,783$ 49. $413 \times 1,810$ 50. $-581 \times 1,970$ 51. $-563 \times 2,617$

52. $615 \times 2,913$ 53. $651 \times 2,999$ 54. $-692 \times 2,888$ 55. 713×299

56. $749 \times 2,999$ 57. $-814 \times 2,987$ 58. $889 \times 3,492$ 59. $-886 \times 3,942$

In exercises 60-66, name the property of multiplication that is illustrated.

60. $-3((-5) \cdot 7) = ((-3) \cdot (-5)) \cdot 7$ 61. $(-12) \cdot (5) = 5 \cdot (-12)$ 62. $-4(3 + (-1)) = -4 \cdot 3 + (-4)(-1)$

63. $-17 \cdot 1 = -17$ 64. $-40 = -40 \cdot 1$ 65. $-2[-5 + (-3)] = (-2)(-5) + (-2)(-3)$

66. $3 \cdot (-5) \cdot (-4) \cdot (8) = (-5) \cdot (-4) \cdot 8 \cdot 3$

In exercises 67-71, find by inspection the value of the variable that will make the given statement true, and name the property of multiplication used.

67. $1 \cdot (-8) = x$ 68. $(-3)(-11) = (-11)x$ 69. $(2 \cdot 3)(-5) = 2 \cdot (y \cdot (-5))$

70. $(-12)(-3 + 8) = (-12)a + (-12) \cdot 8$ 71. $a \cdot 1 = -25$

B. **In exercises 72-91, find the quotient.** Division.

72. $84 \div (-12)$ 73. $(-54) \div 6$ 74. $108 \div (-6)$ 75. $305 \div (-5)$ 76. $\dfrac{-32}{4}$

77. $\dfrac{-20}{-4}$ 78. $\dfrac{-75}{-5}$ 79. $\dfrac{-45}{0}$ 80. $\dfrac{56}{0}$ 81. $\dfrac{-42}{1}$

82. $\dfrac{840}{-1}$ **83.** $\dfrac{-240}{-60}$ **84.** $\dfrac{-25}{-1}$ **85.** $\dfrac{0}{4}$ **86.** $\dfrac{-72}{12}$

87. $\dfrac{78}{-6}$ **88.** $\dfrac{-117}{13}$ **89.** $\dfrac{343}{7}$ **90.** $\dfrac{-85}{-5}$ **91.** $\dfrac{-729}{9}$

In exercises 92-111, estimate the quotient and compare it with the actual quotient using a calculator.

92. $285 \div 26$ **93.** $394 \div 24$ **94.** $(-444) \div 37$ **95.** $494 \div 39$ **96.** $525 \div 46$

97. $655 \div 43$ **98.** $695 \div (-43)$ **99.** $713 \div 45$ **100.** $777 \div 51$ **101.** $791 \div 56$

102. $1,032 \div (-25)$ **103.** $1,212 \div 27$ **104.** $1,332 \div 28$ **105.** $1,671 \div 29$ **106.** $1,855 \div 31$

107. $2,241 \div 32$ **108.** $2,359 \div 36$ **109.** $2,743 \div 29$ **110.** $(-3,142) \div 54$ **111.** $3,859 \div 59$

 In exercises 112-121, divide using a calculator. Round the quotient as indicated.

112. $-12,204 \div (-27)$; to the nearest hundreds

113. $-15,394 \div 43$; to the nearest tens

114. $131,456 \div (-35)$; to the nearest hundreds

115. $4,268 \div (-4)$; to the nearest thousands

116. $-77,625 \div (-345)$; to the nearest tens

117. $(-1,461,184) \div (-578)$; to the nearest hundreds

118. Subtract the quotient of -72 and 8 from the product of -4 and -5.

119. Find the sum of the product of 6 and -12 and the quotient of -45 and -5.

120. What integer should be multiplied by -5 to get the product 60?
(*Hint:* The product is positive, so both the factors must have like signs.)

121. What integer should be used as a divisor of 45 to get the quotient of -9?

Applications

122. Over a period of 18 months, a company loses $76,500 in its stock market account. What is the company's average loss per month, expressed as a signed number?

123. During a 12-month period, the total tax deduction from Jim Johnson's salary amounts to $4,140. Express the deduction as a signed number, and use this to find his average monthly tax deduction.

124. Mrs. Marrison loses 48 pounds in 12 weeks. Express the total weight loss as a signed number, and use it to find her average weekly loss.

1.4   EXPONENTS; ORDER OF OPERATIONS; EVALUATING NUMERICAL EXPRESSIONS

Objectives 📖

After completing this section, you will be able to:

A. Identify the base and the exponent of the exponential form of the product, and evaluate the product;

B. Multiply or divide an integer by a power of 10; and

C. Use the rules for the order of operations to evaluate numerical expressions.

IMPORTANT VOCABULARY 💾

1.   The symbol 5^4 (read : "the fourth **power** of 5", or "5 raised to the fourth **power**") represents the repeated product $5 \times 5 \times 5 \times 5$, and is called the **exponential form** of the product.

2.   In 5^4, 5 is called the **base**, and 4 is called the **exponent**.

3.   The exponents 2 and 3 are often read as **"squared"** and **"cubed"**.

   4^2 is read as **"4 squared"** ;

   $7^3 = 343$ is read as **"7 cubed** is equal to three hundred forty-three".

4.   The symbols of grouping are:

   Parentheses ( ),   braces { },   brackets [ ] and the **fraction bar** $\frac{\square}{\square}$.

5.   A **numerical expression** is an expression involving numbers, symbols of operations $(+, -, \times, \div)$, exponents, and grouping symbols.

6.   To **simplify** means to write in the simplest form.

1.4 A.   Identifying the Base and the Exponent of the Exponential form of the Product and Evaluate the Product

The product $4 \times 4 \times 4 \times 4 \times 4$ is written as 4^5, and is read: the fifth power of 4, or 4 raised *to the fifth power.*

   $4^5 = 4 \times 4 \times 4 \times 4 \times 4 = 1,024.$

In 4^5, 4 is called the **base**; 5 is called the **exponent** of 4.

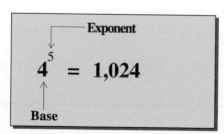

The exponent is a counter. It counts the number of times the base is used as a factor.

• If 1 is used as the exponent, the value is always equal to the base.

   That is, $3^1 = 3$; $5^1 = 5$; $9^1 = 9$.

   Rule :   For any whole number a, $a^1 = a$ or $a = a^1$.

• Let us consider a few more examples for illustration.

$$3 = 3^1$$

$$3 \times 3 = 3^2$$ Read as "the square of 3", *or* "3 **squared**".

$$3 \times 3 \times 3 = 3^3$$ Read as "the cube of 3", *or* "3 **cubed**".

$$3 \times 3 \times 3 \times 3 = 3^4$$ Read as "the fourth power of 3", *or* "3 raised **to the** fourth **power**".

$$3 \times 3 \times 3 \times 3 \times 3 = 3^5$$ Read as "the fifth power of 3", *or* "3 raised **to the** fifth **power**".

$$3 \times 3 \times 3 \times 3 \times 3 \times 3 = 3^6$$ Read as "the sixth power of 3" *or* "3 raised **to the** sixth **power**".

• To evaluate a number written in exponential form, the base is used as a factor as many times as the exponent; thus,

$$4^3 = 4 \times 4 \times 4 = \mathbf{64} \; ; \quad 5^4 = 5 \times 5 \times 5 \times 5 = \mathbf{625}.$$

• If the base is 1, then whatever the exponent is, the value is always one;

thus, $1^1 = 1;$ $1^3 = 1 \cdot 1 \cdot 1 = 1;$ $1^{10} = 1.$

> ***Rule:***   For any whole number a, $1^a = 1$.

***Rule* 1:**   If the exponent is 1, the value is the same as the base.

      $(-3)^1 = -3$ $(-8)^1 = -8$ $(-150)^1 = -150$

***Rule* 2:**   If the exponent is not 1, use the base as a factor as many times as the exponent and compute the product.

      $\mathbf{(-4)^3} = (-4)(-4)(-4)$ The product of an odd number of negative factors is negative.

           $= -64 = -\mathbf{4^3}$

   and $\mathbf{(-3)^6} = (-3)(-3)(-3)(-3)(-3)(-3)$ The product of an even number of negative factors is positive.

           $= 729 = \mathbf{3^6}$

Observe that, when the base is a negative number, the value of the exponential expression is negative or positive depending on whether the exponent is an *odd number* or an *even number*.

      $(-3)^6 = 3^6$ The exponent is an even number, so the value is positive.

      $(-4)^3 = -(4^3)$ The exponent is an odd number, so the value is negative.

• It is very important to distinguish between expressions of the type $(-3)^3$ and -3^3.

      $(-3)^3$ is read as "the cube of negative 3".

      $\mathbf{(-3)^3} = (-3) \cdot (-3) \cdot (-3) = \mathbf{-27}$

      -3^3 is read as "the opposite of the cube of 3".

      $\mathbf{-3^3} = -[3 \cdot 3 \cdot 3] = \mathbf{-27}$

Both give the same answer, but do not mean the same. In fact, if the exponent is even then the two expressions will not be equal.

      $-3^2 \neq (-3)^2$ …why?

   -3^2 is read as "the opposite of the square of 3".

$-3^2 = -[3 \cdot 3] = -9$

$(-3)^2$ is read as "the square of negative 3".

$(-3)^2 = (-3) \cdot (-3) = 9$

Both do not give the same answer.

$$-3^2 \neq (-3)^2$$

Procedure for finding the value of a number written in exponential form:

Step 1 • Identify the base and the exponent.

Step 2 • If the **exponent is 1**, then the value is the base.

• If the **base is 1**, then the value is 1 for any exponent.

• If the exponent is not one, use the base as a factor as many times as the exponent and compute the product.

Warm-Up

1. Name the base and the exponent; then evaluate each power.

(a) 3^4

(b) 6^3

(c) 1^9

(d) -3^4

(e) $(-3)^4$

Example 1 Identify the base and the exponent; then find the value.

(a) 2^4 (b) 4^3 (c) 1^6 (d) -2^4 (e) $(-2)^4$

Solutions

(a) 2^4 The base is 2, and the exponent is 4.

Use 2 as a factor 4 times.
$2^4 = 2 \cdot 2 \cdot 2 \cdot 2$
$= 4 \cdot 2 \cdot 2$
$= 8 \cdot 2$
$= 16$

$2^4 = 16$.

(b) 4^3 The base is 4, and the exponent is 3.

Use 4 as a factor 3 times.
$4^3 = 4 \cdot 4 \cdot 4$
$= 16 \cdot 4$
$= 64$

$4^3 = 64$.

(c) 1^6 The base is 1 and the exponent is 6.

$1^6 = 1$.

(d) -2^4 The base is 2, and the exponent is 4.
$-2^4 = -[2 \times 2 \times 2 \times 2]$
$= -16$

(e) $(-2)^4$ The base is −2, and the exponent is 4.
$(-2)^4 = (-2)(-2)(-2)(-2)$
$= 16$

Example 2 Evaluate 15^4 using a calculator.

Solution A calculator with an exponent key $\boxed{x^y}$ or $\boxed{y^x}$ or $\boxed{\wedge}$ can be used to compute the value of numerical expressions containing exponents:

ENTER $\boxed{15}$ $\boxed{x^y}$ $\boxed{4}$ $\boxed{=}$ 50625;

therefore, $15^4 = 50{,}625$.

Exponents are evaluated before other operations (+, −, ×, ÷).

Procedure to find the value of an expression involving exponents and one more operation:

Step **1** Evaluate all the numbers written in exponential form.

Step **2** Perform the other operation.

Example 3 Evaluate the following expressions:

(a) $4^3 + 15$ (b) $32 - 3^3$

(c) $5 \cdot 2^3$ (d) $\dfrac{6^2}{4}$

Solutions

(a) $4^3 + 15 = \mathbf{4 \cdot 4 \cdot 4} + 15$ • Evaluate 4^3.
$= 64 + 15$ • Add.
$= \mathbf{79}$

(b) $32 - 3^3 = 32 - \mathbf{3 \cdot 3 \cdot 3}$ • Evaluate 3^3.
$= 32 - 27$ • Subtract.
$= \mathbf{5}$

(c) $5 \cdot 2^3 = 5 \cdot \mathbf{2 \cdot 2 \cdot 2}$ • Evaluate 2^3.
$= 5 \cdot 8$ • Multiply.
$= \mathbf{40}$

(d) $\dfrac{6^2}{4} = \dfrac{\mathbf{6 \cdot 6}}{4}$ • Evaluate 6^2.
$= \dfrac{36}{4}$ • Divide.
$= \mathbf{9}$

1.4 B. Multiplying or Dividing an Integer by a Power of 10

• **Powers of 10:** We observe the following interesting results when the base is 10:

$$10^1 = 1\underset{\text{one zero}}{0}; \qquad 10^2 = 10 \times 10 = 1\underset{\text{two zeros}}{00}$$

$$10^3 = 10 \times 10 \times 10 = \mathbf{1000} \qquad\qquad 10^4 = 10 \times 10 \times 10 \times 10 = \mathbf{10{,}000}$$

three zeros   four zeros

In general, **to evaluate any exponent with base 10, we write the number 1, followed by as many zeros as is the exponent.**

$$10^8 = 1\,00{,}000{,}000$$

eight zeros

With this observation, it becomes easy to multiply a whole number by a base ten number.

- **Multiply a whole number by a base ten number.** We know that to multiply a number by 10, we merely have to attach a zero to the right of the number.

$$5 \times 10 = \mathbf{50}; \qquad 23 \times 10 = \mathbf{230}; \qquad 705 \times 10 = \mathbf{7{,}050}$$

Similarly, if a whole number is multiplied by 10^n, where n is a whole number, then we attach n zeros to the right of the number;

thus,

$$56 \times 10^3 = 56 \times 1000 = \mathbf{56{,}000} \qquad\qquad \text{Attach three zeros to the right of 56.}$$

$$125 \times 10^5 = 125 \times 100{,}000 = \mathbf{12{,}500{,}000}. \qquad\qquad \text{Attach five zeros to the right of 125.}$$

- **Dividing a whole number by a base ten number.** Since division is the inverse of multiplication, dividing a number by 10 or 100 or 1000,… will eliminate the last 1 or 2 or 3, … zeros on the right of the number;

so, $32{,}500 \div 10 = 3{,}250$ and $32{,}500 \div 10^2 = 325.$

Use your calculator to verify the results.

Procedure to multiply or divide an integer by 10^n, where n is a whole number.

Step 1   Identify the exponent of 10.

Step 2   If the number is to be multiplied, write the number and attach as many zeros to its right as the exponent of 10.

If the number is to be divided, eliminate the same number of zeros from the right of the number as the exponent. The value eliminated is the remainder.

Warm-Up

4. Evaluate by inspection.

(a) 302×10^6

(b) $43{,}800 \div 10^2$

(c) $375{,}290 \div 10^3$

Example 4   Evaluate by inspection.

(a) 432×10^4 (b) $65{,}000 \div 10^2$ (c) $1{,}250{,}960 \div 10^3$

Solutions

(a) $432 \times 10^4 = 4{,}320{,}000$ The exponent of 10 is 4. To multiply, append 4 zeros to the right of the number.

(b) $65{,}000 \div 10^2 = 650$ The exponent of 10 is 2. To divide, eliminate 2 zeros from the right of the number.

(c) $1{,}250{,}960 \div 10^3 = 1{,}250 \text{ R } 960$ Eliminate three places. The value eliminated is the remainder.

• Notice that :

1 million = 10^6, 1 billion = 10^9, and 1 trillion = 10^{12}

Using these facts it is easy to write amounts that we read in newspapers or articles.

Example 5   Write $36 billion in numeral form.

Solution

$36 billion = $36 × 10^9 Replace billion by "× 10^9".

          = $36,000,000,000   Rewrite, replacing "× 10^9"

                        by 9 zeros.

Example 6   Write 30,250,000 in short form using a power of 10.

Solution

30,250,000   From the given number,

= 30,25**0,000** ⟶   Count the number of zeros that appear continuously on the extreme right. There are 4.

             ⟶

= 3,025 × 10^4 Eliminate 4 zeros, and multiply the remaining number by 10^4.

---

5. Write $14 trillion in numeral form.

6. Write in short form using a power of 10:

            17,250,900

Answers:

4. **(a)** 302,000,000 **(b)** 438 **(c)** 375 R 290

5. $14,000,000,000,000

6. 172,509 × 10^2

1.4 C.   Using the Rules of Operations to simplify Numerical Expressions

A **numerical expression** is a combination of numbers, operations (+, −, ×, and ÷), and exponents.

In previous sections, the expressions involved only one of these operations. Now we shall learn to evaluate numerical expressions which may involve *any* combination of these operations on whole numbers.

To do this, it is necessary to have some laws or rules of order in which the various operations should be performed, so that people, calculators, and computers get the same results. In the absence of such rules, it is possible to interpret even simple numerical expressions like 4 · 5 + 7 in two different ways:

    4 · 5 + 7 = **20** + 7   First multiply,   or   4 · **5 + 7** = 4 · **12**   First add,

               = **27**   then add.   = **48**   then multiply.

We get two different results from the same numerical expression. In order to avoid such a situation, universally accepted *rules for the order of operations* are used.

RULES FOR EVALUATING NUMERICAL EXPRESSIONS INVOLVING GROUPING SYMBOLS

Rule 1   Evaluate any expression(s) within *grouping symbols first*. If grouping symbols are imbedded then start with the innermost grouping.

Rule 2   If an expression involves different operations, perform these operations in the order given below:

   ▸   Evaluate the exponents first, from left to right.

   ▸   Then evaluate multiplications and divisions, from left to right.

   ▸   Finally, evaluate additions and subtractions from left to right.

For example,

     25 − **6 ÷ (−3)** + **8 · 4**

     = 25   **− (−2)**   +   32   • Simplify division (6 ÷ (−3) = −2) and multiplication (8 · 4 = 32).

     = 25 + 2 + 32 = **59**.   • Subtract and then add in order of appearance from left to right.

Warm-Up

7. Simplify.

(a) $3 \times 5 + 4$

(b) $21 - 15 \div (-3)$

(c) $24 \div (-2) + 15$

8. Evaluate.

$12 \times 2 \div (-6) + 16$

9. Perform the indicated operations and simplify.

(a) $3 \cdot (-4)^3 - 8 \cdot 3^2 + 11$

(b) $75 \div 15 \cdot 2^4 - 3 \cdot (-8) - 4$

Example 7 Simplify the following numerical expressions:

(a) $3 \times 2 + 4$ (b) $5 + 2 \times (-3)$ (c) $7 - 8 \div (-2)$

Solutions

(a) $3 \times 2 + 4 = 6 + 4$ Multiply first, then add.

$= 10$

(b) $5 + 2 \times (-3) = 5 + (-6)$ Multiply first, then add.

$= -1$

(c) $7 - 8 \div (-2) = 7 - (-4)$ Divide first, then subtract.

$= 11$

Example 8 Evaluate the following numerical expression:

$$15 - 21 \div 7 \times (-4) + 25$$

Solution

$15 - 21 \div 7 \times (-4) + 25$ • First divide.

$= 15 - 3 \times (-4) + 25$ • Multiply before adding or subtracting.

$= 15 - (-12) + 25$ • Subtract, $15 - (-12) = 15 + 12$

$= 27 + 25$ • Add.

$= 52$

Example 9 Perform the indicated operations and simplify.

(a) $5 \cdot 2^3 - 2 \cdot 4^2 + (-25) - 7 \cdot 3$

(b) $49 \div (-7) \cdot 3^3 + 7 \cdot 4 - 17$

Solutions

(a) $5 \cdot 2^3 - 2 \cdot 4^2 + (-25) - 7 \cdot 3$ • Evaluate exponents. $2^3 = 8$, $4^2 = 16$.

$= 5 \cdot 8 - 2 \cdot 16 + (-25) - 7 \cdot 3$ • Multiply from left to right.

$= 40 - 32 + (-25) - 21$ • Add and subtract from left to right.

$= 8 - 25 - 21$

$= -17 - 21 = -38$

(b) $49 \div (-7) \cdot 3^3 + 7 \cdot 4 - 17$ Evaluate exponent.

$= 49 \div (-7) \cdot 27 + 7 \cdot 4 - 17$ Divide.

$= -7 \cdot 27 + 7 \cdot 4 - 17$ Multiply.

$= -189 + 28 - 17$ Add.

$= -161 - 17$ Subtract.

$= -178$

Evaluating Numerical Expressions using a Calculator

Most calculators are programmed to follow the rules for order of operations. Using a scientific calculator, the procedure is simple. Just enter all the symbols in the given expression in the order you see them from left to right.

 Example 10   Evaluate the expression (a) in Example 9 on a calculator.

Solution   The expression is: $5 \cdot 2^3 - 2 \cdot 4^2 + (-25) - 7 \cdot 3$

ENTER 5 × 2 x^y 3 – 2 × 4 x^y 2

+ ((−) 25) – 7 × 3 = −38

The value is −38, which is the same as obtained earlier in Example 9 a.

Warm-Up

10. Evaluate the expression using a calculator.

$3 \cdot 4^3 - 8 \cdot 3^2 + 11$

Answers:

7. (a) 19   **(b)** 26   **(c)** 3

8. 12   **9. (a)** −253   **(b)** 100

10. 131

 Note   Use parentheses keys for all types of grouping symbols. There are no keys for other grouping symbols such as brackets. Exponents are entered using x^y, or ^ or y^x.

If the expression involves any of the grouping symbols: ( ) parentheses, [ ] brackets, { } braces, or fraction bars then the expressions within these grouping symbols are simplified first, starting at the innermost grouping symbol. For example, let us simplify the following expression:

$4 - \{6 - [-2 + (7 - (1 + 5))]\}$ Evaluate (1 + 5) since this is the innermost grouping.

$= 4 - \{6 - [-2 + (7 - 6)]\}$ Evaluate (7 − 6), the next innermost grouping.

$= 4 - \{6 - [-2 + 1]\}$ Evaluate [−2 + 1].

$= 4 - \{6 - (-1)\}$ Evaluate {6 − (−1)}.

$= 4 - \{6 + 1\}$ 6 − (−1) = 6 + 1

$= 4 - 7$

$= -3$

Example 11   Simplify the following expressions:

(a) $2(5 + 3) - 10$ **(b)** $5 + 2(4 + 3)$

(c) $17 + 3(5 - 10 \div 2)$ **(d)** $-35 + (-18) \div 3$

(e) $5 - 2(4 + 3)$ **(f)** $-4(3) + 5[7 - 6(-4)^2]$

Warm-Up

11. Simplify the following expressions:
(a) $2(3 + 7) - 15$

Solutions

(a) $2(\mathbf{5 + 3}) - 10$ • Simplify within parentheses.

$= \mathbf{2(8)} - 10$ • Multiply.

$= \mathbf{16} - 10$ • Subtract.

$= 6$

(b) $9 + 2(4 + 3)$

(b) $5 + 2(\mathbf{4 + 3})$ • Simplify within parentheses.

$= 5 + \mathbf{2(7)}$ • Multiply.

$= 5 + \mathbf{14}$ • Add.

$= 19$

(c) $21 - 5(12 - 4 \times 2)$

(c) $17 + 3(5 - \mathbf{10 \div 2})$ • Simplify within parentheses. First divide $10 \div 2$,

$= 17 + 3(\mathbf{5 - 5})$ then subtract $5 - 5$.

$= 17 + \mathbf{3(0)}$ • Multiply.

$= 17 + 0$ • Add.

$= 17$

negative   plus   negative

(d) $-24 + (-65) \div 5$

(d) $-35 + (\mathbf{-18}) \div \mathbf{3}$ • First perform the division:

$(-18) \div 3 = \frac{-18}{3} = -6$

$= -\underbrace{35 + (-6)}$ • Now perform the addition.

$= -(35 + 6)$

$= -(41) \text{ or } -41$

(e) $-5 - 2(3 - 7)$

(e) $5 - 2(\mathbf{4 + 3})$ • Simplify within parenthesis first.

$= 5 - \mathbf{2 \cdot 7}$ • Multiply.

$= 5 - 14$ • Subtract.

$= -(14 - 5)$

$= -9$

minus   negative

(f) $-5(4) + 2[15 - 3(-2)^3]$

(f) $-4(3) + 5[7 - 6(\mathbf{-4})^2]$ • Simplify within the brackets.
(i) Evaluate the exponent.

$= -4(3) + 5[7 - \underbrace{6(16)}]$ (ii) Multiply.

$= -4(3) + 5\underbrace{[7 - 96]}$ (iii) Subtract.

$= -4(3) + 5[-89]$ • Perform multiplications, from left to right, in the order they appear.

$= -12 + [-445]$

$= -(12 + 445)$ • Add the two integers.

$= -(457) = \mathbf{-457}$

Important Note

It should be noted that in the above expressions, parentheses are placed around negative integers except when they appear in the beginning of the expression. This is done to avoid any confusion with the meaning of the sign "−". Recall "−" is used for *minus* as well as for *negative numbers*. In the absence of such parentheses, there is a possibility of making an error.

We know, $(-4)^2 = (-4) \times (-4) = 16$, but in the absence of parentheses around − 4, the expression will mean -4^2, read as "the negative of 4^2", and equal to − 16. Omitting parentheses, can lead to a wrong answer. In general, for a non-zero integer x, $-x^2 \neq (-x)^2$.

Example 12 Simplify the expression:

$$10^3 - 2[(13+3) \div 2^4 + 18 \div 3^2]$$

Solution

$$10^3 - 2[(\mathbf{13+3}) \div 2^4 + 18 \div 3^2]$$
• Simplify within parentheses, the inner most grouping symbol.

$$= 10^3 - 2[\quad 16 \quad \div \mathbf{2^4} + 18 \div \mathbf{3^2}]$$
• Simplify within the brackets:
  (i) Simplify the exponent.

$$= 10^3 - 2[\quad 16 \quad \div \mathbf{16} + 18 \div 9]$$
  (ii) Divide.

$$= 10^3 - 2[\quad\quad 1 \quad + \quad 2]$$
  (iii) Add.

$$= \quad 10^3 - 2[3]$$

$$= 1{,}000 - 2[3]$$
• Simplify the exponent.

$$= 1{,}000 - 6$$
• Multiply.

$$= \mathbf{994}$$
• Subtract.

 Example 13 Find the value using a calculator.

$$5(2)^3 + 25 \div (-5)^2 (-7+3) - 20$$

Solution

$$5(2)^3 + 25 \div (-5)^2(-7+3) - 20$$

plus   negative   minus

Recall that we use $\boxed{y^x}$, $\boxed{x^y}$, or $\boxed{\wedge}$ key to evaluate exponents.

We enter all the numbers and symbols in the order in which they appear from left to right, including parenthesis.

ENTER

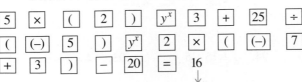

Final Display

12. Evaluate the expression:

$$100 + 2[3(4^2 - 6) + 2^3]$$

13. Find the value using a calculator.

(a) $8(-9+5) - 45 \div (-3)^2$

(b) $[(-4)8 + 30](-4) - 36 \div 12$

Answers:

11. (a) 5   **(b)** 23   **(c)** 1

     (d) − 37   **(e)** 3   **(f)** 58

12. 176   **13. (a)** − 37   **(b)** 5

Exercise 1.4

A. In exercises 1-20, (a) identify the base and exponent and (b) find the value.

1. 3^5 **2.** 4^3 **3.** $(-2)^5$ **4.** -3^3 **5.** 1^{48} **6.** $(-3)^4$ **7.** $(-5)^4$

8. -2^8 **9.** -10^3 **10.** $(-2)^2$ **11.** $(-7)^2$ **12.** 10^4 **13.** -6^4 **14.** 46^1

15. $(-6)^2$ **16.** 2^6 **17.** -20^3 **18.** 15^2 **19.** -12^2 **20.** 36^1

In exercises 21-32, rewrite the given product by using exponents.

21. $7 \cdot 7 \cdot 7 \cdot 7 \cdot 7 \cdot 7$ **22.** $4 \cdot 4 \cdot 4 \cdot 4 \cdot 4$ **23.** $10 \cdot 10 \cdot 10$ **24.** $12 \cdot 12 \cdot 12 \cdot 12$

25. $5 \cdot 5 \cdot 5 \cdot 5$ **26.** $3 \cdot 3 \cdot 3$ **27.** $2 \cdot 2 \cdot 2 \cdot 5 \cdot 5$ **28.** $7 \cdot 7 \cdot 7 \cdot (-4) \cdot (-4) \cdot (-4)$

29. $8 \cdot 8 \cdot 8 \cdot 9 \cdot 9$ **30.** $13 \cdot 13 \cdot 13 \cdot 12 \cdot 12 \cdot 12$ **31.** $6 \cdot 6 \cdot 6 \cdot 6 \cdot (-11) \cdot (-11)$ **32.** $8 \cdot 8 \cdot 12 \cdot 12 \cdot 12 \cdot 5 \cdot 5$

In exercises 33-40, use a calculator to find the value.

33. 21^3 **34.** 64^2 **35.** 35^3 **36.** 2^{15} **37.** 12^6 **38.** 5^7 **39.** 8^5 **40.** 23^4

In exercises 41-61, simplify the numerical expression.

41. $2^3 - 5$ **42.** $3^2 + 7$ **43.** $12 + 3^3$ **44.** $5^2 - 100$ **45.** $2^3 \cdot 3^2$ **46.** $(-5)^2 \cdot 2^4$

47. $4^3 \cdot (-2)^3$ **48.** $10^3 \cdot 3^2$ **49.** $16^3 \div 4^6$ **50.** $7^4 \div 49$ **51.** $9^3 - 3^6$ **52.** $-10^2 + 45$

53. $45 \cdot 6^2$ **54.** $7^2 - 150$ **55.** $-81 \div 3^3$ **56.** $4^2 \cdot 3$ **57.** $25 \div 5^2$ **58.** $2^6 + 8^2$

59. $7^2 - 6^2$ **60.** $8^2 - 2^6$ **61.** $3^5 - 5^3$

B. In exercises 62-82, multiply or divide by inspection.

62. 36×10^2 **63.** 7×10^6 **64.** 130×10^3 **65.** $25,300 \div 10^2$ **66.** $4,500 \div 10^2$

67. $253,000,000 \div 10^3$ **68.** 16×10^5 **69.** 39×10^4 **70.** 120×10^2

71. $708,000 \div 10^3$ **72.** $1,702,000 \div 10^3$ **73.** $1,378,000,000 \div 10^5$ **74.** $3,591 \times 10^4$

75. $\dfrac{302,000}{10^2}$ **76.** 705×10^8 **77.** $\dfrac{49,260,000,000}{10^6}$ **78.** $2,345 \div 10^2$

79. $12,450 \div 10^3$ **80.** $41,599 \div 10^3$ **81.** $14,179 \div 10^3$ **82.** $29 \div 10$

In exercises 83-91, write the dollar amount in numeral form.

83. \$40 million   **84.** \$675 billion   **85.** \$405 million   **86.** \$30 trillion   **87.** \$12 billion

88. \$39 million   **89.** \$473 billion   **90.** \$1,072 trillion   **91.** \$199 billion

C. In exercises 92-184, simplify the expression.

92. $48 + 72 \div 9$ **93.** $24 \div 3 + 5$ **94.** $7 + 15 \div 5$ **95.** $4 \times 3 + 9$ **96.** $5 \times 2 + 8$

97. $7 \times 3 - 10$ **98.** $36 - 4 \cdot 6$ **99.** $85 - 15 \cdot 4$ **100.** $10 \div 5 - 2$ **101.** $20 \div 4 + 7$

102. $7 + 3 \times 2$ **103.** $15 + 9 \div 3 - 10$ **104.** $6 \cdot 3 \div 2 + 13$ **105.** $19 + 6 \times 2$ **106.** $19 - 6 \times 2$

107. $40 \div 10 + 25 \div 5$ **108.** $10 \div 5 + 20 \div 10$ **109.** $4 + 6 \div 3 - 14 \div 7$ **110.** $10 - 4 \div 4 - 9$ **111.** $21 \div 7 - 2$

112. $25 \div 5 - 5$ **113.** $25 - 5 \div 5$ **114.** $2^5 - 6 \cdot 2 + 4 \div 4$ **115.** $16 \div 2^3 + 9$

116. $-4 + (-6) \div (2 \cdot 3)$ **117.** $-4 + (-6) \times 3 \div 2$ **118.** $-4 + (-6 \div 2) \times 3$

119. $(-4)(-6) \div 3 + 2$ **120.** $(-4) - (-6) \times 3 \div 2$ **121.** $-2 + 7 - 3 \div [(-2) - 1]$

122. $7 - 4[8 - 7(2 - 3)]$ **123.** $-9(4) - 24 \div (-6)$ **124.** $-28 \div (-4)\, 7 - 7^2$

125. $(4^2 - 3^2)(-8) \div (9 - 7)^2$ **126.** $9(-1 + 2^2) - 7 - 6 \cdot 2^2$ **127.** $2 - 5[(-10) \div (-5) \cdot 2 - 35]$

128. $4 \div 2^2 + 3 \cdot 2^2$ **129.** $2(-1 + 3^2) - 4 - 3 \cdot 2^3$ **130.** $3^3 \div (-9) \cdot 4 + 5(-2)$

131. $3^3 \div (-9) \cdot 2 - 5 + 4(-5)$ **132.** $50 - 20(3^2 \div 3 \cdot 2 + 14 \div 7)$ **133.** $9 - 11[(3 - 5^2) \div 2 + 5]$

134. $(4^2 - 2^2) - 27 \div (-3) - 3^2$ **135.** $(6^2 - 5^2)(-2) + 9 \div 3$ **136.** $(6 + 9 \div 3) + 4 - 2 \cdot 3$

137. $(5 - 10 \div 5) - 2 \cdot 4 - 3^2$ **138.** $8(-2 - 3^2) + 4 + 2 \cdot 3^2$ **139.** $9 \div 3^2 + 2 \cdot 3^2$

140. $5^3 \div 25 + 25 \div 5$ **141.** $-18 \div (-6)\, 4 - 3^2$ **142.** $3(3^2 - 3) - 5 - 2 \cdot 3^2$

143. $4(2^4 - 4) + 6 - (3^2 - 2^2)$ **144.** $2(4^2 - 3^2) - 2 - 5 \cdot 2^2$ **145.** $(6^2 \div 4 \div 3 - 5) - (3^2 - 1)$

146. $5(-2^2 - 1) - 20 - 3 \cdot 2^2$ **147.** $4 - [(-10) \div 5 + 35 \div 7]$ **148.** $3 - 2[(-6) \div (-2) - 2^3 \div 4]$

149. $7 + 4[9 \div (2^2 - 1) - (3^3 - 20)]$ **150.** $[(15 - 2 \cdot 5) \div 5 - 15 \div 5] + 2$ **151.** $[(4^2 \div 8 \cdot 2 - 2) - (3 - 4)]$

152. $4^3 \div (-4^2) \cdot 2 + 6 + 2(-3)$ **153.** $5^2 \div (2^2 + 1) + (6 + 8 \div 4)$ **154.** $(3^3 - 25) - [8 \div (-2) + 2]$

155. $(6^2 - 3 \cdot 10 + 4 \div 2) - 2^3$ **156.** $40 - 10(5^3 \div 5^2 \cdot 2 + 15 \div 5)$ **157.** $-9(4) - 24 \div (-2)^2$

158. $13 - 2[10 \div 2 + 3(5 - 4)]$ **159.** $8 - 5 + 4^2 \div [(-3) - 1]$ **160.** $9 - 3 + 6^2 \div [7 - 1]$

161. $[(-3)^2 - (-6)^2] - (5 - 1) \div 2$ **162.** $[49 \div 7 + (3 \cdot 4 - 3^2)] \div 10$ **163.** $[48 \div (-6) - (4 \cdot 2 - 2^2)] \div 6$

164. $2^4 \div (-8) \cdot 3 + 2(-3)$ **165.** $13 - 7[(4 - 2^4) \div 4 - 1]$ **166.** $15 - 3[16 \div (8 - 2^2) + 2]$

167. $-18 + 4[18 \div (13 - 2^2) - 3]$ **168.** $-19 - 5[4^2 \div (2^5 - 2^4) - 2]$ **169.** $4^3 \div (-16) \cdot (-2) + 3 + 2(-5)$

170. $5 - 4[(-4) \div (-2) \cdot 3 - 5]$ **171.** $9 - 3[(-25) \div (5) \cdot 2 + 12]$ **172.** $21 - 2[(-7) \cdot 6 \div 3 - (3^2 - 5^2)]$

173. $-7[(-24) \div (8) \cdot 2 + (2^4 - 2^3)]$ **174.** $11[(-35) \div (-7) \cdot 3 + (10 - 5^2)]$ **175.** $14[(-6) \div (-3) \cdot 2 - (3^2 - 6)]$

176. $-13[(-63) \div (7) \cdot (-2) - (4^2 - 3^2)]$ **177.** $19[(-36) \div (-9) \cdot (2) + (3^2 - 2^2)]$ **178.** $-8(-3) + 4[9 - 2(2^2 - 3^2)]$

179. $4 \cdot (5)^2 - 50 \div (-5)^2 \cdot (-6 + 3) + 20$ **180.** $31 - 6[5^2 \div 5 \cdot (-2) + 20 \div 2]$ **181.** $10 - 5(4^2 \div 4 \cdot 2 - 12 \div 6)$

182. $20 - 4[(4^2 - 8) \div 2 - (-1)]$ **183.** $30 + 3[18 \div (2^2 + 2) - 13]$ **184.** $60 - 12[(8 - 2^2) \div 2 + 3]$

1.5 CHAPTER SUMMARY

Part I   Important Vocabulary and Symbols

INTEGERS

1.   The set of **integers** is the set of all whole numbers and their opposites.

   Integers: $\ldots -3, -2, -1, 0, 1, 2, 3, \ldots$

2.   The **positive integers** are the integers that are greater than zero: $1, 2, 3, 4, \ldots$

3.   The **negative integers** are the integers that are less than zero: $-1, -2, -3, -4, \ldots$

> The number 0 is neither positive nor negative.

4.   The **absolute value** of an integer, a, is denoted by the symbol $\left| a \right|$, and represents the distance of point a from the origin on the number line.

   Absolute values are always positive or zero.

$$\left| -5 \right| = -(-5)$$
$$= 5$$
$$\left| -5 \right| = 5$$

5.   The **opposite** of an integer 'a' is denoted by '$-a$', and is read as "**opposite of a**" or "**negative a**", or "**additive inverse** of a".

   The opposite of a positive number is a negative number, and the opposite of a negative number is a positive number.

   The opposite   (or the additive inverse) of 4   is -4.

   The opposite   (or the additive inverse) of -5 is 5.

   The opposite   (or the additive inverse) of 0 is 0 itself.

6.   **Inverse Property for Addition:** The sum of an integer and its additive inverse is 0.

   $4 + (-4) = 0$; $(-2) + 2 = 0$

7.   The grouping symbols are :

   Parentheses ( ),   **braces** { },   **brackets** [ ] and the **fraction bar** $\frac{\Box}{\Box}$.

8.   A **numerical expression** is an expression involving numbers, symbols of operations $(+, -, \times, \div)$, exponents, and grouping symbols.

9.   To **simplify** a numerical expression means to perform all the operations and find the answer as a single number.

Part II **Procedures and Rules**	**Examples**

1. On a number line, positive integers lie to the right of 0 and negative integers lie to the left of 0.

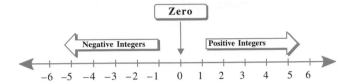

2. To find the **opposite** of an integer, just change its sign.

> The opposite of 0 is 0 itself.

3. The **absolute value** of a number:

(a) is the number itself, if the number is positive.

(b) is opposite of a number, if the number is negative.

Part III   Operations with Integers

4.   *Rule 1*   To add two or more integers with *like* signs, add their absolute values and use the common sign with the sum obtained.

5.   *Rule 2*   To add two integers with *unlike* signs, subtract their absolute values (the smaller from the larger) and use the sign of the integer that has the larger absolute value.

6. To add a group of integers:

   Step 1   Add all the positive numbers, and all the negative numbers separately.

   Step 2   Add the two sums obtained in step 1.

Procedure to estimate the sum or the difference of integers.

7.   *Step 1*   Determine whether you wish to round to the largest or next to the largest place value of the integers.

   Step 2   Round all numbers to that place value.

   Step 3   Add or subtract to get the estimate.

8.   *Rule 3*   To subtract a number from another number, change the sign of the number to be subtracted and add.

Examples

1.

$$\xleftarrow{\quad\;} \overset{}{-3}\;\; -2 \;\; -1 \;\; 0 \;\; 1 \;\; 2 \;\; 3 \xrightarrow{\quad\;}$$

2.

Number	*The opposite*
-15	15
4	-4
0	0

3.

Number	*The absolute value*
12	$\lvert 12 \rvert = 12$
-5	$\lvert -5 \rvert = -(-5) = 5$
0	$\lvert 0 \rvert = 0$

4. (a) $\quad 4+5 = 9$

    (b) $-3+(-12) = -(3+12)$
$$= -15$$

5. (a) $\quad 4+(-8) = -(8-4)$
$$= -4$$

    (b) $\quad -23+15 = -(23-15)$
$$= -8$$

    (c) $\quad -3+7 = +(7-3)$
$$= 4$$

6. Find the sum:
$$-44+37+(-59)+45$$
$$= [-44+(-59)] + [37+45]$$
$$= [-103] + [82]$$
$$= -(103-82)$$
$$= -21.$$

7. Estimate the sum or the difference.

  (a) $-389+(-214)$
$$\approx -400+(-200) \quad \text{Rounded to the largest place value.}$$
$$\approx -600$$

  (b) $-29{,}732+9{,}827$
$$\approx -30{,}000+10{,}000 \quad \text{Rounded to the largest place value.}$$
$$\approx -20{,}000$$

8. (a) $-15-4 = -15+(-4) = -19$

    (b) $7-(-8) = 7+(8) = 15$

Examples

9. (a) $6(5) = 30$

   (b) $(-3)(-8) = 24$

   (c) $8(-5) = -40$

   (d) $6 \div 2 = \dfrac{6}{2} = 3$

   (e) $8 \div (-2) = \dfrac{8}{-2} = -4$

   (f) $-(28) \div (-7) = \dfrac{-28}{-7} = 4$

10. Estimate the product.

    $497 \times 1{,}249 \approx 500 \times 1{,}000$
    $\approx 500{,}000$

11. (a) $(3)(4)(5) = 60$

    (b) $(-2)(-3)(5)(-1)(-4)$
    $= +(2 \cdot 3 \cdot 5 \cdot 1 \cdot 4)$
    $= 120$

    (c) $5(-3)(-1)(-2) = -(5 \cdot 3 \cdot 1 \cdot 2)$
    $= -30$

12. Estimate the quotient

    $459 \div (-23)$

    $-23\overline{)459}^{\,-2} \longrightarrow -23\overline{)459}^{\,-20}$

    The estimate is -20.

13. $(-5)^1 = -5, \qquad 8^1 = 8$

    $(-3)^4 = 81$

    $(-5)^3 = -125.$

14. $28 \div (-4)(2) - 12 \div 3 + (-5^2)$

    $= 28 \div (-4)(2) - 12 \div 3 + 25$

    $= \dfrac{28}{-4} \cdot (2) - 12 \div 3 + 25$

    $= -7(2) - 12 \div 3 + 25$

    $= -14 - 4 + 25$

    $= -(14 + 4) + 25$

    $= -18 + 25$

    $= 7.$

---

9. **Rule 4** To multiply (divide) two integers, multiply (divide) their absolute values. If the integers are of like signs, the result is positive; if the integers are of unlike signs, the result is negative.

10. Estimating a product:

    Step 1 Front-end round each factor.

    Step 2 Multiply the rounded factors.

11. **Rule 5** To multiply several numbers (factors) together, multiply their absolute values. If the number of negative factors is even, the product is positive, and if the number of negative factors is odd, the product is negative.

12. Estimating a quotient:

    Step 1 Carefully locate the position of the first digit in the quotient.

    Step 2 Enter that digit or a close estimate of its value.

    Step 3 Fill in the remaining places with zeros.

EXPONENTS

13. *Rules of exponents.*

    1. If the exponent is 1, then $a^1 = a$.

    2. (Negative number)^n is negative for odd exponents and positive for even exponents.

ORDER OF OPERATIONS

14. To simplify a numerical expression involving more than one operation:

    Rule 1 **Parentheses** - Do the operations within grouping symbols starting with the innermost grouping.

    Rule 2 If an expression involves different operations then perform these operations in the following order:

    - **Exponents** - Simplify the exponents.
    - Do **multiplication** and **division** as they appear from left to right.
    - Do **addition** and **subtraction** as they appear from left to right.

1.6 REVIEW EXERCISE

In exercises 1-6, graph the given set of integers.

1. $\{-3, -1, 0, 4, 5\}$
2. $\{-5, -4, -2, 2, 4, 5\}$
3. $\{0, 3, -6, -8, 7\}$
4. $\{4, 5, 6, -2, -5, -7\}$
5. $\{-15, -13, -11, -10, -9\}$
6. $\{21, 22, 25, 27, 30\}$

In exercises 7-18, find the opposite of the given number.

7. -12
8. -19
9. 16
10. 9
11. $-(-3)$
12. $-(-25)$
13. $-(-5)$
14. -3
15. $-(+4)$
16. $-(+21)$
17. 0
18. 24

In exercises 19-24, find the absolute value of the given number.

19. -47
20. $-(-25)$
21. $-[-(-27)]$
22. 45
23. 0
24. -19

In exercises 25-30, determine whether the given inequality statement is true or false. If it is false, re-write the statement to make it true.

25. $-18 > 7$
26. $-24 > -25$
27. $15 < \left|-20\right|$
28. $\left|-35\right| < \left|20\right|$
29. $-(-9) < 9$
30. $\left|-4\right| \leq \left|-16\right|$

In exercises 31-36, find the possible values of n for which the given statement is true.

31. $\left|n\right| = 16$
32. $\left|n\right| = 0$
33. $\left|n\right| \leq 2$
34. $\left|n\right| < 4$
35. $\left|n\right| = -5$
36. $\left|n\right| = \left|-5\right|$

In exercises 37-42, find the sum.

37. $(-45) + 36$
38. $24 + (-18)$
39. $-8 + (-9)$
40. $-14 + (-36)$
41. $(-15) + (+10)$
42. $(+15) + (-10)$

In exercises 43-46, find the difference.

43. $-75 - 40$
44. $19 - 24$
45. $-28 - (-39)$
46. $218 - (-100)$

In exercises 47-50, estimate the sum or the difference, then compare with the actual sum or difference by using a calculator.

47. $2,378 + 3,984$
48. $35,349 - (-27,421)$
49. $-28,904 + 39,182$
50. $38,712 + (-19,608)$

In exercises 51-62, simplify the numerical expression.

51. $-12 + (-8) + (-16)$
52. $-120 - 48 + 35$
53. $17 + \left|-5\right| - (-8)$
54. $-(-11) + \left|-13\right| - \left|-7\right|$
55. $\left|-10\right| + \left|-18\right| - \left|-27\right|$
56. $\left|-14\right| - \left|-19\right| + \left|-25\right|$
57. $\left|-23\right| - (-8) - \left|25\right|$
58. $\left|-75\right| + 10 - \left|-8\right| - 12$
59. $28 - \left|-65\right| + \left|-15\right| - 4$
60. $\left|-42\right| - (32) - \left|-9\right| - 7$
61. $17 - \left|-52\right| - (-32) + \left|-7\right|$
62. $21 + \left|-23\right| - \left|-7\right| - 13$

63. What should be added to -54 to get the sum equal to 40?

64. What should be subtracted from -15 to get the difference equal to -12?

65. The original manuscript for a book was 785 pages long. The final copy submitted for publication was 643 pages long. What was the change in the length of the text? Express the change as a signed number.

In exercises 66-69, find the product.

66. $4(-8)(-5)(6)(-3)$
67. $-10(-7)(-2)(9)(-4)$
68. $16(-3)(-5)(0)(-12)$
69. $(-75)(0)(-26)(69)$

In exercises 70-73, find the quotient.

70. $\dfrac{-85}{-5}$
71. $\dfrac{48}{-4}$
72. $\dfrac{-75}{-1}$
73. $\dfrac{-36}{0}$

In exercises 74-77, estimate the product or the quotient and compare it with the actual value using a calculator.

74. $495 \times 2,989$
75. $-8,967 \times 5,879$
76. $895 \div 19$
77. $1,985 \div 39$

In exercises 78-111, follow the rules for the order of operations and simplify the expression.

78. $-8 + 2 \cdot (-3)$

79. $-15 + (-24) \div 3$

80. $6 + (-9) \div (-3)$

81. $(12 - 15) \cdot (15 - 12)$

82. $(-3 + 5)(8 - 9)$

83. $(-2)^3 + 8$

84. $(-3)^2 - 3^2$

85. $2 - 5^2 + 7$

86. $(2 - 5)^2 + 7$

87. $-3^3 - 3(-3)^3$

88. $-3(2)^3 + (-2)^3$

89. $8 - [-5 - (-2)]$

90. $2 - [(+3) - (-5)]$

91. $2(-3)^2 - 7(+3) + 8$

92. $15 \div 5 + 10 \cdot 2$

93. $3(-2)^4 - (-2)^3 - 7(-2)^3$

94. $15 \div (-5) \cdot 2 - 8$

95. $8(3 - 5) - 2$

96. $5 - 2(5 - 7)$

97. $4 \div 2^2 + 3 \cdot 2^2$

98. $12 \cdot 3^2 + 48 \div (-2)^3$

99. $3(9 - 4^2) + 16 \div 2 \cdot 5$

100. $5^2 - 3^3 + 16 \cdot 2 \div 4$

101. $6 + (12 \cdot 6 + 3^2) \div 9(-5)$

102. $15 + 6(-3) - 10^2 + 3 \cdot 5^2$

103. $-12 + [8^2 \div 2 \cdot 3 - 16 \cdot 6]$

104. $5^2 \div (-5)(-3) - 2(4 \cdot 3)$

105. $20 \cdot 2 \div (-10) + 4(-5)$

106. $20 \div (-10) \cdot 2 + 4(-5)$

107. $14 \cdot 2 + (-39) \div (-13) - 7$

108. $5^3 - 60 + 3(-12)$

109. $4^2 \div (-8)(-2) + 6(-15 + 3 \cdot 5)$

110. $2(-5)^2 + 16(-3) - 23 - 10$

111. $(-6)^2 \div (3)(-2) + 2(-5 + 1 \cdot 5)$

1.7 SELF TEST

1. Graph the following set of integers on a number line $\{-5, -3, -1, 0, 4, 7\}$.

2. Graph the set of whole numbers less than 5.

3. What are the integer values of x if $|x| \le 4$?

4. What are the integer values of n satisfying the inequality $|n| > 5$?

5. Complete the blanks.

   (a) $-(-14) = $ _____

   (b) $|-35| = $ _____

   (c) $-|-7| = $ _____

   (d) $-|-12| = $ _____

In problems 6-9, find the sum, or the difference.

6. $-7 + (-3)$

7. $46 - (-18)$

8. $-10 + (-3) + 15$

9. $-20 + 35 - 75$

In problems 10-11, estimate the sum or the difference. Then compare with the actual sum or difference by using a calculator.

10. $893 + 986$

11. $6,895 - 5,987$

In problems 12-17, find the product or the quotient.

12. $(-2)(-7)(-5)(-3)$

13. $3(-4)(-10)(-5)$

14. $-25 \cdot 3 \cdot (-14) \cdot 0 \cdot 9$

15. $(-84) \div 7$

16. $(-175) \div 0$

17. $0 \div 17$

In problems 18-19, estimate the product or the quotient. Then compare with the actual product or quotient by using a calculator.

18. $7,961 \times 989$

19. $-5,132 \div 49$

In problems 20-21, simplify the given numerical expression.

20. $(-5)(-3)^2 + 32 - (-4)^2$

21. $36 \div (-4)(3) - 16 \div 2 \cdot (-4) + 3(9) \div 3$

22. Fill in the blanks using appropriate signed numbers.

   (i) $(-5)^3 = $ _____

   (ii) $-[-(-3)] = $ _____

   (iii) $(-2)^6 = $ _____

   (iv) $-|-5| = $ _____

   (v) $-|26| = $ _____

   (vi) $|-12| = $ _____

   (vii) $-(-3)^4 = $ _____

   (viii) $-4(-4)^3 = $ _____

Applications with Integers

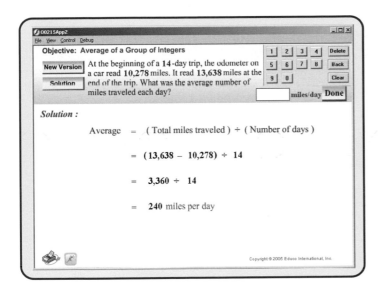

Objective: Average of a Group of Integers

New Version

Solution

At the beginning of a **14**-day trip, the odometer on a car read **10,278** miles. It read **13,638** miles at the end of the trip. What was the average number of miles traveled each day?

1	2	3	4	Delete
5	6	7	8	Back
9	0			Clear

_____ miles/day **Done**

Solution :

Average = (Total miles traveled) ÷ (Number of days)

= $(13,638 - 10,278) \div 14$

= $3,360 \div 14$

= **240** miles per day

Applications with Integers

APPLICATIONS OF INTEGERS

Introduction

In this chapter, we shall study the translation of phrases or statements into algebraic expressions or equations. This chapter is divided into the following four sections:

2.1 *Translations; Simplifying and Evaluating Expressions; and Computing Averages;*

2.2 *Solving Equations with Integers;*

2.3 *Applications using Integers; and*

2.4 *Basic Geometry.*

2.1 TRANSLATIONS; SIMPLIFYING AND EVALUATING EXPRESSIONS

IMPORTANT VOCABULARY 💾

1. Algebraic expressions that are products of numbers, variables, and powers of variables are called **algebraic terms.**

    For example,

    $5x$, x, $-3x^2$, $2xy^3$, p^2q, and $9ab$ are all algebraic terms.

2. Several terms added together form an **algebraic expression**.

    $3x^2 + 4xy^2 - 3$ is an algebraic expression and its terms are :

    $3x^2$, $4xy^2$, and -3.

    Note: $3x^2 + 4xy^2 - 3 = 3x^2 + 4xy^2 + (-3)$

3. A term consisting of only a number, such as -3, is called a **constant term.**

4. A term which includes a variable such as $3x$ or $4xy^2$ is called a **variable term**.

> **Objectives**
>
> After completing this section, you will be able to:
>
> A. Translate phrases or statements into algebraic expressions;
>
> B. Identify coefficients of the terms of an expression;
>
> C. Simplify expressions by combining like terms;
>
> D. Evaluate an algebraic expression; and
>
> E. Find the average of a group of numbers.

5. The numerical factor of a variable term is called the **numerical coefficient** or simply the **coefficient** of the term. The variables together with their powers is called the variable part of the term.

    In the term $-4x^2z$, -4 is the *coefficient*, and x^2z is the *variable part*.

6. **Like terms** have the same variable part (if any). Examples:

    $4, 12,$ and -6 are like terms because each term is a constant;

    $2a$, $-3a$ and $8a$ are like terms because the variable part of each term is the same (a); and

    $-2x^2z^3$ and $\dfrac{3}{2}x^2z^3$ are like terms because the variable part of each term is the same (x^2z^3).

7. Terms which are not like terms are called **unlike terms.**

    For example, $4a$ and $-5b$ are unlike terms because the variable parts are not the same.

    Similarly $2x$ and x^2 are unlike terms.

2.1 A.   Translate Phrases or Statements into Algebraic Expressions

- Words such as *plus*, *increased by*, and *sum* indicate addition.

  Examples: Three *plus* eight   translates to $3 + 8$;

        x increased by seven   translates to $x + 7$;

        The *sum* of twenty-one and fifteen   translates to $21 + 15$.

- Words such as *minus*, *decreased by*, and *difference* indicate subtraction.

  Examples: Five *minus* eleven   translates to $5 - 11$;

        Twelve *decreased* by nine   translates to $12 - 9$;

        Five *less than* twenty-nine   translates to $29 - 5$;

        The *difference* of 17 and 2   translates to $17 - 2$.

- Words such as *times*, and *product*, indicate multiplication.

  Examples: Two *times* five   translates to $2(5)$ or $2 \cdot 5$;

        The *product* of seven and x translates to $7 \cdot x$ or $7x$.

- Words such as *quotient*, and *divided by* indicate division.

  Examples: Twelve *divided* by seven   translates to $12 \div 7$ or $\dfrac{12}{7}$;

        The *quotient* of x and five   translates to $x \div 5$ or $\dfrac{x}{5}$.

- Words such as *is*, *gives*, and *equals* usually indicate equality (=).

  Examples:

  'Two times five increased by seven *equals* seventeen'   translates to $2 \cdot 5 + 7 = 17$.

  'Three subtracted from the product of four and fifteen *gives* fifty-seven' translates to $4(15) - 3 = 57$.

  'The quotient of x and 3 *is* five' translates to $\dfrac{x}{3} = 5$.

- Some times we say *a number* without giving a value. This means that we are talking about an unknown number. An *unknown* number may be translated as x, y, z (any letter of alphabet).

  Examples: 'The sum of a *number* and 11' translates to $x + 11$.

       'The difference between two times *a number* and seven'   translates to $2x - 7$.

       '5 times *a number* plus 4' translates to $5x + 4$.

  We practice this translation process in more details in the following examples.

Warm-Up

1. Translate each of the following into mathematical symbols:

   (a) The sum of 27 and 15

Example 1   Translate each of the following into mathematical symbols:

(a) The sum of 4 and 11

(b) Fifteen subtracted from twenty

(c) The product of 5 and a number

(d) The quotient of a number and another number

Solutions

(a)   The **sum** of 4 and 11,

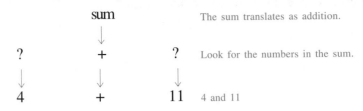

The sum translates as addition.

Look for the numbers in the sum.

4 and 11

(b)   Fifteen **subtracted** from twenty,

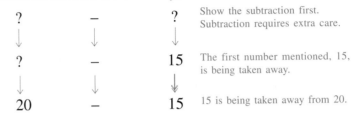

Show the subtraction first.
Subtraction requires extra care.

The first number mentioned, 15, is being taken away.

15 is being taken away from 20.

(b) Two hundred five subtracted from three hundred.

(c)   The **product** of 5 and a number,

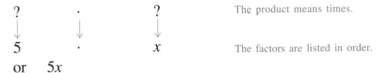

The product means times.

The factors are listed in order.

or   5*x*

(c) The product of a number and 7.

(d)   The **quotient** of a number and another number,

Translate the division first.

$\dfrac{m}{n}$

(d) The quotient of a number and 5.

Example 2   Translate the following into algebraic expressions:
(a) Five times a number plus 4
(b) The difference between three times a number and twenty-two

2. Translate the following words, phrases, or sentences into algebraic expressions:

(a) Seven times a number plus 15.

Solutions

(a)   Five times a number plus 4,

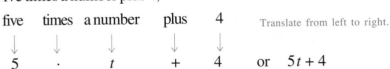

Translate from left to right.

or $5t + 4$

(b) The difference between four times a number and one.

(b)   The difference between **three times a number** and **twenty-two,**

or $3x - 22$

Answers:

1. (a) $27 + 15$ (b) $300 - 205$ (c) $7x$ (d) $\dfrac{x}{5}$

2. (a) $7x + 15$ (b) $4x - 1$

• One of the primary objectives for the study of mathematics is to solve application problems. These are always first expressed in word statements. These statements are converted into mathematical symbols, equations, and inequalities. We use universally accepted symbols for this conversion. Some of these symbols are defined in the following chart.

Word Statement	Translation into Symbols
Seven is *less than* eleven.	7 < 11 is less than
Five *plus* seven	5 + 7 plus
Twenty *minus* nine	20 – 9 minus
Four *more than* seventeen	17 + 4 more than
Four *is not equal* to three.	4 ≠ 3 is not equal to
Thirteen *is greater than or equal* to twelve.	13 ≥ 12 is greater than or equal to
Twelve *is less than or equal to* thirteen.	12 ≤ 13 is less than or equal to
Fifteen *is greater than* five.	15 > 5 is greater than
Six is *less than* twelve.	6 < 12 is less than

In order to solve application problems it is necessary to translate the word statements and sentences in the problems into mathematical expressions and equations. Relational symbols such as the ones discussed in the above chart will serve as convenient tools in this process of translation.

Words such as *plus, increased by,* and *sum* indicate **addition**.
Words such as *minus, decreased by,* and *less than* indicate **subtraction**.
Words such as *times, product,* and *"of"* indicate **multiplication**.
Words such as *quotient,* and *divided by* indicate **division**.

Warm-Up

3. Translate the following statements into symbols.

(a) Thirteen increased by four equals seventeen.

(b) Four times nine decreased by sixteen equals twenty.

(c) Eighteen divided by three is less than seven.

(d) Six multiplied by four equals twenty-four.

Example 3   Translate the following statements into symbols.

Solutions

Statements   **Conversion to symbols**

(a) Fourteen decreased by three equals eleven.

14 decreased by 3 equals 11.

$$14 - 3 = 11$$

(b) Two times five increased by seven equals seventeen.

2 times 5 increased by 7 equals 17.

$$2 \cdot 5 + 7 = 17$$

(c) Six divided by two equals three.

6 divided by 2 equals 3.

$$\frac{6}{2} = 3$$

(d) The product of seven and three is greater than twenty. $\rightarrow$ 7 multiplied by 3 is greater than 20.

$$7 \quad \cdot \quad 3 \quad > \quad 20$$

(e) Five is greater than the quotient of eight and four. $\rightarrow$ 5 is greater than 8 divided by 4.

$$5 \quad > \quad 8 \quad \div \quad 4$$

(e) Nine is greater than or equal to the quotient of twenty-one and three.

Answers:

3. (a) $13 + 4 = 17$

(b) $4 \times 9 - 16 = 20$ (c) $18 \div 3 < 7$

(d) $6 \times 4 = 24$ (e) $9 \geq (21 \div 3)$

Variables, Changing Phrases, and Sentences into Expressions and Equations

A variable is a symbol used to represent an unknown number or a quantity. It is denoted by a letter such as: x, y, z, p, t, and so forth. Operations on variables are performed in the same way as operations on numbers. The examples given below illustrate how variables are used to construct algebraic expressions and equations.

Example 4   Translate the following phrases into algebraic expressions:

(a)   The sum of *a number* and 11

(b)   3 subtracted from *a number*

(c)   The product of 11 and *a number*

(d)   The quotient of *a number* and 4

(e)   The quotient of 4 and *a number*

(f)   5 times *a number* plus 4

(g)   The difference between twice *a number* and 7

Warm-Up

4.   Translate the following phrases into algebraic expressions:

(a) The **difference** between three times a number and 4.

(b) The quotient of 7 and twice a number.

> **Note**   The word a "number", without specification, means an unknown number. An *unspecified* number may be translated as x, y, z (any letter).

Solutions

(a)   The sum of a number and 11

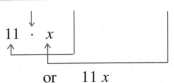

> **Note**   "and" does not mean add. It is simply a conjunction.

(b)   3 subtracted from a number"

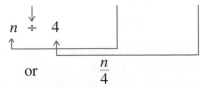

> **Note**   In subtraction it is important to carefully read to determine which number is being subtracted and which is the original number. Often the number mentioned first is the number being subtracted (last).

(c)   The product of 11 and a number

$$11 \cdot x$$

or $11\,x$

Recall that $11 \cdot x$ and $11x$ mean the same.

$11\,x$ is preferred.

(d)   The quotient of a number and 4

$$n \div 4$$

or $\dfrac{n}{4}$

> **Note** $\dfrac{n}{4}$ is preferred.

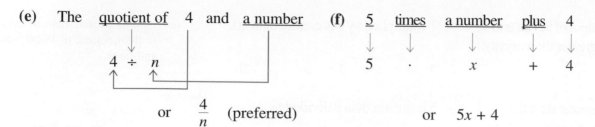

(e) The quotient of 4 and a number

$$4 \div n$$

or $\dfrac{4}{n}$ (preferred)

(f) 5 times a number plus 4

$$5 \cdot x + 4$$

or $5x + 4$

(g) The difference between two times a number and 7

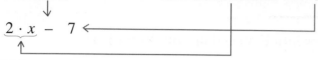

$$2 \cdot x - 7$$

> **Note** When reading words like "sum of" (or difference, product, or quotient of) note the operation first, then find the quantities being added (subtracted, multiplied, or divided) which are usually connected by "and". In addition or multiplication there may be more than two quantities involved.

Distinguishing Between "An Expression and an Equation"

An **equation** is a statement that expresses equality between two algebraic expressions.
$3x + 5 = 2$; $x^2 - x = 2x + 1$; $2x^3 + 3xy - 5y = 0$ are all examples of equations.
The equality symbol $(=)$ must be present if the statement is to qualify as an equation.

- **The sum of four times a number and 7 is 91.**

  Since **is** means "$=$", this will translate into an equation.

  four times a number plus seven equals 91

  $$4 \cdot x + 7 = 91$$

  Thus, the given word statement translates to the equation $4x + 7 = 91$.

- **Two times the difference of a number and seven.** Since a word meaning "$=$" is not present, this phrase translates as an expression:

  $$2(x - 7)$$

  The difference between an expression and equation is that an equation contains an '$=$' sign and an expression does not contain an '$=$' sign.

Procedure to decide whether a statement, in words or in mathematical symbols, is an equation or an expression:

    Step **1**   Translate the word statement into mathematical symbols. Use a letter of the alphabet for the unknown number.

    Step **2**   **a.** If the result does not contain an '$=$' sign, it is an expression.

              b. If the result contains an '$=$' sign, it is an equation.

Warm-Up

5. Identify if the following is an expression or an equation:

   (a) $2x + 3y = 4$

   (b) $5x - 17$

Example 5 Identify whether the following is an equation or an expression:

   (a) $4x^2 - 5y$ **(b)** $4x^2 - 5y = 0$

   (c) $7x^2 = 9x - 12$ **(d)** $(3x + y)x - 2y$

Solutions

   (a) $4x^2 - 5y$ is an expression.   There is no '$=$' sign.

(b) $4x^2 - 5y = 0$ is an equation. The '=' sign is present.

(c) $7x^2 = 9x - 12$ is an equation. The '=' sign is present.

(d) $(3x + y)x - 2y$ is an expression. There is no '=' sign.

(c) $\dfrac{x^2 + 1}{2x - 3}$

(d) $\dfrac{x^2 + 1}{2x - 3} = 1$

Example 6 Translate the following into mathematical symbols and identify each result as an expression or an equation.

(a) Seventeen times a number decreased by five.

(b) Seventeen times a number decreased by five equals eleven.

(c) Five added to two times a number.

(d) Five added to two times a number is twenty-four.

6. Translate the following into mathematical symbols, and identify the result as an expression or an equation:

(a) 3 times a number increased by 4.

(b) 3 times a number increased by 4 equals twelve.

(c) Eighteen subtracted from twice a number.

(d) Eighteen subtracted from twice a number is fifteen.

Solutions

(a) Seventeen times a number decreased by five.

$17x - 5$.   • x is used for the unknown number.

It is an expression.   • The result does not contain an '=' sign.

(b) Seventeen times a number decreased by five equals eleven.

$17x - 5 = 11$.   • x is used for the unknown number.

It is an equation.   • The result contains an '=' sign.

(c) Five added to two times a number.

$5 + 2y$.   • y is used for the unknown number.

It is an expression.   • The result does not contain an '=' sign.

(d) Five added to two times a number is twenty-four.

$5 + 2x = 24$. x is used for the unknown number. Result contains '=' sign.

It is an equation.

Answers:

4. (a) $3x - 4$ (b) $\dfrac{7}{2x}$

5. (a) Equation   (b) Expression
   (c) Expression   (d) Equation

6. (a) $3x + 4$ (expression)
   (b) $3x + 4 = 12$ (equation)
   (c) $2y - 18$ (expression)
   (d) $2y - 18 = 15$ (equation)

2.1 B. Identifying Coefficients of the Terms of an Expression and Evaluating Expressions for a Given Value of the Variable.

• The expression $3x^2 + 4x - 5$ is an algebraic **expression in** x.

This expression has three **terms:** $3x^2$, $4x$, and -5.

Each variable term has two components: the **coefficient** and the **variable part.** For example,

Expression:	$3x^2 + 4x - 5$	or	$3x^2 + 4x + (-5)$
Terms:	$3x^2$,	$4x$,	-5 (a constant term)
Coefficients:	3,	4,	
Variable parts:	x^2,	x,	

Warm-Up

7. Identify the numerical coefficient, and the variable part of the following terms:

(a) $16x$

(b) $-3x^3$

(c) z^3

Answers:

7. (a) 16 ; x (b) –3 ; x^3 (c) 1; z^3

Example 7   Identify the numerical coefficient and the variable part of the following terms:

(a) $2x^3$ (b) $-3x^2$ (c) y

Solutions

Term		Numerical Coefficient	Variable part
(a)	$2x^3$	2	x^3
(b)	$-3x^2$	-3	x^2
(c)	y	1	y

2.1 C.   Simplifying Expressions by Combining Like Terms

1.   Like and Unlike Terms

- Terms which differ only in **numerical coefficients** and have identical variable parts (variables together with their exponents) are called **like terms**.

   Examples: $2x$ and $-3x$; $-3xy^2$ and $-5xy^2$; ay^2z and $4ay^2z$ are pairs of **like terms**.

- Terms which are not like terms are called **unlike terms**.

   For example, $7x^3$ and $-4xy^2$ are **unlike terms** since their variable parts are not identical.

Warm-Up

8. Identify the groups of like terms from the following terms:

$6y^3$; $2x^2y$; -3 ; $-5x^2y$; 7 ; $-8y^3$; 14

Example 8   From the following list of terms, identify the groups of like terms.

$$3x^2, \ -5xyz^2, \ -4x^2, \ -9, \ 6x^2, \ 12xyz^2, \ 15, \ x^2.$$

Solutions

(a) $3x^2, -4x^2, 6x^2$, and x^2 are like terms.   Each term has x^2 as variable part.

(b) $-5xyz^2$ and $12xyz^2$ are like terms.   The variable part of each term is xyz^2.

(c) -9 and 15 are like terms.   Both are *constants*.

2.   Combining Like Terms

Like terms of an algebraic expression can be combined by using the *distributive property* of multiplication over addition in reverse order.

Recall, $(b + c)\,a = ba + ca$.

Switching sides we get: $ba + ca = (b + c)a$. We call this the distributive property in reverse order.

Example:

$$5x + 7x = (5 + 7)\,x$$

$$= 12x \qquad \text{since } 5 + 7 = 12.$$

The distributive property is true even if we have more than two terms in the sum.

$$7x + 5x + 9x = \underbrace{(7 + 5 + 9)}x$$

$$= 21x.$$

Like terms of an algebraic expression are combined by finding the sum of coefficients and attaching the sum obtained to the common variable part. This process is called **combining like terms.**

To combine the like terms in the expression $3x^2y + 4x^2y - 2x^2y + x^2y$, we add their coefficients.

$$3 + 4 + (-2) + 1 = 6 ;$$ The common variable part is x^2y.

so, $\quad 3x^2y + 4x^2y + (-2x^2y) + x^2y = [3 + 4 + (-2) + 1]\ x^2y$

$$= 6x^2y.$$

- *Unlike terms* cannot be combined (added).

  $2a + 3b \qquad$ cannot be combined or simplified.

  $4x^2 + 5xy \qquad$ cannot be combined or simplified because the variable parts of the two terms are not the same.

- In an expression, some terms may be **like terms** and others may be **unlike terms**.

  For example,

  $4x + 5x - 3x^2y$: The first two terms $4x$ and $5x$ are like terms; therefore, they can be combined.

  $$= \underbrace{(4 + 5)}\ x - 3x^2y \qquad \text{The sum of the coefficients is the coefficient of the variable part } x.$$

  $$= 9x - 3x^2y. \qquad \longleftarrow \qquad \text{These two terms cannot be combined.}$$

Similarly,

$$4x + 5x + 3x^2 + 5xy$$

like terms $\quad$ unlike terms

$$= (4 + 5)\ x \ + \ 3x^2 + 5xy \qquad \text{Like terms can be combined.}$$

$$= 9x \qquad + \ 3x^2 + 5xy. \qquad \text{Unlike terms, cannot be combined further.}$$

Procedure to combine the like terms:

$\quad$ *Step* **1** $\quad$ Add the coefficients of the like terms.

$\quad$ *Step* **2** $\quad$ Prefix the sum to the common variable part.

Example 9 $\quad$ Simplify the expressions by combining like terms.

$\quad$ **(a)** $4x + 7x$ $\qquad\qquad$ **(b)** $-7p + 5p$

$\quad$ **(c)** $18t^2 - 21t^2$ $\qquad$ **(d)** $22y^2 + 10y - 30y^2$

Solutions

$\quad$ **(a)** $\quad 4x + 7x \quad = (4 + 7)\ x \qquad$ • The sum of coefficients is $4+7 = 11$.

$\qquad\qquad\qquad\quad = \mathbf{11x} \qquad$ • The common variable part is x. Attach 11 to x.

$\quad$ **(b)** $\quad -7p + 5p \quad = (-7 + 5)\ p \qquad$ Add the numerical coefficients and attach the sum to the common variable part p.

$\qquad\qquad\qquad\quad\ = -2p$

Warm-Up

9. Simplify by combining like terms.

$\quad$ **(a)** $2y + 13y$

$\quad$ **(b)** $-15x + 27x$

93

(c) $5p^2 - 13p^2$

(d) $4x^2 - 3xy + 6x^2$

(c) $18t^2 - 21t^2 = (18 - 21)t^2$ The variable part of both terms is t^2.

$$= -3t^2$$

(d) $22y^2 + 10y - 30y^2 = 22y^2 - 30y^2 + 10y$ Terms can be added in any order.

$$= (22 - 30)y^2 + 10y$$ Combine like terms.

$$= -8y^2 + 10y$$

Recall that the **distributive property** provides an alternative method for evaluating expressions that involve groupings of terms and multiplication. $-3(4 + -2)$ can be simplified using order of operations or using the distributive property.

Using the order of operations: $-3(4 + (-2)) = -3(2)$ Simplifiy inside the parentheses first.

$$= -6$$

Using the distributive property: $-3(4 + (-2)) = (-3)(4) + (-3)(-2)$

$$= -12 + 6 = -6$$

It is easier to use the order of operations rather than the distributive property when evaluating numerical expressions. This is **not** the case in working with algebraic expressions.

Consider: $-3(x - 2)$

The terms inside the parentheses cannot be added because they are unlike terms. However, using the distributive property we are able to simplify the expression as follows:

$$-3(x - 2) = -3(x - 2)$$
$$= (-3)(x) + (-3)(-2)$$
$$= -3x + 6$$

Procedure to simplify algebraic expressions:

Step **1**   Use the distributive property to perform multiplication.

Step **2**   Combine like terms.

Warm-Up

10. Write the products without grouping symbols using the distributive law.

(a) $9(2x + 3y)$

(b) $5x(3x - 4)$

(c) $-5(7 + x)$

Example 10   Write the following products without grouping symbols using the distributive property.

(a) $2(x + y)$ **(b)** $3x(2 + y)$

(c) $-2(x + 3y)$ **(d)** $-4x(3x - 7y^2 + 4)$

Solutions

(a) $2(x + y) \quad = 2x + 2y$ Distributive property.

(b) $3x(2 + y) \quad = 3x(2) + 3x(y)$ Distributive property.

$$= 3 \cdot 2 \cdot x + 3x \cdot y$$ Numbers can be multiplied in any order.

$$= 6x + 3xy$$

(c) $-2(x + 3y) \quad = (-2)x + (-2)(3y)$ Distributive property.

$$= -2x + (-2)(3)y$$
$$= -2x + (-6)y$$
$$= -2x - 6y$$

(d) $-4x(3x - 7y^2 + 4)$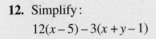

$$= (-4x)(3x) + (-4x)(-7y^2) + (-4x)(4)$$

$$= (-4)(3)(x \cdot x) + (-4)(-7)(xy^2) + (-4)(4)x$$

$$= -12x^2 + 28xy^2 - 16x$$

Example 11   Simplify the following expression:
$$3(x + 4) - 2(x - 5) + 1$$

Solution

$$3(x + 4) - 2(x - 5) + 1$$

$= 3x + 12 - 2x + 10 + 1$ Multiply using Distributive Property.

$= 3x - 2x + 12 + 10 + 1$ Combine like terms.

$= x + 23$

Example 12   Simplify the following expression.
$$2b(a + 2) - a(3 - b) + 2(a + b - 1)$$

Solution

$2b(a + 2) - a(3 - b) + 2(a + b - 1)$ • Use distributive property:
$2b(a + 2) = 2 \cdot b \cdot a + 2 \cdot b \cdot 2$
$= 2ab + 4b$

$= 2ab + 4b - 3a + ab + 2a + 2b - 2$ $-a(3 - b) = -3a + ab$

$= 2ab + ab + 4b + 2b - 3a + 2a - 2$ Rearrange terms.

$= (2 + 1)ab + (4 + 2)b + (-3 + 2)a - 2$ • Combine like terms:

$= 3ab + 6b - a - 2$ Simplify.

 Note   When multiplying "$b \cdot a$", it is customary to write the resulting product algebraically as "ab". This makes it easier to recognize terms.

11. Simplify:
$$x^2 - 3x^2 + 5x - 3 + 1.$$

12. Simplify:
$$12(x - 5) - 3(x + y - 1)$$

Answers:

8. $6y^3$ and $-8y^3$; $2x^2y$ and $-5x^2y$;
   -3, 7, and 14.

9. **(a)** $15y$ **(b)** $12x$ **(c)** $-8p^2$ **(d)** $10x^2 - 3xy$

10. (a) $18x + 27y$ **(b)** $15x^2 - 20x$
   (c) $-35 - 5x$ **(d)** $-8x^2 - 14xy^2 + 18xy$

11. $-2x^2 + 5x - 2$ **12.** $9x - 3y - 57$

2.1 D.   Evaluating an Algebraic Expression

•   Variables are the building blocks for algebraic expressions. A **variable** is a symbol which is used to represent an unknown number. Operations on variables are performed in the same way as operations on numbers.

For example,

   (a) $x \cdot x$ is written as x^2.

   (b) $2 \cdot x$, written as $2x$, denotes the product of 2 and x.

   (c) $x^2 + x$ means the sum of x^2 and x.

   (d) $x - 2$ means 2 subtracted from x.

   (e) $x \cdot y$ is written as xy ; $3xy$ means $3 \cdot x \cdot y$.

- Algebraic expressions are created using variables, numbers, operations, and grouping symbols. For example:

$$3x^2 + 5, \quad x(x + 2), \quad 6x + 5yz - 7, \quad \text{and} \quad 5x^2 + (x - 1)2y + 4$$

are some examples of algebraic expressions.

If an algebraic expression involves only one variable, say x, we say that it is an algebraic expression in one variable or specifically, **an algebraic expression in x.**

If there are two variables, x and y, we say that it is an algebraic expression in two variables or an algebraic expression in x and y.

- Recall the rules to evaluate *numerical expressions*. To evaluate an algebraic expression for given value(s) of the variable(s), we first replace the variable(s) by their given values, and then simplify the resulting numerical expression using the order of operations. Use parentheses when replacing variables by values.

For example, let us evaluate $4x - 3y + 1$ for $x = 5$ and $y = 2$:

$$\begin{aligned}
4x - 3y + 1 &= 4(\mathbf{5}) - 3(\mathbf{2}) + 1 \\
&= 20 - 6 + 1 \\
&= 14 + 1 \\
&= \mathbf{15}
\end{aligned}$$

Replace x by 5 and y by 2.

First, perform all multiplications from left to right.

Then perform addition and subtraction from left to right.

Procedure for evaluating an algebraic expression:

Step 1 Substitute the value(s) for the variable(s) using parentheses.

Step 2 Simplify the resulting expression using the order of operations.

Warm-Up

13. Find the numerical value of:

(a) $5y$ for $y = 3$

(b) $2x^2 - 3$ for $x = 4$

(c) $(4x - 7)^2 + 4$ for $x = 1$

Example 13 Find the numerical values of :

(a) $3x$ when $x = 2$

(b) $4y^2 + 5$ when $y = 3$

(c) $(3x - 2)^2 + 1$ when $x = 4$

Solutions

(a) $3x$ when $x = 2$ is $\mathbf{3\,(2)} = \mathbf{6}$

(b) $4y^2 + 5$ when $y = 3$

$$\begin{aligned}
&= 4\,(\mathbf{3})^2 + 5 \\
&= \mathbf{4 \cdot 9 + 5} \\
&= 36 + 5 = \mathbf{41}
\end{aligned}$$

First evaluate the exponent, 3^2;

next multiply $4 \cdot 9$ and then add.

(c) $(3x - 2)^2 + 1$ when $x = 4$

$$\begin{aligned}
&= (3\,(\mathbf{4}) - 2)^2 + 1 \\
&= (\mathbf{12 - 2})^2 + 1 \\
&= \mathbf{10}^2 + 1 \\
&= 100 + 1 = \mathbf{101}
\end{aligned}$$

Simplify within parentheses.

Simplify the exponent.

Example 14 Evaluate the following expressions for the given values of the variables.

(a) $3x - 5y$ for $x = 4, y = 2$

(b) $5x^2 - 2yz + 8$ for $x = 3, y = 2, z = 4$

(c) $(x^2 + 3y)(3y + 7)$ for $x = 1, y = 1$

Solutions

(a) $3x - 5y$ for $x = 4$, and $y = 2$

$= 3(\mathbf{4}) - 5(\mathbf{2})$ Substitute $x = 4$, $y = 2$.

$= 12 - 10$ Multiply, then subtract.

$= \mathbf{2}$

(b) $5x^2 - 2yz + 8$ for $x = 3, y = 2$, and $z = 4$

$= 5(\mathbf{3})^2 - 2(\mathbf{2})(\mathbf{4}) + 8$

$= \mathbf{5 \cdot 9} - 16 + 8$

$= 45 - 16 + 8 = \mathbf{37}$

(c) $(x^2 + 3y)(3y + 7)$ for $x = 1$, and $y = 1$

$= (\mathbf{1}^2 + 3(\mathbf{1}))(3(\mathbf{1}) + 7)$

$= (1 + 3)(3 + 7)$

$= (4)(10) = \mathbf{40}$

Example 15 Evaluate the expressions.

(a) $2x + 5$ for $x = -2$ (b) $-4x^2 + 5x - 3$ for $x = -3$

Solutions

(a) $2x + 5$ for $x = \mathbf{-2}$

$= 2(\mathbf{-2}) + 5$ Substitute -2 for x.

$= -4 + 5$ Multiply.

$= \mathbf{1}$ Add.

(b) $-4x^2 + 5x - 3$ for $x = -3$

$= -4(\mathbf{-3})^2 + 5(\mathbf{-3}) - 3$ Substitute -3 for x.

$= -4(\mathbf{9}) + (\mathbf{-15}) - 3$ Simplify exponents.

$= -36 + (-15) - 3$ Multiply.

$= -(36 + 15 + 3)$

$= \mathbf{-54}$ Add.

Example 16 Evaluate the expressions for the given value of the variable.

(a) $2x^3 - 5x^2 + 7x - 36$ for $x = 3$;

(b) $6y^4 - 5y^3 + 3y + 1$ for $y = -2$

Warm-Up

14. Evaluate:

(a) $2a + 5b$ for $a = 3, b = 4$

(b) $3x^2 + 4yz - 3$ for $x = 1, y = 2, z = 2$

(c) $(a^2 + 2b)(2b - 5)$ for $a = 2, b = 1$

15. Evaluate.

(a) $5x + 4$ for $x = -2$

(b) $3x^2 - 4x + 2$ for $x = -1$

16. Evaluate.

(a) $4x^2 + 5x - 12$ for $x = 2$

Solutions

(a) $2x^3 - 5x^2 + 7x - 36; \quad x = 3$ Replace x by 3, using parentheses.

$= 2(3)^3 - 5(3)^2 + 7(3) - 36$ Simplify the exponents,

$= 2 \cdot 27 - 5 \cdot 9 + 7 \cdot 3 - 36$ Next, multiply,

$= 54 \quad - 45 \quad + 21 - 36$ and then add and subtract, in the order in which they appear from left to right.

$= \qquad 9 \qquad + 21 - 36$

$= \qquad\qquad 30 \qquad - 36$

$= -(36 - 30) = -6$

(b) $x^3 + 4x^2 + 2x + 3$ for $x = -3$

(b) $6y^4 \quad - \quad 5y^3 \quad + 3y + 1 \; ; \quad y = -2$

$= 6 \cdot (-2)^4 - 5 \cdot (-2)^3 + 3 \cdot (-2) + 1$ Replace y by -2, **using parentheses around -2.**

$= 6 \cdot (16) \quad - 5 \cdot (-8) \quad + (-6) + 1$ $(-2)^4 = 2^4 = 16;$ $(-2)^3 = -2^3 = -8.$

$= 96 \quad - (-40) \quad + (-6) + 1$

$= 96 + \quad 40 \quad + (-6) + 1$

$= \qquad 136 \qquad + (-6) + 1$

$= \qquad\qquad 130 \qquad + 1$

$= \quad \mathbf{131}$

Answers:

13. (a) 15   (b) 29   (c) 13

14. (a) 26   (b) 16   (c) –18

15. (a) – 6   (b) 9

16. (a) 14   (b) 6

2.1 E.   Finding the Average of a Group of Numbers

- The concept of average is a frequently used mathematical concept. Let us consider two examples of the use of the term average.

    1. "How much do they pay you in that company, Allen?", a friend asked. "On an average, $50 a week", he replied.

    2. Suppose the height of three friends, James, Peter, and Joe, are 184 cm, 170 cm, and 180 cm, respectively. Instead of telling the height of each individual, we might say that the average height of three persons is 178 cm.

What do we actually mean when we use the word "average"?

In the first case, Allen might have been paid $35, $45, $50, and $70, respectively, in the first, second, third, and the fourth weeks of the month, totalling "35 + 45 + 50 + 70 = 200" in 4 weeks. If the total amount of $200 was to be paid *equally* in four weeks, he would get $50 a week.

In the same manner, the total height of the three friends (184 + 170 + 180 = 534) comes out to be 534 cm. If it is assumed that they all are of the *same* height, then the height of each would be

        (534 cm ÷ 3) = 178 cm.

- The average is a representative value of a group of numbers.

  The average of a group of numbers is found by first adding the numbers in the group, and then dividing the sum by the count of numbers in the group.

  The average of 44, 50, and 56 is $(44 + 50 + 56) \div 3 = 150 \div 3 = 50$.

Procedure for finding an average:

    Step **1**   Add all the numbers and obtain the sum.

    Step **2**   Divide the sum by the count of numbers in the group.

Example 17   Find the average of the group of numbers:

    (a) 87 and 115   **(b)** 27 ,35, 48, 52, and 73

    (c) 2395, 4089, and 5132

Solutions

  (a) $87 + 115 = 202$ • Add the numbers in the group.

          Average $= 202 \div 2 =$ **101**   • There are 2 numbers; so, divide the sum by 2.

  (b)   Sum of the numbers:

$$27 + 35 + 48 + 52 + 73 = \mathbf{235}$$

     There are 5 numbers :

     Average $= 235 \div 5 =$ **47**

  (c)   Sum of the numbers:

$$2,395 + 4,089 + 5,132 = 11,616$$

     There are 3 numbers :

     Average $= 11,616 \div 3 =$ **3,872**

Example 18   Find the average of 567, 917, 855, and 345 using a calculator.

Solution   We shall first add all the numbers, and then divide by 4, since there are 4 numbers.

ENTER | (| | 567 | | + | | 917 | | + | | 855 | | + |

ENTER | 345 | |) | | ÷ | | 4 | | = | 671 ← Final display

The average is **671**.

Observe that the use of parentheses means to add the numbers first before dividing by 4.

Warm-Up

17. Find the average of the group of numbers:

    (a) 35 and 47

    (b) 14, 15, 20, and 23

    (c) 438, 561, and 732

18. Find the average of the group of numbers using a calculator:

    7,895, 8,053, and 8,769

Warm-Up

19. The weekly gasoline expenses, in dollars, of eight students in a college, are given below. Find the average weekly gasoline expense.

$34, $45, $60, $45, $35, $50,$72, $35

20. A total of 4,354 students registered for classes during the first week of registration. What was the average number of students who registered per day?

Answers:

17. (a) 41   (b) 18   (c) 577

18. 8,239   **19.** $ 47   **20.** 622 students/day

Example 19   Weekly earnings, in dollars, of 10 employees of a software company are: $2,780; $2,030; $3,300; $850; $2,540; $1,760; $1,360; $2,100; $1,580; $1,800. What is the average earnings of the workers?

Solution   The total earnings of the ten employees

$$= 2,780 + 2,030 + 3,300 + 850 + 2,540 + 1,760 + 1,360 + 2,100 + 1,580 + 1,800$$

$$= \$20,100$$

The number of workers = 10

The average = $ 20,100 \div 10 =$ **$2,010**

Example 20   At the beginning of a 14-day trip, the odometer on a car read 10,278 miles. It read 13,638 miles at the end of the trip. What was the average number of miles traveled each day?

Solution   Average = (Total miles traveled) ÷ (Number of days)

$$= (13,638 - 10,278) \div 14$$

$$= 3,360 \div 14$$

$$= 240 \text{ miles per day}$$

Exercise 2.1

A. In exercises 1-10, translate the word statement into mathematical symbols.

1. Eight plus two is equal to ten.

2. Twenty divided by four equals five.

3. The quotient of thirty and five is six.

4. The product of five and six is 30.

5. Three times five added to four equals nineteen.

6. Nine decreased by five is four.

7. Seventeen minus two times five is equal to seven.

8. Twenty two divided by two is less than three plus twelve.

9. Nine raised to the power of four is not the same as four raised to the power of nine.
   (*Hint*: Symbol for not equal to is ≠.)

10. Three to the power of five plus seven is greater than two hundred.

In exercises 11-20, change the given phrase to an algebraic expression. Use *x* to represent the unknown.

11. Four times a number

12. Seven decreased by twice a number

13. Quotient of eleven and a number

14. Twenty minus the quotient of seven and a number

15. Five added to the product of a number and two

16. Five added to three times a number

17. A number increased by nine

18. Nine added to a number

19. Three times the difference between 9 and a number

20. Eight less than three times a number

In exercises 21-29, translate the given phrase or statement into symbols by using *x* for the unknown:

21. A number decreased by 6 is 19.

22. 15 is 3 more than a number.

23. If a number is multiplied by 3 and the product is increased by 10, the result is 25.

24. If two times a number is decreased by 8, the result is 6.

25. The sum of *x* and 5 is 9.

26. 5 times *x* equals 40.

27. The product of 7 and *x* is 63.

28. Nine plus five is greater than 10.

29. Fifteen minus 8 is less than 9.

In exercises 30-50, translate the word statement into symbols.

30. Eight plus five is greater than ten.

31. Twelve minus ten is less than fifteen.

32. Sixteen divided by four equals four.

33. Six multiplied by eight is greater than twelve.

34. The quotient of thirty and five is less than nine.

35. Twenty-six divided by thirteen equals two.

36. The product of five and six is not equal to twenty-one.

37. The quotient of forty-eight and twelve is equal to four.

38. Three times five added to four makes (equals) nineteen.

39. Five times three subtracted from twenty is not equal to six.

40. Nine decreased by five is less than or equal to four.

41. Three raised to fourth power is the same as nine squared.

42. Seventeen minus two times five is greater than three.

43. Twelve plus eighteen is equal to thirty-five minus five.

44. Twenty-two divided by eleven is less than three minus two.

45. Seven multiplied by six is equal to eighty four divided by two.

46. Three raised to the power six is not the same as (is not equal to) six raised to power three.

47. Six squared minus three squared equals twenty-seven.

48. Nine squared minus five squared equals fifty-six.

49. Three to the power four plus seven is greater than fifty.

50. Six raised to third power minus four squared is equal to two times ten squared.

In exercises 51-58, identify whether the given representation is an equation or an expression.

51. $3x^3 - 57x + y$

52. $4x^2 - 7x = \dfrac{8}{x+1}$

53. $5 + \dfrac{x}{3x-1} = 0$

54. $\dfrac{x^3 + 7x}{3x^2 + 5 - 1} = 0$

55. $8a^2 - 6ab + b^2$

56. $3ab - 4a^2 = b^2$

57. $6x^2y + 4 + y^2 = 2$

58. $4x^2 - 7x + \dfrac{8}{x+1}$

B. In exercises 59-63, identify the coefficient and the variable part of each term.

59. $-9x^2$

60. $4x^3$

61. $-5x$

62. $-9x^5$

63. $15x^2$

In exercises 64-67, determine whether or not the given pair of terms are like terms.

64. 13, 14

65. $2x, 3y$

66. $-x^2, 15x^2$

67. $2xy^2, 3x^2y$

In exercises 68-71, identify the like terms from a given set of terms.

68. $4, 5x^2y, -13x^2y, 2x, 3y$ **69.** $-2, 3, 5x, 2y, 3x^2y^2$ **70.** $6, -7xy, 5xy, x^2, y^2$ **71.** $2x, 3y, -5x^3y, 4yx^3, x^2$

C. **In exercises 72-83, simplify the given expression by combining like terms, wherever possible.**

72. $3x - 5x$ **73.** $-8y + 13y$ **74.** $-6xy - 7xy$

75. $3y - 7x + 4y(x + y)$ **76.** $-3x + 4x^2 + 7x - 5(x^2 - 1)$ **77.** $53 + 7(x + 2)$

78. $2 + x + 15 - 7x$ **79.** $-4p + 2(7 - 8p) - 48$ **80.** $2(7 - a) - 4a + 9$

81. $2xy + 4x - 3xy + 7x - y$ **82.** $3y^2 + 7y + 8x - 4y + 5x - 2y^2$ **83.** $3x^2 + x^2 - 5b + 2b$

In exercises 84-93, first simplify, then evaluate the expression for the given value of the variable.

84. $3x + 7 - 4x^2 - 4 + 5x - x^2$; $x = -2$ **85.** $5y^2 + 7 - 5y^2 + 8y - 15$; $y = -3$

86. $5x^2 - x^2 + 6x^2 + 2x - 7x$; $x = 4$ **87.** $-7 - 9x - 15x - 19 - 5x$; $x = -5$

88. $-4y + 5y^2 - 4y + 5y^2 + 6$; $y = -1$ **89.** $3y^2 - 4y + 2 + y^2 - 5$; $y = 2$

90. $x^3 + 3x^3 + 5x - 4x^2 + 1$; $x = -2$ **91.** $2(y^2 + 3y - 5) + 3(y^2 + 5y - 4)$; $y = -2$

92. $5(x^2 + 2x - 3) + 2(x^2 - x + 3)$; $x = -1$ **93.** $2x^2 - 5x + x^2 - 3 + 2x + 5 - 4x^2$; $x = 3$

D. **In exercises 94-103, evaluate the expression for $x = 2$, and $x = 9$.**

94. $2x + 3$ **95.** $3x - 5$ **96.** $x^2 + 1$ **97.** $25 - 2x$ **98.** $3x^2 + 15$ **99.** $47 - 4x$

100. $x^2 + 3x - 6$ **101.** $10x + x^2 + 3$ **102.** $3x^3$ **103.** $4x^2 + 5x - 12$

In exercises 104-119, evaluate the expression for the given value(s) of the variable(s).

104. $3m^2 - 4m + 1$; $m = 3$ **105.** $3x^4 + 5x^3 - 4$; $x = 2$ **106.** $x^2 + 5xy - 3y^2$; $x = 1$, $y = 1$

107. $4p^2 - 7p + 2$; $p = 4$ **108.** $4x - 2(x - 2y)$; $x = 1$, $y = 2$ **109.** $2a^2 - 5b$; $a = 6$, $b = 4$

110. $(2x + 3y)(2x - 3y)$; $x = 3$, $y = 2$ **111.** $5x^2 + (3y) - (5y)$; $x = 2$, $y = 3$ **112.** $3p + 4(7 - q)$; $p = 5$, $q = 2$

113. $x^2(3x + 1) - 4x + 5$; $x = 2$ **114.** $x^2 + 5x - 36$; $x = 9$ **115.** $y^3 - 3y^2 - y - 12$; $y = -2$

116. $-3a^2 + 5a + 2$; $a = -4$ **117.** $2y(2y + 2) + y - 12$; $y = 3$ **118.** $5x^3 - 3x^2 + 4x + 6$; $x = -1$

119. $2x^5 + 3x^4 - 4x^3 + 3x^2 - 5x - 1$; $x = 2$

E. **In exercises 120-132, find the average of the group of numbers.**

120. 8 and 12 **121.** $7, 3, 11$ **122.** $11, 10, 21$ **123.** $7, 5, 9, 11$

124. $2, 8, 9, 5$ **125.** $12, 7, 15, 14$ **126.** $4, 6, 9, 11, 15$ **127.** $3, 8, 1, 6, 7$

128. $12, 11, 17, 19, 31$ **129.** $468, 1481, 392, 1219, 85$ **130.** $24, 35, 37, 42, 45, 51$

131. $52, 89, 68, 124, 72, 80, 56, 115$ **132.** $35, 68, 120, 44, 56, 75, 82, 170, 92, 58$

133. The number of books issued in a college library on 20 different days is given in the following table:

305   500   450   489   365   296   413   503   437   482

386   429   455   427   474   399   325   373   455   397

Find the average number of books issued per day.

134. The heights of 10 students are 178, 173, 175, 181, 179, 171, 179, 175, 173, and 176 cm. Find their average height.

135. The population of a city increased from 225,000 to 245,000 in 5 years. What was the average increase per year?

2.2 SOLVING EQUATIONS WITH INTEGERS

IMPORTANT VOCABULARY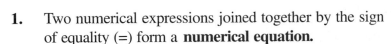

1. Two numerical expressions joined together by the sign of equality (=) form a **numerical equation.**

$$3 \cdot 4 - 5 = 7 \text{ is a numerical equation.}$$

2. An equation containing at least one unknown (variable) is called an **algebraic equation.**

$$x + 3 = 7 \text{ is an equation in the variable } x;$$
$$2y = 6 \text{ is an equation in the variable } y.$$

3. A value of the unknown which makes the equation a true statement is called a **solution.**

$$x = 4 \text{ is a solution of the equation } x + 3 = 7.$$

We also say that $x = 4$ **satisfies** the equation $x + 3 = 7$.

4. To **solve** an equation means to find its solution or to find a value for the unknown that when substituted in the equation makes the equation a true statement.

5. The procedure of solving equations is based on the principles of equality which say that if we perform the same operations on both sides of an equation, the resulting equation will have the same solution as the original equation.

6. Two equations which have the same soluion are called equivalent equations.

7.

THE PRINCIPLES OF EQUALITY
The Addition Principle: Adding the same number to both sides of an equation yields an equivalent equation.
The Division Principle: Dividing both sides of an equation by the same non-zero number yields an equivalent equation.

2.2A. Determine if a number is a solution of an equation.

- Two numerical expressions joined together by an equality (=) symbol form an **equation.**

    $7 + 4 = 11$, $13 - 4 = 9$ are examples of **True** equations.

- Equations may include variables.

    Equations may look like:

    $$x = 4 ; \quad \text{or} \quad n + 4 = 7 ; \quad \text{or} \quad y - 2 = 5.$$

    These equations will be true only when the variable is replaced by a specific number that makes both sides equal.

    For example,

    $x = 4$ is true only when x is replaced by **4**.

    $n + 4 = 7$ is true only when n is replaced by **3**.

    $y - 2 = 5$ is true only when y is replaced by **7**.

- The numbers that make the equations *true* statements are called **solutions**.

To find out if a number is a *solution* of an equation, we replace the variable by this number and simplify the expressions on both sides of the equation. If the simplification results in a true statement, the number is a solution; otherwise, it is not a solution.

The procedure for identifying which number from a given set of numbers is a solution.

Verify for each number in the set, one by one, whether or not it is a solution of the equation.

Warm-Up

1. Identify the solution from the given set.

   (a) $4x - 5 = 7$; $\{1, 2, 3\}$

   (b) $4x - 12 = x$; $\{5, 3, 4\}$

Example 1   Identify the solution of each of the following equations from the given set:

(a) $2x + 9 = 5x$; $\{0, -2, 3\}$

(b) $3x - 7 = 11$; $\{3, 4, -5\}$

Solutions

(a) $x = 0$:   Substitute 0 for x.

$$2x + 9 = 5x$$
$$\rightarrow \quad 2(0) + 9 = 5(0)$$
$$\rightarrow \quad 0 + 9 = 0$$
$$\rightarrow \quad 9 = 0 \quad \text{False}$$

0 is not a solution.

$x = -2$: Substitute -2 for x.

$$2(-2) + 9 = 5(-2)$$
$$\rightarrow \quad -4 + 9 = -10$$
$$\rightarrow \quad 5 = -10 \quad \text{False}$$

-2 is not a solution.

$x = 3$:   Substitute 3 for x.

$$2(3) + 9 = 5(3)$$
$$\rightarrow \quad 6 + 9 = 15$$
$$\rightarrow \quad 15 = 15 \quad \text{True}$$

$x = 3$ is a solution of $2x + 9 = 5x$.

(b)   Substitute 3, 4 and -5, one by one, for x in the given equation $3x - 7 = 11$.

$x = 3$:   Substitute 3 for x.

$$3x - 7 = 11$$
$$3(3) - 7 = 11$$
$$9 - 7 = 11$$
$$2 = 11 \quad \text{False}$$

$x = 3$ does not satisfy the equation; so, it is **not a solution**.

$x = 4$:   Substitute 4 for x.

$$3x - 7 = 11$$
$$3(4) - 7 = 11$$
$$12 - 7 = 11$$
$$5 = 11 \quad \text{False}$$

$x = 4$ does not satisfy the equation; therefore, it is **not a solution**.

$x = -5$: Substitute -5 for x.　　$\mathbf{3x - 7 = 11}$

$$3\,(-5) - 7 = 11$$
$$-15 - 7 = 11$$
$$-22 = 11 \quad \text{False}$$

$x = 5$ is **not a solution**; therefore, $3x - 7 = 11$ *does not* have a solution in the set $\{3, 4, -5\}$.

Answers:

1. (a) $x = 3$　　　(b) $x = 4$

2.2B. Solving One-step Equations using the Addition, Multiplication, or Division Principles

Consider the statement: "What number should be added to 4 to get the number 20?". This statement when translated into symbols give us the equation $x + 4 = 20$. To solve this using arithmetic, we would write the related subtraction problem: $20 - 4 = x$.

The solution is 16. We can verify the solution by substituting 16 into the original equation.

$$x + 4 = 20$$
$$(16) + 4 = 20 \quad \text{True}$$

The process of solving the same equation in algebra is more elaborate. One side of the equation is identified as the *left side* and the other is identified as the *right side*, with the "=" sign separating the sides.

We imagine that the sides are perfectly balanced.

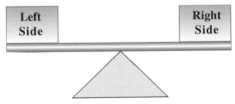

The equation $x + 4 = 20$ is illustrated below.

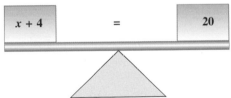

In algebra, our task is to keep the balance by performing the same operation on both sides, with the goal of getting x alone on the left side. We keep in mind the inverse and identity properties as we do this. We are aware of two facts:

$$4 + (-4) = 0 \qquad \text{Inverse property for Addition}$$
$$x + 0 = x \qquad \text{Identity property for Addition}$$

As we work with the equation, our goal is to keep the sides in balance with each other. Any time we change a side by adding (multiplying by, dividing by) a new number, we do the same to the other side, too.

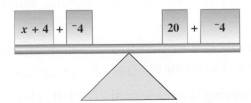

When we add the same number to both sides, we are using the Addition Principle of Equality.

The Addition Principle of Equality:

Adding the same number to both sides of an equation yields an equivalent equation.

Both sides, when simplified, yield the solution.

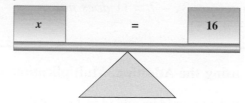

The above problem is shown below, when solved algebraically. Notice how the "=" signs are always below each other, and how the left and right sides are always distinct.

$x + 4 = 20$	Given equation
$x + 4 + (-4) = 20 + (-4)$	Addition Principle
$x + 0 = 16$	Inverse Property
$x = 16$	Identity Property

Warm-Up	**Example 2** Solve the equations: **(a)** $x + 7 = 5$ **(b)** $-13 = x - 8$.

Solutions

2. Solve and check.

(a) $y + 12 = -2$

(a)

$$x + 7 = 5$$
$$\longrightarrow \quad x + 7 - 7 = 5 - 7 \qquad \bullet \text{ Add } -7 \text{ to both sides.}$$
$$x + 0 = -2 \qquad \bullet \text{ Simplify both sides.}$$
$$x = -2 \qquad \bullet \ x + 0 = x$$

The solution is -2.

Check:
$$x + 7 = 5$$
$$\downarrow$$
$$(-2) + 7 = 5 \quad \longrightarrow \quad 5 = 5 \quad \text{True}$$

(b) $-8 = x - 3$

(b)

$$-13 = x - 8$$
$$\longrightarrow \quad -13 + 8 = x - 8 + 8 \qquad \text{Addition Principle.}$$
$$\longrightarrow \quad -5 = x + 0 \qquad \text{Simplying both sides.}$$
$$-5 = x \quad \text{or} \quad x = -5$$

The solution is -5.

Check:
$$-13 = x - 8$$
$$\downarrow$$
$$-13 = (-5) - 8 \quad \longrightarrow \quad -13 = -13 \quad \text{True}$$

- The same balancing principle is used for equations involving "**multiplication**". Here the inverse operation "**division**" will be used.

Consider the equation $-3x = 21$. If we were to solve this using arithmetic, we would simply use the related division fact: $21 \div (-3) = x$. The solution is -7.

The algebraic method of solving is more formal. The left side is $-3x$ and the right side is 21. To solve the equation is to get the x alone on the left side.

We are aware of two facts.

$$\frac{-3}{-3} = 1$$
  A non-zero number divided by itself equals 1.

$$1 \cdot x = x$$
  Identity Property for Multiplication.

Our strategy is to get a "1" to replace "−3" in the original equation. Whatever operation we use, we must keep the "balance" by doing the same operation on both the left and right sides of the equation. Study the algebraic method for solving the equation below.

$$-3x = 21$$
  Original equation.

$$\frac{-3 \cdot x}{-3} = \frac{21}{-3}$$
  Division Principle of Equality.

$$1 \cdot x = -7$$
  Division of a number by itself = 1.

$$x = -7$$
  Identity Property for Multiplication.

In the above solution, we solved the equation by dividing both the right and left sides by −3 and then simplifying. When we divide both sides by −3, we are using the Division Property of Equality.

The Division Principle of Equality:

Dividing both sides of an equation by the same non-zero number yields an equivalent equation.

Example 3 Solve the following equations:

(a) $3x = -18$ **(b)** $-15x = 45$ **(c)** $-4 = -x$

Solutions

(a) $3x = -18$
  • Write the given equation.

$$\frac{3x}{3} = \frac{-18}{3}$$
  • The coefficient of x is 3. Divide both sides by 3.

$$x = -6$$
  • Simplify.

The solution is −6.

Check: $3x = -18$
$$3(-6) = -18 \rightarrow -18 = -18 \quad \text{True}$$

Remark:

While solving equations, it is usual to express division in the fraction form: $-18 \div 3 = \frac{-18}{3}$.

Also, an expression such as $\frac{3x}{3}$ means the same as $\frac{3}{3} \cdot x$.

(b) $-15x = 45$

$$\frac{-15 \cdot x}{-15} = \frac{45}{-15}$$
  • Write the given equation.

  • Coefficient of x is −15. Divide both sides by −15.

$$1 \cdot x = -3$$
  • Perform division on both sides. Coefficient of x will become 1.

$$x = -3$$

The solution is −3.

Warm-Up

3. Solve and check.

(a) $4x = -64$

(b) $-9x = 63$

(c) $-12 = -2x$

Answers:

2. (a) $y = -14$ (b) $x = -5$

3. (a) $x = -16$ (b) $x = -7$
     (c) $x = 6$

Check: $-15x = 45$
$$-15(\mathbf{-3}) = 45$$
$$45 = 45 \quad \text{True}$$

(c) $-4 = -x$
- Switch sides so that the variable x is on the left side.

$-x = -4$
- Rewrite $-x = -1 \cdot x$.

$-1 \cdot x = -4$

$$\frac{-1 \cdot x}{-1} = \frac{-4}{-1}$$
- Division Principle of Equality: Divide both sides by -1.

$$x = 4$$

The solution is 4.
- Replace the variable by the solution, using parentheses.

Check: $-4 = -x$
$$-4 = -(\mathbf{4}) \quad \text{True}$$

2.2C. Solving Equations with Several Steps using the Addition and Division Principles

Consider an equation that is slightly more complex : $4x + 9 = 65$

The left side is $4x + 9$ and the right side is 65. The left side involves both addition and multiplication. Our goal is to get x alone on the left side. Which one should be eliminated first, the 9 or the 4? Does it matter?

Before algebraic symbolism was invented, this equation would have been stated as a puzzle.

Start with a number.	x
Multiply by 4.	$4x$
Add 9.	$4x + 9$
The result is 65.	$4x + 9 = 65$

Before continuing your reading, try to solve the puzzle.

Before algebra, mathematicians solved this type of problem by working in reverse: working from the end back to the beginning as well as working with inverse operations.

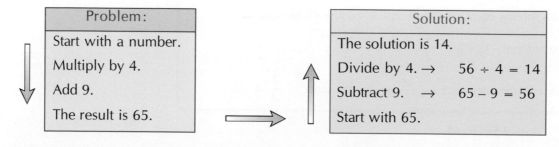

Observe the solution below. In solving an equation with a multiplication and an addition, the addition is eliminated first. This is precisely the reverse of the order of operations, from the last, back to the beginning. Study the algebraic solution for the equation, shown below:

$$4x + 9 = 65 \qquad \text{Given equation.}$$

$$4x + 9 + (-9) = 65 + (-9) \qquad \text{Add } (-9) \text{ to both sides.}$$

$$4x = 56 \qquad \text{Simplify.}$$

$$\frac{4x}{4} = \frac{56}{4} \qquad \text{Divide both sides by 4.}$$

$$x = 14 \qquad \text{Simplify, to get the final solution.}$$

The solution is 14.

Check:
$$4x + 9 = 65$$
$$\downarrow$$
$$4(\mathbf{14}) + 9 = 65$$
$$56 + 9 = 65$$
$$65 = 65 \qquad \text{True}$$

Procedure to solve an equation that includes both multiplication and addition.

Step 1 Add the same number to both sides to eliminate the constant term.

Step 2 Divide both sides by the same number to eliminate the factor of the variable.

Step 3 Check the solution.

Example 4 Solve the following equations:

(a) $3x - 1 = -13$ (b) $-14 = 4y + 2$

(c) $7 - x = -12$

Solutions

(a)
$$3x - 1 = -13 \qquad \bullet \text{ Write the given equation.}$$
$$3x - 1 + \mathbf{1} = -13 + \mathbf{1} \qquad \bullet \text{ Add 1 on both sides.}$$
$$3x = -12 \qquad \bullet \text{ Simplify.}$$
$$\frac{3x}{3} = \frac{-12}{3} \qquad \bullet \text{ Divide both sides by 3.}$$
$$x = -4 \, ;$$

The solution is $x = -\mathbf{4}$.

Check: $3x - 1 = -13$
$$\downarrow$$
$$3(-\mathbf{4}) - 1 = -13 \longrightarrow -12 - 1 = -13 \longrightarrow -13 = -13 \, ; \quad \text{True}$$

(b)
$$-14 = 4y + 2 \qquad \text{It is easier to work with the variable on the left.}$$
$$4y + 2 = -14 \qquad \bullet \text{ Rewrite the equation by switching the sides.}$$
$$4y + 2 - \mathbf{2} = -14 - \mathbf{2} \qquad \bullet \text{ Subtract 2 from both sides.}$$
$$4y + 0 = -16 \qquad \bullet \text{ Simplify.}$$
$$4y = -16 \qquad \bullet \text{ Divide both sides by 4.}$$
$$\frac{4y}{4} = \frac{-16}{4} \qquad \bullet \text{ Simplify.}$$
$$y = -\mathbf{4} \, ;$$

The solution is $y = -\mathbf{4}$.

Warm-Up

4. Solve the equations:

(a) $-6x - 2 = 28$

(b) $7x - 5 = -40$

Check:

$$-14 = 4y + 2 \quad \text{Use the given equation.}$$

$$-14 = 4(-4) + 2 \quad \longrightarrow \quad -14 = -16 + 2$$

$$-14 = -14 ; \quad \textbf{True}$$

(c) $5 - x = 7$

(c)

$7 - x = -12$	• Write the given equation.
$7 + (-x) = -12$	• Rewrite the subtraction as addition of the opposite.
$7 + (-x) + (-7) = -12 + (-7)$	• Add –7 to both sides.
$-x = -19$	
$-1 \cdot x = -19$	• Rewrite $-x$ as $-1 \cdot x$.
$\dfrac{-1 \cdot x}{-1} = \dfrac{-19}{-1}$	• Divide both sides by –1.
$x = \textbf{19}$	

The solution is 19.

Check:

$$7 - x = -12$$

$$7 - (\textbf{19}) = -12 \qquad \text{Use the given equation.}$$

$$-12 = -12 \qquad \textbf{True}$$

5. Solve and check.

(a) $-3x + 4 - 9 = -21 + 7$

Example 5 Solve the equations :

    (a) $2x - 6 + 8 = -17 - 5$

    (b) $4 - 4(x - 2) = -11 + 3$

Solutions

 Note   In equations of this type, we combine like terms on both sides before using the properties. The result is a simpler equation.

(a)

$2x - 6 + 8 = -17 - 5$	Write the given equation.
$2x - \underbrace{6 + 8} = \underbrace{-17 - 5}$	Combine the like terms on both sides. The equation reduces to the form $ax + b = c$.
$2x + 2 = -22$	
$2x + 2 - 2 = -22 - 2$	Add –2 (or subtract 2) to both sides.
$2x = -24$	Simplify both sides.
$\dfrac{2x}{2} = \dfrac{-24}{2}$	Divide both sides by 2.
$x = -12.$	Simplify.

The solution is $x = \textbf{–12}$.

Check:

$$2x - 6 + 8 = -17 - 5 \quad \text{Original equation}$$

$$2(\mathbf{-12}) - 6 + 8 = -17 - 5$$

$$-24 - 6 + 8 = -17 - 5 \longrightarrow -22 = -22; \quad \text{True}$$

(b) $\quad 4 - 4(x - 2) = -11 + 3 \quad \bullet$ Write the given equation.

$$4 - 4x + 8 = -11 + 3 \quad \bullet \text{ Use distributive property.}$$
$$-4(x - 2) = -4x + 8$$

$$-4x + 12 = -8 \quad \bullet \text{ Add } -12 \text{ to both sides (or, equivalently, subtract 12 from both sides).}$$

$$-4x + \underbrace{12 - \mathbf{12}}_{= 0} = -8 - \mathbf{12} \quad \bullet \text{ Simplify by combining like terms.}$$

$$-4x = -20 \quad \bullet \text{ Divide both sides by the coefficient of } x, \text{ that is } -4.$$

$$\frac{-4x}{\mathbf{-4}} = \frac{-20}{\mathbf{-4}} \quad \bullet \text{ Simplify by performing division on both sides.}$$

$$x = \mathbf{5}.$$

Check:

$$4 - 4(x - 2) = -11 + 3$$

$$4 - 4(\mathbf{5} - 2) = -11 + 3$$

$$4 - 4 \cdot 3 = -8$$

$$-8 = -8; \quad \text{True}$$

(b) $-5(x - 7) + 10 = -28 + 13$

Answers:

4. (a) $x = -5$ (b) $x = -5$ (c) $x = -2$

5. (a) $x = 3$ (b) $x = 12$

Exercise 2.2

A. In exercises 1-20, an equation and a set of numbers are given. Identify which number in the set is a solution of the equation.

1. $x + 10 = 16$; $\{3, 4, 5, 6\}$

2. $x - 7 = 14$; $\{17, 19, 21, 23\}$

3. $17 = x + 6$; $\{7, 8, 9, 10, 11, 12\}$

4. $3x = 21$; $\{1, 2, 3, 4, 5, 6, 7\}$

5. $y - 5 = 20$; $\{21, 22, 23, 24, 25, 30\}$

6. $x + 14 = 20$; $\{3, 5, 6, 9\}$

7. $4x = 25 - 5$; $\{0, 1, 2, 3, 4, 5\}$

8. $\dfrac{x}{5} = 3$; $\{10, 15, 20, 25\}$

9. $x + 8 = 22 - 14$; $\{0, 1, 2, 3, 4\}$

10. $72 = 8p$; $\{7, 8, 9, 10, 11\}$

11. $x + 2 = -5$; $\{-5, -6, -7, -8\}$

12. $y - 8 = -4$; $\{-2, -1, 0, 1, 2, 3, 4\}$

13. $-3 = 2x - 1$; $\{0, -1, -2, -3\}$

14. $-11 = 3x + 1$; $\{-2, -3, -4, -5, -6\}$

15. $-5x = 30$; $\{-3, -4, -5, -6\}$

16. $4y = -9 + 5$; $\{2, 1, 0, -1, -2, -3\}$

17. $\dfrac{x}{-7} + 1 = 3$; $\{7, 14, -7, -14, -21\}$

18. $5 - t = 12$; $\{-3, -4, -5, -6, -7\}$

19. $-18 = 5y - 18$; $\{-3, -2, -1, 0, 1\}$

20. $4 + t = -3 + 7$; $\{0, -1, -2, -3, -4\}$

B. In exercises 21-68, solve for the variable and check your solution.

21. $x + 3 = 11$

22. $x + 5 = 15$

23. $x - 2 = 50$

24. $z - 17 = 13$

25. $z - 8 = 8$

26. $14 = x + 14$

27. $z + 8 = 8$

28. $14 = x - 14$

29. $x + 0 = 4$

30. $y + 175 = 390$

31. $x - 105 = 395$ **32.** $x + 17 = 41$ **33.** $x + 1{,}297 = 1{,}300$ **34.** $p - 75 = 125$ **35.** $x + 13 = 16$

36. $12 + y = 16$ **37.** $y + 6 = 15$ **38.** $18 + x = 11 + 9$ **39.** $x + 7 = -2$ **40.** $x + 11 = 5$

41. $x - 8 = -11$ **42.** $x - 9 = -12$ **43.** $-21 = y + 4$ **44.** $-17 = y - 19$ **45.** $-7 = y - 12$

46. $-10 = y - 13$ **47.** $-8 = t - 8$ **48.** $-12 = t + 4$ **49.** $t + 6 = -6$ **50.** $t + 9 = -9$

51. $x + 20 = -100$ **52.** $-43 = p - 40$ **53.** $-17 = x - 9$ **54.** $t + 1 = -2$ **55.** $-12 = x - 3$

56. $14 = -x$ **57.** $-n = 125$ **58.** $-m = -17$ **59.** $-5x = 30$ **60.** $-3x = 12$

61. $-12x = 144$ **62.** $-8x = -96$ **63.** $9x = -63$ **64.** $13x = -52$ **65.** $65 = -13y$

66. $-72 = 8y$ **67.** $108 = -9x$ **68.** $36 = -6x$

C. **In exercises 69-90, use the basic properties to solve the given equation.**

69. $11 - x = 20$ **70.** $-15 = 77 - x$ **71.** $x + 17 - 10 = -9 + 16$ **72.** $3 - 3x - 4x = -3 + 27$

73. $-20 - 4 = 6y + y - 3y$ **74.** $6(x + 1) = 24$ **75.** $5x + 2x = -35 + 15 + 20$ **76.** $3 - 2(x - 2) = -4 + 9$

77. $2p - 5p - 7 = 14$ **78.** $3y - 27 - y = -19$ **79.** $2(x + 3) = 2$ **80.** $p - 4p = -25 + 3 + 25$

81. $-2(x - 2) = 2x$ **82.** $5y + 20 - 13y + 4 = 0$ **83.** $5(y + 1) = 20$ **84.** $2u + 7u - 4u = 17 - 3 + 6$

85. $4 - 2(x - 3) = 19 - 5$ **86.** $2x - 3(x + 4) = 25 - 32$ **87.** $-2x + 4(3 - x) = 4 - 16$

88. $-2(x + 3) - 3(2 - x) = -19 + 23$ **89.** $4x - 2(7 - x) - 5x = -18$

90. $-10(x - 4 + 9) + 6x + 3(x - 8) = -41 + 25$

2.3 APPLICATIONS USING INTEGERS

Introduction

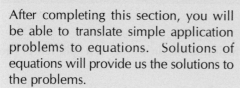

Objectives

After completing this section, you will be able to translate simple application problems to equations. Solutions of equations will provide us the solutions to the problems.

Solving problems is the main purpose for learning mathematics. In this section we will develop the skills necessary for translating application problems, and then use our knowledge of mathematics to solve these problems. At every stage in this book we will be revisiting the process of solving application problems with varying degrees of complexities depending on the mathematical concepts being discussed.

Translating and Solving Application Problems

- We have already discussed earlier how to solve equations. We will use this skill in solving some application problems. The procedures are summarized in the following steps:

> **Basic Steps for Solving Word Problems**
>
> **1.** Read the problem carefully. Read it again, until you understand the problem and you are able to identify what is given and what is to be determined.
>
> **2.** If possible draw figures or diagrams that might be helpful. Translate the problem into an equation.
>
> **3.** Solve the equation and interpret the solution.
>
> **4.** Verify your solution by using the *original* statement of the problem.

Often we are able to translate an application directly into an equation. Some require slight re-wording so that the numbers are clearly named.

Example 1   Marguerite spent $26 less on food this week than Jan did. If Jan spent $92 this week, how much did Marguerite spend?

Solution   We are given the relationship between the two week's food expenses. We are also given Jan's food expense, $92. We are asked to find Marguerite's expense.

We need to rewrite the satement using a form of the word "is" and naming the numbers, rather than the people.

<u>Marguerite's food expense</u> was $26 less than <u>Jan's food expense</u>.

Reword using "was".

M   =   J   – $26   Be careful writing the subtraction.

M = $92 – $26   Since we know Jan's amount, replace J by $92.

M = $66   Solve.

Marguerite spent $66, which is $26 less than Jan spent ($92).

Example 2   After writing three checks for $560, $250, and $179, Peter Martinez has $536 left in his account. How much money was in the account originally?

Solution   We are looking for the original amount. Let x be the original amount. We are given the amounts of three checks and the final amount, $536. The checks will be subtractions. We will start with the original amount.

Original Amount – 1st check – 2nd check – 3rd check = Final Amount

$$x \quad - \quad \$560 \quad - \quad \$250 \quad - \quad \$179 \ = \ \$536$$

Rewrite subtraction as addition.

$$x \quad + (-560) + (-250) + (-179) = 536$$

Combine like terms.

$$x + (-989) = 536$$

Add 989 to both sides.

$$x + (-989) + 989 = 536 + 989$$

$$x = 1525$$

The original amount in the account was **$1525**.

To check, start with $1525 and deduct the amount of each check that was written. Verify that the final balance is $536.

- **The Sum of the Parts = The total**

Many addition and subtraction problems involve a total that is the sum of several parts. Sometimes we are trying to find the total and sometimes we are trying to find one or more of the parts.

Example 3   To buy a used car, Walter Jones pays $300 down and the rest in 18 monthly payments. If the car costs him $2,352, what is his monthly payment?

113

Solution   We are looking for the monthly payment. Let x be the monthly payment. We are given the total amount, $2,352, and the downpayment, $300. The total is the sum of the downpayment and all the monthly payments.

$$\text{Downpayment} + 18 \text{ monthly payments} = \text{Total Cost}$$

$$\$300 + 18 \cdot x = \$2352$$

$$300 + 18x = 2352$$

Add −300 to each side.

$$300 + 18x + (-300) = 2352 + (-300)$$

Combine like terms.

$$18x = 2052$$

Divide both sides by 18.

$$\frac{18x}{18} = \frac{2052}{18}$$

$$x = 114$$

The monthly payments were each **$114**.

How would you verify that the answer is correct?

$114 \cdot 18 + 300$ must be equal to $2352.

• **Applications involving Unit Rates**

Most application problems involving multiplication or division of numbers are rate problems. This type of problem is discussed in detail in Chapter 5. Rates involve relationships between numbers with different labels. The application problems most often encountered involve unit rates, in which one of the amounts is 1. Five candy bars in one packet relates *5 candy bars to 1 packet*.

If 5 candy bars are in one packet, we expect to find 10 candy bars in 2 packets, and 20 candy bars in 4 packets. If we have twice as many packets, we expect twice as many candy bars. Examine the diagram below. Note that 4 numbers are involved, two for each case.

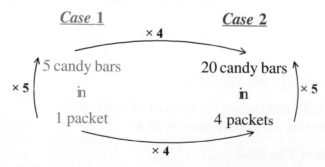

Warm-Up

4. A fruit seller bought 26,175 apples. If 111 apples were found rotten, and the remaining apples were packed in 362 boxes, find the number of apples in each box. (Use calculator for calculations, if necessary).

Example 4   There are 5 candy bars in a packet. How many candy bars are there in 24 packets? If these candy bars are to be distributed among 12 children. How many candy bars will each child receive?

Solution   There are two problems here. We are asked to find the number of candy bars and then we are asked to find how many candy bars each child will receive.

First, let us find the total number of candy bars. Let the number of candy bars in 24 packets be x. We are given that there are 5 candy bars in 1 packet. The candy bars and packets are related. It is a rate problem. We will show a diagram involving the 4 numbers.

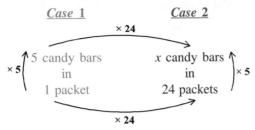

From the diagram, we see that we can multiply 5 candy bars by 24 to find x.

$$x = 5 \cdot 24 = \mathbf{120}$$

There are **120 candy bars** altogether in the 24 packets.

Next, we are asked to find how many candy bars each child will receive. Let this number of candy bars be y. We know that we have 120 candy bars for 12 children.

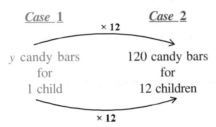

Using the diagram we can easily see that:

$$y \cdot 12 = 120$$
$$12y = 120 \qquad \text{Rewrite in the usual from.}$$
$$\frac{12y}{12} = \frac{120}{12} \qquad \text{Divide both sides by 12.}$$
$$y = 10$$

Each child will get **10 candy bars**.

Work backwards to verify.

Example 5

A new Ford Explorer should get 16 miles per gallon for city driving and 21 miles per gallon on the highway. In a week when all of the driving was city driving, the vehicle logged 432 miles. How many gallons of gas were used?

Solution

We are asked to find the number of gallons of gas used. Let x represent the number of gallons used. We are told the millage, 432 miles, and city mpg is 16 miles per gallon.

This is a rate problem, involving miles and gallons. We will show a diagram involving the 4 numbers.

5. A new Ford Explorer should get 20 miles per gallon for city driving and 24 miles per gallon on the highway. In a particular day when all the driving was highway driving, the vehicle logged 168 miles. How many gallons of gas were used?

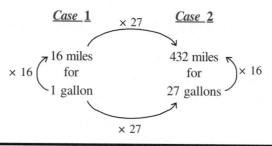

Using the diagram we can easily see that:

$$x \cdot 16 = 432$$

$$16x = 432 \qquad \text{Rewrite in the usual form.}$$

$$\frac{16x}{16} = \frac{432}{16} \qquad \text{Divide both sides by 16.}$$

$$x = 27$$

27 gallons of gasoline were used. To verify, replace x in the diagram and check all the resulting multiplication relations, as shown below.

Answers:

1. 12,428
2. $3,848; $3,800
3. $235
4. 72 apples in each box
5. 7 gallons

Exercise 2.3

In exercises 1-45, translate into equations and solve.

Checking Accounts

1. Jeanne has $2750 in her college checking account. She writes a check for $670 for her food bill at the dining hall. How much is left in her account?

2. Andy had $6,400 in his checking account. If he writes a check for three thousand five hundred thirty-eight dollars, how much is left in his account?

3. A shopkeeper had $13,750 in his checking account. He writes a check for $6,870. How much is left in his account?

4. A glass company had $34,875 in its checking account. If the treasurer of the company writes a check for two thousand three hundred forty-five dollars, how much is left in the account?

5. Derek had $3,625 in his checking account. He wrote a check for $469 to buy a fax modem for his computer. How much was left in his account?

6. In the beginning of January, Mr. Philip had a balance of $6,850 in his checking account. During January he made deposits of $640, $780, and $1,540. He wrote checks for $1,100, $1,200, and $1,550. What was his checking account balance at the end of the month?

7. In January, Mr. Lemen opened a checking account and deposited $2,575. In February he deposited $600 and wrote checks for $740 and $1,305. Estimate the balance in his account at the end of February and find the actual balance.

8. In February, Mr. Laurant opened a checking account and deposited $1,725. In March, he wrote checks for $45, $37, and $142 and deposited $257. Estimate the balance in his account at the end of March and find the actual balance.

9. Manique deposited $1,265 in her bank account in the first year. In the second year, she deposited $340 more than the first year. In the third year, she deposited $450 more than the amount deposited in the second year. What was the total amount deposited in the three years?

10. The balance in Philip's checking account is $2,129. He wrote checks for $223 and $527, then he deposited $319 from his pay check. What is Philip's new balance?

11. Roza is working for an insurance company. In November 2003, she opened a checking account and deposited $1,850. By the next month her company transferred $750 into her account as a Christmas bonus. During the Christmas week she did a lot of shopping and wrote checks for $250, $365, and $575. Find the balance in her account.

12. John had $5,468 in his checking account. He wrote checks for $145, $88, and $249. Then he deposited $205 back in the account upon the return of some books. How much is left in his account?

13. Addy has $12,670 in his checking account. He wrote checks for $730, $8,450, $385, and $3,800. At all times, he must maintain a minimum balance of $100 in his account. How much more should he deposit in his account so that all his checks are cleared?

14. Edmond had $12,245 in his checking account. If he writes two checks for $3,040 and $6,105, how much is left in his account?

15. Mr. Trear is working for a travel company. In December 2003, he opened a checking account and deposited $2,548. In January 2004, his company transferred $1,250 into his account as a bonus. During January, he wrote checks for $355, $675, and $963. Find the balance in his account.

16. Robin has $2,364 in his checking account. If he writes checks for $72, $109, $634, and $470, find the balance in his account.

17. In the beginning of a month, Ms. Beth had a balance of $560 in her checking account. During the month, she made deposits of $840, $531, and $1,735. She wrote checks for $146, $37, and $1,345. What was her checking account balance at the end of the month?

18. A man opens the checking account and deposits $25,000. During one year, he writes three checks for $7,500, $4,580, and $8,250. The bank credited $625 to his account in interest for that year. Find the balance in the account after one year.

19. Robin kept $5,000 in his checking account for two years. Interest of $400 was credited to his account at the end of the first year and interest of $432 at the end of the second year. After two years, he wrote a check for $3,470. Find the balance in his account.

20. Eric kept $6,000 in his checking account for three years. Interest of $400 was credited to his account at the end of the first year, interest of $450 at the end of second year, and $500 at the end of the third year. At the end of three years he wrote a check for $3,142. Find the balance in his account.

Consumer Items

21. The largest river in the world is the Nile, which is 4,145 miles long. It is 138 miles longer than the second largest river, which is the Amazon in South America. How long is the Amazon river?

22. The largest lake in the world is the Caspian Sea, which has an area of 317,000 square kilometers. It is 288,900 square kilometers larger than the second largest lake, which is Lake Superior. What is the area of Lake Superior?

23. Lowell borrowed $6,548 for a used car. The loan is to be paid in 30 equal monthly payments. How much is each payment (excluding interest)?

24. The Lou family borrows $4,932 to build a sun room on the back of their house. The loan is to be paid off in equal monthly payments of $137 (excluding interest). How many months will it take to pay off the loan?

25. John wants to buy a new car costing $23,000. He will pay $1,500 in taxes and a $575 licensing fee. He plans to make a down payment of $4,200 and finance the remainder through his bank. How much will he finance?

26. Ann wants to buy a car costing $35,000. She will pay $2,000 in taxes and $650 licensing fee. She plans to make a down payment of $7,500 and finance the remainder through his bank. How much will she finance?

27. Dia wants to buy a car costing $31,726. She has only $1,624 for the down payment. Her parents gave her $2,800 for the car. She wants to pay the balance in 22 equal monthly payments. What is Dia's monthly payment?

28. Carrol wants to buy a car costing $36,516 including all taxes and closing costs. She has $6,500 for the down payment. Her friend gave her $2,450 for the car. She wants to pay the balance in 24 equal monthly payments. What is Carrol's monthly payment?

29. Kim sold four houses last year for : $89,050, $210,560, $459,000, and $71,950. What is the total value of her sales? Round to the nearest thousand dollars.

30. Liz sold four lots last year for $95,250, $125,543, $175,899, and $189,346. What is the total value of her sales? Round to the nearest thousand.

31. Jose's total earning are $3,525. He spent $1,215 on clothes, $892 on other items, and saved the rest. How much did he save?

32. Linda spent $1,350 on mortgages payments, $1,225 on clothes and food items, $480 on other items, and saved the rest. How much did she save if her total earnings were $4,566 ?

33. Thomas has refinanced his home and now owes only $253,670. He pays part of the mortgage payment from his inheritance of $250,800. He wants to pay off the rest of the mortgage in 24 monthly installments. What will be his monthly payment?

34. Andy has refinanced his home and now owes only $225,520. He pays $100,000 towards the mortgage from his savings. He wants to pay off the rest of the mortgage in 16 monthly payments. What will be his monthly payment?

35. A woman goes shopping and spends $245 on clothes, $70 on food items, and $63 on magazines. She has $570 left in her purse. What amount did she have in her purse before going shopping?

36. Before going back to college, Chris buys 5 shirts at $49 each and 6 pairs of pants at $79 each. He has $674 left. What amount did he have before going shopping?

37. A car costing $4,500 was sold at a profit of $725. Find the selling price. (*Hint:* Profit = Sales – Costs.)

38. A mini-van costing $4,897 was sold at a profit of $923. Find the selling price.

39. The hard-drive on your computer has 40 gigabytes (GB) storage space available. If the software installation takes 15 GB of space, how much storage space is left after the installation?

40. The Carrol family has the following payments to make each month: rent, $630; car, $210; T.V. set, $28; washer and dryer, $63; and insurance, $112. What is their total monthly payment? If the monthly income of the Carrol family is $ 2,000, find the balance left after making these payments.

41. A welfare association prepares two types of packages for distribution to the needy, the family pack that contains nine cans of vegetables, and the elderly pack that contains four cans of vegetables. How many cans of vegetables are needed for preparing 125 family packs and 50 elderly packs?

42. During a canned vegetable sale Ted buys 14 cans of different vegetables. If the sale price of each can is $ 2, how much does Ted pay for the canned vegetables?

43. A bottling company produces 22,324 cans of Diet Cola. How many 12-can packages can be made? How many cans will be left over?

44. Copies of this book are generally despatched from the warehouse in cartons containing 24 books each. How many cartons are required to despatch 2,880 books?

45. A map has a scale of 170 miles to an inch. The distance between Washington DC and Atlanta is 850 miles. How far apart are they on the map?

2.4 BASIC GEOMETRY

IMPORTANT VOCABULARY

Geometry offers us a practical setting in which we use arithmetic and basic algebra skills. In order to construct buildings, design and use instruments, we must have a working knowledge of geometric figures. Engineers, architects, home builders, computer scientists, and many others rely on the knowledge of geometry. In this chapter we review some of the basic concepts of Geometry that will be used throughout this book.

> **Objectives** 📖
>
> After completing this section, you will be able to identify terms and basic concepts about:
>
> A. Lines and angles,
>
> B. Properties of angles,
>
> C. Polygons, triangles, and quadrilaterals; and
>
> D. Solve perimeter and area applications.

2.4 A. Lines and Angles

- **To become familiar with the basic terms of Geometry**

The basic terms used in Geometry includes the notion of a point, a line, an angle, and other related terms. We shall briefly review these terms and some of the very basic concepts associated with these terms.

Point: As soon as the tip of our pen or pencil comes in contact with a paper (Figure 2.1), or the sharp edge of a piece of chalk comes in contact with the writing board (Figure 2.2) a **point** is plotted.

A point is represented by a dot.

A point has no dimensions such as length, width or thickness.

We generally use capital letters to name points (Figure 2.3).

Figure 2.1   **Figure 2.2**

Figure 2.3

Line: When a pencil runs along the edge of a ruler, it leaves a trace on the paper in the form of a straight line (Figure 2.4).

Figure 2.4

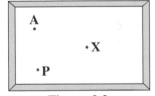

A 'straight - line' (or a 'line')

Through two given points, we can draw exactly one line. (See Figure 2.5). There is exactly one line LM that passes through points L and M. A line is infinitely long, continuing forever in both directions.

Figure 2.5

Line segment:

If we mark two different points, say P and Q, on a line, then the portion of the line between P and Q is called a **segment**, and is named as PQ; P and Q are the end points of the segment PQ (Figure 2.6).

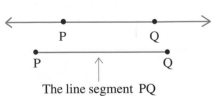

The line segment PQ

Figure 2.6

A line segment has a *length*, but it has no width or thickness.

We can measure the length of a line segment with the help of a scale or ruler. In Figure 2.7, the length of the segment AB is 8 cm.

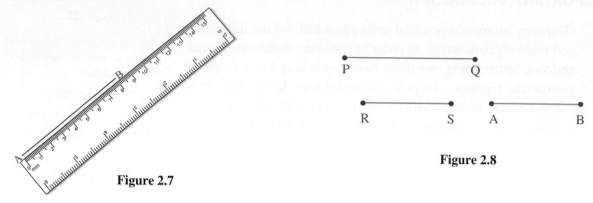

Figure 2.7

Figure 2.8

We can *compare* two line segments by comparing the measurements of their lengths. In Figure 2.8, the segment RS is shorter than PQ. The segments RS and AB seem to be equal.

Ray: A ray is a part of a line which starts from a point and extends endlessly towards one side. The word **ray** comes from the sun's rays. The sun's rays begin at the Sun and travel endlessly.

We use the initial point along with one more point on the ray to represent a ray. The initial point is written first to describe a ray.

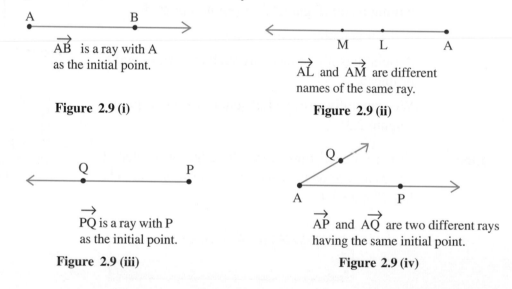

$\overrightarrow{AB}$ is a ray with A
as the initial point.

Figure 2.9 (i)

$\overrightarrow{AL}$ and $\overrightarrow{AM}$ are different
names of the same ray.

Figure 2.9 (ii)

$\overrightarrow{PQ}$ is a ray with P
as the initial point.

Figure 2.9 (iii)

$\overrightarrow{AP}$ and $\overrightarrow{AQ}$ are two different rays
having the same initial point.

Figure 2.9 (iv)

Angles: An angle (symbol: $\angle$) is a figure formed by two rays having a common initial point called the **vertex** of the angle. (Figure 2.10)

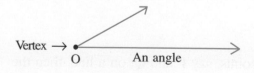

Vertex → O   An angle

Figure 2.10

Any two points, one on each of the two arms of the angle, along with the vertex can be used to name an angle. The angle shown in Figure 2.11 below is written as ∠AOB and read as **angle AOB**. It should be noted that the common initial point, or the vertex, is written in the middle.

Figure 2.11	Figure 2.12

An angle may also be denoted by the single letter at its vertex, or by some different letter or symbol designed for this purpose. Observe in Figure 2.12, ∠QOP, ∠POQ, ∠O, and ∠x are different names of the same angle.

- **To identify types of angles by degree measure**

Measuring an angle: Just as segments are measured in terms of inches or centimeters, angles are measured in terms of *degrees* or *radians*. We will only use degrees as measurement of angles in this book.

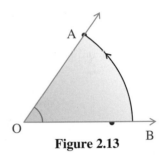

Figure 2.13

Measure an angle in degrees: We place the vertex of the angle at the center of a circle of some fixed radius as shown in Figure 2.14a. Divide the circumference into 360 equal parts, called **degrees,** denoted by the symbol ° .

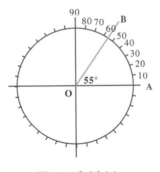

Figure 2.14 (a)

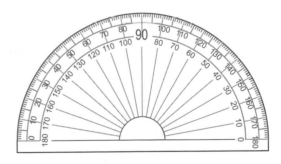

Figure 2.14 (b)

The number of degrees along the circumference between the two arms OA and OB of the angle in Figure 2.14 (a) is its degree measure which is 55°. Usually, we use a *protractor* as in Figure 2.14 (b), to measure angles in degrees.

Types of angles:

The angle of 360° is called a **complete angle** or a full circle (Figure 2.15).

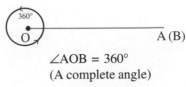

∠AOB = 360°
(A complete angle)
Figure 2.15

The angle of 180° is called a **straight angle** (Figure 2.16).

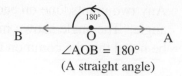

∠AOB = 180°
(A straight angle)

Figure 2.16

The angle of 90°, one fourth of a complete revolution, is called a **right angle** (Figure 2.17).

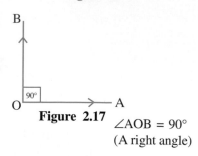

Figure 2.17

∠AOB = 90°
(A right angle)

An angle less than 90° and greater than 0° is called an **acute** angle (Figure 2.18) and an angle greater than 90° and less than 180° is called an **obtuse** angle (Figure 2.19).

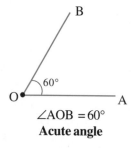

∠AOB = 60°
Acute angle

Figure 2.18

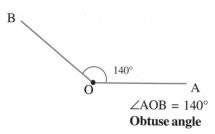

∠AOB = 140°
Obtuse angle

Figure 2.19

Warm-Up

1. Identify the type of angles.

(a)

(b)   (c)

(d)   (e)

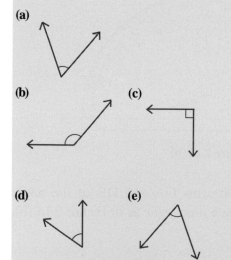

Example 1   Identify the type of the following angles:

(a)   (b)   (c)

(d)   (e)

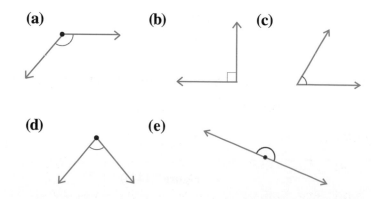

Solutions

(a)   Obtuse, since it is greater than 90° by inspection.

(b)   Right angle, indicated by a small square at the vertex.

(c)   Acute angle, since it is less than 90° by inspection.

(d)   Acute angle, since it is little less than 90° by inspection.

(e)   Straight angle

Example 2 In the following figure identify all the acute angles and right angles.

Solution

There are *five* acute angles in the drawing.

These are: ∠1, ∠2, ∠3, ∠6, and ∠7.

There are four right angles; namely,
∠4, ∠5, ∠8, and ∠9.

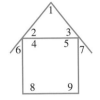

2. Identify all the acute, obtuse, and right angles.

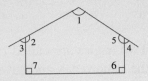

Answers:

1. (a) Acute   (b) Obtuse
    (c) Right angle   (d) Acute
    (e) Acute

2. Acute: 3, 4
    Obtuse: 1, 2, 5
    Right: 6, 7

2.4 B. Properties of Angles

- Two angles are called *complementary* if their sum is 90° (a right angle). The **complement** of an angle equals 90° minus the angle. (Obtuse angles do not have complements.)

  ∠BAC and ∠CAD are complements.

  $60° + 30° = 90°$

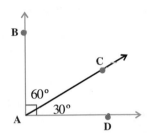

- Two angles are *supplementary* if their sum is 180° (a straight angle). The supplement of an angle is 180° minus the angle.

  ∠QPR and ∠RPS are supplementary.

  $45° + 135° = 180°$

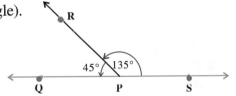

Example 3 Find the complements of the following angles:

  (a) 40°   (b) 20°   (c) 0°

Solutions

(a) The complement of 40° is $90° - 40° = $ **50°**.

(b) The complement of 20° is $90° - 20° = $ **70°**.

(c) The complement of 0° is $90° - 0° = $ **90°**.

Example 4 Find the supplements of the following angles:

  (a) 40°   (b) 120°   (c) 90°

Solutions

(a) The supplement of 40° is $180° - 40° = $ **140°**.

Warm-Up

3. Find the complements of the following angles:

  (a) 53°

  (b) 27°

  (c) 90°

4. Find the supplements of the following angles:

  (a) 95°

  (b) 37°

  (c) 140°

(b)   The supplement of   120° is 180° – 120° = **60°**.

(c)   The supplement of   90°   is 180° – 90° = **90°**.

- Two angles are called *congruent* if they have the same measure. Two angles are *adjacent* if they share the same vertex and have a common side. Two angles formed by intersecting lines are called *vertical angles* if they are opposite each other (not adjacent).

Vertical angles have *equal* measure.

∠APB and ∠CPD are vertical angles, ∠APD and ∠BPC are also vertical angles.

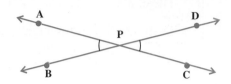

∠APB is adjacent to ∠APD. It is also adjacent to ∠BPC.

Warm-Up

5.   Find the measure of the angles whose measurements are not shown in the figure.

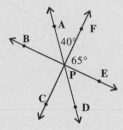

Answers:

5.   ∠APB = 75° , ∠BPC = 65°,
     ∠CPD = 40°, ∠DPE = 75°

Example 5   Find the measure of the unknown angles.

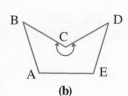

Solution

∠APB and ∠DPE = 45° are vertical; hence, they are equal. Therefore, ∠APB = **45°**.

∠BPC = 20° and ∠EPF are vertical; hence they are equal. So, ∠EPF = **20°**.

∠APF is the supplement of ∠FPD = 20° + 45° = 65°

Therefore, ∠APF = 180° – 65° = **115°**.

∠CPD = ∠APF = 115° ;   vertical angles.

2.4 C.   Polygons: Triangles and Quadrilaterals

- A **polygon** is a closed geometric figure whose sides are line segments and each segment meets another segment at its end point. A polygon is called a **convex polygon** if the measure of each angle is less than 180°.

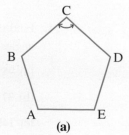

(a)   **Figure 2.20**   (b)

In Figure 2.20 ABCDE is a polygon. However Figure 2.20 (a) is a convex polygon since the measure of each angle is less than 180° and Figure 2.20 (b) is a nonconvex polygon since ∠BCD is greater than 180°. Polygons are named according to the number of sides they have. The most frequently used polygons are listed in the following table.

Number of sides	3	4	5	6	8
Polygon Name	Triangle	Quadrilateral	Pentagon	Hexagon	Octagon
Shape	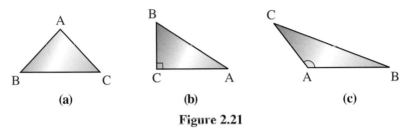				

- A **triangle** is a polygon having three sides, and is usually named by its vertices (Figures 2.21 a-c).

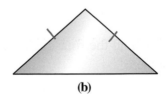

(a) (b) (c)

Figure 2.21

In terms of angles, there are three types of triangles:

1. **Acute triangle:**   A triangle in which *all the three* angles are acute (smaller than 90°) is called an acute triangle. The triangle ABC in Figure 2.21(a) is an acute-triangle.

2. **Right triangle:**   A triangle in which *one* of the angles is a right angle is called a right triangle. The sides forming a right angle are called **legs**, and the side opposite to the right angle is called the **hypotenuse.** The triangle in Figure 2.21(b) is a right-triangle.

3. **Obtuse triangle:**   If one of the angles is obtuse (larger than 90°), then the triangle is called an obtuse triangle. The triangle ABC in Figure 2.21(c) is an obtuse-triangle.

In terms of the sides, there are three types of triangles (Figures 2.22a-c).

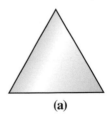

(a)   (b)   (c)

Figure 2.22

1. **Equilateral** triangle
   (All sides equal)

2. **Isosceles** triangle
   (Two sides equal)

3. **Scalene** triangle
   (No two sides equal)

Example 6   Identify the following triangles as acute, obtuse, or right triangle.

(a)    (b)    (c)

 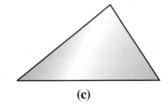

(b)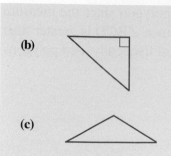

(c)

Solutions

(a) One of the angles is a right angle; therefore, it is a right triangle.

(b) Each of the angles is less than a right angle; therefore, it is an acute triangle.

(c) One of the angles is clearly greater than a right angle. It is an obtuse triangle.

7. Identify the triangle as equilateral isosceles, or scalene.

Example 7 Identify the following triangles as equilateral, isosceles, or a scalene triangle.

(a)   **(b)**   **(c)**

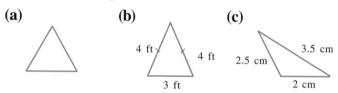

Solutions

(a) All sides seem to be equal; therefore, it is possibly an equilateral triangle.

(b) Two of its sides are equal; therefore, it is an isosceles triangle.

(c) No two sides are equal; therefore, it is a scalene triangle.

Answers:

6. (a) obtuse   (b) right   (c) obtuse

7. equilateral

- **Special Quadrilaterals:**

A **quadrilateral** is a polygon having four sides; hence, it has four vertices. It is usually named by its vertices taken clockwise or counter-clockwise. The quadrilateral in Figure 2.23 is named as ABCD.

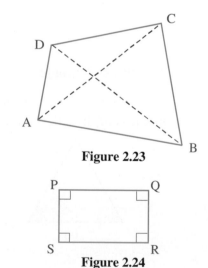

Figure 2.23

A **rectangle** is a quadrilateral in which all the four angles are right angles. Figure 2.24 is a rectangle.

Figure 2.24

A **square** is a quadrilateral with all its angles right angles and all its sides equal (Figure 2.25).

Observe that a square is both a rectangle and a parallelogram.

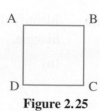

Figure 2.25

Example 8 Identify the following quadrilaterals as; a square, rectangle, or neither.

(a) (b) (c) (d)

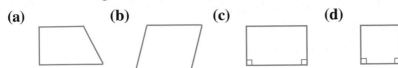

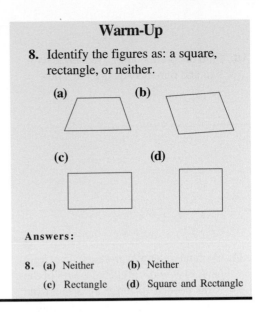
Solutions

(a) Neither

(b) Neither

(c) All the four angles are right angles; therefore, the figure is a rectangle.

(d) All the four angles are right angles and all the sides are equal; therefore, the figure is a square. It is also a rectangle.

2.4 D. Perimeter and Area

We discuss here, two basic geometry facts about rectangles and squares, namely, the **perimeter** and the **area**.

A **rectangle** is a four-sided figure whose opposite sides are equal in length and whose adjacent sides are at right angles. The longer sides are called its length and the shorter sides are the width. A rectangle is a square if all the sides are equal in length.

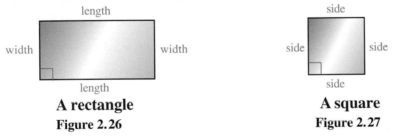

A rectangle

Figure 2.26

A square

Figure 2.27

The total distance around the figure is called the **perimeter**.

The perimeter of a rectangle = length + width + length + width.

The perimeter of a square = side + side + side + side.

Rectangle: $P = l + w + l + w$ **Square:** $P = s + s + s + s$

or

$$P = 2l + 2w$$

or

$$P = 4s$$

The variables P, l, w, and s represent the perimeter, length, width, and side of a square, respectively.

Example 9 Find the perimeter of the polygon in Figure 2.28.

Solution

$$P = 9\,m + 9\,m + 9\,m + 8\,m + 8\,m$$

$$= (9 + 9 + 9 + 8 + 8)\,m$$

$$= 43\,m.$$

8 m   8 m

9 m   9 m

9 m

Figure 2.28

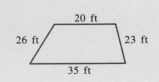

Warm-Up

10. Find the perimeter of a rectangle with 9 in and 6 in as two adjacent sides.

11. A rectangular playground is 45 m long and 30 m wide. Find the length of the wire needed to fence all around the field. Also, find the cost of fencing if the fencing costs $3 per meter.

Example 10 Find the perimeter of the rectangle with 4 in and 3 in as two adjacent sides.

Solution

$$\text{Perimeter} = 4\text{ in} + 3\text{ in} + 4\text{ in} + 3\text{ in}$$
$$= (4 + 3 + 4 + 3)\text{ in}$$
$$= 14\text{ in}$$

or

$$\text{Perimeter} = 2\,l + 2\,w$$
$$= 2\,(4\text{ in}) + 2\,(3\text{ in})$$
$$= 8\text{ in} + 6\text{ in} = 14\text{ in}$$

Example 11 A rectangular field is 130 m long and 80 m wide. Find the length of wire needed to fence all around the field. Also, find the total cost of the fencing if it sells at the rate of $3 per meter.

Solution

Length of wire needed to fence all around the field

$$= \text{the perimeter of the field}$$
$$= 2(130\text{ m}) + 2(80\text{ m})$$
$$= 420\text{ m}$$

For the second part of the problem :

Cost of 1 m of fencing $= \$3$;

therefore, the cost of 420 m of wire $= 420 \times \$3$
$$= \$1,260$$

- The **area** of a rectangle or square is the amount of space it encloses. Area is measured in square units, such as square inches (in^2) or square cm (cm^2).

  Consider a rectangular region that is 8 cm by 4 cm. Fill the region with square units as shown. Observe that there are 32 square units.

$$\text{The number of square units} = 8 \times 4$$
$$= 32$$

$$\text{Area} = 32 \times 1\text{cm}^2$$
$$= 32\text{ cm}^2$$
$$= 8\text{ cm} \times 4\text{ cm}$$
$$= (8 \times 4)\text{ cm}^2$$

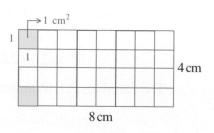

Area of a rectangle = length × width

Rectangle

Square

$$\textbf{Area of rectangle} = \text{length} \times \text{width} = l \cdot w$$
$$\textbf{Area of square} = \text{side} \times \text{side} = s \cdot s = s^2$$

Example 12   Find the area of a rectangle whose length is 3 ft and width is 5 ft.

Solution

$$\text{Area} = \text{length} \times \text{width}$$
$$= 3\,\text{ft} \times 5\,\text{ft}$$
$$= 15\,\text{ft} \times \text{ft}$$
$$= 15\,\text{ft}^2$$

12. Find the area (in sq m) of a rectangle whose length is 4 m and width is 3m.

Example 13   Find the perimeter and area of a square whose side is 4 cm.

Solution

Area $= 4\,\text{cm} \times 4\,\text{cm}$	**Perimeter** $= 4 \cdot s$
$= 16\,\text{cm} \times \text{cm}$	$= 4 \cdot 4\,\text{cm}$
$= 16\,\text{cm}^2$	$= 16\,\text{cm}$

13. Find the perimeter and area of square with a side equal to 3 cm.

Example 14   A square that is 8 in on a side is placed inside a rectangle that has a length of 24 in and a width of 20 in. What is the area of the region inside the rectangle that surrounds the square? (For each figure, **the area is the product of the length and the width.**)

14. Find the perimeter of a rectangle that has a length 35 ft and a width of 25 ft. Also, find its area.

Solution   In this case, a picture is very helpful. We have to find the shaded area. The shaded area will be the difference between the areas of the rectangle (the larger area) and the square (smaller area).

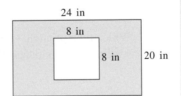

Area of rectangle $= 24 \times 20 = 480\,\text{in}^2$

Area of Square $= 8 \times 8 = 64\,\text{in}^2$

Shaded area (the desired area) $=$
$$\begin{array}{r} \overset{7\ 10}{48\cancel{0}}\ \text{in}^2 \\ -\ 6\,4\ \ \text{in}^2 \\ \hline 4\,1\,6\ \ \text{in}^2 \end{array}$$

Exercise 2.4

A. In exercises 1-5, identify the figure as a ray, line, line segment, or angle.

1.
2.
3.
4.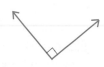
5.

In exercises 6-8, identify and name all the segments and angles.

6.
7.
8.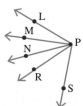

In exercises 9-15, identify the angle as an acute, obtuse, or right angle.

9.
10.
11.

12.
13.
14.
15.

In exercises 16-18, answer the question using the figure.

16.  Which type of angle is between the hands? Will the angle become larger or smaller in five minutes time?

17.  Identify the type of the angle between the hands. Identify another time when the hands form the same angle.

18. Which type of angle is between the hands? After 10 minutes time, what type of angle will it become?

B. **In exercises 19-26, find the complement of the angle.**

19. 16°　　　**20.** 82°　　　**21.** 35°　　　**22.** 90°　　　**23.** 42°　　　**24.** 45°　　　**25.** 37°　　　**26.** 89°

In exercises 27-34, find the supplement of the angle.

27. 90°　　　**28.** 0°　　　**29.** 12°　　　**30.** 120°　　　**31.** 140°　　　**32.** 70°　　　**33.** 110°　　　**34.** 139°

In exercises 35-38, find the measure of the missing angle(s).

35. 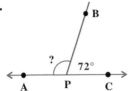　　　**36.** 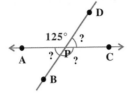　　　**37.** 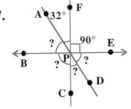　　　**38.**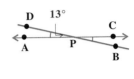

C. **39.**　Identify the following triangles as acute, right, or obtuse.

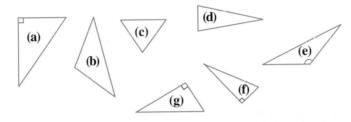

40.　Classify the following triangles as equilateral, isosceles, or scalene.

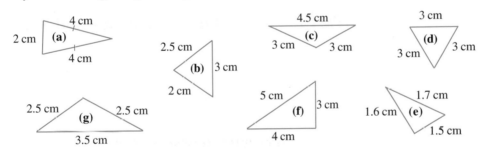

41.　Identify the following quadrilaterals as a rectangle, square, or neither.

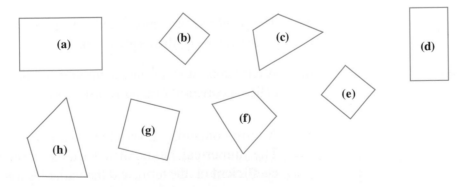

D. **42.**　The length of a rectangle exceeds its width by 7 ft. If the length is 18 ft, find the width and the area of the rectangle.

43. Find the area of a rectangular garden that measures 30 ft by 25 ft. Now assume that there is a 3 ft wide track around the entire garden. Compute the area of the track. The track is to be covered with concrete. If concrete costs $3 per sq ft, what will be the total cost of covering the track?

(*Hint:* The dimensions of the outer rectangle are 36 ft by 31 ft.
Total cost will be area of the track × $3).

44. A window is in the shape of a square surmounted by an isosceles triangle (two sides equal). If the square is 25 inches on each side and each of the two equal sides of the triangle is 18 inches long, what is the perimeter of the window?

(*Hint:* Draw a figure such as and label the sides as per given dimensions)

45. How much fencing will be needed for an 18 ft by 11 ft rectangular barnyard?

46. Find the perimeter of a square that is 4 cm on a side.

2.5   CHAPTER SUMMARY

Examples

1. 4, −5, 317 are all constants.

2. $3x^2 - 4xy$, $2x - y^2 + 4$ are algebraic expressions.

3. 5, $-3x^2$, $2xy^3$, and $9ab$ are terms.

4. The terms of $3x^2 + 4xy^2 - 3$ are:
$3x^2$, $4xy^2$, and -3.
Here, -3 is a constant term.

5. In $-4x^2z$,
-4 is the *coefficient* and
x^2z is the *variable part*.

6. 4, 12, and −6 are **like** terms.

$-2x^2z^3$ and $\frac{3}{2}x^2z^3$ are also **like** terms.

$4a$ and $-5a^2$ are **unlike** terms.

Part I   Important Vocabulary and Symbols

EXPRESSIONS

1. An integer has a constant value and is called a **constant.**

2. **Algebraic expressions** are the expressions formed by using variables, numbers, operation symbols, and/or grouping symbols.

3. The **products** of numbers and powers of variables are called **terms of the expression.**

4. A term consisting of only a number and no variable part is called a **constant** or a **constant term.**

5. A term containing a variable is called a **variable term.** The numerical factor of a variable term is called the **coefficient** of the term, and the variables together with the powers are called the **variable part.**

6. **Like terms** have the same variable part, if any.

7. Translating Phrases or Statements into Algebraic Expressions

(a) An unknown represented by a letter of the alphabet (x, y, a, b, ...) is called a **variable**.

(b) Words such as **plus**, **increased by**, and **sum** indicate addition.

(c) Words such as **minus**, **decreased by**, and **difference** indicate subtraction.

(d) Words such as **quotient** and **divided by** indicate division.

(e) Words such as **times**, and **product** indicate multiplication.

(f) Words such as *is*, **gives**, and **equals** indicate equality (=).

(g) Phrases such as "**is less than**", "**is less than or equal to**", "**is greater than**", and "**is greater than or equal to**" are indicated by the symbols <, ≤, >, and ≥, respectively.

Examples

7. (a) x, y, ... represent unknown numbers.

(b) "A number plus eight" translates to $x + 8$.

"A number increased by 5" translates to $x + 5$.

"The sum of a number and 7" translates to $x + 7$.

(c) "A number minus 7" translates to $x - 7$.

"A number decreased by 8" translates to $x - 8$.

"The difference of a number and 9" translates to $x - 9$.

(d) "A number divided by 8" translates to $\dfrac{x}{8}$.

"The quotient of a number and 9" translates to $\dfrac{x}{9}$.

(e) "Five times a number" translates to $5x$ or $5 \cdot x$.

"The product of 6 and a number" translates to $6x$ or $6 \cdot x$.

(f) "The quotient of a number and 7 is 8" translates to $\dfrac{x}{7} = 8$.

"7 added to a number gives 8" translates to $x + 7 = 8$

"6 subtracted from a number equals 10" translates to $x - 6 = 10$.

(g) "A number is less than 5" is translated as $x < 5$.

"Three times a number is less than or equal to 8" is translated as $3x \leq 8$.

"A number is greater than 5" is translated as $x > 5$.

"Two times a number is greater than or equal to 10" is translated as $2x \geq 10$.

8. Distinguishing between an Expression and an Equation

Procedure to decide whether a statement, in words or in mathematical symbols, is an equation or an expression:

Step 1   Translate the word statement into mathematical symbols. Use a letter of the alphabet for the unknown number.

8. "Two times the sum of a number and 5" translates to $2(x + 5)$. It is an expression since it does not contain the equality symbol (=).

"Three times a number decreased by 4 equals 11" translates to $3x - 4 = 11$. It is an equation since it contains the equality symbol.

Step 2 (a) If the result does not contain an '=' sign, it is an expression.

(b) If the result contains an '=' sign, it is an equation.

9. (a) $5x + 6y = (5+6)x = 11x$

9. Simplifying an Expression by Combining Like Terms

(a) **Procedure for combining like terms**

Step **1** Add the coefficients of the like terms.

Step **2** Attach the common variable part.

(b) $\begin{aligned} -2(x+3y)+y &= -2x+(-2)(3)y+y \\ &= -2x-6y+1y \\ &= -2x+(-6+1)y \\ &= -2x-5y \end{aligned}$

(b) **Procedure** to use the Distributive Property for simplifying expressions:

Step **1** Write the products as sums using the Distributive Property: $a(x + y) = ax + ay$.

Step **2** Simplify by combining like terms.

10. Evaluate: $5x - 4y$ for $x = 3$ and $y = 2$.

$\begin{aligned} 5x - 4y &= 5(\mathbf{3}) - 4(\mathbf{2}) \\ &= 15 - 8 = 7 \end{aligned}$

10. Evaluating an Algebraic Expression

Step **1** Substitute the value for the variable(s) using parentheses.

Step **2** Evaluate the resulting numerical expression using the order of operations.

11. Find the average of 14, 15, 20, 23.

$\begin{aligned} \text{Average} &= \frac{14+15+20+23}{4} \\ &= \frac{72}{4} \\ &= 18 \end{aligned}$

11. Finding the Average of a Group of Numbers.

Step **1** Add all the numbers and obtain the sum.

Step **2** Divide the sum by the count of numbers in the group.

12. Solving equation

(a) $3 - 1 = 7 - 5$ is a numerical equation.

(b) $x + 3 = 7$ is an algebraic equation since it contains the variable x.

(c) $x = 4$ is a solution of $x + 3 = 7$, since

$\begin{aligned} 4 + 3 &= 7 \\ 7 &= 7 \quad \text{True} \end{aligned}$

(d) Identify the solution of $x + 4 = 7$ from the set $\{2, 3\}$.

$\begin{aligned} \mathbf{2} + 4 = 7 & \qquad \text{False} \\ \mathbf{3} + 4 = 7 & \qquad \text{True} \end{aligned}$

Therefore, $x = 3$ is a solution of the equation.

12. Solving Equations

(a) Two expressions involving numbers joined together by the sign of equality (=) form a **numerical equation.**

(b) An equality containing at least one unknown (variable) is called an **algebraic equation.**

(c) A value of the unknown which makes an equation a true statement is called a **solution**.

(d) To find which number from a given set of numbers is a solution of the equation, we substitute each number, one by one, in the equation. The number that makes the equation a true statement is a solution.

(e) Solving an equation of the type $x + a = b$ or $x - a = b$

    Step 1   Switch the sides of the equation, if necessary, so the variable is on the left side. It is common to keep the variable on the left side of the equal sign, although it is not required.

    Step 2   Add or subtract a number on both sides of the equation to isolate the variable on the left side, and simplify the right side.

    Step 3   Check the solution by substituting the value of the variable obtained in step 2 in the original equation.

(f) **Procedure** to solve a linear equation of the type $ax + b = c$ or $ax - b = c$.

    Step 1   Use the Addition Property of Equality to move all variable terms on one side and constant terms on the other side.

    Step 2   Solve the equation using the Multiplication Property of Equality.

    Step 3   Check the solution using substitution.

13. **Basic Steps for Solving Word Problems**

    (a) Read the problem carefully until you understand the problem. Identify the unknown number. Choose a letter of the alphabet as the variable to represent the numerical value of the unknown quantity.

    (b) If possible draw figures or diagrams that might be helpful and decide what operations are needed.

    (c) Perform these operations.

    (d) Verify your answer by using the *original* statement of the problem.

14. **Basic Geometry Vocabulary**

    (a) A **point** is represented by a dot and has no dimensions. Points are usually named by capital letters.

    (b) We can draw a line through any two points. The line continues forever on both sides.

    (c) If P and Q are two points on a line, then the portion of the line between P and Q is called the **segment** PQ of the line.

    (d) A **ray** is a portion of a line from a point towards one direction only. If P and Q are two points on a line, then a line from P towards Q is named as ray PQ.

(e) Solve the equation $x + 4 = 9$:

$$x + 4 + (-4) = 9 + (-4) \quad \text{(Addition Property)}$$
$$x + 4 - 4 = 9 - 4$$
$$x = 5$$

Check:
$$x + 4 = 9$$
$$5 + 4 = 9$$
$$9 = 9; \text{ True.}$$

Hence, the solution $x = 5$ is correct.

(f) Solve: $3x - 5 = 13$

$$3x - 5 + 5 = 13 + 5 \quad \text{Addition Property}$$
$$3x = 18$$
$$\frac{1}{3} \cdot 3x = \frac{1}{3} \cdot 18 \quad \text{Multiplication Property}$$
$$x = 6.$$

Check:
$$3x - 5 = 13$$
$$3(6) - 5 = 13$$
$$18 - 5 = 13$$
$$13 = 13; \text{ True.}$$

Hence, the solution $x = 6$ is correct.

13. The **difference** between two sides of a rectangular lot is 20 yards. If the smaller side measures 25 yards, find the measure of the longer side.

(a) Let x be the longer side of the rectangle.

(b) $x - 25 = 20$

(c)
$$x - 25 + 25 = 20 + 25$$
$$x = 45 \text{ yd}$$

Check:

(d)
$$x - 25 = 20$$
$$45 - 25 = 20 \quad \text{Substitute 45 for } x.$$
$$20 = 20; \text{ True}$$

Hence, the solution is correct.

14. (a)   ○ Point   P

(b) Line $\overleftrightarrow{PQ}$ P   Q

(c) Segment $\overline{PQ}$ P   Q

(d) Ray $\overrightarrow{PQ}$ P   Q

(e)

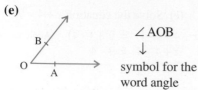

∠AOB
↓
symbol for the
word angle

(e) An **angle** is a figure formed by two rays having a common **vertex.** The angle shown in the figure is read as angle AOB, angle BOA, or angle O.

(f)

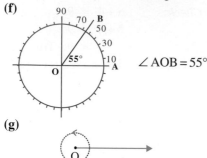

∠AOB = 55°

(f) An **angle is measured** in terms of degrees or radians, we shall use only degree measure in this text.

(g)

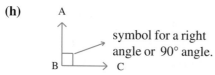

(g) There are 360° in a complete circle.

(h)

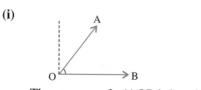

symbol for a right
angle or 90° angle.

(h) Right angle: An angle of 90° is called a right angle.

(i)

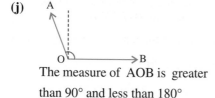

The measure of ∠AOB is less than 90° and greater than 0°

(i) Acute angle: An angle less than 90° and greater than 0° is called an acute angle.

(j)

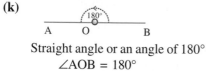

The measure of AOB is greater than 90° and less than 180°

(j) Obtuse angle: An angle greater than 90° and less than 180° is called an obtuse angle.

(k)

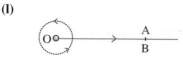

Straight angle or an angle of 180°
∠AOB = 180°

(k) Straight angle: An angle of 180° is called a straight angle.

(l)

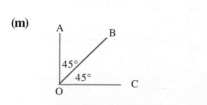

(l) Complete angle: One complete revolution or an angle of 360° is called a complete circle or full circle.

(m)

A   B
45°
45°
O   C

(m) Congruent angles: Two angles are congruent if they have the same measure.

∠AOB and ∠BOC are congruent since each has a measure of 45°.

(n) **Adjacent angles:** Two angles are adjacent if they share the same vertex and a side.

(n)

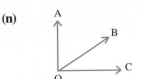

∠AOB and ∠BOC are adjacent since they share the common vertex O and common side OB.

(o) **Vertical angles:** Two angles formed by intersecting lines are vertical angles if they are opposite each other (not adjacent).

Vertical angles have equal measures.

(o)

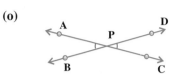

∠APB and ∠DPC are vertical angles and have equal measures.

(p) **Polygons:** A polygon is a closed geometric figure whose sides are line segments and each segment meets another segment at its end point.

(p)

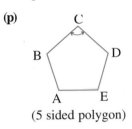

(5 sided polygon)

(q) **Acute triangle:** A triangle in which *all three* angles are acute (smaller than 90°) is called an acute triangle.

(q)

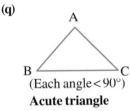

(Each angle < 90°)
Acute triangle

(r) **Right triangle:** A triangle in which *one* of the angles is a right angle is called a right triangle.

(r)

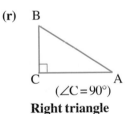

(∠C = 90°)
Right triangle

(s) **Obtuse triangle:** If one of the angles is obtuse (larger than 90°), then the triangle is called an obtuse triangle.

(s)

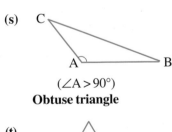

(∠A > 90°)
Obtuse triangle

(t) **Equilateral triangle:** A triangle that has all sides equal is an equilateral triangle.

(t)

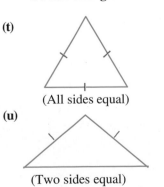

(All sides equal)

(u) **Isosceles triangle:** A triangle that has two equal sides is an isosceles triangle.

(u)

(Two sides equal)

(v)

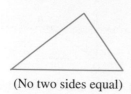

(No two sides equal)

(v) **Scalene triangle:** A triangle that has no two sides equal is a scalene triangle.

(w)

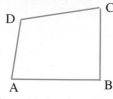

(Four sided polygon)

(w) **Quadrilateral:** A polygon having four sides is called a quadrilateral.

(x)

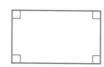

(All the four angles are right angles)

(x) **Rectangle:** A rectangle is a quadrilateral in which all the four angles are right angles.

(y)

(All the angles are right angles and all the four sides are equal).

(y) **Square:** A square is a quadrilateral in which all the four angles are right angles and all the four sides are equal.

15. **(a)** Find the perimeter of the given quadrilateral.

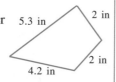

$P = 2\,\text{in} + 2\,\text{in} + 4.2\,\text{in} + 5.3\,\text{in}$
$= 13.5\,\text{in}$

(b) Find the area of the given rectangle.

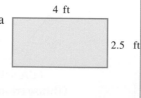

$P = l \cdot w$
$= 4 \cdot 2.5$
$= 10\,\text{ft}^2$

15. **Perimeter and area of polygons**

(a) **Perimeter:** The perimeter of a geometric figure is the distance around the figure and is generally denoted by **P.**

Rectangle: $\quad P = 2l + 2w$

Sqaure: $\quad P = 4 \cdot s$

(b) **Area:** The area of a geometric figure is the measure of the space enclosed by the boundary of the figure and is measured in square units.

Rectangle: $\quad A = l \cdot w$

Square: $\quad A = s \cdot s$
$\qquad\qquad = s^2$

2.6 REVIEW EXERCISE

In exercises 1-17, change the phrase to an algebraic expression. Use *x* to represent the unknown variable.

1. A number multiplied by two

2. A number increased by nine

3. Nine decreased by a number

4. Seven decreased by twice a number

5. Nine times a number added to seven

6. Nine added to a number

7. Nine added to two times a number

8. The quotient of eleven and a number

9. The quotient of seven times a number and eight added to the number

10. Twenty minus the quotient of seven and a number

11. The quotient of seven and the sum of a number and eight

12. Five added to the product of a number and two

13. A number multiplied by ten decreased by the square of the number

14. Four added to three-fifths of a number

15. Three subtracted from the square of a number

16. The quotient of five subtracted from a number and two added to the number

17. The quotient of seven added to a number and ten subtracted from the number

In exercises 18-32, change the word statement to an equation. Find the solution of the equation in the set {0, 1, 2, 4, 5}.

18. The sum of three times a number and four is nineteen.

19. Seven subtracted from four times a number is one.

20. The difference of three times a number and ten equals twenty-one.

21. One added to twice a number is 5.

22. The quotient of sixteen and twice a number is four less than the number.

23. The sum of three and twice a number is twelve.

24. Five times a number exceeds three times the number by four.

25. The difference of three and twice a number is the number.

26. Nine and three times a number adds up to twenty-one.

27. The difference of the square of a number and the number is zero.

28. Two times a number equals five times the number.

29. The quotient of two and a number is the sum of the number and one.

30. The quotient of a number and eight is the quotient of two and the number.

31. Two times the square of a number decreased by one is equal to the number.

32. Explain the difference between an algebraic expression and an equation.

In exercises 33-44, simplify the given expression by combining like terms.

33. $4x + 9x$

34. $12x - 5x$

35. $-7x - 5x + x$

36. $14y - 9y - 10y$

37. $3(2x - 4) + 3x + 7$

38. $5x - 12 + x - 3$

39. $-9x - 11x + 6$

40. $-15y - 3(y + 1) - 4$

41. $2x^2 - 5x + x^2 + x - 4$

42. $5y^2 - 2(2y - 1) - y^2 + 3$

43. $-2x^2 + x + x(x^2 - 3)$

44. $2(3x - 5) + 3(x + 2)$

In exercises 45-66, evaluate the given expression for the given value(s) of the variable.

45. $a - b$ for $a = -2$, $b = -3$

46. $5 - 2x$ for $x = -6$

47. $5 + 2(n - 3)$ for $n = -1$

48. $2 - n(n - 2)$ for $n = -6$

49. $4(3 + x) + 2x$ for $x = 8$

50. $2x^2 + 3x - 5$ for $x = -2$

51. $2x^2 - x - 3$ for $x = -5$

52. $3x^2 - y^2$ for $x = -2$, $y = -5$

53. $x^2 - xy + y^2$ for $x = -3$, $y = 3$

54. $2(2x + 3) - 3(x + 3)$ for $x = -2$

55. $6(x - 5) - 3(2 - x)$ for $x = -4$

56. $x + y(z - 4)$ for $x = -2$, $y = 3$, $z = -1$

57. $(x - y) - (y - z)$ for $x = -1$, $y = 2$, $z = -3$

58. $14xy + 5x^2 - 6y$ for $x = -3$, $y = 2$

59. $2x^2 - 3y^2 + 5x - 8$ for $x = 3$, $y = -1$

60. $x^2 - 5(3 - x) + 6$ for $x = -1$

61. $-2x^3 + 3(x - 8) - 4$ for $x = 2$

62. $a^2 - b^2 - (b - c)(b + c)$ for $a = -2$, $b = -1$, $c = -3$

63. $3(a - 2b) + 2a^2 - b^2$ for $a = -1$, $b = -2$

64. $7x^2y + 8xy^2 - 11xy - 2x - 3y$ for $x = -3$, $y = -2$

65. $3xy^2 - 5x^2y + 2x - 3y + 4$ for $x = -2$, $y = -3$

66. $15ab + 7a^2 - 8a - 4b$ for $a = 2$, $b = -1$

In exercises 67-75, solve the equation and check your answer.

67. $x - 3 = -8$

68. $x + 4 = -9$

69. $-42 = x + 20$

70. $-12 = -17 + y$

71. $x - 8 = -8$

72. $2x - 15 = 13$

73. $5x + 173 = 23$

74. $3x + 2x - x + 12 = 32$

75. $4x + 9x - 3x + 73 = 173$

In exercises 76-97, find the average of the given set of numbers.

76. $3, 7, 11, 15, 19$

77. $-4, -1, 2, 8, 10$

78. $10, -2, 5, -7, -11$

79. $-9, -7, -12, -16$

80. $20, 21, 30, 33$

81. $-6, 8, 13, 17$

82. $30, -6, -25, -15, -18, -26$

83. $-4, -8, -12, -16, -15$

84. $-18, 14, -20, -10, 34$

85. $26, -34, -18, 38, -12$

86. $20, 20, 20, 20, 20$

87. $-15, -15, -15, -15$

88. $\$25, \$15, \$12, \$28$

89. $\$19, \$13, \$24, \$10, \$14$

90. 7 ft, 6 ft, 3 ft, 5 ft, 4 ft

91. 54 ft, 45 ft, 41 ft, 36 ft

92. $10°, 15°, -5°, -8°, -7°, -3°, 5°$

93. $-11°, -7°, 5°, 10°, 13°$

94. $30, 45, -75, -48, -62$

95. $-50, 59, -72, 79, -106$

96. $14, 14, 13, 17, 18, 14$

97. $35, 22, 25, 11, 5, 25, 17$

98. Carlos works for 3 hours on Monday, 4 hours on Tuesday, 3 hours on Wednesday, 5 hours on Thursday and Friday, and 4 hours on Saturday. On an average, how many hours does he work each day?

99. The rain gauge at the water reservoir records the following rainfall during a four- month period:

7 cm , 8 cm , 6 cm, and 7 cm.

What is the average monthly rainfall for the 4 months?

100. Courtnay is advised by his doctor to go for a long morning walk by his doctor. He walks 2 km on the first day, 3 km on the second day, 4 km on the third day, and 3 km on the forth day. How many kilometers on an average, does he walk each day?

101. On a four-day trip, a car was driven the following number of miles each day:

320, 290, 310, and 340.

What was the average number of miles driven per day?

102. According to recent estimates, a particular brand of Toyota car can be expected to cover 247 miles (city) on 13 gallons of gasoline. What is the average number of miles expected per gallon?

103. The following temperatures were recorded for seven days in Atlanta :

39°, 40°, 35°, 37°, 36°, 38°, 41°

What was the average temperature during these seven days?

104. The following price per pound of salmon were found at five fish markets:

$8, $7, $8, $9, $8

What was the average price per pound?

105. Identify each of the following statements as true or false. Change each false statement to make it true.

(a) Adjacent angles can be complementary.

(b) Adjacent supplementary angles add up to 180°.

(c) If two lines intersect, then one pair of vertical angles always consists of acute angles and the other of obtuse angles.

(d) Two adjacent angles are always supplementary.

(e) A horizontal and a vertical line intersect at a right angle.

106. Name each pair of supplementry angles and each pair of vertical angles in the figure below.

(Linear pair of angles add up to 180°)

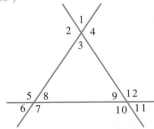

107. Find the measure of the angle which is complement of itself.

108. Find the angle which is equal to its supplement.

109. Two supplementary angles differ by 40°. Find the angles.

141

110. If the complement of an angle is 20°, then find the supplement of the angle.

111. The supplement of an acute angle is obtuse. What can you say about

    a) the supplement of a right angle?

    b) the complement of an acute angle?

    c) the complement of an obtuse angle?

In exercises 112-118, find the measure of the unknown angle (s).

112.

113.
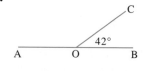

114.
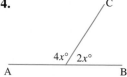

115.
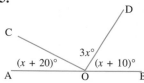

116.
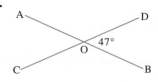

117.
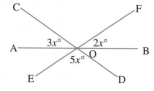

118.
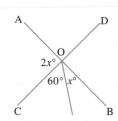

In exercises 119-124, find the perimeter of the figure.

119.
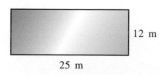

120.
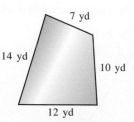

121.
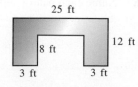

122.
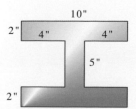

123.
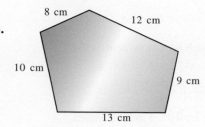

124.
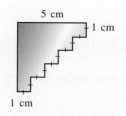

125. The perimeter of the triangle in the figure is 150 yd. Find the lengths of the sides of the triangle.

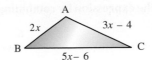

126. The sides of a triangular lot are $3x$, $2x + 3$, and $5x - 3$ meters. Find the lengths of the sides of the lot if the cost of fencing its perimeter at the rate of $2 per meter is $1,800.

In exercises 127-132, find the area of the shaded region in the figure.

127.

128.

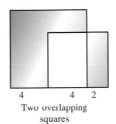

Two overlapping squares

129.

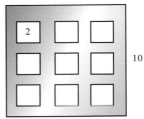

Frame and holes are squares

130.

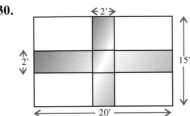

131.

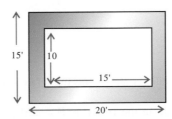

132.

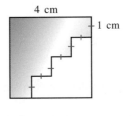

133. The perimeter of the floor of a 100 ft long rectangular swimming pool is 260 ft. What is the floor area of the swimming pool?

134. The floor of a living room is 20 ft long and 18 ft wide. How many yards of 6 feet wide carpet is required for wall to wall carpeting of the room? **(1 yard = 3 ft).**

135. The largest painting according to the Guiness Book of Records is 5,000 ft by 12 ft. If a 1 ft wide frame is placed around this painting, what would be the area of the front of the frame?

2.7 SELF TEST

1. Translate the following word phrases or statements into symbols:
   (a) Five added to the quotient of a number and eleven.
   (b) Seven times the difference between three and a number.
   (c) Twelve exceeds two times a number by five.
   (d) Six times a number minus seven equals twenty-nine.
   (e) Two times a number increased by seven is less than or equal to twenty-seven.

2. Identify whether the following is an expression or an equation.
   (a) $3x^2 + 50$ (b) $4x - 5 = 7$

3. Identify the numerical coefficient and the variable part of the term $-15x^3$.

4. Identify the like terms from the following group of terms.
   4, $5x$, $6y$, $15xy$, x^2, y^2, $-13xy$, $9xy$, $2x^2y^2$

In exercises 5-8, simplify the expression by combining like terms.

5. $4x^2 - 5x + 6 - 14$

6. $3(2y^2 - 5y + 6) + 4(-y^2 + 2y - 3)$

7. $-3x + 5y - y + 5$

8. $2(x - 4) - 3(7 - x)$

9. Over a period of 12 months, a company gains $471,600 in its stock market account. What is the company's average gain per month?

10. Identify the solution of the equation $3x - 8 = 7$ from the set $\{0, 3, 5\}$.

In exercises 11-15, use the basic properties to solve the equation.

11. $x + 7 = 9$

12. $-3x = 15$

13. $5x - 21 = -6$

14. $5 - x = 13$

15. $-4 = -x + 9$

16. Identify all the rays, segments, and angles in the figure.

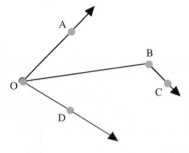

17. Two angles are supplementary. One angle is 50°. Find the other angle.

18. Given that the perimeter of the triangle in the figure is P = 320 yd, find the lengths of the sides of the triangle.

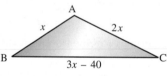

19. Find the measure of the unknown angles.

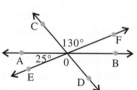

In exercises 20-23, find the perimeter and the area of the shaded region in the figure.

20.

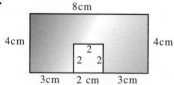

21.

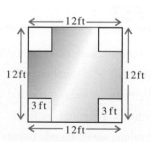

22.

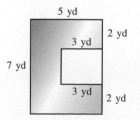

23.

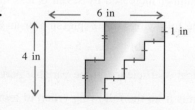

24. A lot is 60 m by 40 m. A house 40 m by 25 m is built on the lot. How much area is left?

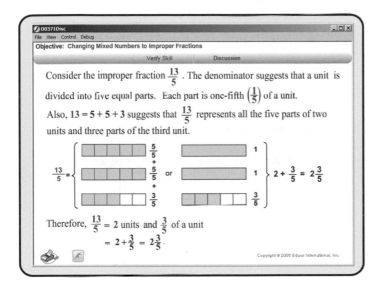

Introduction to Rational Numbers

INTRODUCTION TO RATIONAL NUMBERS

Introduction

The main focus of this chapter is to define **Rational Numbers and related concepts.** We will also define special types of numbers, called prime numbers, and state the **Fundamental Theorem of Arithemtic**. We will discuss methods to find common multiples and the least common multiples of two or more numbers. These concepts are essential to operations with fractions. We will discuss the meaning of fractions, equivalent fractions, and how to simplify fractions.

This chapter is divided into eight sections:

3.1 DIVISIBILITY TESTS, DIVISORS, MULTIPLES, AND FACTORS

IMPORTANT VOCABULARY

1. If a whole number can be divided evenly (without a remainder) by a second whole number, then the first is said to be **divisible** by the second; and the second is said to be a **factor** or **divisor** of the first.

   > 8 is a *divisor* of 48 since $48 \div 8 = 6$ with no remainder.
   >
   > We also say that 48 is *divisible* by 6.
   >
   > 8 is also a factor of 48, since $6 \cdot 8 = 48$.

> **Objectives**
>
> After completing this section, you will be able to:
>
> A. Use divisibility tests to determine whether or not an integer is divisible by 2, 3, 4, 5, 6, 8, 9, 10, 25, 50, or 100; and
>
> B. Apply the concept of divisibility to determine whether or not one number is a multiple of another.

2. A **multiple** of a natural number is the product of the natural number and some other natural number.

   > 120 is a multiple of 8: $120 = 8 \times 15$.
   >
   > 45 is a multiple of 9: $45 = 9 \times 5$.

    Note 120 is a multiple of 8 because 8 can be multiplied by some number to get 120.

3. **Even integers** are divisible by 2. Every even integer can be expressed in the form **$2n$** where n may be any integer, positive or negative, even or odd.

4. **Odd integers** are not divisible by 2. Every odd integer can be expressed in the form **$2n + 1$** where n may be any integer.

3.1 A. Tests for Divisibility; Even and Odd Integers

- **Even and Odd integers:** Recall the definition of an even integer. An even integer is an integer whose ones digit is an even digit (0, 2, 4, 6, or 8). Hence, we may say that:

  An integer is even if and only if it is divisible by 2.

  Every even integer can be expressed as **$2n$** where n is any integer.

  Odd integers are integers whose ones digit (1, 3, 5, 7, or 9) *is not divisible by* 2.

  An integer is an odd integer if and only if it is not divisible of 2.

  Every odd integer can be expressed as 1 added to an even integer: $2n + 1$.

  The even integers are: $..., -8, -6, -4, -2, 0, 2, 4, 6, 8, ...$

  The odd integers are: $..., -9, -7, -5, -3, -1, 1, 3, 5, 7, 9, ...$

  It is interesting to note that:

  a. Every integer is either even or odd.

  b. If 1 is added to or subtracted from an even integer, we get an odd integer and vice-versa.

Warm-Up

1. Determine if each of the following integers is even or odd, then express it in the form $2n$ or $2n + 1$.

(a) 217

(b) 2268

Example 1 Determine if each of the following integers is even or odd, then express it in the form $2n$ or $2n + 1$.

(a) 478   (b) 3,759

Solutions

(a) 478 is even, since its last digit is 8.

Since 478 is an even integer, it is divisible by 2. It can be expressed in the form $2n$.

$478 \div 2 = 239$,

or 478 can be written as 2(239)

or as $2n$ where $n = 239$.

(b) 3,759 is an odd integer, since it equals 1 added to the even integer 3,758. It can be expressed in the form $2n + 1$.

$$3,759 = 3,758 + 1$$
$$= 2 \cdot 1,879 + 1 \quad \text{Since } 3,758 \div 2 = 1,879$$

or

$$= 2 \cdot n + 1$$

where $n = 1,879$.

TESTS FOR DIVISIBILITY

Divisibility by 2:   An integer is divisible by 2 only if its ones digit is even (0, 2, 4, 6, or 8).

Examples: − 218, 4,000, and 214 are divisible by 2.

315, − 479, and − 3,547 are not divisible by 2.

Divisibility by 3:   An integer is divisible by 3 only if the sum of its digits is divisible by 3.

Examples: 321 is divisible by 3 because 3 + 2 + 1 = 6 is divisible by 3.

5,013 is divisible by 3 because 5 + 0 + 1 + 3 = 9 is divisible by 3.

4,073 is not divisible by 3 because 4 + 0 + 7 + 3 = 14 is not divisible by 3.

Divisibility by 4:   An integer is divisible by 4 only if the last two digits (that is, the digits in the tens and ones places) are zeros or form an even number divisible by 4.

Examples: 4,016, − 3,524, and 1,03,500 are divisible by 4.

− 3,153, 434, and 5,762,034 are not divisible by 4.

Divisibility by 5:   An integer is divisible by 5 only if its ones digit is either 0 or 5.

Examples: 345, 4,095 and − 4,755 are divisible by 5.

472, and − 5,089 are not divisible by 5.

Divisibility by 8:   An integer is divisible by 8 only if the last three digits (units group) are zeros or form a number divisible by 8.

(Use division to test the last three digits.)

Examples: 5,242,000 is divisible by 8   (the last three digits are 000)

4,320,440 is divisible by 8.   (440 ÷ 8 = 55)

9,324,182 is not divisible by 8.   (182 is not divisible by 8.)

Divisibility by 9:   An integer is divisible by 9 only if the sum of its digits is divisible by 9.

Examples: − 819 is divisible by 9.   (8 + 1 + 9 = 18 is divisible by 9)

2,073,006 is divisible by 9. (2 + 0 + 7 + 3 + 0 + 0 + 6 = 18)

3,079 is not divisible by 9. (3 + 0 + 7 + 9 = 19)

Divisibility by 10:   An integer is divisible by 10 only if its ones digit is 0.

Examples: − 510 and − 3,170 are divisible by 10.

− 752 and 9,535 are not divisible by 10.

Divisibility by 25:   An integer is divisible by 25 only if its last two digits are 25 or 50 or 75 or 00.

Examples: − 725; − 9,750; 3,275 and 4,372,900 are divisible by 25.

840 and 1,723 are not divisible by 25.

Divisibility by 50:   An integer is divisible by 50 only if its last two digits are 50 or 00.

Examples: − 750 and 2,750, 900 are divisible by 50.

225 and 3,420 are not divisible by 50.

Divisibility by 100:   An integer is divisible by 100 only if its last two digits are 00.

Examples: 2,500 and 7,525,300 are divisible by 100.

1,250 is not divisible by 100.

The following tests also enable us to test an integer for its divisibility by 6, 12, and 15.

An integer is **divisible by 6** if it is divisible by its factors 2 and 3.

An integer is **divisible by 12** if it is divisible by its factors 3 and 4.

An integer is **divisible by 15** if it is divisible by its factors 3 and 5.

Many integers, such as 7, 19, and 23, have no divisibility tests. To test for divisibility of such integers we need to perform division.

Summary of divisibility tests:
i.   Test for divisibility by 2, 5, 10, 25, 50 or 100 by inspecting the last digit(s).
ii.   Test for divisibility by 4 or 8 by dividing the last 2 or 3 digits by 4 or 8, respectively.
iii.   Test for divisibility by 3 or 9 by checking the sum of the digits for divisibility by 3 or 9.
iv.   Test for divisibility by 6, 12, or 15 by applying the test for 3 and then the test for 2, 4, or 5, respectively.

Warm-Up

2. **(a)** Is 478 divisible by 2? by 3?

(b) Is 243 divisible by 2 ? by 3 ?

Example 2   Determine divisibility by 2, 3, 4, 5, 6, 8, 9, 10, 12, 15, 25, 50, and 100 by applying the divisibility tests.

     (a)   3,784   **(b)**   864,540

     (c)   735,600   **(d)**   3,455

Solutions

(a)   **3,784**

     i.   Examine the last digit(s).

        3,784 is divisible by **2** (since it is even), but not by 5, 10, 25, 50 or 100.

     ii.   The last two digits are divisible by **4.** $84 \div 4 = 21$

        The last three digits are divisible by **8.** $784 \div 8 = 98$

          3,784 is divisible by 4 and by 8.

     iii.   Examine the sum of the digits.

        $3 + 7 + 8 + 4 = $ **22.** 3,784 is *not* divisible by 3 or 9, since 22 is not.

     iv.   3,784 is not divisible by 6, 12, or 15, since it is not divisible by 3;

        hence, 3,784 is found to be divisible by 2, 4, and 8 only when the divisibility tests are used.

(b)   **864,540**

     i.   Examine the last digit(s).

        864,540 is divisible by 2, 5, and 10, but not by 25, 50, or 100.

     ii.   864,**540** is divisible by 4 (since $40 \div 4 = 10$).

     iii.   864,**540** is not divisible by 8, since 540 is not divisible by 8.

iv. $8 + 6 + 4 + 5 + 4 + 0 = \mathbf{27}$; therefore, 864,540 is divisible by both 3 and 9.

v. Since 864,540 is divisible by 2 and 3, it is divisible by 6.
Since it is divisible by 3 and 4, it is divisible by 12.
Since it is divisible by 3 and 5, it is divisible by 15.
Hence, 864,540 is divisible by 2, 3, 4, 5, 6, 9, 10, 12, and 15.

(c) **735,600**

i. Examine the last digit(s).
735,600 is divisible by 2, 5, 10, 25, 50, and 100.

ii. 735,600 is divisible by 4 since the last two digits are zeros, and by 8 since $600 \div 8 = 75$.

iii. $7 + 3 + 5 + 6 + 0 + 0 = 21$; hence, 735,600 is divisible by 3 but not by 9.

iv. Since it is divisible by 2 and 3, it is divisible by 6.
Since it is divisible by 3 and 4, it is divisible by 12.
Since it is divisible by 3 and 5, it is divisible by 15;

hence, 735,600 is divisible by 2, 3, 4, 5, 6, 8, 10, 12, 15, 25, 50, and 100.

(d) **3,455**

i. Examine the last digit(s). 3,455 is divisible only by 5, not by 2, 10, 25, 50, or 100.

ii. Since it is odd, it cannot be divisible by 4 or 8.

iii. $3 + 4 + 5 + 5 = 17$, which is not divisible by 3 or 9.

iv. Since 3,455 is not divisible by 3, it cannot be divisible by 6, 12, or 15;

hence, the tests only show divisibility by 5.

Example 3 Determine divisibility of the following numbers by 7, 11, 37, or 59.

(a) 935 (b) 11,977

Solutions

Check by division since there is no special divisibility test for these numbers.

(a) 935 is divisible by 11, but not by 7, 37, or 59.

(b) 11,977 is divisible by 7 and 59, but not by 11 and 37.

(c) Is 437,890 divisible by 5? by 9?

(d) Is 1,535 divisible by 5? by 10?

(e) Is 20,400 divisible by 2? by 4? by 10? by 3? by 5?

(f) Is 243,789 divisible by 3?

(g) Is 9,507 divisible by 3? by 9?

(h) Is –1,552 divisible by 4? by 10?

3. (a) Is 861 divisible by 11? by 21?

(b) Is 6,250 divisible by 29? by 41?

Answers:

1. (a) Odd, 2(108) + 1
   (b) Even, 2(1134)

2. (a) Yes ; No (b) No ; Yes (c) Yes ; No
   (d) Yes ; No (e) Yes ; Yes ; Yes ; Yes ; Yes
   (f) Yes (g) Yes ; No (h) Yes ; No

3. (a) No; Yes (b) No; No

3.1 B.   Multiples of Integers, Factors, and Divisors

A **multiple** of an integer is the product of that integer with another integer. For example, -35 is a multiple of 5, since $-35 = 5 \times (-7)$. -35 is a multiple of (-7) as well. When two or more integers are multiplied together, the product obtained is a *multiple* of each of the numbers multiplied. Each of the numbers is a *factor* of the product.

If an integer is a **multiple** of another integer, then the first number is **divisible** by the second number. For example, 48 is a *multiple* of 6 since $48 = 6 \cdot 8$,

      and $48 = 6 \cdot 8 \quad \longrightarrow \quad 48 \div 6 = 8 \quad \longrightarrow \quad 48$ is *divisible* by 6.

Conversely, if an integer is divisible by another integer, then the first number must be a **multiple** of the second number. For example, 579 is *divisible* by 3 since $579 \div 3 = 193$,

      and $579 \div 3 = 193 \quad \longrightarrow \quad 579 = 3 \cdot 193 \quad \longrightarrow \quad 579$ is a *multiple* of 3.

The relationship between the terms 'factor', 'multiple', 'divisible', and 'divisor' is illustrated below:

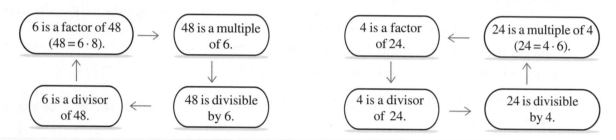

6 is a factor of 48 $(48 = 6 \cdot 8)$. → 48 is a multiple of 6.

6 is a divisor of 48. ← 48 is divisible by 6.

4 is a factor of 24. ← 24 is a multiple of 4 $(24 = 4 \cdot 6)$.

4 is a divisor of 24. → 24 is divisible by 4.

Warm-Up

4. Write each fact as a multiplication or a division fact in two other ways.

   (a) $42 = 6 \cdot 7$

   (b) $(-120) \div 5 = -24$

Example 4   Write each fact as a multiplication or a division fact in two other ways.

   (a) $-35 = 5 \cdot (-7)$ **(b)** $48 \div (-2) = -24$

Solutions

   (a) • $(-35) \div 5 = -7$
           • $(-35) \div (-7) = 5$

   (b) • $(-2) \times (-24) = 48$
           • $48 \div (-24) = -2$

5. Describe this multiplication fact as many ways as possible using the terms "factor", "multiple", "divisible", and "divisor".

   $9 \times 7 = 63$

Example 5   Describe this multiplication fact as many ways as possible using the terms "factor", "multiple", "divisible", and "divisor".

   $-3 \times 7 = -21$

Solution -3 is a factor of -21.   7 is a factor of -21.

              -21 is a multiple of -3. -21 is a multiple of 7.

              -21 is divisible by -3. -21 is divisible by 7.

              -3 is a divisor of -21.   7 is a divisor of -21.

Example 6   List the multiples of:

    (a) 3   **(b)** – 3   **(c)** 5   **(d)** 0

Solutions

  (a)   ..., –9, –6, –3, 0, 3, 6, 9, ...

       We multiply 3 by 0, then by 1, –1, 2, –2, and so forth.

  (b)   ..., –9, –6, –3, 0, 3, 6, 9, ...

       The multiples of –3 are the same as the multiples of 3.

  (c)   ..., – 15, –10, – 5, 0, 5, 10, 15, ...

       We multiply 5 by 0, then by 1, –1, 2, –2, and so forth.

  (d)   0

       Zero has only 1 multiple: 0

       $0 \cdot a = 0$ for all integers a.

       Every integer other than 0 has infinitely many multiples.

Warm-Up

6. List the multiples of

  (a) 4

  (b) – 4

  (c) 9

  (d) 1

Answers:

 4. **(a)** $42 \div 6 = 7$, $42 \div 7 = 6$

   (b) $(- 120) \div (- 24) = 5$, $(- 24) \cdot 5 = - 120$

 5. 7 is a factor of 63 and so forth.

 6. **(a)** ..., – 12, – 8, – 4, 0, 4, 8, 12, ...

   (b) ..., – 12, – 8, – 4, 0, 4, 8, 12, ...

   (c) ..., – 27, – 18, – 9, 0, 9, 18, 27, ...

   (d) ..., – 3, – 2, – 1, 0, 1, 2, 3, ...

Exercise 3.1

A. In exercises 1-18, identify whether the given integer is even or odd. Then write the even integer as $2n$ and the odd integer as $2n + 1$, for some integer n.

1. 319   **2.** 473   **3.** 9,210   **4.** 0   **5.** 5,799   **6.** 9,975

7. 10,064   **8.** 11,531   **9.** 876   **10.** 253,238   **11.** 44,683   **12.** 44,638

13. 1   **14.** 12,373   **15.** 24,863   **16.** 3,570   **17.** 394   **18.** 1,756

In exercises 19-48, using the tests for divisibility, determine which of the numbers 2, 3, 4, 5, 9, 10, 25, 50, and 100 are divisors of the given integer.

19. 72   **20.** –90   **21.** 45   **22.** 54   **23.** 77   **24.** 65

25. –136   **26.** 312   **27.** –253   **28.** 441   **29.** 874   **30.** 950

31. 1,044   **32.** –5,350   **33.** 7,623   **34.** 8,145   **35.** –3,570   **36.** 4,562

37. 9,000   **38.** 2,741   **39.** 3,500   **40.** 6,471   **41.** 6,387   **42.** 8,450

43. 888   **44.** –8,888   **45.** 1,818   **46.** 1,881   **47.** 3,735   **48.** 1,623

B. In exercises 49-56, write each fact as a multiplication or a division fact in two other ways.

49. $8 \cdot 9 = 72$ **50.** $75 \div (5) = 15$ **51.** $-40 \div 4 = -10$ **52.** $(-7) \times (-5) = 35$

53. $-210 \div 7 = -30$ **54.** $(-7) \cdot (-4) = 28$ **55.** $(-99) \div (-9) = 11$ **56.** $(-9100) \div (-91) = 100$

In exercises 57-67, determine whether the first number is a multiple of the second.

57. 1,131 ; 13   **58.** 6,790 ; 6   **59.** 45,774 ; 8   **60.** 9,972 ; 4   **61.** 76,905 ; 9   **62.** 17,370 ; 9

63. 14,545 ; 15   **64.** 6,816 ; 7   **65.** 3,948 ; 12   **66.** 4,736 ; 6   **67.** 27,525 ; 15

68. Give an example of each of the following:

  (a) A number which is a multiple of 3 but not of 9.   **(b)** A number which is a multiple of 4 but not of 8.

  (c) A number which is a multiple of 5 but not of 10.   **(d)** A number which is a multiple of 8 but not of 6.

  (e) A number which is a multiple of 6 but not of 12.   **(f)** A number which is a multiple of 12 but not of 15.

In exercises 69-78, identify whether or not the statement is true.

69. An odd integer can never be divisible by an even integer.

70. If *n* represents any integer, then $2n$ represents an even integer, and $2n + 1$ represents an odd integer.

71. An integer may be divisible by 6 and not divisible by 12. Give two examples to justify your answer.

72. If an integer is divisible by both 3 and 5, then it is divisible by 15.

73. If an integer is divisible by both 4 and 6, then it may not be divisible by 24.

74. An integer may be divisible by both 3 and 6 but not divisible by 18. Give two examples.

75. If an integer is divisible by 8, then it is divisible by 4.

76. An integer may be divisible by 3, 6, and 12 but not divisible by 9. Give two examples.

77. If an integer is divisible by 4, then it may or may not be divisible by 8. Give two examples of each type.

78. An integer may be divisible by 5 and not divisible by 10. Give four examples.

3.2   PRIME FACTORS

Objectives

After completing this section, you will be able to:

A. Identify whether a whole number is prime or composite; list all the prime numbers less than 50 using the 'Sieve of Eratosthenes'; and

B. Find the prime factorization of a composite number.

IMPORTANT VOCABULARY

1. A **prime number** is a whole number greater than 1 with **exactly two** different factors or divisors, 1 and the number itself.

    2, 3, 5, 7 are examples of prime numbers.

    2 is the smallest prime number.

2. A **composite number** is a whole number greater than 1 **with more than two** different factors.

    4, 6, 14 are examples of composite numbers.

    Every *even* number other than 2 is a composite number.

3. When a number is expressed as a product of prime numbers, it is said to be the **prime factorization** of that number.

    $15 = 3 \cdot 5$ and $18 = 2 \cdot 3 \cdot 3$ are the prime factorizations of 15 and 18.

    $16 = 2 \cdot 8$ is *not* a prime factorization of 16, because 8 is not prime.

4. The **Sieve of Eratosthenes** is a technique developed by the famous Greek mathematician Eratosthenes that helps in finding prime numbers.

5. **The Fundamental Theorem of Arithmetic** states that every composite number has exactly one prime factorization.

3.2 A.   Determining whether a Whole Number is Prime or Composite

1. A **prime number** is a whole number greater than 1 with exactly two factors, 1 and itself.

    A whole number greater than 1 which is not prime is a **composite number.**

The whole numbers 0 and 1 are neither prime nor composite numbers. 1 is the only number which has exactly one factor, namely, itself.

$$1 = 1 \times 1$$

Both 0 and 1 have special properties in multiplication and division which complicate their inclusion as prime numbers.

> Special properties of 0 and 1.
>
> - $0 \times$ (any number) $= 0$
> $0 \times a = a \times 0 = 0$ Zero factor property
> - Division by 0 is not defined.
> $\dfrac{a}{0}$ is undefined.
> - $1 \times$ (any number) $=$ the number itself
> $1 \times a = a \times 1 = a$
>   Any number divided by 1 $=$ the number itself
> $\dfrac{a}{1} = a$

Example 1   Identify the integers in the set that are prime numbers.
$$\{4, 5, 6, 7, 8\}$$

Solution   4 is not prime, since $4 = 1 \cdot 4$, and also $= 2 \cdot 2$.

5 **is prime**, since 5 can only be written as $1 \cdot 5$, with only two factors.

6 is not prime, since $6 = 1 \cdot 6$, and also $= 2 \cdot 3$.

7 **is prime**, since 7 can only be written as $1 \cdot 7$, with only two factors.

8 is not prime, since $8 = 1 \cdot 8$, and also $= 2 \cdot 4$.

 Note   The smallest prime number is 2.
2 is the only prime number that is even.
Every even number, other than 2, is composite.

Example 2   Verify that the given even numbers below are composite numbers.
   (a)   268   **(b)** -14 **(c)** -602

Solutions

   (a)   268 is composite,   since $268 = 1 \cdot 268$
                             and also $= 2 \cdot 134$

   (b) -14 is composite,   since $-14 = 1 \cdot (-14)$
                             and also $= 2 \cdot (-7)$

   (c) -602 is composite,   since $-602 = 1 \cdot (-602)$
                             and also $= 2 \cdot (-301)$

Warm-Up

1. Identify the integers in the set that are prime numbers.

   $\{11, 12, 13, 14, 15\}$

2. Verify that the odd numbers below are composite numbers.
   (a)   21
   (b)   35
   (c)   49
   (d)   63

Answer:
1.   11, 13

2. Listing Prime Numbers (The Sieve of Eratosthenes)

There is no formula for finding all the prime numbers. We can list all the prime numbers up to a certain number, say 50, by using a technique developed by the Greek mathematician named Eratosthenes (born 230 B.C.). The method is known as the **Sieve of Eratosthenes.**

To list the positive multiples of a number, say 5, we need to multiply 5 by each natural number.

Natural Numbers:	1	2	3	4	5 ...	13 ...	21 ...
Multiples of 5:	5	10	15	20	25 ...	65 ...	105 ...

In the above list, 5, 10, 15, ... are respectively called the 1st (first) multiple of 5, the 2nd (second) multiple of 5, the 3rd (third) multiple of 5, and so on.

Note that none of the multiples of a number, except possibly the number itself, can be prime. Each multiple has the number as a factor. To list all the prime numbers up to 50 by the ***Sieve of Eratosthenes***, we proceed by eliminating multiples of primes, as described in the following steps:

***Step* 1** List all the natural numbers from 1 to 50, in rows of ten, as shown below.

1	2	3	4	5	6	7	8	9	10
11	12	13	14	15	16	17	18	19	20
21	22	23	24	25	26	27	28	29	30
31	32	33	34	35	36	37	38	39	40
41	42	43	44	45	46	47	48	49	50

***Step* 2** Cross out 1 (since 1 is not a prime number). The next number is 2, which is a prime number. Circle 2, and cross out all other multiples of 2 since they are not prime.

~~1~~	(2)	3	~~4~~	5	~~6~~	7	~~8~~	9	~~10~~
11	~~12~~	13	~~14~~	15	~~16~~	17	~~18~~	19	~~20~~
21	~~22~~	23	~~24~~	25	~~26~~	27	~~28~~	29	~~30~~
31	~~32~~	33	~~34~~	35	~~36~~	37	~~38~~	39	~~40~~
41	~~42~~	43	~~44~~	45	~~46~~	47	~~48~~	49	~~50~~

Note that except 2, all the other even numbers have been crossed out.

***Step* 3** The next available number is 3. It is a prime. Circle 3, and cross out all other multiples of 3 since they are not prime.

~~1~~	(2)	(3)	~~4~~	5	~~6~~	7	~~8~~	~~9~~	~~10~~
11	~~12~~	13	~~14~~	~~15~~	~~16~~	17	~~18~~	19	~~20~~
~~21~~	~~22~~	23	~~24~~	25	~~26~~	~~27~~	~~28~~	29	~~30~~
31	~~32~~	~~33~~	~~34~~	35	~~36~~	37	~~38~~	~~39~~	~~40~~
41	~~42~~	43	~~44~~	~~45~~	~~46~~	47	~~48~~	49	~~50~~

Note that except 3, all other multiples of 3 have been crossed out.

***Step* 4** The next available number is 5. It is a prime. Circle 5, and cross out every other multiple of 5 that is not crossed out yet. If we continue the process we will obtain the following table in which all the composite numbers are crossed out and the prime numbers are circled:

~~1~~	(2)	(3)	~~4~~	(5)	~~6~~	(7)	~~8~~	~~9~~	~~10~~
(11)	~~12~~	(13)	~~14~~	15	~~16~~	(17)	~~18~~	(19)	~~20~~
~~21~~	~~22~~	(23)	~~24~~	25	~~26~~	~~27~~	~~28~~	(29)	~~30~~
(31)	~~32~~	~~33~~	~~34~~	35	~~36~~	(37)	~~38~~	~~39~~	~~40~~
(41)	~~42~~	(43)	~~44~~	~~45~~	~~46~~	(47)	~~48~~	~~49~~	~~50~~

All the prime numbers up to 50 therefore, are:

2, 3, 5, 7, 11, 13, 17, 19, 23, 29, 31, 37, 41, 43, and 47.

> **Remark:** Eratosthenes probably made holes in the paper instead of crossing out the numbers; therefore , his paper must have looked like a sieve. This may be the reason why this method is known as the Sieve of Eratosthenes.

3. **Determining Prime Numbers (General Method):** To determine whether a large odd number is prime or composite, we test its divisibility by the prime numbers listed above (2, 3, 5, 7, 11, 13, 17, 19, 23, 29, ...) , one by one in order. We can use the divisibility tests for 2, 3, and 5, and the actual division for the remaining numbers. If the number is divisible by any of these primes, then the number is composite. It should be noted here that in testing whether a number is prime or composite:

(i) We need to test only the odd numbers because every even number other than 2 is a composite number and 2 is a prime.

(ii) We do not test the divisibility of an odd number by a composite number. If a number is *not* divisible by 3, then it can not be divisible by any of its multiples such as 6 or 9 (Think! Why?). Similarly, if a number is not divisible by 5, it will not be divisible by any other number which is a multiple of 5 such as 10 or 15, and so on.

(iii) We continue dividing the number by prime numbers until either we get a remainder of 0 or we find that the quotient is smaller than the divisor.

Procedure to determine whether a number is prime or composite:

Check the divisibility by successive prime numbers starting with 2, using the divisibility tests, or by actual divisions.

1. **Stop** when you find a remainder of 0. This will mean that the prime divisor is a factor of the number, and that the **number is a composite number.**

OR

2. **Stop** when the quotient is smaller than the prime divisor. This means that the number has no larger prime factor and is, therefore, **itself a prime number.**

Example 3 Determine whether the given number is prime or composite.

(a) 549   (b) 749,235

Solutions

(a) 549 is divisible by 3. $5 + 4 + 9 = 18$ which is divisible by 3.

3 is a factor of 549.

549 is a composite number, since it has more than two factors, 1 and 549. It also has 3 as a factor.

(b) 5 is a factor of 749,235.   The ones digit is 5.

Therefore, it is a composite number, with more than two factors.

Warm-Up

3. Identify the given number as prime or composite.

(a) 657

(b) 649,530

155

Warm-Up

4. Determine whether the given number is prime or composite.

(a) 767

(b) 719

Answers:

3. (a) Composite (b) Composite

4. (a) Composite (b) Prime

Example 4 Determine whether the given number is prime or composite.

(a) 473   (b) 257

Solutions

(a)   Verify that 473 is not divisible by 2, 3, and 5.   The tests for divisibility by 2, 3, and 5 fail.

It is not divisible by 7: $473 \div 7 = 67 \ R \ 4$

It is divisible by 11: $473 \div 11 = 43 \ R \ 0$

                 $\longrightarrow$ 11 is a factor of 473;

therefore, 473 is a composite number.

(b)   Verify that 257 is not divisible by 2, 3, and 5.

It is not divisible by 7: $257 \div 7 = 36 \ R \ 5$

It is not divisible by 11: $257 \div 11 = 23 \ R \ 4$

It is not divisible by 13: $257 \div 13 = 19 \ R \ 10$

It is not divisible by 17: $257 \div 17 = 15 \ R \ 2$

Since the quotient is *less than* the divisor, we conclude that 257 is a prime number.

 Note In example 4b, if we further divide the number by larger primes such as 19 or 23, the quotient would only get smaller. If any of these larger numbers were a divisor, we would have obtained its smaller quotient as a factor in the previous steps. Thus, when the quotient is less than the divisor and the remainder is not 0, there is no need trying for larger prime divisors.

3.2 B.   Prime Factorization; Fundamental Theorem of Arithmetic; Factors of Composite Numbers

- **Prime Factorization**

A number is said to be factored if it can be written as a product of two or more whole numbers; thus, 12 can be factored in many ways. For example:

$$1 \cdot 12, \qquad 2 \cdot 6, \qquad 3 \cdot 4, \qquad 2 \cdot 2 \cdot 3.$$

Each of these is called a **factorization** of 12. However, the factorization $2 \cdot 2 \cdot 3$ is of special interest, since all the factors are prime numbers. Such a factorization is called **prime factorization.**

A **prime factorization** is a representation of a whole number as a product of two or more prime numbers.

$12 = 2 \cdot 2 \cdot 3$ is a prime factorization, since 2, 2, 3 are primes.

- **The Fundamental Theorem of Arithmetic**

We know that multiplication is a commutative and associative operation: the factors may be written in any order. Consider the prime factorization of the number 42:

$$42 = 2 \cdot 3 \cdot 7$$

We might write: $42 = 7 \cdot 2 \cdot 3$ or $3 \cdot 7 \cdot 2$ or $7 \cdot 3 \cdot 2$, and so on.

Each of these is the *same* prime factorization of 42. They all contain the same prime factors. This fact holds good for any composite number and is called the Fundamental Theorem of Arithmetic.

The fact that all factorizations of a composite number yields the same set of prime factors is historically known as the Fundamental Theorem of Arithmetic.

> **The Fundamental Theorem of Arithmetic**
> Every composite number has **exactly one** prime factorization.

We will follow the convention of writing the factors in ascending order (smaller to larger) such as $42 = 2 \cdot 3 \cdot 7$.

Let us determine the prime factorization of the number 72.

$$72 = 2 \cdot \mathbf{36}$$

- Start with the smallest prime 2. 72 is divisible by 2. Divide 72 by 2 to obtain the quotient 36.

$$= 2 \cdot 2 \cdot \mathbf{18}$$

- 36 is also divisible by the smallest prime, that is 2. Divide 36 by 2 to obtain the quotient 18.

$$= 2 \cdot 2 \cdot 2 \cdot \mathbf{9}$$

- 18 is also divisible by 2, and $18 = 2 \cdot 9$.

$$= 2 \cdot 2 \cdot 2 \cdot 3 \cdot \mathbf{3}$$

- The quotient 9 is *not* divisible by 2 so try the next prime (3). 9 is divisible by 3, and $9 = 3 \cdot 3$.

The quotient is prime, so we stop here.

The prime factorization of 72, therefore, is

$$\mathbf{72 = 2 \cdot 2 \cdot 2 \cdot 3 \cdot 3} \quad \text{or} \quad \mathbf{2^3 \cdot 3^2} \quad \text{(using exponents)}.$$

Note that we will arrive at the same prime factorization even if, instead of starting with the smallest prime factor, we start by expressing 72 as a product of two factors in any manner, say:

$$72 = \mathbf{9} \cdot \mathbf{8} \qquad \text{or} \qquad 72 = \mathbf{4} \cdot \mathbf{18}$$
$$= 3 \cdot 3 \cdot 2 \cdot 4 \qquad\qquad\qquad = 2 \cdot 2 \cdot 2 \cdot 9$$
$$= 3 \cdot 3 \cdot 2 \cdot 2 \cdot 2 \qquad\qquad = 2 \cdot 2 \cdot 2 \cdot 3 \cdot 3$$
$$= 3^2 \cdot 2^3 \qquad\qquad\qquad\quad = 2^3 \cdot 3^2$$
$$= 2^3 \cdot 3^2$$

Procedure to find the prime factorization of a composite number:

Step **1**   Factor the given number into any factor pair, using divisibility tests or division.

Step **2**   Factor each composite factor into a factor pair.

Step **3**   Continue the process until all factors are prime.
The **prime factorization** is the product of all the prime factors.

Example 5   Find the prime factorization of 45.

Solution

STEPS

$$45 = 3 \cdot \mathbf{15}$$

- 2 is not a divisor of 45. The next prime is 3, and 3 is a divisor of 45 $(4 + 5 = 9)$.
  Divide by 3; the first quotient is 15.

$$= 3 \cdot 3 \cdot \mathbf{5} \,;$$

- 2 is not a divisor of 15. The next prime is 3, and 3 is a divisor of 15. Divide by 3; the second quotient is 5 which is a prime.

thus, the prime factorization of 45 is:

$$45 = \mathbf{3 \cdot 3 \cdot 5} \quad \text{or} \quad \mathbf{3^2 \cdot 5}.$$

> **Warm-Up**
>
> **5.** Find the prime factorization of 60.

Warm-Up

6. Find the prime factorization of:

(a) 90

(b) 124

(c) 352

Example 6 Find the prime factorization of:

(a) 240   (b) 184   (c) 252

Solutions

(a) $240 =$ $24 \cdot 10$

$= 3 \cdot 8 \cdot 2 \cdot 5$

$= 3 \cdot 2 \cdot 2 \cdot 2 \, ;$

- Since the ones digit is 0, we know that 10 is a factor.
- Since the sum of the digits of 24 is divisible by 3, 3 is a factor of 24.
- Except for 8, all other factors are prime. Also, $8 = 2 \cdot 2 \cdot 2$.

thus, the prime factorization of 240 is:

$240 = 3 \cdot 2 \cdot 2 \cdot 2 \cdot 2 \cdot 5$

$= 2 \cdot 2 \cdot 2 \cdot 2 \cdot 3 \cdot 5$

$240 = 2^4 \cdot 3 \cdot 5 \, .$ (Using exponents)

- Rearrange the factors in increasing order.

(b) $184 =$ $2 \cdot 92$

$= 2 \cdot 2 \cdot 46$

$= 2 \cdot 2 \cdot 2 \cdot 23 \, ;$

- Since the ones digit is 4, we start with 2 as a factor.
- 92 is even; so, 2 is a factor. Divide 92 by 2. $92 \div 2 = 46$.
- 46 is even, so, 2 is a factor. Divide 46 by 2. $46 \div 2 = 23$.

thus, the prime factorization of 184 is:

- Since the quotient 23 is itself a prime, we get the prime factorization.

$184 = 2 \cdot 2 \cdot 2 \cdot 23$ or $2^3 \cdot 23.$

(c) $252 =$ $2 \cdot 126$

$= 2 \cdot 2 \cdot 63$

$= 2 \cdot 2 \cdot 3 \cdot 21$

$= 2 \cdot 2 \cdot 3 \cdot 3 \cdot 7 \, ;$

- 252 is even; divide by 2.
  126 is also even; divide by 2.
- 63 is divisible by 3: $63 = 3 \cdot 21$
  21 is divisible by 3: $21 = 3 \cdot 7$
- Since 7 is prime, we stop.

hence, the prime factorization of 252 is:

$252 = 2 \cdot 2 \cdot 3 \cdot 3 \cdot 7$ or $2^2 \cdot 3^2 \cdot 7.$

• Factors of Composite Numbers

To find all of the factors of a composite number, we list the factor pairs in order, starting with 1 times the number;

$72 = \mathbf{1} \cdot 72$

$= \mathbf{2} \cdot 36$ Divide by 2 to find the factor 36.

$= \mathbf{3} \cdot 24$ Divide by 3 to find the factor 24.

$= \mathbf{4} \cdot 18$

$= \mathbf{6} \cdot 12$

$= \mathbf{8} \cdot 9$

$= \mathbf{9} \cdot 8$ Factors start to repeat.

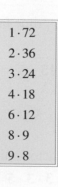

$1 \cdot 72$
$2 \cdot 36$
$3 \cdot 24$
$4 \cdot 18$
$6 \cdot 12$
$8 \cdot 9$
$9 \cdot 8$

As soon as the list repeats a pair, we know that we have the complete list. We can now list the factors of 72 from lowest to highest.

The factors of 72 are 1, 2, 3, 4, 6, 8, 9, 12, 18, 24, 36, 72

Procedure to find all of the factors of a number.

Step 1   List all the factor pairs in order of the first factor, starting with 1 times the number.

Step 2   List all the factors that appear in the factor pairs.

Example 7   Write 68 as a product of two factors in all possible ways. Then list all the factors of 68.

Solution

First find the factor pairs for 68.

$$68 = 1 \cdot 68$$
$$68 = 2 \cdot 34$$
$$68 = 4 \cdot 17$$

Then list the factors.

The factors of 68 are: 1, 2, 4, 17, 34, and 68.

Warm-Up

7.   Write 154 as a product of two factors in all possible ways.

Answers:

5. $2^2 \cdot 3 \cdot 5$

6.   (a) $2 \cdot 3^2 \cdot 5$ (b) $2^2 \cdot 31$ (c) $2^5 \cdot 11$

7. $1 \cdot 154$, $2 \cdot 77$, $7 \cdot 22$, $11 \cdot 14$

Exercise 3.2

A.   **In exercises 1-10, determine whether the given number is prime or composite.**

1.   32   2.   45   3.   77   4.   89   5.   94
6.   23   7.   861   8.   599   9.   15,734   10. 2,430

B.   **In exercises 11-18, find the prime factorization for the given number.**
(Use the divisibility tests for 2, 3, 4, 5, 9, and 10.)

11. 66   12. 112   13. 48   14. 180   15. 54   16. 600   17. 294   18. 288

In exercises 19-33, write the given number as a product of two factors in all possible ways, then list all the factors of the number.

19. 18   20. 30   21. 28   22. 56   23. 75
24. 37   25. 325   26. 219   27. 97   28. 63
29. 140   30. 286   31. 365   32. 116   33. 65

34.   Find two whole numbers such that their product is 30 and their sum is 11.

35.   Find two natural numbers such that their product is 56 and their sum is 15.

36.   Find two natural numbers such that their product is 120 and their sum is 22.

37.   Find the whole numbers such that their product is 72 and their sum is 22.

38. Find the whole numbers such that their product is 99 and their sum is 36.

39. Find the whole numbers such that their product is 125 and their sum is 30.

40. Find the whole numbers such that their product is 98 and their sum is 21.

41. Find the whole numbers such that their product is 99 and their sum is 20.

42. Find two positive integers such that their product is 84 and their sum is 20.

43. Find two positive integers such that their product is 90 and their sum is 21.

44. Find two positive integers such that their product is 105 and their sum is 26.

45. Find two positive integers such that their product is 108 and their sum is 24.

46. Find two positive integers such that their product is 144 and their sum is 30.

47. Find two positive integers such that their product is 182 and their sum is 27.

48. Find two positive integers such that their product is 24 and their difference is 2.

49. Find two positive integers such that their product is 48 and their difference is 2.

50. Find two positive integers such that their product is 120 and their difference is 7.

51. Find two positive integers such that their product is 150 and their difference is 19.

52. Find two positive integers such that their product is 140 and their difference is 31.

53. Find two positive integers such that their product is 130 and their difference is 21.

54. Find two positive integers such that their product is 104 and their difference is 22.

55. Find two positive integers such that their product is 135 and their difference is 6.

56. Find two positive integers such that their product is 225 and their difference is 16.

57. Find two positive integers such that their product is 96 and their difference is 4.

58. Find two positive integers such that their product is 168 and their difference is 2.

59. Find all primes up to 100 using the Sieve of Eratosthenes.

60. The pairs of prime numbers that have a difference of 2 are called **twin primes**. Some examples of twin primes are (3, 5), (5, 7). Find the next three pairs of twin primes.

61. A set of three consecutive prime numbers that have a difference of 2 is called a **prime triplet.** Find a prime triplet.

62. A natural number is a **perfect number**, if the sum of all its possible factors including 1 and the number itself, is two times the number. Show that 6 is a perfect number.

63. A natural number is a **deficient number**, if the sum of all its possible factors including 1 and the number itself, is less than two times the number. Show that 10 is a deficient number.

64. A natural number is an **abundant number**, if the sum of all its possible factors including 1 and the number itself, is greater than two times the number. Show that 100 is an **abundant** number.

65. Identify each of the following numbers as perfect, deficient, or abundant.

    (a) 2   **(b)** 4   **(c)** 6   **(d)** 12   **(e)** 15   **(f)** 132   **(g)** 216

3.3 LEAST COMMON MULTIPLES

IMPORTANT VOCABULARY 💾

The **Least Common Multiple** (LCM) of a group of whole numbers is:

1. The smallest number that is a multiple of each of the numbers in the group.

2. The smallest number divisible by each of the given numbers.

3. The smallest number that has each of the given numbers as a factor.

The above three definitions are equivalent.

> **Objectives** 📖
>
> After completing this section, you will be able to:
>
> A. Find the Least Common Multiple (LCM) of a set of natural numbers and of a set of algebraic terms; and
>
> B. Recognize the application of the LCM in real life situations.

3.3 A. Finding the Least Common Multiple (LCM)

1. Finding the LCM of a set of natural numbers

We discuss below two methods for finding the LCM of numbers.

- **Listing Method**

The LCM of a set of natural numbers can be found by **listing the multiples** of each number and finding the smallest multiple that is common to all the lists.

For example, let us find the LCM of the numbers 4 and 6.

Multiples of 4:	4	8	**12**	16	20	**24** ...
Multiples of 6:	6	**12**	18	**24**	30	**36** ...

The common multiples in the two lists are 12, 24, ..., and the **smallest** of these is 12 ; therefore, the LCM of 4 and 6 is **12**.

We can shorten this method by listing only the multiples of the larger number. We check each until we find one that is a multiple of the other numbers as well. Stop the process as soon as the multiple is found. This method is most useful for multiples that can be easily determined, even mentally.

Example 1 Using the listing method find the LCM of:

(a) 20 and 15   (b) 6, 15, and 18.

Solutions

(a) Check only the multiples of the larger number, 20.

Multiples of 20:   20 40 60 80 ...

Checking for divisibility by 15, we find that 60 is the LCM.

(b) Check only the multiples of 18.

18 36 54 72 90 108

Warm-Up

1. Using the listing method find the LCM of:

(a) 30 and 45

(b) 9, 15, and 24.

Since all multiples of 18 are multiples of 6 and 3, we can determine divisibility by 15 by checking for divisibility by 5. We find that 90 is the LCM.

- **Prime Factoring Method**

The prime factoring method is the method commonly used for finding the LCM in algebra.

To find the LCM of 36 and 126, we write the prime factorization of both numbers.

$$36 = 2 \cdot 2 \cdot 3 \cdot 3$$
$$126 = 2 \cdot 3 \cdot 3 \cdot 7$$

Since the LCM must be divisible by 36, the LCM should have $2 \cdot 2 \cdot 3 \cdot 3$ among its factors. Similarly, the LCM must be divisible by 126, so it should also have $2 \cdot 3 \cdot 3 \cdot 7$ among its factors.

To find the LCM, write down all the prime factors of the first number.

$$2 \cdot 2 \cdot 3 \cdot 3$$

Then check to see if all the prime factors of the next number are present. If any factor is missing include that factor in the expression

$$2 \cdot 2 \cdot 3 \cdot 3 \cdot 7 ; \qquad \text{7 was missing.}$$

so, the LCM $= 2 \cdot 2 \cdot 3 \cdot 3 \cdot 7 = 252$.

We are able to find both 36 and 126 in the factorization of the LCM, 252.

> *Your skill in using this method depends on your ability to find prime factorizations.*

Procedure to find a Least Common Multiple of a set of natural numbers:

Step **1** Write each number as a product of its prime factors.

Step **2** Start with the prime factorization of the first number.

Step **3** Check each number in turn, and write down any factor in its prime factorization that is not yet included.

Step **4** The LCM is the product of all the identified prime factors.

Warm-Up	**Example 2** Find the LCM of the given set of numbers:

2. Find the LCM of:

(a) 15, 14, and 24

(a) 10, 15, and 20 (b) 32, 45, and 108

Solutions

(a) **LCM of 10, 15, 20:**

Step 1
$$10 = 2 \cdot 5$$
$$15 = 3 \cdot 5$$
$$20 = 2 \cdot 2 \cdot 5$$

Step 2   Identify the prime factors of the first number.

$$10 = 2 \cdot 5 \qquad \text{Start with: } \ 2 \cdot 5$$

Step 3   Identify additional factors of the other numbers.

$$15 = \mathbf{3} \cdot 5 \qquad 3 \text{ is needed.} \qquad 2 \cdot 5 \cdot \mathbf{3}$$
Include it.

$$20 = 2 \cdot 2 \cdot \mathbf{5} \qquad \text{Another 2 is needed. Include it.}$$
$$2 \cdot 5 \cdot 3 \cdot \mathbf{2}$$

Step 4   LCM $= 2 \cdot 2 \cdot 3 \cdot 5$ by writing the factors in ascending order

$$= 60.$$

(b)   **LCM of 32, 45, 108:**

$$32 = 2 \cdot 2 \cdot 2 \cdot 2 \cdot 2$$
$$45 = \mathbf{5} \cdot \mathbf{3} \cdot \mathbf{3}$$
$$108 = 2 \cdot 2 \cdot 3 \cdot 3 \cdot \mathbf{3}$$

$$\text{LCM} = \overbrace{2 \cdot 2 \cdot 2 \cdot 2 \cdot 2}^{\text{Factors of 32}} \cdot \overbrace{5 \cdot 3 \cdot 3}^{\text{From 45}} \cdot \underset{\text{From 108}}{3} = \mathbf{4,320.}$$

Example 3   Find the LCM of 96, 108, and 180.

Solution

Prime factorization:

$$96 = 2 \cdot 2 \cdot 2 \cdot 2 \cdot 2 \cdot 3$$
$$108 = 2 \cdot 2 \cdot 3 \cdot \mathbf{3} \cdot \mathbf{3}$$
$$180 = 2 \cdot 2 \cdot 3 \cdot 3 \cdot \mathbf{5}$$

$$\text{The LCM} = \underbrace{2 \cdot 2 \cdot 2 \cdot 2 \cdot 2 \cdot 3}_{= \ 96} \cdot \underbrace{\overset{\text{from 180}}{\mathbf{3} \cdot \mathbf{3}}}_{\text{from 108}} \cdot \mathbf{5} = \mathbf{4,320.}$$

2. Finding the LCM of a Set of Algebraic Terms

The method of finding the LCM of a set of algebraic terms is similar to that for finding the LCM of a set of numbers. Each variable is regarded as a prime factor. Consider the following algebraic terms.

$$45, \ 27a, \ 6ax^2, \ 18a^3x$$

Warm-Up

(b) 112, 140, and 168

3.   Find the LCM of 16, 28, 40, and 77.

Examples:

$$45 = 3 \cdot 3 \cdot 5; \qquad\qquad 27a = 3 \cdot 3 \cdot 3 \cdot a$$

$$6ax^2 = 2 \cdot 3 \cdot a \cdot x \cdot x; \qquad\qquad 18a^3x = 2 \cdot 3 \cdot 3 \cdot a \cdot a \cdot a \cdot x$$

Start with the term having the largest number of factors:

$$18\,a^3\,x = 2 \cdot 3 \cdot 3 \cdot a \cdot a \cdot a \cdot x$$

Check $6ax^2$. An additional x is needed as a factor for LCM.
$$\underbrace{2 \cdot 3 \cdot 3 \cdot a \cdot a \cdot a \cdot x}_{\text{Factors of } 18a^3x} \cdot \overset{\text{from } 6ax^2}{x}$$

Check $27a$. An additional **3** is needed as a factor for LCM.
$$\underbrace{2 \cdot 3 \cdot 3 \cdot a \cdot a \cdot a \cdot x \cdot x}_{\text{LCM of } 18a^3x, \text{ and } 6ax^2} \cdot \overset{\text{from } 27a}{3}$$

Check 45. An additional **5** is needed as a factor for LCM.
$$\underbrace{2 \cdot 3 \cdot 3 \cdot a \cdot a \cdot a \cdot x \cdot x \cdot 3}_{\text{LCM of } 18a^3x, \ 6ax^2, \text{ and } 27a} \cdot 5$$

The LCM $= 2 \cdot 3 \cdot 3 \cdot a \cdot a \cdot a \cdot x \cdot x \cdot \mathbf{3} \cdot \mathbf{5} = 270\,a^3x^2$. $\qquad\overset{\downarrow}{\text{from } 45}$

Observe that the number 270 is the LCM of the coefficients (6, 18, 27, and 45) of the given terms.

Warm-Up

4. Find the LCM of the terms:

$$13xy^2z, \ 39xyz^2, \ 52x^2yz$$

Answers:

1. (a) **90** (b) **360**

2. (a) **840** (b) **1,680**

3. **6160**

4. $156x^2y^2z^2$

Example 4 Find the LCM of the following terms:

$$27x^2y^3, \quad 36xy, \quad \text{and } 54\ y^2z$$

Solution First, we find the prime factors of $27x^2y^3$, $36xy$, and $54\ y^2z$

$$27x^2\,y^3 = 3 \cdot 3 \cdot 3 \cdot x \cdot x \cdot y \cdot y \cdot y$$

$$36xy = \mathbf{2} \cdot \mathbf{2} \cdot 3 \cdot 3 \cdot x \cdot y$$

$$54y^2z = 2 \cdot 3 \cdot 3 \cdot 3 \cdot y \cdot y \cdot \mathbf{z}$$

$$\text{LCM} = \underbrace{3 \cdot 3 \cdot 3 \cdot x \cdot x \cdot y \cdot y \cdot y}_{27x^2\,y^3} \cdot \overset{\text{from } 36xy}{\underbrace{\mathbf{2} \cdot \mathbf{2}}} \cdot \overset{\text{from } 54y^2z}{z}$$

$$= \mathbf{108}\ x^2y^3z$$

3.3 B. Application of the LCM

Study the following examples carefully to understand and recognize the application of finding an LCM. Generally, the words such as 'regular intervals', 'least quantity', or ' the smallest number' indicate the use of the concept of LCM.

Example 5   Three bells ring at regular intervals of 16, 18, and 20 minutes, respectively. At what time will they ring together again if they start simultaneously at 12 noon? How many times will each bell ring during that time?

Solution   We wish to know after how many minutes they will again strike together. When the bells ring together again, each will have already rung some number of times. Since the first bell rings after every 16 minutes, the solution must be a multiple of 16. Similarly, the solution must be a multiple of 18 and a multiple of 20 to allow the other two bells also to ring simultaneously with the first one.

The solution, thus, is the LCM of 16, 18, and 20.

$$
\left.\begin{array}{l}
16 = 2 \cdot 2 \cdot 2 \cdot 2 \\
18 = 2 \cdot 3 \cdot 3 \\
20 = 2 \cdot 2 \cdot 5
\end{array}\right\}
\begin{array}{l}
\text{LCM} = 2 \cdot 2 \cdot 2 \cdot 2 \cdot 3 \cdot 3 \cdot 5 \\
\qquad = 720.
\end{array}
$$

Thus, the bells will ring together again after **720 minutes** or **12 hours**. If they start simultaneously at 12 noon, they will all ring together at 12 midnight. Note that, by 12 midnight,

the first bell will have rung 45 times, because

$$720 = 16 \cdot \mathbf{45}.$$

The second bell will have rung 40 times, because

$$720 = 18 \cdot \mathbf{40}.$$

The third bell will have rung 36 times, because

$$720 = 20 \cdot \mathbf{36}.$$

Example 6   Rosa and Terri have each been saving coins. Rosa saved dimes and Terri saved quarters. Both of them went shopping together and they bought the same item, each spending all of their coins. What is the least amount the item could cost?

Solution   The least amount the item could cost is the smallest number that is divisible by **10** (1 dime = 10 ¢) and **25** (1 quarter = 25 ¢).

That number is the LCM of 10 and 25.

$$
\left.\begin{array}{l}
10 = 2 \cdot 5 \\
25 = 5 \cdot 5
\end{array}\right\}
\quad \text{LCM} = 2 \cdot 5 \cdot 5 = 50
$$

The least amount the item could cost is 50¢; that is, 5 dimes or two quarters.

Warm-Up

5. Three bells ring at regular intervals of 10, 15, and 30 minutes, respectively. At what time will they ring together again if they start simultaneously at 8 AM? How many times will each bell ring during that time?

6. Linda and Patricia have each been saving coins. Linda saved nickels and Patricia saved quarters. Both of them went shopping together and they bought the same item, each spending all of their coins. What is the least amount the item could cost?

7. Candies are to be packed in four different sized packets containing 40, 60, 80, or 100 candies, respectively. Find the smallest number of candies required so that an exact number of any kind of packets can be made from it. Also, find the number of packets of each kind that will be made from this number.

Example 7 Candies are to be packed in four different sized packets containing 200, 350, 500, or 800 candies respectively. Find the smallest number of candies required so that an exact number of any kind of packets can be made from it. Also, find the number of packets of each kind that will be made from this number.

Solution For an exact number of packets containing 200 candies, the number of candies must be a multiple of 200. So is the case with the other three kinds of packets that contain 350, 500 or 800 candies each. Thus, the desired number is the LCM of 200, 350, 500, and 800. Since 200 is a factor (divisor) of 800, it is sufficient to find the LCM of 350, 500, and 800.

$$350 = 5 \cdot 5 \cdot 7 \cdot 2$$
$$500 = 5 \cdot 5 \cdot \mathbf{5} \cdot 2 \cdot 2$$
$$800 = 2 \cdot 2 \cdot \mathbf{2} \cdot \mathbf{2} \cdot \mathbf{2} \cdot 5 \cdot 5$$

$$LCM = \underbrace{5 \cdot 5 \cdot 7 \cdot 2}_{\text{Factors of 350}} \cdot \overbrace{\mathbf{5} \cdot 2}^{\text{from 500}} \cdot \underbrace{\mathbf{2} \cdot \mathbf{2} \cdot \mathbf{2}}_{\text{from 800}} = 28,000.$$

The smallest number of candies required for any kind of packets to be exact in numbers is **28,000**.

Likewise, by grouping the factors of 28,000 we get:

$$28,000 = \mathbf{200} \cdot 140; \qquad 28,000 = \mathbf{350} \cdot 80;$$
$$28,000 = \mathbf{500} \cdot 56; \qquad \text{and} \quad 28,000 = \mathbf{800} \cdot 35.$$

We find that:

140 packets can be made that contain 200 candies each;

or 80 packets can be made that contain 350 candies each;

or 56 packets can be made that contain 500 candies each;

or 35 packets can be made that contain 800 candies each.

Answers:

5. 8.30 AM; 3, 2, and 1.

6. 25¢

7. 1,200; 30, 20, 15, and 12.

Exercise 3.3

A. In exercises 1-18, find the LCM of the group of whole numbers.

1. 12 and 15   **2.** 8 and 12   **3.** 12 and 16   **4.** 9 and 15   **5.** 6, 9 and 12

6. 3, 5 and 7   **7.** 5, 15 and 20   **8.** 15, 45 and 90   **9.** 35, 40 and 72   **10.** 4, 8 and 10

11. 15, 12 and 20   **12.** 4, 15 and 20   **13.** 3, 6, 12 and 25   **14.** 12, 9, 10 and 24   **15.** 25, 40 and 15

16. 2, 7 and 11   **17.** 24, 15 and 100   **18.** 128, 144, 180 and 300

In exercises 19-32, find the LCM of the set of numbers.

19. 6, 15, 24   **20.** 12, 16, 24, 36   **21.** 10, 12, 30   **22.** 12, 18, 24   **23.** 5, 7, 8   **24.** 6, 4, 18   **25.** 18, 24, 30

26. 10, 18, 90   **27.** 18, 36, 66   **28.** 21, 35, 14   **29.** 63, 35, 49, 126   **30.** 20, 35, 70   **31.** 27, 30, 35, 42   **32.** 17, 5, 68, 12

In exercises 33-43, find the LCM of the set of algebraic terms.

33. $4x^2, 6x, 18y^3, x^2y$

34. $25a, 10b^2, 14ab$

35. $9x^2y, 6xy^3, 15$

36. $6x^2y, 12y^2, 20xy$

37. b^2x^2, bx, ab

38. $6x, 10x^2, 14x$

39. $14xy, 10y^2, 25x$

40. $xy^3, 20x^3, 15xy^2$

41. $10xy, 15x^2, 35y$

42. $8ab, 20b, 10a^2$

43. $10a^2, 15ab, 25ab^3$

B. Applications

44. (a) Find the LCM for 20, 28, 45, and 35.

    (b) Identify how many times each number divides into the LCM.

45. Find the smallest number which is exactly divisible by 65, 70, 75, and 80. Also, find how many times each of these numbers divide into that smallest number.

46. Find the smallest number that is exactly divisible by 14, 16, 28, and 40. How many times will each of these numbers divide into that smallest number.

47. Find the largest number of 3 digits that is exactly divisible by 4, 6, and 12. Think ? You need the LCM.

48. Determine two numbers close to 1000 which are exactly divisible by 2, 3, 4, 5, and 6. Think? You need the LCM.

49. Four bells ring at intervals of 8, 12, 18, and 20 minutes, respectively. At what time will they ring together if they start ringing simultaneously at 4 a.m? How many times will each of them ring before and including that time?

50. Four bells ring at regular intervals of 4, 7, 12, and 84 seconds, respectively. The bells ring together at 6 a.m. When will they again ring together? How many times will they ring together in 28 minutes?

51. Coffee is to be packed in 100g, 200g, 250g or 500g packets. Find the least quantity of coffee required so that an exact number of any kind of packets can be made from it. Also find the number of packets of each kind that will be made from this quantity.

52. All students in a class can be divided into groups of 3, 5, 10, and 15. What is the least number of students this class can have?

53. All students in a class can be divided into groups of 4, 6, 8, and 12. What is the least number of students this class can have?

54. Andy has a camera that takes 24 exposures per roll of film and Eric has a camera that takes 36 per roll of film exposures. Both of them want to take the same number of photographs and use up the entire roll. How many rolls should each buy?

55. In a morning walk, three persons start together. At what distance from the starting point will they step together again if their steps measure 80 cm, 85 cm, and 90 cm respectively?

56. Four different sized boxes can hold 24 lb, 36 lb, 48 lb, and 54 lb, respectively. Find the least amount of weight which will exactly fit any of these types of boxes.

57. A school bus picking up children in a neighborhood stops at every fourth block and another school bus starting from the same place stops at every sixth block. Which is the first block at which both the buses will stop?

58. Martin, Laurent, and Jacob have each been saving coins. Martin saved nickels, Laurent saved dimes, and Jacob, quarters. The boys went shopping together and they bought the same item, each spending all of his coins. What is the least amount each could pay?

59. Three sales persons have dinner together whenever all three are in New York city at the same time. The first sales person visits New York city every 12 days, the second every 15 days, and the third, after 18 days.

    (a) How frequently do the three sales persons have dinner together?

    (b) How many trips to New York will each sales person make between any two such dinners?

60. If any one number in a group of numbers is an even number, then the LCM of the group is an even number. True or False? Justify your answer.

3.4   RATIONAL NUMBERS: IDENTIFYING AND GRAPHING

IMPORTANT VOCABULARY

Objectives

After completing this section, you will be able to:

A.   Identify rational numbers; and

B.   Graph rational numbers on a number line.

1.   A **fraction,** such as $\frac{3}{5}$ (read as **three-fifths**), is the name for a number.

2.   A fraction has three components:

   (i)   A horizontal line called the **fraction bar ;**

   (ii)   A number above the fraction bar called the **numerator**; and

   (iii)   A number below the fraction bar called the **denominator.**

$$\text{Fraction bar} \longleftarrow \frac{2 \longrightarrow \text{Numerator}}{7 \longrightarrow \text{Denominator}}$$

3.   The term **rational number** is the technical term for a *fraction.*

4.   A **rational number** is a number that can be written in the form $\frac{a}{b}$, where a and b are integers and $b \neq 0$.

3.4 A.   Identifying Rational Numbers

We have been working with the set of integers. We have seen that when we add, subtract, or multiply two integers, the answer is always an integer. This is not true for division of integers.

When we divide one integer by another integer, the result (quotient) may be an integer, or it may not be an integer.

For example, $12 \div (-3) = \frac{12}{-3} = -4$ is an integer;

but $(-3) \div 12 = \frac{-3}{12} = \frac{-1}{4}$ is not an integer.

This does not mean that we can not divide two integers. It simply means that when we divide two integers, we do not *always* get another integer.

$$\frac{1}{4} \ , \ \frac{2}{3} \ , \ \frac{-3}{4} \ , \ \frac{5}{-7} \ , \ \frac{-13}{-95}$$

These are just a few of the infinitely many numbers that we can obtain when we divide an integer by another integer. Such numbers are called **fractions** or **rational numbers.** Unless stated otherwise, we will use the terms *fraction* and *rational number* to mean the same thing. The word *rational* has the root word *ratio*. A rational number is a ratio or comparison of two integers, using division.

In chapters 1 and 2, we have emphasized that **division by 0 is not defined**. We reinforce the same thing here again: **We cannot divide by 0.**

> *Definition*
>
> A rational number is a number that can be written as a ratio $\frac{a}{b}$, where
>
> a and b are integers, and $b \neq 0.$ $\dfrac{a \longrightarrow \text{Numerator}}{b \longrightarrow \text{Denominator}}$

- In Chapter 2, we used the fraction form of a number to indicate division. Examples:

$$\frac{-14}{2} = -7 ; \qquad \frac{25}{5} = 5 ; \qquad \frac{9}{-3} = -3 ; \qquad \frac{-12}{-4} = 3$$

With this concept, a division represented in fraction form, every integer can be written in the form of a fraction with a denominator of 1.

$$0 = \frac{0}{1} \;, \quad 1 = \frac{1}{1} \;, \quad 2 = \frac{2}{1} \;, \quad 3 = \frac{3}{1} \;, \cdots$$

$$-1 = \frac{-1}{1} \;, \quad -2 = \frac{-2}{1} \;, \quad -3 = \frac{-3}{1} \;, \cdots \text{ and so on.}$$

Every integer is a rational number.

We shall make no distinction between an integer n and the rational number $\frac{n}{1}$; thus, $n = \frac{n}{1}$ for each integer n.

Example 1   Which of the following numbers are rational numbers?

$$-5, \quad \frac{-3}{5}, \quad 0, \quad \frac{-5}{0}, \quad \frac{-12}{3}, \quad 4, \quad \frac{0}{-2}, \quad \frac{3}{-1}$$

Solution

Only $\frac{-5}{0}$ is not rational. In fact $\frac{-5}{0}$ is undefined. All other numbers are rational numbers. The number -5 can be written as $\frac{-5}{1}$.

The number 4 can be written as $\frac{4}{1}$.

The number 0 can be written as $\frac{0}{1}$.

- **Proper and Improper Fractions:** Non-negative fractions whose numerators are *less than* the denominators are called *proper fractions*. If the numerator is greater than or equal to the denominator then the fraction is called an improper fraction.

Examples: $\frac{1}{2}, \frac{3}{8}, \frac{7}{9}$, and $\frac{9}{11}$ are **proper** fractions.

$4, \frac{5}{2}, \frac{7}{5}, \frac{9}{9}$, and $\frac{21}{19}$ are **improper** fractions.

The value of an improper fraction in which the numerator is *equal* to the denominator is always 1, as reflected in the following examples:

$$\frac{8}{8} = 1 ; \qquad \frac{25}{25} = 1 ; \qquad \frac{4}{4} = 1 ; \qquad \frac{-6}{-6} = 1$$

- **Algebraic fractions** or rational expressions are fractions where the numerator or the denominator contains variable(s) instead of just integers.

Some examples of algebraic fractions are given below:

$$\frac{3x}{2y} \; ; \qquad \frac{3ax^2}{5by} \; ; \qquad \frac{12xy^2}{8x^2z} \; ; \qquad -\frac{ab}{5a^2x}$$

- **Positive and Negative Rational Numbers:** Recall that the quotient of two integers with *like* signs is always positive $\left(\dfrac{45}{5} = 9 \; ; \; \dfrac{-24}{-6} = 4\right)$ and the quotient of two integers with *unlike* signs is negative $\left(\dfrac{-35}{7} = -5 \; ; \; \dfrac{18}{-3} = -6\right)$. Rational numbers like $\dfrac{1}{5}, \dfrac{3}{8},$ and $\dfrac{-4}{-9}$ are *positive rationals*; rational numbers like $\dfrac{-35}{7}, \dfrac{18}{-3}, \dfrac{-5}{3},$ and $\dfrac{2}{-7}$ are *negative rationals*.

Let us observe the following three relationships:

$$-\frac{15}{3} = -(15 \div 3) \; ; \qquad \frac{-15}{3} = (-15) \div 3 \; ; \qquad \frac{15}{-3} = 15 \div (-3) \; ;$$
$$= -5 \qquad\qquad\qquad = -5 \qquad\qquad\qquad = -5$$

therefore, $\qquad -\dfrac{15}{3} = \dfrac{-15}{3} = \dfrac{15}{-3}.$

We can conclude that a negative sign in a rational number can be placed in any one of the three positions without changing the meaning or the value of that number. Also, since $\dfrac{-18}{-6} = 3$, and $\dfrac{18}{6} = 3$, we observe that $\dfrac{-18}{-6} = \dfrac{18}{6}$; thus, we have the following rule:

RULE FOR THE PLACEMENT OF NEGATIVE SIGNS

If a and b are two integers and $b \neq 0$, then

- $\dfrac{-a}{b} = \dfrac{a}{-b} = -\dfrac{a}{b}$
- $\dfrac{-a}{-b} = \dfrac{a}{b}$

- $-\dfrac{-a}{b} = \dfrac{-(-a)}{b} = \dfrac{a}{b},$ and
- $-\dfrac{a}{-b} = \dfrac{a}{-(-b)} = \dfrac{a}{b}.$

Warm-Up

2. Write one or more equivalent variations of each rational number that differs from the given number only in signs.

(a) $\dfrac{4}{3}$ \qquad (b) $-\dfrac{4}{5}$

(c) $\dfrac{-7}{-3}$ \qquad (d) $\dfrac{-5}{8}$

(e) $\dfrac{7}{-9}$

Example 2 Write one or more equivalent variations of each rational number that differs from the given number only in signs.

(a) $-\dfrac{5}{6}$ \quad (b) $\dfrac{15}{17}$ \quad (c) $\dfrac{4}{-3}$ \quad (d) $\dfrac{-8}{-9}$ \quad (e) $\dfrac{-1}{2}$

Solutions

(a) $-\dfrac{5}{6}$ is equivalent to $\dfrac{-5}{6}$ and $\dfrac{5}{-6}$.

(b) $\dfrac{15}{17}$ is equivalent to $\dfrac{-15}{-17}, -\dfrac{15}{-17},$ and $-\dfrac{-15}{17}$.

(c) $\dfrac{4}{-3}$ is equivalent to $\dfrac{-4}{3}$ and $-\dfrac{4}{3}$.

(d) $\dfrac{-8}{-9}$ is equivalent to $-\dfrac{8}{-9}$ and $-\dfrac{-8}{9}$.

(e) $\dfrac{-1}{2}$ is equivalent to $-\dfrac{1}{2}$ and $\dfrac{1}{-2}$.

Now we can define *positive* and *negative* rational numbers:

- A rational number of the form $\dfrac{a}{b}$ is **positive** if either both a and b are positive integers or both a and b are negative integers.

  Example: $\dfrac{15}{3} = 15 \div 3 = \mathbf{5}$; $\dfrac{-15}{-3} = (-15) \div (-3) = \mathbf{5}$

  therefore, $\dfrac{-15}{-3} = \dfrac{15}{3}$.

- A rational number of the form $\dfrac{a}{b}$ is **negative** if a and b have opposite signs.

  Examples: $\dfrac{-15}{3} = (-15) \div 3 = \mathbf{-5}$;

  $\dfrac{15}{-3} = (15) \div (-3) = \mathbf{-5}$;

  therefore, $\dfrac{-15}{3} = \dfrac{15}{-3} = -5 = -\dfrac{15}{3}$.

3.4 B. Graphing Rational Numbers on a Number Line

Just as we graphed integers on a number line, we can also graph the rational numbers (fractions) on a number line. To represent rational numbers on a number line, it is necessary to consider them as fractions (or parts) of a whole. We can interpret the numerator and the denominator of, say, $\dfrac{2}{3}$ in different ways.

$\dfrac{2}{3}$ ⟶ The *numerator* counts the actual number of pieces of a unit.

⟶ The *denominator* describes the total number of pieces in a whole or a unit.

$\dfrac{2}{3}$ can be read "2 out of 3" equal parts in a unit or "two-thirds" of a unit.

To illustrate $\dfrac{7}{3}$ requires that several units be broken into thirds, so that we can count 7 thirds.

Consider the following number line:

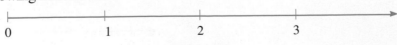

0   1   2   3

Figure 3.1

Divide each of these units into three equal parts as shown in Figure 3.2.

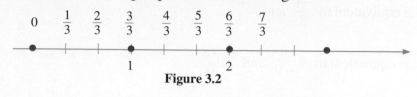

Figure 3.2

$\dfrac{1}{3}, \dfrac{2}{3}, \dfrac{3}{3}, \dfrac{7}{3}$ represent distances from zero (0).

In Figure 3.3, each unit is divided into 4 equal parts. Each segment is $\dfrac{1}{4}$ of a unit.

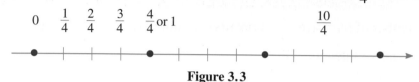

Figure 3.3

$\dfrac{1}{4}, \dfrac{2}{4}, \dfrac{3}{4}$, and $\dfrac{10}{4}$ represent distances from zero (0).

Warm-Up
3. Represent the fractions $\dfrac{1}{3}$ and $\dfrac{5}{3}$ on a number line.

Example 3   Graph the fractions $\dfrac{2}{5}$ and $\dfrac{8}{5}$ on a number line.

Solution

Step 1   Draw a number line, indicating 0, 1, and 2.

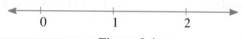

Figure 3.4

Step 2   Divide each of these units into five equal pieces because the denominator of both fractions is 5. Mark the ends of each piece with a tick mark (Figure 3.4a).

Step 3   **(i)**   For $\dfrac{2}{5}$, count 2 pieces starting from the point 0, because the numerator is 2. Mark the point with a dot.

This dot is the graph of $\dfrac{2}{5}$.

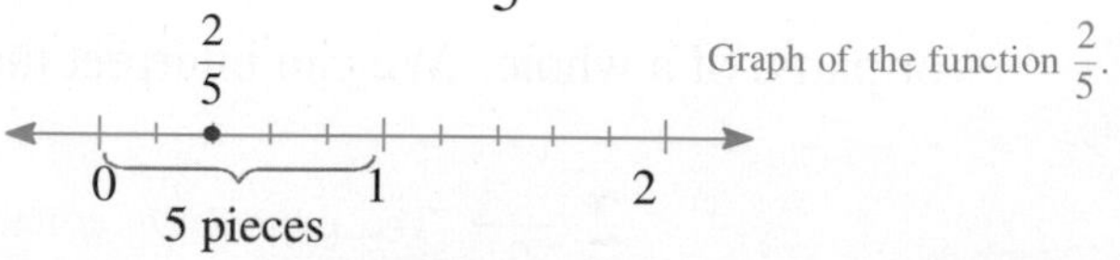

Graph of the function $\dfrac{2}{5}$.

Figure 3.4a

(ii)   For $\dfrac{8}{5}$, count to the end of the 8th piece from 0, or 3 pieces from 1. Mark with a dot.

This dot is the graph of $\dfrac{8}{5}$.

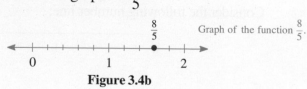

Graph of the function $\dfrac{8}{5}$.

Figure 3.4b

The unit may also be shown on a ruler. The fraction $\dfrac{7}{10}$ represents the distance from 0 to the arrow in Figure 3.5:

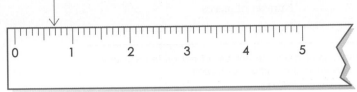

Figure 3.5

When using a ruler, representing the denominator correctly requires accurately counting the number of pieces in a whole.

Example 4   Use a ruler to measure (in cm) the following objects. Express your answer as fractions.

    (a)   The diameter of a quarter

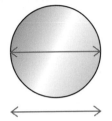

    (b)   The length of this nail

Solutions

    (a)   First count the pieces in 1 cm on your ruler. There are 10 pieces in 1 cm; so, the denominator for the length (in cm) of the diameter of a quarter must be

$$\frac{?}{10}.$$

Next count the actual pieces in the length: $\dfrac{23}{10}$ cm.

    (b)   Similarly the length of the nail is $\dfrac{20}{10}$ cm.

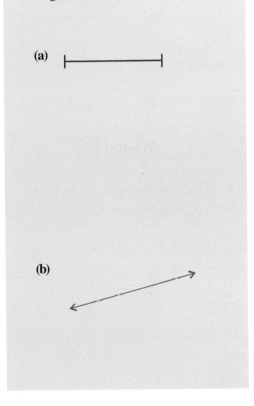

Warm-Up

4.   Use a ruler to measure the following lengths in cm:

    (a)

    (b)

On the number line in Figure 3.6, the number $\dfrac{1}{2}$ lies one-half of the way between 0 and 1, while $\dfrac{3}{4}$ lies three-fourths of the way between 0 and 1.

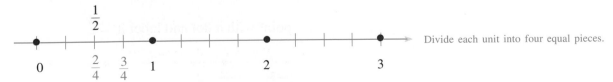

Divide each unit into four equal pieces.

Figure 3.6

The fraction $\frac{3}{4}$ is three of the four equal pieces of a unit.

$\frac{3}{4}$ ⟶ Number of pieces
⟶ Number of equal pieces in a unit

 Note The denominator gives the number of pieces in each unit. The numerator is the number of pieces.

- In order to graph a negative rational number, it is necessary to use the $-\frac{a}{b}$ form of the number.

The **negative rational number** $-\frac{3}{4}$ lies on the opposite side of 0 at a distance $\frac{3}{4}$ from 0.

Figure 3.7 shows the points on a number line representing the rational numbers $-\frac{3}{4}$, $-\frac{5}{4}$, and $-\frac{6}{4}$.

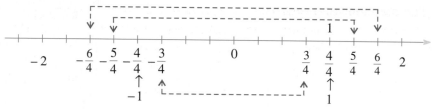

Figure 3.7

Warm-Up

5. Graph the fractions $\frac{-2}{5}$ and $\frac{-9}{5}$ on a number line.

Example 5 Graph the fractions $\frac{-4}{7}$ and $\frac{-16}{7}$ on a number line.

Solution Since both fractions are negative, the points representing them are on the left of 0.

Step 1

Draw a number line and mark the points representing $-1, -2, -3, \ldots$ Since the fractions are negative, they will be represented by points on the negative side of 0.

Step 2

Divide each of the units into 7 equal pieces because the common denominator is 7.

Step 3 For $-\frac{4}{7}$, count **four** pieces on the left of 0. Mark the point with a dot and label it $-\frac{4}{7}$.

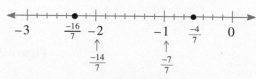

Figure 3.8

For $-\dfrac{16}{7}$, count 16 pieces from 0 (towards the left) or two pieces from -2 (towards the left).

Mark the point with a dot and label it $-\dfrac{16}{7}$.

Example 6 Graph the fractions $\dfrac{3}{2}$ and $-\dfrac{4}{5}$ on the same number line.

Solution $\dfrac{3}{2}$ is positive; therefore, its graph will be on the right of 0.

$-\dfrac{4}{5}$ is negative; therefore, its graph will be on the left of 0.

Draw a number line and divide each unit to the right of 0 into two equal pieces and count three pieces from 0 or one piece from 1. Mark this point with a dot.

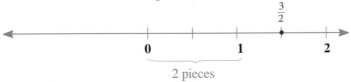

Divide each unit to the left of 0 into 5 equal pieces and count 4 pieces from 0 towards the left. Mark this point with a dot.

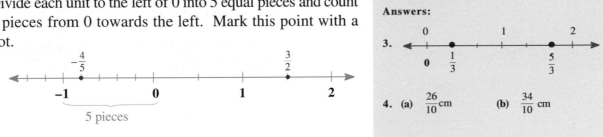

The graph of $\dfrac{3}{2}$ and $-\dfrac{4}{5}$ is shown below.

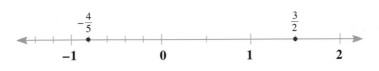

 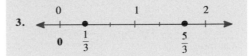
● **Absolute Values of Rational Numbers:** The absolute value of a rational number is its distance from 0 on the number line; thus, the absolute value of $\dfrac{-3}{4}$ is $\dfrac{3}{4}$ and the absolute value of $\dfrac{3}{4}$ is also $\dfrac{3}{4}$.

Both points have the same distance from zero on the number line in Figure 3.7.

Symbolically, we represent the absolute value of $\dfrac{a}{b}$ by $\left|\dfrac{a}{b}\right|$; thus, in Figure 3.7,

$$\left|\dfrac{-6}{4}\right| = \dfrac{6}{4}\,; \qquad \left|-\dfrac{5}{4}\right| = \dfrac{5}{4}\,; \qquad \left|\dfrac{6}{4}\right| = \dfrac{6}{4}\,.$$

The absolute value of 0 is 0, and the absolute value of a non-zero rational number is always positive.

In general terms, we may define the absolute value of $\dfrac{a}{b}$ as follows:

$$\left|\frac{a}{b}\right| = \frac{|a|}{|b|} \; ; \quad b \neq 0 \; ; \quad |0| = 0.$$

Warm-Up

7. Find the indicated absolute values.

(a) $\left|\dfrac{-7}{8}\right|$

(b) $\left|\dfrac{9}{-13}\right|$

(c) $\left|\dfrac{-4}{-11}\right|$

Answers:

7. (a) $\dfrac{7}{8}$ (b) $\dfrac{9}{13}$ (c) $\dfrac{4}{11}$

Example 7   Find the indicated absolute values.

(a) $\left|\dfrac{-3}{7}\right|$ (b) $\left|\dfrac{11}{-15}\right|$ (c) $\left|\dfrac{-4}{-13}\right|$

Solution

(a) $\left|\dfrac{-3}{7}\right| = \dfrac{|-3|}{|7|}$ Using $\left|\dfrac{a}{b}\right| = \dfrac{|a|}{|b|}$ for $b \neq 0$.

$\qquad\quad = \dfrac{3}{7}$

(b) $\left|\dfrac{11}{-15}\right| = \dfrac{|11|}{|-15|}$ Using $\left|\dfrac{a}{b}\right| = \dfrac{|a|}{|b|}$ for $b \neq 0$.

$\qquad\quad = \dfrac{11}{15}$

(c) $\left|\dfrac{-4}{-13}\right| = \dfrac{|-4|}{|-13|}$ Using $\left|\dfrac{a}{b}\right| = \dfrac{|a|}{|b|}$ for $b \neq 0$.

$\qquad\quad = \dfrac{4}{13}$

Exercise 3.4

A. In exercises 1-12, identify the rational number.

1. $\dfrac{1}{2}$ 2. $\dfrac{-3}{4}$ 3. $\dfrac{7}{0}$ 4. 10 5. -8 6. $-\dfrac{9}{12}$

7. $\dfrac{7}{5-5}$ 8. $-\dfrac{0}{9}$ 9. $\dfrac{7-7}{4}$ 10. $-\dfrac{12}{0}$ 11. $\dfrac{9}{-7}$ 12. $\dfrac{-0}{-12}$

In exercises 13-16, write two equivalent variations of the rational number that differ from the given number only in signs.

13. $-\dfrac{4}{5}$ 14. $\dfrac{-5}{7}$ 15. $\dfrac{15}{-7}$ 16. $\dfrac{7}{5}$

In exercises 17-22, write the fraction represented by the shaded unit.

17. 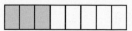   18.    19.

20. 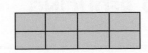   **21.**   **22.**

B. In exercises 23-26, write the fraction represented by the point below the arrow in the given figure.

23.    **24.**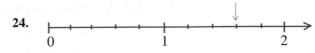

25.    **26.**

In exercises 27-39, represent the fraction on a number line.

27. $\dfrac{3}{4}$ **28.** $\dfrac{5}{8}$ **29.** $-\dfrac{4}{6}$ **30.** $\dfrac{7}{5}$ **31.** $-\dfrac{8}{3}$ **32.** $\dfrac{5}{3}$ **33.** $\dfrac{9}{4}$

34. $-\dfrac{7}{4}$ **35.** $\dfrac{5}{7}$ **36.** $-\dfrac{3}{7}$ **37.** $-\dfrac{8}{10}$ **38.** $\dfrac{3}{5}$ **39.** $\dfrac{4}{10}$

In exercises 40-53, represent the pair of fractions on the same number line.

40. $-\dfrac{2}{3}$ and $\dfrac{1}{3}$ **41.** $\dfrac{2}{5}$ and $\dfrac{7}{5}$ **42.** $-\dfrac{4}{10}$ and $-\dfrac{7}{10}$ **43.** $-\dfrac{3}{4}$ and $\dfrac{5}{4}$ **44.** $-\dfrac{4}{5}$ and $\dfrac{3}{5}$

45. $\dfrac{2}{3}$ and $-\dfrac{2}{3}$ **46.** $\dfrac{3}{6}$ and $-\dfrac{5}{6}$ **47.** $\dfrac{7}{2}$ and $-\dfrac{4}{2}$ **48.** $\dfrac{-3}{8}$ and $-\dfrac{9}{8}$ **49.** $\dfrac{14}{5}$ and $-\dfrac{3}{5}$

50. $\dfrac{1}{4}$ and $\dfrac{9}{4}$ **51.** $-\dfrac{5}{6}$ and $\dfrac{7}{6}$ **52.** $\dfrac{1}{2}$ and $-\dfrac{3}{2}$ **53.** $\dfrac{5}{8}$ and $-\dfrac{5}{8}$

In exercises 54-59, use the ruler to measure the length (l) in inches and centimeters.

54. 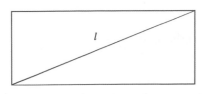   **55.**    **56.**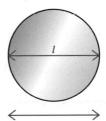

57. 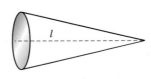   **58.** 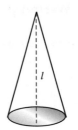   **59.**

In exercises 60-70, find the indicated absolute value.

60. $\left|\dfrac{5}{9}\right|$ **61.** $\left|\dfrac{-7}{3}\right|$ **62.** $\left|\dfrac{8}{-3}\right|$ **63.** $\left|\dfrac{0}{-4}\right|$ **64.** $\left|-\dfrac{4}{5}\right|$ **65.** $\left|\dfrac{-7}{-9}\right|$

66. $\left|\dfrac{129}{-130}\right|$ **67.** $\left|\dfrac{-9}{-17}\right|$ **68.** $\left|\dfrac{-13}{19}\right|$ **69.** $\left|\dfrac{19}{-70}\right|$ **70.** $\left|\dfrac{80}{-101}\right|$

3.5 BUILDING EQUIVALENT FRACTIONS AND REDUCING FRACTIONS

Objectives 📖

After completing this section, you will be able to:

A. Build a fraction; and

B. Reduce fractions.

3.5 A. Building Equivalent Fractions

• Consider the four units shown in Figure 3.9.

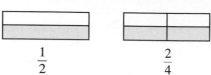 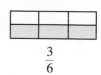

$$\frac{1}{2} \qquad \frac{2}{4} \qquad \frac{3}{6} \qquad \frac{4}{8}$$

Figure 3.9

Since the shaded portions in each of the four units (rectangles) represent the same part of the whole, the fractions represented by them are equal ; that is,

$$\frac{1}{2} \;=\; \frac{2}{4} \;=\; \frac{3}{6} \;=\; \frac{4}{8}.$$ Such fractions are called **equivalent fractions.**

Each of these fractions can be derived from the fraction $\frac{1}{2}$ by multiplying both the numerator and the denominator by the same number.

$$\frac{1}{2} = \frac{1 \cdot 2}{2 \cdot 2} = \frac{2}{4} \;\; ; \;\; \frac{1}{2} = \frac{1 \cdot 3}{2 \cdot 3} = \frac{3}{6} \;\; ; \;\; \frac{1}{2} = \frac{1 \cdot 4}{2 \cdot 4} = \frac{4}{8}$$

We generalize the above observation in the following statement:

> The value of a fraction is not changed if both the numerator and the denominator are multiplied by the same non-zero number.

$$\frac{3}{5} = \frac{3 \cdot 4}{5 \cdot 4} = \frac{12}{20}; \qquad \frac{7}{6} = \frac{7 \cdot 5}{6 \cdot 5} = \frac{35}{30}$$

$\frac{4}{4} = 1$ and $\frac{5}{5} = 1$, if we multiply any number by 1, the value is not changed.

This process is called **building equivalent fractions.**

Warm-Up

1. Build the given fraction as indicated.

   (a) $\dfrac{3}{4} = \dfrac{?}{32}$

Example 1 (a) Build $\dfrac{5}{6}$ as indicated: $\dfrac{5}{6} = \dfrac{?}{42}$.

(b) Build $\dfrac{4}{9}$ as indicated: $\dfrac{4}{9} = \dfrac{24x}{?}$.

Solutions

(a) To build a fraction, we multiply both the numerator and the denominator by the same non-zero number:

$$\frac{5}{6} = \frac{5 \cdot 7}{6 \cdot 7} = \frac{35}{42}$$

Note that the new denominator is 42.

Since $42 = 6 \cdot 7$, we multiply both the numerator and the denominator by 7.

(b) $\dfrac{4}{9} = \dfrac{24x}{?}$

    The new numerator is $24x$:

$$24x = 4 \cdot 6 \cdot x ;$$

$$= \dfrac{4 \cdot 6 \cdot x}{?}$$

    that is, the numerator (4) has been multiplied by $6 \cdot x$. We also multiply the denominator by $6 \cdot x$.

$$= \dfrac{4 \cdot 6 \cdot x}{9 \cdot 6 \cdot x}$$

$$= \dfrac{24\,x}{54\,x}$$

(b) $\dfrac{11}{15} = \dfrac{?}{45p}$

Answers:

1. (a) $\dfrac{24}{32}$ (b) $\dfrac{33p}{45p}$

3.5 B. Reducing Fractions to Lowest Terms

We have established that the fractions $\dfrac{2}{4}$, $\dfrac{3}{6}$, and $\dfrac{4}{8}$ in Figure 3.9 are equal to the fraction $\dfrac{1}{2}$.

$$\frac{2}{4} = \frac{2 \cdot 1}{2 \cdot 2} = \frac{1}{2} ; \qquad \frac{3}{6} = \frac{3 \cdot 1}{3 \cdot 2} = \frac{1}{2} ; \qquad \frac{4}{8} = \frac{4 \cdot 1}{4 \cdot 2} = \frac{1}{2}$$

The cancellation shown in the above illustration is equivalent to dividing by the common factor.

We generalize this in the following statement:

> The value of a fraction remains unchanged if both the numerator and the denominator are divided by the same non-zero number.

Examples:

$$\frac{35}{30} = \frac{5 \cdot 7}{5 \cdot 6} = \frac{7}{6} ; \qquad \text{5 is a common factor.}$$

$$\frac{12}{20} = \frac{4 \cdot 3}{4 \cdot 5} = \frac{3}{5} . \qquad \text{4 is a common factor.}$$

This process of dividing the numerator and the denominator by the common factor is called **reducing the fraction to lower terms**, or simply **reducing the fraction.** A fraction can be reduced only if the numerator and the denominator have a common factor other than 1.

A fraction is said to have been **simplified or reduced** if the numerator and the denominator have no factor in common, other than 1.

• To reduce fractions, we proceed as follows.

> Write the numerator and the denominator as products of prime factors and cancel the common prime factors.

For example:

$$\frac{84}{144} = \frac{2 \cdot 2 \cdot 3 \cdot 7}{2 \cdot 2 \cdot 2 \cdot 2 \cdot 3 \cdot 3} = \frac{7}{2 \cdot 2 \cdot 3} = \frac{7}{12}$$

$\dfrac{84}{144}$ could have been reduced using several applications of one of the previous methods:

Identifying and dividing out a common factor as in

$$\frac{84}{144} = \frac{84 \div 4}{144 \div 4} = \frac{21}{36} \qquad \text{Divide out 4.}$$

$$\frac{21}{36} = \frac{21 \div 3}{36 \div 3} = \frac{7}{12} \qquad \text{Divide out 3.}$$

or identifying and cancelling common factors:

$$\frac{84}{144} = \frac{\cancel{4} \cdot \cancel{3} \cdot 7}{\cancel{4} \cdot \cancel{3} \cdot 12} = \frac{7}{12} .$$

Procedure to reduce a fraction to lowest terms:

Method 1   Identify a common factor. Rewrite the numerator and the denominator as factor pairs having a common factor. Cancel the common factor. Repeat if a common factor can still be found.

Method 2   Replace the numerator and the denominator by their prime factorizations. Cancel the common factors.

Warm-Up

2. Reduce the following fractions to lowest terms:

(a) $\dfrac{8}{30}$

(b) $\dfrac{15}{28}$

(c) $\dfrac{-18}{-81}$

Example 2   Reduce the given fractions to lowest terms.

(a) $\dfrac{4}{12}$ (b) $\dfrac{14}{15}$ (c) $\dfrac{-12}{30}$ (d) $\dfrac{84}{-90}$

Solutions

(a) $\dfrac{4}{12} = \dfrac{\cancel{2} \cdot \cancel{2}}{\cancel{2} \cdot \cancel{2} \cdot 3}$
- $4 = 2 \cdot 2$
- $12 = 2 \cdot 2 \cdot 3$
- Cancel the common factors.

$= \dfrac{1}{3}$

(b) $\dfrac{14}{15} = \dfrac{2 \cdot 7}{3 \cdot 5}$
- $14 = 2 \cdot 7$;
- $15 = 3 \cdot 5$
- There are no common factors. The fraction can not be reduced. Or, we say that the fraction is already in its lowest terms.

$= \dfrac{14}{15}$

(c) $\dfrac{-12}{30} = \dfrac{(-1) \cdot 12}{30}$

Recall that $-a = (-1) \cdot a$
- $-12 = (-1) \cdot 2 \cdot 2 \cdot 3$
- $30 = 2 \cdot 3 \cdot 5$
- Cancel the common factors.

$= \dfrac{(-1) \cdot 2 \cdot \cancel{2} \cdot \cancel{3}}{\cancel{2} \cdot \cancel{3} \cdot 5}$

$= \dfrac{(-1) \cdot 2}{5}$

$= \dfrac{-2}{5}$

(d) $\dfrac{84}{-90} = -\dfrac{84}{90}$

- We can place the negative sign before the fraction bar.

$= -\dfrac{2 \cdot 2 \cdot 3 \cdot 7}{2 \cdot 3 \cdot 3 \cdot 5}$

- $84 = 2 \cdot 42 = 2 \cdot 2 \cdot 21 = 2 \cdot 2 \cdot 3 \cdot 7$
- $90 = 9 \cdot 10 = 3 \cdot 3 \cdot 2 \cdot 5 = 2 \cdot 3 \cdot 3 \cdot 5$

$= -\dfrac{2 \cdot 7}{3 \cdot 5}$

- Cancel out common factors.

$= -\dfrac{14}{15}$

- Write the product of the remaining factors for both the numerator and the denominator.

(d) $\dfrac{27}{-12}$

Example 3 Reduce $\dfrac{12xy}{27xy}$ to lowest terms.

Solution

$\dfrac{12xy}{27xy} = \dfrac{2 \cdot 2 \cdot 3 \cdot \cancel{x} \cdot \cancel{y}}{3 \cdot 3 \cdot 3 \cdot \cancel{x} \cdot \cancel{y}}$

- Write the prime factorizations of both the numerator and the denominator.

$= \dfrac{4}{9}$

- Cancel out common factors.

3. Reduce $\dfrac{34ax^2}{-51xb^2}$.

Answers:

2. (a) $\dfrac{4}{15}$ (b) $\dfrac{15}{28}$ (c) $\dfrac{2}{9}$ (d) $-\dfrac{9}{4}$

3. $\dfrac{2ax}{-3b^2}$

Exercise 3.5

A. In exercises 1-14, build three fractions equivalent to the given fraction by multiplying with $\dfrac{3}{3}, \dfrac{4}{4}, \dfrac{6}{6}$.

1. $\dfrac{3}{5}$ **2.** $\dfrac{2}{7}$ **3.** $\dfrac{1}{8}$ **4.** $\dfrac{6}{11}$ **5.** $\dfrac{4}{5}$ **6.** $\dfrac{9}{10}$ **7.** $\dfrac{15}{16}$

8. $\dfrac{5}{9}$ **9.** $\dfrac{3}{7}$ **10.** $\dfrac{7}{3}$ **11.** $\dfrac{8}{11}$ **12.** $\dfrac{17}{6}$ **13.** $\dfrac{13}{18}$ **14.** $\dfrac{18}{13}$

In exercises 15-34, build the given fraction as indicated.

15. $\dfrac{3}{4} = \dfrac{?}{20}$ **16.** $\dfrac{1}{2} = \dfrac{?}{10}$ **17.** $\dfrac{3}{5} = \dfrac{18}{?}$ **18.** $\dfrac{7}{9} = \dfrac{?}{36}$

19. $\dfrac{6}{7} = \dfrac{18}{?}$ **20.** $-\dfrac{5}{3} = -\dfrac{?}{18}$ **21.** $\dfrac{3}{7} = \dfrac{?}{35}$ **22.** $\dfrac{5}{6} = \dfrac{-10x}{?}$

23. $\dfrac{-4}{5x} = \dfrac{?}{20x}$ **24.** $\dfrac{9}{12} = \dfrac{27x}{?}$ **25.** $\dfrac{17}{15} = \dfrac{?}{45x}$ **26.** $\dfrac{19}{20} = \dfrac{?}{60y}$

27. $\dfrac{5y}{3} = \dfrac{20y}{?}$ **28.** $\dfrac{?}{12y} = \dfrac{7}{4}$ **29.** $\dfrac{-13}{18} = \dfrac{39y}{?}$ **30.** $\dfrac{15y}{?} = \dfrac{3}{7}$

31. $\dfrac{2x}{y} = \dfrac{?}{3xy}$ **32.** $\dfrac{5x}{3y} = \dfrac{10x^2}{?}$ **33.** $\dfrac{7x}{?} = \dfrac{21xy}{9y}$ **34.** $\dfrac{?}{12xy} = \dfrac{5y}{6x}$

B. In exercises 35-78, reduce the fraction to lowest terms.

35. $\dfrac{4}{6}$ **36.** $\dfrac{6}{8}$ **37.** $\dfrac{6}{15}$ **38.** $\dfrac{12}{20}$ **39.** $\dfrac{32}{50}$ **40.** $\dfrac{35}{15}$ **41.** $\dfrac{15}{18}$

42. $\dfrac{21}{35}$ **43.** $\dfrac{8}{36}$ **44.** $\dfrac{10}{38}$ **45.** $\dfrac{12}{39}$ **46.** $\dfrac{25}{40}$ **47.** $\dfrac{21}{42}$ **48.** $\dfrac{36}{45}$

49. $\dfrac{35}{63}$ **50.** $\dfrac{18}{78}$ **51.** $\dfrac{42}{105}$ **52.** $\dfrac{45}{120}$ **53.** $\dfrac{108}{144}$ **54.** $-\dfrac{26}{39}$ **55.** $\dfrac{66}{84}$

56. $\dfrac{75}{125}$ **57.** $\dfrac{172}{236}$ **58.** $\dfrac{200}{240}$ **59.** $-\dfrac{7}{28}$ **60.** $-\dfrac{20}{36}$ **61.** $\dfrac{20x}{25}$ **62.** $\dfrac{15}{25x}$

63. $\dfrac{12xy}{60x}$ **64.** $\dfrac{24x}{36xy}$ **65.** $\dfrac{-27x}{54xy}$ **66.** $\dfrac{25xy}{-15y}$ **67.** $\dfrac{28uv}{49u}$ **68.** $\dfrac{-42u}{72uv}$ **69.** $\dfrac{35v}{-56uv}$

70. $\dfrac{-60u}{84v}$ **71.** $\dfrac{-72a^2}{180a}$ **72.** $\dfrac{150a}{270a^2}$ **73.** $\dfrac{26ab}{-39a^2b}$ **74.** $\dfrac{52b^2}{78ab}$ **75.** $\dfrac{18xy^2}{-27x^2y}$

76. $\dfrac{-50xy}{75x^2y}$ **77.** $\dfrac{xy^2}{-120x^2y}$ **78.** $\dfrac{90xy}{135x^2y^2}$

3.6 LEAST COMMON DENOMINATOR; COMPARING FRACTIONS

Objectives

After completing this section, you will be able to:

A. Build fractions to equivalent fractions with the same denominator; and

B. Compare fractions.

In order to add, subtract, or compare fractions, the denominators must be the same. In this section we will learn how to build fractions, so they have the same denominators: the Least Common Denominator (LCD). We will then be able to compare fractions.

> **Definition:**
>
> The Least Common Denominator (LCD) of two or more fractions is the Least Common Multiple (LCM) of the denominators.

3.6 A. Building Fractions to Equivalent Fractions with the same denominator

*We use the Least Common Denominator (**LCD**) to convert given fractions to equivalent fractions, each with the same denominator.*

The LCD is the LCM of the denominators. Recall the method to find the LCM of numbers.

Consider the fractions $\dfrac{2}{5}$, $\dfrac{3}{10}$, $\dfrac{7}{15}$.

The LCD = LCM of 5, 10, 15

$\qquad$ = 30

$5 = 5$

$10 = 2 \cdot 5 \qquad$ LCM $= 3 \cdot 5 \cdot 2 = 30$

$15 = 3 \cdot 5$

Next, build each fraction to one with a denominator of 30.

$$\frac{2}{5} = \frac{?}{30} \qquad\qquad \frac{3}{10} = \frac{?}{30} \qquad\qquad \frac{7}{15} = \frac{?}{30}$$

$$\frac{2}{5} \cdot \frac{6}{6} = \frac{12}{30} \qquad\qquad \frac{3}{10} \cdot \frac{3}{3} = \frac{9}{30} \qquad\qquad \frac{7}{15} \cdot \frac{2}{2} = \frac{14}{30}$$

Therefore, $\dfrac{2}{5} = \dfrac{12}{30}$; $\dfrac{3}{10} = \dfrac{9}{30}$; and $\dfrac{7}{15} = \dfrac{14}{30}$.

Procedure to change a group of fractions to equivalent fractions using the least common denominator (LCD):

Step 1 Find the LCD (the LCM of the denominators) for the given fractions.

Step 2 Build each fraction to an equivalent fraction, having the LCD as the denominator.

Example 1 Build the following fractions to equivalent fractions, each with the same denominator:

(a) $\dfrac{4}{5}, \dfrac{3}{4}$ (b) $-\dfrac{4}{9}, \dfrac{11}{15}$ (c) $\dfrac{2}{3}, \dfrac{11}{20}, \dfrac{4}{15}, -\dfrac{7}{6}$

Solutions

(a) The LCD of $\dfrac{4}{5}$ and $\dfrac{3}{4}$ is 20.

$$\frac{4}{5} = \frac{4}{5} \cdot \frac{4}{4} = \frac{16}{20} \qquad 20 \div 5 = 4$$

$$\frac{3}{4} = \frac{3}{4} \cdot \frac{5}{5} = \frac{15}{20} \qquad 20 \div 4 = 5$$

$5 = 5$

$4 = 2 \cdot 2$

LCD $= 2 \cdot 2 \cdot 5$

Therefore, the fractions $\dfrac{4}{5}$ and $\dfrac{3}{4}$ are equivalent to $\dfrac{16}{20}$ and

$\dfrac{15}{20}$, respectively, each with 20 as the denominator.

(b) The LCD of $-\dfrac{4}{9}$ and $\dfrac{11}{15}$ is 45.

$9 = 3 \cdot 3$

$15 = 3 \cdot 5$

LCD $= 3 \cdot 3 \cdot 5$

$$-\frac{4}{9} = -\frac{4}{9} \cdot \frac{5}{5} = -\frac{20}{45} \qquad \bullet \ \ 45 \div 9 \ = 5 \ \text{(additional factor for 9)}$$

$$\frac{11}{15} = \frac{11}{15} \cdot \frac{3}{3} = \frac{33}{45} \qquad \bullet \ \ 45 \div 15 = 3 \ \text{(additional factor for 15)}$$

Therefore, $-\dfrac{4}{9} = -\dfrac{20}{45}$ and $\dfrac{11}{15} = \dfrac{33}{45}$.

Warm-Up

1. Build the following fractions to equivalent fractions with the same denominator:

(a) $\dfrac{3}{4}, \dfrac{5}{8}$

(b) $\dfrac{7}{12}, \dfrac{6}{10}$

(c) $\dfrac{2}{9}, \dfrac{-5}{12}, \dfrac{13}{8}$

Answers:

1. (a) $\dfrac{6}{8}, \dfrac{5}{8}$ (b) $\dfrac{35}{60}, \dfrac{36}{60}$

(c) $\dfrac{16}{72}, \dfrac{-30}{72}, \dfrac{117}{72}$

(c) The LCD of $\dfrac{2}{3}, \dfrac{11}{20}, \dfrac{4}{15},$ and $-\dfrac{7}{6}$ is 60.

$$\begin{aligned} 3 &= 3 \\ 20 &= 2 \cdot 2 \cdot 5 \\ 15 &= 3 \cdot 5 \\ 6 &= 2 \cdot 3 \\ \text{LCD} &= 2 \cdot 2 \cdot 3 \cdot 5 = 60 \end{aligned}$$

$$\dfrac{2}{3} = \dfrac{2}{3} \cdot \dfrac{20}{20} = \dfrac{40}{60}$$

$$\dfrac{11}{20} = \dfrac{11}{20} \cdot \dfrac{3}{3} = \dfrac{33}{60} \qquad 60 \div 3 = 20 \text{ (additional factor for 3)}$$

$$\dfrac{4}{15} = \dfrac{4}{15} \cdot \dfrac{4}{4} = \dfrac{16}{60} \qquad 60 \div 20 = 3 \text{ (additional factor for 20)}$$

$$\qquad 60 \div 15 = 4 \text{ (additional factor for 15)}$$

$$\dfrac{-7}{6} = -\dfrac{7}{6} \cdot \dfrac{10}{10} = -\dfrac{70}{60} \qquad 60 \div 6 = 10 \text{ (additional factor for 6)}$$

Therefore, $\dfrac{2}{3} = \dfrac{40}{60}, \dfrac{11}{20} = \dfrac{33}{60}, \dfrac{4}{15} = \dfrac{16}{60},$ and $-\dfrac{7}{6} = -\dfrac{70}{60}.$

3.6 B.   Comparing Fractions

1. Let us first compare two fractions, say, $\dfrac{2}{7}$ and $\dfrac{5}{7}$, having the same denominators. Figure 3.10 shows that the shaded portion representing the fraction $\dfrac{2}{7}$ is smaller than the shaded portion representing the fraction $\dfrac{5}{7}$.

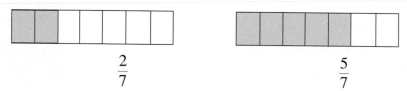

$$\dfrac{2}{7} \qquad\qquad \dfrac{5}{7}$$

Figure 3.10

We say that $\dfrac{2}{7}$ is smaller than $\dfrac{5}{7}$, and write the same fact symbolically as $\dfrac{2}{7} < \dfrac{5}{7}.$

less than

We can also say that $\dfrac{5}{7}$ is greater than $\dfrac{2}{7}$, or in symbols, $\dfrac{5}{7} > \dfrac{2}{7}.$

The above observation can be generalized as a Rule.   greater than

> **Rule:** If two fractions have the same denominator, the one with the larger numerator is larger.

$$\dfrac{5}{9} > \dfrac{2}{9} \qquad \text{because} \qquad 5 > 2.$$

$$\dfrac{13}{21} > \dfrac{8}{21} \qquad \text{because} \qquad 13 > 8.$$

$$\dfrac{15}{91} > \dfrac{7}{91} \qquad \text{because} \qquad 15 > 7.$$

2. If the fractions to be compared do not have a common denominator, we first build the fractions to equivalent fractions with the LCD as the common denominator and then compare the new fractions.

Let us compare $\dfrac{7}{9}$ and $\dfrac{5}{12}$.

We first build these fractions to equivalent fractions with the LCD as the common denominator.

LCD = LCM of 9 and 12 which is 36.

$$\frac{7}{9} = \frac{7}{9} \cdot \frac{4}{4} = \frac{28}{36}, \quad \text{and} \quad \frac{5}{12} = \frac{5}{12} \cdot \frac{3}{3} = \frac{15}{36}.$$

Now we compare $\dfrac{28}{36}$ and $\dfrac{15}{36}$. Since $28 > 15$, $\dfrac{28}{36} > \dfrac{15}{36}$; therefore, $\dfrac{7}{9} > \dfrac{5}{12}$.

Procedure to compare two given fractions.

Step 1 Change the given fractions to equivalent fractions with the same denominator.

Step 2 Compare the new fractions, by comparing the numerators.

Step 3 Replace the new fractions by the original fractions.

Example 2 Identify the larger of the two fractions: $\dfrac{3}{9}$, $\dfrac{5}{12}$.

Write a true inequality statement.

Solution

Step 1 The LCD of 9 and 12 = 36.

$9 = 3 \cdot 3$
$12 = 4 \cdot 3$
LCM $= 4 \cdot 3 \cdot 3 = 36$

Build equivalent fractions in order to compare the fractions.

$$\frac{3}{9} = \frac{?}{36}$$

$$\frac{3}{9} = \frac{3}{9} \cdot \frac{4}{4} = \frac{12}{36}$$

$$\frac{5}{12} = \frac{?}{36}$$

$$\frac{5}{12} = \frac{5}{12} \cdot \frac{3}{3} = \frac{15}{36}$$

Step 2 $\dfrac{15}{36}$ is larger than $\dfrac{12}{36}$ since $15 > 12$;

Step 3 Therefore, $\dfrac{5}{12}$ is larger than $\dfrac{3}{9}$.

The true statement of inequality is: $\dfrac{5}{12} > \dfrac{3}{9}$.

Warm-Up

2. Identify the smaller of the two fractions:
$\dfrac{5}{6}, \dfrac{3}{4}$

3. Identify the statement as True or False.

(a) $\dfrac{3}{4} > \dfrac{7}{9}$

(b) $\dfrac{11}{16} > \dfrac{13}{20}$

Example 3 Identify the statement as True or False.

(a) $\dfrac{2}{5} > \dfrac{3}{4}$ (b) $\dfrac{11}{30} < \dfrac{7}{18}$

Solutions

(a) The LCD of 4 and 5 = 20.

Build equivalent fractions in order to compare the fractions.

$$\frac{2}{5} = \frac{2}{5}\cdot\frac{4}{4} = \frac{8}{20} \qquad 20 \div 5 = 4$$

$$\frac{3}{4} = \frac{3}{4}\cdot\frac{5}{5} = \frac{15}{20} \qquad 20 \div 4 = 5$$

$$\frac{2}{5} > \frac{3}{4} \text{ means } \frac{8}{20} > \frac{15}{20} \;\rightarrow\; 8 > 15 \quad \text{False}$$

The statement is **False**.

(b) The LCD of 30 and 18 = 90 (Verify)

Build equivalent fractions in order to compare the fractions.

$$\frac{11}{30} = \frac{11}{30}\cdot\frac{3}{3} = \frac{33}{90} \qquad 90 \div 30 = 3$$

$$\frac{7}{18} = \frac{7}{18}\cdot\frac{5}{5} = \frac{35}{90} \qquad 90 \div 18 = 5$$

$$\frac{11}{30} < \frac{7}{18} \text{ means } \frac{33}{90} < \frac{35}{90} \;\rightarrow\; 33 < 35 \quad \text{True}$$

The statement is **True**.

• To check whether two given fractions are equivalent, we may use one of the following two methods.

Procedure for checking whether two given fractions are equivalent.

Method 1 Reduce each fraction to lowest terms. If equivalent, the reduced fractions will be identical.

Method 2 Compute the cross products. If equivalent, the cross products will be identical.

Method **1:** Reduce both the fractions and verify if they are the same.

Consider the following two pairs of fractions.

(a) $\dfrac{3}{12}$ and $\dfrac{8}{32}$ (b) $\dfrac{12}{15}$ and $\dfrac{4}{16}$

(a) $\dfrac{3}{12} = \dfrac{\cancel{3} \cdot 1}{\cancel{3} \cdot 4} = \dfrac{1}{4}$; $\qquad \dfrac{8}{32} = \dfrac{\cancel{8} \cdot 1}{\cancel{8} \cdot 4} = \dfrac{1}{4}$

Since both fractions reduce to the same fraction, they are equivalent.

(b) $\dfrac{12}{15} = \dfrac{\cancel{3} \cdot 4}{\cancel{3} \cdot 5} = \dfrac{4}{5}$; $\qquad \dfrac{4}{16} = \dfrac{\cancel{4} \cdot 1}{\cancel{4} \cdot 4} = \dfrac{1}{4}$

Since both fractions do not reduce to the same fraction, they are not equivalent.

Method 2:   Find the cross products, if both products are the same then the fractions are equivalent.

Let us check whether $\dfrac{3}{12}$ and $\dfrac{8}{32}$ are equivalent.

$\dfrac{3}{12} \diagdown\!\!\!\!\diagup \dfrac{8}{32} \longrightarrow \begin{array}{l} 12 \cdot 8 = 96 \\ 3 \cdot 32 = 96 \end{array} \Bigg\} \rightarrow \dfrac{3}{12}$ and $\dfrac{8}{32}$ are equivalent, or $\dfrac{3}{12} = \dfrac{8}{32}$.

First fraction   Second fraction

Let us check whether $\dfrac{12}{15}$ and $\dfrac{4}{16}$ are equivalent.

$\dfrac{12}{15} \diagdown\!\!\!\!\diagup \dfrac{4}{16} \longrightarrow \begin{array}{l} 15 \cdot 4 = 60 \\ 12 \cdot 16 = 192 \end{array} \Bigg\} \rightarrow \dfrac{12}{15}$ and $\dfrac{4}{16}$ are not equivalent.

First fraction   Second fraction   or $\dfrac{12}{15} \neq \dfrac{4}{16}$

Observe from the illustration above that finding the cross products is much easier. Therefore, we will use method 2 in the following example.

Example 4   Check whether the following fractions are equivalent:

(a) $\dfrac{5}{16}$ and $\dfrac{3}{8}$ **(b)** $\dfrac{65}{85}$ and $\dfrac{26}{34}$

Solutions

(a) $\dfrac{5}{16} \diagdown\!\!\!\!\diagup \dfrac{3}{8} \longrightarrow \begin{array}{l} 16 \cdot 3 = \mathbf{48} \\ 5 \cdot 8 = \mathbf{40} \end{array} \Bigg\}$ not equal

Since the two cross products are not equal, $\dfrac{\mathbf{5}}{\mathbf{16}} \neq \dfrac{\mathbf{3}}{\mathbf{8}}$.

(b) $\dfrac{65}{85} \diagdown\!\!\!\!\diagup \dfrac{26}{34} \longrightarrow \begin{array}{l} 26 \cdot 85 = 2210 \\ 65 \cdot 34 = 2210 \end{array}$

Since the two products are equal, we conclude $\dfrac{\mathbf{65}}{\mathbf{85}} = \dfrac{\mathbf{26}}{\mathbf{34}}$.

Warm-Up

4. Check whether the following fractions are equal or not:

(a) $\dfrac{5}{6}$ and $\dfrac{4}{5}$

(b) $\dfrac{14}{35}$ and $\dfrac{24}{60}$

- When a group of numbers is arranged in order from the smallest to the largest, they are said to be arranged in **ascending** order; and when they are arranged from the largest to the smallest, they are in **descending** order.

Procedure to list a group of fractions in order.

Step **1** Find the LCD of all the fractions in the group.

Step **2** Build each fraction to an equivalent fraction with the LCD as the common denominator.

Step **3** Arrange the new fractions in the desired order by comparing numerators.

Step **4** Replace each new fraction by the original fraction.

Warm-Up

5. List the following in ascending order:

$$\frac{9}{12}, \frac{17}{20}, \frac{11}{15}$$

Example 5 Arrange the following fractions in descending order:

$$\frac{3}{4}, \frac{5}{6}, \frac{7}{12}, \frac{12}{15}$$

Solution

LCD = LCM of 4, 6, 12, and 15 = 60 (Verify.)

Build each fraction to the LCD in order to compare the fractions.

$$\frac{3}{4} = \frac{3}{4} \cdot \frac{15}{15} = \frac{45}{60} \qquad 60 \div 4 = 15$$

$$\frac{5}{6} = \frac{5}{6} \cdot \frac{10}{10} = \frac{50}{60} \qquad 60 \div 6 = 10$$

$$\frac{7}{12} = \frac{7}{12} \cdot \frac{5}{5} = \frac{35}{60} \qquad 60 \div 12 = 5$$

$$\frac{12}{15} = \frac{12}{15} \cdot \frac{4}{4} = \frac{48}{60} \qquad 60 \div 15 = 4$$

The fractions equivalent to the given fractions with common denominator are:

$$\frac{45}{60}, \frac{50}{60}, \frac{35}{60} \text{ and } \frac{48}{60}$$

- List the new fractions in the descending order of the numerators.

$$\frac{50}{60} > \frac{48}{60} > \frac{45}{60} > \frac{35}{60}$$

$$\rightarrow \frac{5}{6} > \frac{12}{15} > \frac{3}{4} > \frac{7}{12}$$

- Replace each fraction by the original fraction.

The list in descending order is: $\dfrac{5}{6}, \dfrac{12}{15}, \dfrac{3}{4}, \dfrac{7}{12}$.

6. Find the missing numerator or denominator.

(a) $\dfrac{?}{16} = \dfrac{99}{144}$

Example 6 Find the missing numerator or denominator in two equivalent fractions.

(a) $\dfrac{3}{7} = \dfrac{?}{35}$ (b) $\dfrac{7}{?} = \dfrac{147}{336}$

Solutions

(a) Let the missing numerator be x;

so, $\dfrac{3}{7} = \dfrac{x}{35}$.

We can now solve this equation for x by equating the cross products.

$$\dfrac{3}{7} \; \underset{\diagdown}{\overset{\diagup}{=}} \; \dfrac{x}{35} \quad \longrightarrow \quad \begin{array}{l} 7 \cdot x \\ 3 \cdot 35 \end{array}$$

$$\rightarrow \quad 7x = 3 \cdot 35$$

$$\rightarrow \quad x = 15$$

$$\dfrac{\cancel{7}x}{\cancel{7}} = \dfrac{3 \cdot \cancel{35}^{5}}{\cancel{7}}$$

$$x = 15$$

Therefore, the missing numerator is **15**.

(b) Let the missing denominator be x.

$$\dfrac{7}{x} = \dfrac{147}{336} \qquad \text{Find the cross products.}$$

$$\rightarrow \quad 147 \cdot x = 7 \cdot 336 \qquad \text{Solve this equation for } x.$$

$$\rightarrow \quad \dfrac{\overset{1}{\cancel{147}}\, x}{\underset{1}{\cancel{147}}} = \dfrac{7 \cdot 336}{147} \quad \rightarrow \quad x = 16$$

Therefore, the missing denominator is **16**.

(b) $\dfrac{9}{6} = \dfrac{108}{?}$

Answers:

2. $\dfrac{3}{4}$ **3. (a)** False   **(b)** True

4. (a) Not Equal   **(b)** Equal

5. $\dfrac{11}{15}; \dfrac{9}{12}; \dfrac{17}{20}$ **6. (a)** 11   **(b)** 72

Exercise 3.6

A. **In exercises 1-20, convert the fractions to equivalent fractions with the LCD as the common denominator.**

1. $\dfrac{4}{9}, \dfrac{7}{12}$ **2.** $\dfrac{2}{3}, \dfrac{3}{4}$ **3.** $\dfrac{8}{9}, \dfrac{5}{2}, \dfrac{3}{5}$ **4.** $\dfrac{1}{3}, \dfrac{4}{5}, \dfrac{6}{7}$ **5.** $\dfrac{2}{5}, \dfrac{1}{4}, \dfrac{7}{10}$

6. $\dfrac{2}{3}, \dfrac{3}{4}, \dfrac{3}{8}$ **7.** $\dfrac{7}{8}, \dfrac{4a}{9}, \dfrac{11}{24}$ **8.** $\dfrac{3x}{10}, \dfrac{2x}{15}, \dfrac{9x}{35}$ **9.** $\dfrac{a}{6}, \dfrac{a}{8}, \dfrac{a}{10}$ **10.** $\dfrac{4}{3x}, \dfrac{5}{6x}, \dfrac{1}{9x}$

11. $\dfrac{3}{2x}, \dfrac{9}{4}, \dfrac{x}{8}$ **12.** $\dfrac{6a}{13b}, \dfrac{7b}{2a}, \dfrac{4}{13ab}$ **13.** $\dfrac{5}{6x}, \dfrac{x}{8}, \dfrac{5}{4x}$ **14.** $\dfrac{x}{a}, \dfrac{5a}{bx}, \dfrac{8x}{3ab}$ **15.** $\dfrac{4a}{9b}, \dfrac{5b}{3ab}, \dfrac{3}{2a}$

16. $\dfrac{3c}{2d}, \dfrac{4}{5c}, \dfrac{7d}{3c}$ **17.** $\dfrac{1}{5x}, \dfrac{3y}{x}, \dfrac{7x}{2y}$ **18.** $\dfrac{2x}{y}, \dfrac{3y}{2x}, \dfrac{5}{4xy}$ **19.** $\dfrac{4x}{3y}, \dfrac{2x}{3y}, \dfrac{y}{2x}$ **20.** $\dfrac{3x}{4y}, \dfrac{5y}{6x}, \dfrac{7}{12xy}$

B. **In exercises 21-35, insert the appropriate symbol (>, or =, or <) to make the statement true.**

21. $\dfrac{11}{2} \; \square \; \dfrac{5}{2}$ **22.** $\dfrac{16}{5} \; \square \; \dfrac{10}{3}$ **23.** $\dfrac{5}{6} \; \square \; \dfrac{3}{4}$ **24.** $\dfrac{15}{27} \; \square \; \dfrac{25}{45}$ **25.** $\dfrac{6}{51} \; \square \; \dfrac{51}{6}$

26. $\dfrac{3}{8} \;\square\; \dfrac{9}{24}$ **27.** $\dfrac{5}{7} \;\square\; \dfrac{7}{9}$ **28.** $\dfrac{19}{4} \;\square\; \dfrac{4}{19}$ **29.** $\dfrac{20}{35} \;\square\; \dfrac{12}{21}$ **30.** $\dfrac{56}{72} \;\square\; \dfrac{105}{135}$

31. $\dfrac{9}{13} \;\square\; \dfrac{9}{16}$ **32.** $\dfrac{42}{35} \;\square\; \dfrac{24}{20}$ **33.** $\dfrac{7}{8} \;\square\; \dfrac{4}{21}$ **34.** $\dfrac{9}{10} \;\square\; \dfrac{44}{50}$ **35.** $\dfrac{36}{30} \;\square\; \dfrac{117}{90}$

In exercises 36-50, determine whether the given fractions are equivalent.

36. $\dfrac{3}{8}$ and $\dfrac{4}{11}$ **37.** $\dfrac{4}{5}$ and $\dfrac{12}{15}$ **38.** $\dfrac{12}{14}$ and $\dfrac{36}{42}$ **39.** $\dfrac{10}{26}$ and $\dfrac{15}{65}$ **40.** $\dfrac{16}{18}$ and $\dfrac{80}{90}$

41. $\dfrac{8}{12}$ and $\dfrac{18}{27}$ **42.** $\dfrac{15}{21}$ and $\dfrac{50}{80}$ **43.** $\dfrac{16}{28}$ and $\dfrac{40}{70}$ **44.** $\dfrac{14}{18}$ and $\dfrac{35}{45}$ **45.** $\dfrac{10}{22}$ and $\dfrac{15}{32}$

46. $\dfrac{16}{20}$ and $\dfrac{28}{35}$ **47.** $\dfrac{20}{50}$ and $\dfrac{26}{65}$ **48.** $\dfrac{60}{70}$ and $\dfrac{66}{67}$ **49.** $\dfrac{35}{45}$ and $\dfrac{49}{61}$ **50.** $\dfrac{54}{66}$ and $\dfrac{72}{88}$

In exercises 51-70, arrange the fractions in ascending order.

51. $\dfrac{2}{3}, \dfrac{1}{3}, \dfrac{1}{2}$ **52.** $\dfrac{1}{2}, \dfrac{3}{4}, \dfrac{5}{6}$ **53.** $\dfrac{2}{3}, \dfrac{13}{15}, \dfrac{11}{20}$ **54.** $\dfrac{2}{5}, \dfrac{3}{4}, \dfrac{5}{2}$ **55.** $\dfrac{3}{4}, \dfrac{7}{5}, \dfrac{5}{8}$

56. $\dfrac{4}{9}, \dfrac{8}{3}, \dfrac{7}{4}$ **57.** $\dfrac{4}{5}, \dfrac{9}{10}, \dfrac{13}{10}$ **58.** $\dfrac{2}{3}, \dfrac{3}{4}, \dfrac{4}{5}$ **59.** $\dfrac{3}{4}, \dfrac{2}{5}, \dfrac{4}{7}$ **60.** $\dfrac{5}{6}, \dfrac{4}{5}, \dfrac{3}{2}$

61. $\dfrac{5}{6}, \dfrac{2}{3}, \dfrac{3}{2}$ **62.** $\dfrac{2}{3}, \dfrac{3}{5}, \dfrac{7}{15}$ **63.** $\dfrac{3}{5}, \dfrac{2}{7}, \dfrac{9}{35}$ **64.** $\dfrac{5}{6}, \dfrac{4}{7}, \dfrac{19}{42}$ **65.** $\dfrac{3}{4}, \dfrac{5}{6}, \dfrac{7}{12}$

66. $\dfrac{1}{3}, \dfrac{2}{5}, \dfrac{3}{4}, \dfrac{7}{12}$ **67.** $\dfrac{2}{5}, \dfrac{3}{10}, \dfrac{1}{3}, \dfrac{3}{2}$ **68.** $\dfrac{3}{7}, \dfrac{3}{4}, \dfrac{5}{6}, \dfrac{2}{14}$ **69.** $\dfrac{2}{9}, \dfrac{3}{4}, \dfrac{5}{6}, \dfrac{7}{12}$ **70.** $\dfrac{1}{2}, \dfrac{2}{3}, \dfrac{5}{9}, \dfrac{5}{6}$

In exercises 71-90, find the missing numerator or denominator in the given equivalent fractions.

71. $\dfrac{2}{3} = \dfrac{?}{15}$ **72.** $\dfrac{6}{?} = \dfrac{2}{7}$ **73.** $\dfrac{?}{10} = \dfrac{3}{5}$ **74.** $\dfrac{4}{9} = \dfrac{20}{?}$ **75.** $\dfrac{5}{7} = \dfrac{?}{35}$

76. $\dfrac{7}{?} = \dfrac{42}{54}$ **77.** $\dfrac{?}{12} = \dfrac{21}{36}$ **78.** $\dfrac{5}{6} = \dfrac{55}{?}$ **79.** $\dfrac{15}{20} = \dfrac{?}{24}$ **80.** $\dfrac{26}{39} = \dfrac{18}{?}$

81. $\dfrac{12}{?} = \dfrac{18}{45}$ **82.** $\dfrac{?}{5} = \dfrac{20x}{25}$ **83.** $\dfrac{3}{2x} = \dfrac{?}{10x}$ **84.** $\dfrac{5x}{?} = \dfrac{35x}{77}$ **85.** $\dfrac{?}{3x} = \dfrac{22}{33x}$

86. $\dfrac{5x}{y} = \dfrac{?}{8y}$ **87.** $\dfrac{3y}{7x} = \dfrac{21y}{?}$ **88.** $\dfrac{4u}{11v} = \dfrac{16u}{?}$ **89.** $\dfrac{?}{12\,uv} = \dfrac{5v}{6u}$ **90.** $\dfrac{9u}{7v} = \dfrac{27uv}{?}$

3.7 INTRODUCTION TO MIXED NUMBERS

IMPORTANT VOCABULARY

- A **proper fraction** is a fraction whose numerator has an absolute value *smaller than* the absolute value of the denominator.

  Example:

  $-\dfrac{2}{3}, -\dfrac{1}{3}$ and $\dfrac{2}{3}$ are proper fractions since the absolute value of each numerator is smaller than the absolute value of its denominator.

- An **improper fraction** is a fraction whose numerator has an absolute value *larger than* or *equal* to the absolute value of its denominator.

  Example:

  $-\dfrac{4}{3}, -\dfrac{3}{3}, \dfrac{5}{3}$ and $\dfrac{10}{3}$ are improper fractions since the absolute value of each numerator is greater than or equal to the absolute value of its denominator.

- Numbers such as $4\dfrac{1}{3}$ (read : "Four *and* one-third") and $13\dfrac{2}{5}$ (read : "Thirteen *and* two-fifths") are called **mixed numbers**.

3.7A. Changing Mixed Numbers to Improper Fractions and Improper Fractions to Mixed Numbers

1. **Introduction to Mixed Numbers:** A **mixed number** is the sum of a whole number and a proper fraction. Usually the whole number and the fraction are written side by side without the plus sign. For example,

$$2 + \frac{4}{5} = 2\frac{4}{5} \qquad \text{(Read: "Two and four-fifths")}$$

$$15 + \frac{3}{8} = 15\frac{3}{8} \qquad \text{(Read: "Fifteen and three-eighths")}$$

2. **Changing Improper Fractions to Mixed Numbers**

Consider the improper fraction $\dfrac{13}{5}$. The denominator suggests that a unit is divided into five equal parts.

Each part is one-fifth $\left(\dfrac{1}{5}\right)$ of a unit. Also, $13 = 5 + 5 + 3$ suggests that $\dfrac{13}{5}$ represents all the five parts of two units and three parts of the third unit as illustrated in Figure 3.11.

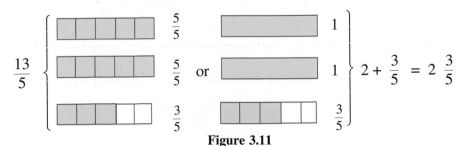

Figure 3.11

191

Therefore, $\dfrac{13}{5}$ = 2 units and $\dfrac{3}{5}$ unit

$$= 2 + \dfrac{3}{5} = 2\dfrac{3}{5}.$$

- Observe that when we divide 13 by 5, the quotient is 2 and the remainder is 3.

$$\dfrac{13}{5} = 13 \div 5 = 2 \text{ R } 3 \,;$$

$$\dfrac{13}{5} = 2 + \dfrac{3}{5}$$

We now generalize the above observation for improper fractions.

$$\text{Improper fraction} = \dfrac{\text{Numerator}}{\text{Denominator}} \qquad (\text{Numerator} \geq \text{Denominator})$$

$$\overset{\textbf{Quotient}}{\text{Denominator} \,\overline{)\,\text{Numerator}}} \qquad\qquad \textbf{Improper fraction} = \textbf{Quotient} + \dfrac{\textbf{Remainder}}{\text{Denominator}}$$

$$\textbf{Remainder} \qquad\qquad\qquad = \textbf{Quotient}\,\dfrac{\textbf{Remainder}}{\text{Denominator}}$$

$$\dfrac{23}{5} = 23 \div 5 = 4 \text{ R } 3 = 4 + \dfrac{3}{5} = 4\dfrac{3}{5}\,;$$

(**Note**: The denominator of the fraction remains the same.)

thus, $\qquad \dfrac{23}{5} \qquad = 4 \quad + \quad \dfrac{3}{5} \qquad = 4\dfrac{3}{5}.$

$$\text{Improper fraction} = \text{Whole} + \text{Proper} = \text{Mixed number}$$
$$\text{number} \quad \text{fraction}$$
$$\text{(Quotient)}$$

- In a mixed number, the fraction part should always be in reduced form. To ensure this, we first reduce the improper fraction to lowest terms and then divide to separate its whole number part.

Let us change $\dfrac{45}{6}$ to a mixed number:

First, reduce. $\qquad\qquad \dfrac{45}{6} = \dfrac{\cancel{3}\cdot 15}{\cancel{3}\cdot 2} = \dfrac{15}{2}.$

Then change to a mixed number. $\quad \dfrac{15}{2} = 7 \text{ R } 1 = 7 + \dfrac{1}{2} = 7\dfrac{1}{2}\,;$

$$\overset{7}{2\,\overline{)\,15}}$$
$$\underline{14}$$
$$1$$

Thus, $\qquad \dfrac{45}{6} = 7\dfrac{1}{2}.$

Procedure to change an improper fraction to a mixed number:

Step 1 Reduce the fraction, if needed, then divide the numerator by the denominator to find the whole number part (the quotient) of the mixed number.

Step 2 Write the remainder over the denominator as the fraction part of the mixed number.

$$\text{Improper fraction} = \text{quotient}\,\dfrac{\text{remainder}}{\text{divisor}}$$

Example 1   Change the improper fraction to a mixed number:

(a) $\dfrac{9}{4}$ (b) $\dfrac{47}{11}$ (c) $\dfrac{-40}{15}$

Solutions

(a) $\dfrac{9}{4} = 9 \div 4 = 2 \text{ R } 1$ (By inspection)

$\qquad = 2 + \dfrac{1}{4}$ The sum of the quotient and the fraction part

$\qquad = \mathbf{2\dfrac{1}{4}}$ Drop the + sign.

(b) $\dfrac{47}{11} = 47 \div 11$

$\qquad = 4 \text{ R } 3$

$\qquad = 4 + \dfrac{3}{11}$

$\qquad = \mathbf{4\dfrac{3}{11}}$

Divisor
$$\overset{\downarrow}{11)\,\overline{47}}\;\;\overset{4}{}$$
$$\underline{44}$$
$$3 \leftarrow \text{Remainder}$$

- Fraction part $= \dfrac{3}{11} \leftarrow$ Divisor
- Write the sum of the whole number part and the fraction part.
- Drop the '+' sign.

(c) $-\dfrac{40}{15} = -\dfrac{\cancel{5}\cdot 8}{\cancel{5}\cdot 3}$

$\qquad = -\dfrac{8}{3}$

$\qquad = -\left(2 + \dfrac{2}{3}\right)$

$\qquad = -\mathbf{2\dfrac{2}{3}}$

- We first reduce the fraction as both the numerator and the denominator are divisible by 5.
- Now, change $\dfrac{8}{3}$ to a mixed number.

Divide :
$$\overset{\text{Divisor}}{\underset{\downarrow}{3)\,\overline{8}}}\;\;\overset{2 \leftarrow \text{ Whole number part}}{}$$
$$\underline{6}$$
$$2 \leftarrow \text{(Remainder)}$$

The fraction part $= \dfrac{2}{3}$.

3. Changing Mixed Numbers to Improper Fractions

Consider the mixed number $2\dfrac{3}{5}$.

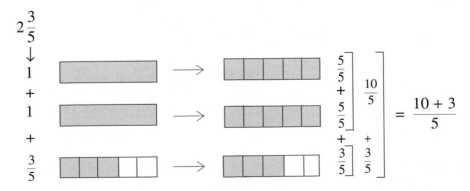

Figure 3.12

$$2\frac{3}{5} = \frac{10+3}{5} = \frac{2 \times 5 + 3}{5}$$

The numerator of the fraction on the right is $2 \times 5 + 3$. Compare this with numbers in the mixed number.

$$2\frac{3}{5} = \frac{\overset{2}{\text{(Whole number part)}} \cdot \overset{5}{\text{(Denominator)}} + \overset{3}{\text{(Numerator)}}}{\underset{5}{\text{Denominator}}}$$

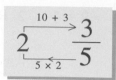

$$= \frac{2 \cdot 5 + 3}{5} = \frac{13}{5}.$$

Generalizing this observation, we get the following procedure.

Procedure to convert a mixed number into an improper fraction:

Step **1**   Multiply the whole number part by the denominator and obtain the product.

Step **2**   Add the numerator to the product to get the numerator of the improper fraction.

Step **3**   Write the improper fraction using this numerator. The denominator remains unchanged. If negative, attach the negative sign to the resulting fraction.

Warm-Up

2. Convert each mixed number into an improper fraction.

(a) $5\frac{3}{4}$

(b) $7\frac{5}{9}$

(c) $-12\frac{1}{4}$

Answers:

1. (a) $2\frac{4}{5}$ (b) $2\frac{3}{5}$ (c) $-2\frac{5}{6}$

2. (a) $\frac{23}{4}$ (b) $\frac{68}{9}$ (c) $-\frac{49}{4}$

Example 2   Convert each mixed number into an improper fraction.

(a) $7\frac{4}{9}$ (b) $3\frac{4}{5}$ (c) $-53\frac{3}{4}$

Solutions

(a) $7\frac{4}{9} = \frac{7 \times 9 + 4}{9}$ Multiply 7 by 9 and add 4 to the product to get the numerator.

$\qquad = \frac{63+4}{9} = \frac{67}{9}$

(b) $3\frac{4}{5} = \frac{3 \times 5 + 4}{5}$ Multiply 5 by 3 and add 4 to the product to get the numerator.

$\qquad = \frac{19}{5}$

(c) $-53\frac{3}{4} = -\frac{53 \cdot 4 + 3}{4}$

$\qquad = -\frac{212+3}{4}$

$\qquad = -\frac{215}{4}$

⚠ **Caution:** **Do not** write $-53\frac{3}{4} = \frac{-53 \cdot 4 + 3}{4}$.

Recall, $-53\frac{3}{4}$ is the opposite of $53\frac{3}{4}$.

$$= -\left(53\frac{3}{4}\right)$$

3.7 B. Graphing Mixed Numbers on a Number Line

Positive and Negative Mixed Numbers: Just like integers and fractions, mixed numbers can also be positive or negative. Some positive and negative mixed numbers are graphed on the number line in Figure 3.12.

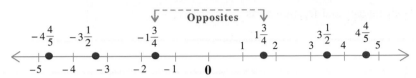

Figure 3.12

Note that $-1\frac{3}{4}$ is the *opposite* of $1\frac{3}{4}$; $-3\frac{1}{2}$ is the *opposite* of $3\frac{1}{2}$.

Example 3   Graph the mixed number on a number line:

(a) $-2\frac{1}{3}$ (b) $-1\frac{3}{4}$ (c) $1\frac{1}{8}$

Solutions

(a) $-2\dfrac{1}{3}$

Move 2 units to the left of 0. Then move an additional $\frac{1}{3}$

unit to the left and graph the point representing $-2\frac{1}{3}$.

(b) $-1\dfrac{3}{4}$

Move 1 unit to the left of 0. Then move an additional

$\frac{3}{4}$ unit to the left and graph the point representing $-1\frac{3}{4}$.

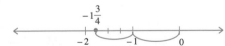

(c) $1\dfrac{1}{8}$

Move 1 unit to the right of 0. Then move an additional

$\frac{1}{8}$ unit to the right and graph the point representing $1\frac{1}{8}$.

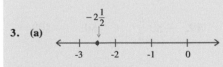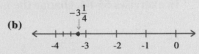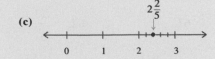

⚠ **Caution:** $-1\frac{3}{4} \ne -1 + \frac{3}{4}$.

$$-1\frac{3}{4} = \text{opposite of } 1\frac{3}{4} = -\left(1\frac{3}{4}\right) = -\left(1 + \frac{3}{4}\right) = -1 - \frac{3}{4}.$$

Both integer and fraction parts are negative.

Exercise 3.7

A. **In exercises 1-12, identify the proper and improper fractions from the given list.**

1. $\frac{1}{3}, \frac{-2}{3}, 5, \frac{6}{5}, -\frac{10}{3}$

2. $\frac{-3}{4}, \frac{-5}{2}, -1, \frac{3}{5}, \frac{-4}{3}$

3. $-15, \frac{5}{7}, -\frac{3}{19}, \frac{19}{-5}$

4. $\frac{13}{4}, \frac{-25}{19}, \frac{7}{9}, -15, \frac{8}{-9}$

5. $-214, \frac{75}{23}, \frac{-19}{36}, \frac{17}{241}$

6. $\frac{8}{3}, -\frac{19}{5}, \frac{-5}{2}, \frac{8}{-3}, \frac{9}{5}$

7. $\frac{9}{7}, -\frac{6}{5}, 2, \frac{4}{3}, \frac{5}{8}$

8. $-2, \frac{3}{4}, -\frac{5}{6}, \frac{8}{7}, -\frac{19}{6}$

9. $\frac{2}{5}, \frac{-7}{8}, -\frac{18}{5}, \frac{5}{2}, \frac{3}{7}$

10. $2, \frac{2}{11}, -\frac{4}{13}, -\frac{15}{7}, -3$

11. $\frac{3}{8}, -\frac{4}{3}, -\frac{5}{2}, \frac{23}{7}, -3$

12. $-\frac{3}{7}, \frac{4}{7}, \frac{21}{8}, -5, -\frac{9}{11}$

In exercises 13-54, change the mixed number to an improper fraction.

13. $1\frac{1}{2}$

14. $-2\frac{1}{3}$

15. $-3\frac{1}{4}$

16. $5\frac{1}{3}$

17. $5\frac{1}{5}$

18. $-8\frac{4}{7}$

19. $4\frac{3}{5}$

20. $6\frac{2}{3}$

21. $7\frac{5}{6}$

22. $8\frac{5}{7}$

23. $-5\frac{2}{3}$

24. $8\frac{5}{8}$

25. $11\frac{7}{9}$

26. $-2\frac{1}{8}$

27. $7\frac{3}{10}$

28. $-7\frac{3}{8}$

29. $1\frac{7}{45}$

30. $6\frac{8}{9}$

31. $75\frac{1}{6}$

32. $-87\frac{2}{3}$

33. $112\frac{5}{8}$

34. $-11\frac{5}{8}$

35. $8\frac{1}{2}$

36. $-10\frac{6}{7}$

37. $2\frac{3}{4}$

38. $82\frac{1}{8}$

39. $20\frac{2}{3}$

40. $11\frac{5}{6}$

41. $-13\frac{1}{8}$

42. $4\frac{7}{8}$

43. $-7\frac{6}{7}$

44. $8\frac{4}{3}$

45. $-5\frac{3}{4}$

46. $15\frac{3}{2}$

47. $-55\frac{3}{10}$

48. $100\frac{9}{11}$

49. $-80\frac{2}{3}$

50. $-200\frac{1}{11}$

51. $13\frac{1}{100}$

52. $5\frac{1}{200}$

53. $144\frac{2}{5}$

54. $321\frac{5}{9}$

In exercises 55-84, change the improper fraction to a mixed number.

55. $\frac{19}{4}$

56. $-\frac{5}{3}$

57. $\frac{7}{3}$

58. $\frac{17}{5}$

59. $-\frac{21}{5}$

60. $-\frac{49}{5}$

61. $\frac{47}{6}$

62. $\frac{53}{7}$

63. $-\frac{55}{8}$

64. $\frac{215}{9}$

65. $\frac{135}{10}$

66. $\frac{1873}{17}$

67. $\frac{911}{100}$

68. $-\frac{533}{50}$

69. $-\frac{753}{9}$

70. $-\frac{327}{11}$

71. $-\frac{513}{12}$

72. $\frac{834}{13}$

73. $-\dfrac{1553}{80}$ **74.** $\dfrac{132}{13}$ **75.** $-\dfrac{1051}{12}$ **76.** $-\dfrac{813}{13}$ **77.** $\dfrac{925}{13}$ **78.** $\dfrac{300}{151}$

79. $\dfrac{177}{160}$ **80.** $-\dfrac{1151}{15}$ **81.** $-\dfrac{903}{10}$ **82.** $\dfrac{-321}{14}$ **83.** $\dfrac{532}{15}$ **84.** $-\dfrac{471}{16}$

B. **In exercises 85-99, graph the mixed number on a number line.**

85. $1\dfrac{4}{5}$ **86.** $-5\dfrac{3}{5}$ **87.** $3\dfrac{1}{3}$ **88.** $-7\dfrac{6}{7}$ **89.** $2\dfrac{4}{5}$

90. $-5\dfrac{1}{4}$ **91.** $2\dfrac{1}{7}$ **92.** $-6\dfrac{2}{5}$ **93.** $3\dfrac{3}{4}$ **94.** $-3\dfrac{5}{6}$

95. $-6\dfrac{1}{6}$ **96.** $2\dfrac{2}{5}$ **97.** $-2\dfrac{1}{5}$ **98.** $-5\dfrac{2}{7}$ **99.** $7\dfrac{3}{8}$

3.8   TRANSLATING ENGLISH EXPRESSIONS; RATIOS, RATES, AND PERCENTS AS FRACTIONS

3.8 A.   Translating English Expressions to Mathematical Expressions Involving Fractions

In the real world we make statements that can be translated into fractions. Fractions can represent a part of a total. To translate statements into fractions, we need to identify the **part of the total**, and **the total**, as illustrated in the following example.

Example 1   Cathy wants to finish a novel as soon as possible. So far she has read only 54 pages.

     (a)   What fraction of the number of pages has she read if there are 180 pages in the novel?

     (b)   What fraction does she still have to read ?

     Reduce each fraction to lowest terms.

Warm-Up

1. Carol completed reading 72 pages out of the total of 288.

     (a)   What fraction of the number of pages has she completed reading?

Solutions

     (a) $\dfrac{\text{Number of pages read (\textbf{Part})}}{\text{Total number of pages (\textbf{Total})}} = \dfrac{54}{180}.$

$$\dfrac{54}{180} = \dfrac{6 \cdot 9}{6 \cdot 30} = \dfrac{9}{30}$$

$$= \dfrac{\cancel{3} \cdot 3}{\cancel{3} \cdot 10} = \dfrac{3}{10}$$

Cathy has read $\dfrac{3}{10}$ of the total number of pages.

$\dfrac{3}{10}$ means 3 out of every 10 pages, or 3 tenths.

(b) What fraction does she still have to complete?

(b) She still has to read $(180 - 54)$ or 126 pages; so, the fraction of the book she still has to read

$$\begin{array}{r} 180 \\ -54 \\ \hline 126 \end{array}$$

$= \dfrac{126}{180}$ ⟵ Number of pages left to read
    ⟵ Total number of pages

$= \dfrac{2 \cdot 3 \cdot 3 \cdot 7}{2 \cdot 3 \cdot 3 \cdot 2 \cdot 5}$

$126 = 2 \cdot 63$
$\quad = 2 \cdot 3 \cdot 3 \cdot 7$
$180 = 2 \cdot 9 \cdot 10$
$\quad = 2 \cdot 3 \cdot 3 \cdot 2 \cdot 5$

$= \dfrac{7}{10}$.

Cathy still has to read $\dfrac{7}{10}$ of the total number of pages.

Answers:

1. (a) $\dfrac{1}{4}$ **(b)** $\dfrac{3}{4}$

3.8 B.   Translating Ratios, Rates, Percents to Fractions

* Fractions are also used to express the *ratio* of one quantity *to* another quantity.

  A ratio is a comparison of two numbers.

  Procedure for finding the *ratio* of one amount *to* another amount

  To find the ratio of a **first amount** to a **second amount**:

  1. Write the fraction: $\dfrac{\text{first amount}}{\text{second amount}}$

  2. Cancel the units.

  3. Reduce the fraction to lowest terms.

Warm-Up

2. Write the ratio of 250 to 375 in lowest form.

Example 2 Write the ratio of 234 to 36 in lowest terms.

Solution Since 234 appears first in the comparison, it is written in the numerator position.

234 to 36 $= \dfrac{234}{36}$ Write the ratio as a fraction.

$= \dfrac{13}{2}$ Simplify.

The ratio of 234 to 36 is $\dfrac{13}{2}$ (or $13 : 2$ or 13 to 2).

3. Jolley and Ela went on a picnic. Jolley spent \$35 and Ela spent \$20. Compare Jolley's expenditure to that of Ela's as a ratio.

Example 3 The length of a rod is 45 inches and that of another is 54 inches. Compare the length of the *second* rod to that of the *first* and express the result as a ratio.

Solution The length of the second rod, 54 in, is mentioned first in the ratio, so it is written first in the numerator position.

$$\text{Second rod to the first rod} = \frac{54 \text{ inches}}{45 \text{ inches}}$$ • Cancel the common units.

$$= \frac{54}{45} = \frac{2 \cdot \cancel{3} \cdot \cancel{3} \cdot 3}{\cancel{3} \cdot \cancel{3} \cdot 5} = \frac{6}{5}$$

The ratio of the length of second rod to the length of the first rod is 6 to 5.

• If different units of measure are used then we usually convert to the smaller unit before comparing amounts using fractions or ratios, as explained below in example 4 and 5.

Warm-Up

Example 4   Sophia spends 40 hours working each week. What is the ratio of time spent working to the total time in a week?

Solution $$\frac{40 \text{ hours}}{7 \text{ days}} = \frac{40 \text{ hours}}{7 \times 24 \text{ hours}} = \frac{40}{168}$$

$$= \frac{\cancel{8} \cdot 5}{\cancel{8} \cdot 21} = \frac{5}{21}$$

4. Ebony has spent 14 months out of the last 2 years in Jamaica. What fraction of the last two years has she spent in Jamaica?

Example 5   What is the ratio of 375 centimeters (cm) to 5 meters (m)?

Centimeters and meters are units of length measurement in the metric system. (1 meter = 100 cm).

5. Find the ratio of 256 cm to 2 m.
    (1 meter = 100 cm).

Solution $$\text{The desired ratio} = \frac{375 \text{ cm}}{5 \text{ m}}$$ • Here, we change units so that they are the same. There are 100 cm in 1 meter. It is convenient to change 5 m to cm:
5 m = 5 × 100 cm = 500 cm.

$$= \frac{375 \text{ cm}}{500 \text{ cm}}$$ • Drop the common unit and reduce the fraction.

$$= \frac{375}{500} = \frac{3 \cdot \cancel{5} \cdot \cancel{5} \cdot \cancel{5}}{2 \cdot 2 \cdot \cancel{5} \cdot \cancel{5} \cdot \cancel{5}}$$

$$= \frac{3}{4}$$

The reduced ratio is $\frac{3}{4}$ (or 3 : 4 , or 3 to 4).

Example 6   The opening soccer game at the new arena was attended by approximately 4,200 Caucasians, 3,600 African Americans, and 15,000 Hispanic Americans. Approximately 1,200 attended who were from other ethnic backgrounds.

   (a) What was the ratio of Hispanic Americans to the total who attended?

   (b) What was the ratio of African Americans to Hispanic Americans?

   (c) What fraction of the total were Caucasians?

6. The opening soccer game at the new arena was attended by approximately 3,600 Caucasians, 4,400 African Americans, and 12,000 Hispanic Americans. Approximately 700 attended who were from other ethnic backgrounds.

   (a) What was the ratio of Hispanic Americans to the total who attended?

Solutions

(a) The ratio of Hispanic Americans to **the total who attended.**

$$\frac{15,000}{4,200 + 3,600 + 15,000 + 1,200}$$

⟵ 1st number: Hispanic Americans
⟵ 2nd number: Total who attended.

$$= \frac{15,000}{24,000}$$

Both are divisible by 1,000.

$$= \frac{15 \cdot \cancel{1000}}{24 \cdot \cancel{1000}}$$

$$= \frac{15}{24} = \frac{3 \cdot \cancel{5}}{3 \cdot \cancel{8}} = \frac{5}{8}$$

Read: "There were 5 Hispanic Americans for every 8 who attended the game".

(b) What was the ratio of African Americans to Hispanic Americans?

(b) $$\frac{3,600}{15,000}$$ African Americans ⟵ 1st amount
Hispanic Americans ⟵ 2nd amount

Note: Both are divisible by 100.

$$= \frac{36 \cdot \cancel{100}}{150 \cdot \cancel{100}}$$

$$= \frac{2 \cdot \cancel{2} \cdot \cancel{3} \cdot 3}{\cancel{2} \cdot \cancel{3} \cdot 5 \cdot 5} = \frac{6}{25}$$ African Americans
Hispanic Americans

Read: 6 African Americans to (every) 25 Hispanic Americans.

(c) What fraction of the total were Caucasians?

(c) What fraction of the total were Caucasians?

$$\frac{4,200}{24,000}$$ Caucasians ⟵ Part represented
Total ⟵ Total amount

Note: Both are divisible by 100.

$$= \frac{42 \cdot \cancel{100}}{240 \cdot \cancel{100}}$$

$$= \frac{\cancel{2} \cdot \cancel{3} \cdot 7}{2 \cdot 2 \cdot \cancel{2} \cdot \cancel{2} \cdot \cancel{3} \cdot 5} = \frac{7}{40}$$

Read: 7 fortieths of the total were Caucasians.

- **Rates are** ratios that involve amounts having different units, as explained below in Example 7.

Warm-Up

7. 180 students attended the event. There were 45 cars in the student parking lot. What was the ratio of students to cars?

Example 7 150 students attended the event. There were 60 cars in the student parking lot. What was the ratio of students to cars?

Solution

$$\text{Ratio of the students to the cars} = \frac{150 \text{ students}}{60 \text{ cars}}$$

$$= \frac{15 \text{ students}}{6 \text{ cars}} = \frac{3 \cdot 5 \text{ students}}{3 \cdot 2 \text{ cars}} = \frac{5 \text{ students}}{2 \text{ cars}}$$

Read : 5 students for every 2 cars.

This is a *rate* comparing students to cars.

- **Unit Rates** are special kinds of rates, where one quantity is compared to a single unit of another quantity. This concept is used in many real life situations as explained in example 8 and 9.

Unit Rates are often used to indicate *division* of a total amount by a number of equal parts.

Example 8 Samuel paid $140 for 7 tickets for a concert. What was the cost per ticket?

Solution What was the cost per ticket?

"Per" means "for each".

In this question, cost (1st amount) is being compared to the tickets (2nd amount).

$$\frac{\text{cost}}{\text{number of tickets}} = \frac{\$140}{7 \text{ tickets}} = \frac{\$20}{1 \text{ ticket}}$$

or $20 per ticket.

Example 9 Seven gallons of milk was shared equally by 5 persons. How much did each person receive?

Solution

$$\text{Share of each person} = \frac{\text{amount}}{\text{number of people}}$$

$$= \frac{7 \text{ gallons}}{5 \text{ persons}}$$

$$= 1\frac{2}{5} \text{ gallons/person.}$$

- Fractions are often used to express **probability**, a measure of the likelihood that an event will take place. The probability that an event occurs $= \dfrac{\text{Number of successful outcomes}}{\text{Total possible outcomes}}$

This is demonstrated in the following example.

Example 10 Before the last game of the season, the hockey team had won 8 games, tied 2 games, and lost 2 games. Based on these outcomes, what is the probability that the final game will be won?

Solution

$$\frac{\text{Number of wins}}{\text{Total games}} = \frac{8}{8 + 2 + 2}$$

Warm-Up

8. Samuel paid $160 for 32 friends to be admitted to the concert. What was the cost per ticket?

9. Three pies are split equally by four friends. How much should each receive?

Warm-Up

10. In a sample of 50 alumni families, 10 had no children; 9 had 1 child; 12 had 2 children; 15 had 3 children; 4 had 4 or more children. Find the probability of an alumni having a family with 2 or fewer children.

Answers:

2. $\dfrac{2}{3}$ 3. 7 to 4   4. $\dfrac{7}{12}$

5. $\dfrac{32}{25}$ 6. (a) $\dfrac{40}{69}$ (b) $\dfrac{11}{30}$ (c) $\dfrac{4}{23}$

7. $\dfrac{4}{1}$ 8. $5 per ticket

9. $\dfrac{3}{4}$ pic per person   10. $\dfrac{31}{50}$

$$= \frac{8}{12} = \frac{2}{3} = \text{ probability that the final game will be done.}$$

Read: "two-thirds" or "2 out of 3".

• Percents as Fractions

A very common use of fractions in everyday life is percents. To understand percents, it is necessary to think of them as fractions.

"Per**cent**" literally means "per **100**".

$$3\% \text{ means 3 per 100 or } \frac{3}{100}.$$

Warm-Up

11. Express the statement below as a fraction in lowest terms.

   (a) The pilots contributed 2% of their salaries to the company buy-out.

   (b) The population increased 10% in 5 years.

Examples 11 Express the statement below as a fraction in lowest terms.

(a)   60% of American households own their homes.

(b)   The sales tax is 5%.

Solutions

(a) $60\% = \dfrac{60}{100} = \dfrac{3 \cdot \mathbf{20}}{5 \cdot \mathbf{20}} = \dfrac{3}{5}.$

Three-fifths of American households own their homes.

OR

Three out of every five American households own their homes.

Answers:

11. (a) The pilots contributed $\frac{1}{50}$ of their salaries.

     OR

    The pilots contributed 1 dollar out of every 50 dollars in their salaries.

(b) The population increased by $\frac{1}{10}$ in five years.

     OR

    There was 1 additional person for every 10 people in the original population after five years.

(b) $5\% = \dfrac{5}{100} = \dfrac{\mathbf{5} \cdot 1}{\mathbf{5} \cdot 20} = \dfrac{1}{20}$ ← Tax
                                                  ← Purchases

The sales tax is $\dfrac{1}{20}$ of the purchase price.

OR

$1 in sale tax is paid for every $20 purchased.

Exercise 3.8

In exercises 1-14, express the results in lowest terms.

1.   Deandra solved 15 problems out of 75 problems assigned. What fraction of the problems has she solved?

2.   Linda solved 12 exercises out of a total of 54. What fraction of the exercises has she solved?

3. Brenda spent $35 out of $120 she had in her purse. What fraction (in lowest terms) of her money in the purse did she spend?

4. The library of the local church receives 43 new books and 58 used books as a donation. What fraction of the books received are new?

5. The college library received 231 new books and 363 used books as a donation. What fraction of the books received were used?

6. If you had $35 and you spent $14 to buy a shirt, what fraction of money did you spend for the shirt? What fraction do you still have?

7. If your credit card limit is $3,000 and the bank statement indicates $2,781 is due, what fraction of the limit is already used?

8. In a class of 40, 12 students received an A. What fraction of the class did not receive an A?

9. In a class of 30, five students received an A and six students a B. What fraction of the class received less than a B?

10. In a class of 33, six students received an A, ten students a B, and nine students a C. What fraction of the class received less than a C?

11. In a math class there are 45 students; 23 of them are male. What fraction of the class is male students?

12. There are 27 students in a pre-algebra class and 18 are female. What fraction of the class is female? What fraction of the class is male?

13. Out of the total of 3,540 students in a college, 2,736 are receiving financial aid. What fraction of students are paying their own educational expenses?

14. Helen has 10 pennies, 5 nickels, 7 dimes, and 12 quarters. What fraction of the total number of coins is in pennies? What fraction of the total value of the coins is in dimes?

In exercises 15-22, write the ratio in lowest terms.

15. 32 to 8

16. 15 to 55

17. $35 to $15

18. 150 to 135

19. 25 ft to 10 ft

20. 120 m to 80 m

21. 195 yd to 270 yd

22. 140 cm to 245 cm

In exercises 23-34, convert the units to similar units and then find the ratio in lowest terms.

Note: 1m = 100 cm, 1yd = 3ft, 1 ft = 12 in

23. 5 m to 35 cm

24. 115 cm to 69 m

25. $25 to 35 dimes

26. 40 dimes to 15 dollars

27. 12 ft to 60 in

28. 13 yd to 91 ft

29. 50 ft to 30 yd

30. 21 dollars to 150 nickels

31. 42 dimes to 280 nickels

32. $12 to 25 pennies

33. 20 yd to 144 in

34. 180 in to 45 yd

35. Two hundred forty students attended an event. There were only 120 cars in the parking lot. What is the ratio of students to cars?

36. A group of 340 persons attending a party reserved all 85 rooms of a hotel. What is the ratio of persons to hotel rooms?

37. Sharman paid $385 for 55 tickets. What was the cost per ticket?

38. Jackson paid $371 for 7 shirts. What was the cost per shirt?

In exercises 39-44, find the cost per item.

39. $585 for 15 items

40. $380 for 19 items

41. $1,284 for 12 items

42. $5,842 for 23 items

43. $1,554 for 42 items

44. $4,984 for 89 items

In exercises 45-48, find the number of miles per gallon of gasoline if you travel:

45. 630 miles on 35 gallons

46. 255 miles on 15 gallons

47. 350 miles on 14 gallons

48. 324 miles on 12 gallons

49. In a sample of 75 students who completed pre-algebra course last semester, 10 received an A; 25 a B; 15 a C; and others received a D, F, or W. Find the probability that a particular student from the same group received:

    (a) C   **(b)** A   **(c)** D, W, or F   **(d)** B

50. Before the last game of the season, the hockey team had won 6 games, tied 3 games, and lost 3 games. What is the probability that the final game will be won?

51. In a sample of 150 alumni families, 25 had no children, 42 had one child, 31 had two children, 40 had three children, and 12 had four or more children. Find the probability of an alumni having a family with:

    (a) 2 children   **(b)** four or more children   **(c)** three or more children

    (d) two or more children   **(e)** three or fewer children

In exercises 52-60, find what fraction of the figure is shaded.

52.

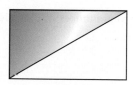

53.

54.

55.

56.

57.

58.

59.

60.

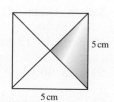

In exercise 61-64, re-word the statement below using a fraction in lowest terms.

61. 28 % of the college students were receiving grants.

62. The tuition rose 15 % in one year.

63. 2 % of the milk is fat.

64. Health insurance pays 80% of the patient's bill.

65. Eight of 32 students in a class received an A. What percent of the class received an A?
(**Hint:** Find, what fraction received an A grade. Then change the fraction to an equivalent fraction with a

denominator of 100. $\frac{a}{100} = a\%$).

66. Twelve out of 60 persons at a party were female. What percent of the persons at the party were female?

67. Fifteen out of 25 students in a class are 25 years or older. What percent of the class is younger than 25 years?

68. In Atlanta, Georgia, there are 50 lawyers for every 1000 people. What is the ratio of lawyers to people? Express the result in lowest terms.

69. Mark earns $60,000 per year and spends $9,000 for maintaining his car. What is the ratio of car expenses to his annual income ?

70. A jet flies 3,600 miles in 6 hours. What is the speed in miles per hour ?

71. Light travels 44,000 miles in 4 seconds. What is the speed of light, in miles per second ?

72. On a map, the distance of 1,764 miles from New York to Denver is 14 cm. Determine the scale of the map.
(Scale means number of miles per cm).

73. Allen College has 100 teachers for every 3,000 students.
   (a) Write the student teacher ratio as a fraction. Reduce the fraction to its lowest terms.
   (b) How large is the faculty, if the school has 2,100 students ?

74. An angle measures 30°.
   (a) Determine the complement of this angle.
   (b) Write the ratio of 30° to its complement as a fraction reduced to lowest terms.

75. An angle measures 120°.
   (a) Determine the supplement of this angle.
   (b) Write the ratio of 120° to its supplement as a fraction reduced to its lowest terms.

76. Samuel spends 8 hours working and 2 hours commuting each day.
   (a) Find the fraction of time spent working to total time spent in a day.
   (b) Find the ratio of time spent in commuting to the time spent in working and commuting.

77. A lawn mower uses a mixture of gasoline and oil. If the tank holds 5 gallons of the mixture containing 2 gallons of oil, find the ratio of the oil to the gasoline.

78. In the 1960 United States presidential election, John F. Kennedy received 303 electoral votes. That was 84 more than the votes for Richard M. Nixon. Write the fraction of the votes received by Nixon to the votes received by Kennedy, reduced to lowest terms.

79. At this time Kathy is 15 years old and Linda is 10 years old. Write the ratio of Linda's age five years later to Kathy's age as a fraction reduced to lowest terms.

80. A family of four members equally shared 14 gallons of milk in two weeks. How much did each member consume weekly ?

81. A strip of paper 48 inches long is cut into two pieces. If the smaller piece is 12 inches, what fraction of the strip is the smaller piece ?

3.9 CHAPTER SUMMARY

| Part I | **Important Terms and Symbols** |

1. **Divisor** and **divisible:** In the true statement $48 \div 6 = 8$; 6 is a **divisor** of 48 ; 48 is **divisible** by 6.

2. **Factor:** In the true statement $48 = 6 \cdot 8$; 6 and 8 are *factors* of 48.

3. **Even integers** are divisible by 2. Every *even* integer can be expressed in the form **2n** where *n* is any integer, positive or negative, even or odd.
$$26 = 2 \cdot \mathbf{13} \; ; \quad 48 = 2 \cdot \mathbf{24} \; ; \quad -34 = 2 \cdot \mathbf{(-17)}$$

4. **Odd integers** are not divisible by 2. Every *odd* integer can be expressed in the form **2n + 1** where *n* is any integer.
$$35 = 2 \cdot \mathbf{17} + 1 \; ; \quad -71 = 2 \cdot \mathbf{(-36)} + 1 \; ; \quad 1 = 2 \cdot \mathbf{0} + 1$$

5. A **prime number** is a whole number greater than 1 with **exactly two** different factors or divisors, 1 and the number itself.

   1 is not a prime number.

   2 is the smallest prime number.

6. A **composite number** is a whole number with **more than two** different factors. Every even number other than 2 is a composite number.

   2 is the only number which is both *even* and *prime*. All other even numbers are composite numbers.

   The whole numbers 0 and 1 are neither prime nor composite.

7. **Prime factorization** is a process of expressing a number as a product of prime factors.
$$24 = 2 \cdot 2 \cdot 2 \cdot 3 \quad \text{is the prime factorization of } 24.$$

8. **The Sieve of Eratosthenes** is a technique developed by the famous Greek mathematician Eratosthenes that helps in finding prime numbers.

9. **The Fundamental Theorem of Arithmetic** states that every composite number has exactly one prime factorization.

10. **Multiple:** The first five multiples of 6 are 6, 12, 18, 24, and 30 since:
$$6 \cdot \mathbf{1} = 6 \, , \quad 6 \cdot \mathbf{2} = 12 \, , \quad 6 \cdot \mathbf{3} = 18 \, , \quad 6 \cdot \mathbf{4} = 24 \, , \quad 6 \cdot \mathbf{5} = 30.$$

11. **LCM** is the abbreviation for the **Least Common Multiple**.

12. A **fraction,** such as $\frac{3}{5}$ (read as **three-fifths**) is the name for a number. A fraction has three components: the numerator, the denominator, and the fraction bar.

    Fraction bar $\longleftarrow \dfrac{\mathbf{13}}{\mathbf{15}} \begin{array}{l} \longrightarrow \text{Numerator} \\ \longrightarrow \text{Denominator} \end{array}$

13. A **rational number** is the *technical* name for any number that can be written as a fraction.

> **Definition:** A rational number is a number that can be written in the form $\dfrac{a}{b}$, where a and b are integers, and $b \neq 0$.

Every integer is also a rational number: $\quad 3 = \dfrac{3}{1} \; ; \quad 0 = \dfrac{0}{1} \; ; \quad -5 = \dfrac{-5}{1}$

14. **Building a fraction** means to write an equivalent fraction whose denominator is a multiple of the denominator of the original fraction.

15. **Reducing a fraction** means to write an equivalent fraction such that the numerator and the denominator have no common factor, except 1.

16. A **proper fraction** is a fraction whose numerator has an absolute value smaller than the absolute value of the denominator.

$$\dfrac{3}{4}, \dfrac{4}{5}, \text{ and } \dfrac{-3}{7} \text{ are proper fractions.}$$

17. An **improper fraction** is a fraction whose numerator has an absolute value larger than or equal to the absolute value of the denominator.

$$\dfrac{4}{3}, \dfrac{-7}{5}, \text{ and } 4 \text{ are improper fractions.}$$

18. A **mixed number** is the sum of a whole number and a proper fraction, written without the plus symbol in between. $2 + \dfrac{2}{3} \; \rightarrow \; \mathbf{2\dfrac{2}{3}}$.

Part II Procedure and Rules

Examples

CRITERIA FOR DIVISIBILITY

1. **Divisibility by 2:** A number is divisible by 2 if its ones digit is even.

   1. 878,50**6** is divisible by 2.

      15,73**5** is not divisible by 2.

2. **Divisibility by 3:** A number is divisible by 3 if the sum of its digits is divisible by 3.

   2. 4,872 is divisible by 3.
      The sum of the digits is 21.

3. **Divisibility by 4:** A number is divisible by 4 if the last two digits are zeros or form a number divisible by 4.

   3. 75,**400** is divisible by 4.

      145,**372** is divisible by 4.

      43,**926** is not divisible by 4.

4. **Divisibility by 5:** A number is divisible by 5 if its last digit is either 0 or 5.

   4. 84,25**0** is divisible by 5.

      293,71**5** is divisible by 5.

      462**9** is not divisible by 5.

5. 325,**000** is divisible by 8.

29,**376** is divisible by 8.

735,**474** is not divisible by 8.

6. 50,391 is divisible by 9;
the sum of the digits is 18.

478, 301, 956 is not divisible by 9;
the sum of the digits is 43.

7. 2,5**70** is divisible by 10.

930,2**58** is not divisible by 10.

8. 25**75** is divisible by 25.
273**40** is not divisible by 25.

9. 5,270,1**50** is divisible by 50.
7,234,2**25** is not divisible by 50.

10. 3,754,**500** is divisible by 100.
352,7**90** is not divisible by 100.

11. 3,438 is divisible by 6 because the last digit is 8(even) and the sum of digits (18) is divisible by 3.

12. 5,724 is divisible by 12 because the last two digits are divisible by 4 and the sum of digits (18) is divisible by 3.

13. 433,725 is divisible by 15 because the last digit is 5 and the sum of digits (24) is divisible by 3.

14. The 15th multiple of 237 $= 15 \times 237$
$= 3,555.$

15. To determine whether 1,344 is a multiple of 6, use the divisibility criteria for 2 and 3.

1,344 is divisible by 2;

1,344 is divisible by 3;

so, 1,344 is divisible by 6.

16. (a) 75 is a composite number as it is divisible by 5.

   (b) 121 is a composite numbers because
$$121 \div 11 = 11 \text{ R } 0$$
↑

5. **Divisibility by 8:** A number is divisible by 8 if the last three digits are zeros or form a number divisible by 8.

6. **Divisibility by 9:** A number is divisible by 9 if the sum of its digits is divisible by 9.

7. **Divisibility by 10:** A number is divisible by 10 if its ones digit is 0.

8. **Divisibility by 25:** A number is divisible by 25 if its last two digits (ones and tens) are 25 or 50, or 75 or 00.

9. **Divisibility by 50:** A number is divisible by 50 if its last two digits are 50 or 00.

10. **Divisibility by 100:** A number is divisible by 100 if its last two digits are 00.

11. **Divisibility by 6:** A number is divisible by 6 if it is divisible both by 2 and 3.

12. **Divisibility by 12:** A number is divisible by 12 if it is divisible both by 3 and 4.

13. **Divisibility by 15:** A number is divisible by 15 if it is divisible both by 3 and 5.

MULTIPLES AND FACTORS

14. To find the nth multiple of a natural number, multiply the natural number by n.

15. To determine whether a natural number is a multiple of another natural number, determine whether the first number is divisible by the second.

PRIME FACTORS

16. To determine whether a number is prime or composite, divide the number by the prime numbers 2, 3, 5, 7, 11, 13, ... Use the divisibility tests for 2, 3, 5, ... one by one, until :

Examples

1. You find a remainder of 0. This will mean that the number is a composite number.

OR

2. You find a quotient smaller than the prime divisor. This will mean that the number is a prime number.

(c) To determine whether 157 is prime or a composite

(i) 157 is not divisible by 2, 3, and 5.

(ii) Divide by 7, 11, 13, ….

$$157 \div 7 = 22 \text{ R } 3$$
— larger than 7

$$157 \div 11 = 14 \text{ R } 3$$
— larger than 11

$$157 \div 13 = 12 \text{ R } 1;$$
— smaller than the divisor 13

so, 157 is a prime number.

17. To find the prime factorization of a composite number:

Step **1** Factor the given number into any two factors.

Step **2** Factor each factor (in step 1) that is not a prime.

Step **3** Continue the process until all the factors are prime.

The **prime factorization** is the product of all the prime factors.

17. $72 = \quad 8 \cdot 9$

$= 4 \cdot 2 \cdot 3 \cdot 3$

$= 2 \cdot 2 \cdot 2 \cdot 3 \cdot 3;$

so, the prime factorization of 72 is

$72 = 2 \cdot 2 \cdot 2 \cdot 3 \cdot 3$ or $2^3 \cdot 3^2$.

18. To find all the factors (divisors) of a composite number:

Step **1** List all the factor pairs, in order, starting with 1 times the number.

Step **2** List all the factors that appear in the factor pairs.

18. To find all the factors (divisors) of 154:

$$154 = 1 \cdot 154$$
$$= 2 \cdot 77$$
$$= 7 \cdot 22$$
$$= 11 \cdot 14$$

The factors of 154 are 1, 2, 7, 11, 14, 22, 77, 154.

FINDING THE LEAST COMMON MULTIPLE (LCM)

19. To find the LCM of a set of integers or algebraic terms.

Step **1** Find the prime factorization of each number or algebraic term.

Step **2** Start with the prime factorization of the first number or the first term.

Step **3** Check each number in turn and write down any factor in its prime factorization that is not yet included.

Step **4** The LCM is the product of all the identified factors.

19. (a) To find the LCM of 45, 36, and 75:

$$45 = 3 \cdot 3 \cdot 5$$
$$36 = 2 \cdot 2 \cdot 3 \cdot 3$$
$$75 = 3 \cdot 5 \cdot 5$$
$$LCM = 3 \cdot 3 \cdot 5 \cdot 2 \cdot 2 \cdot 5$$
$$= 2^2 \cdot 3^2 \cdot 5^2 \text{ or } 900.$$

(b) To find the LCM of $27x^2y^3$, $36xy$, $54y^2z$:

$$27x^2y^3 = 3 \cdot 3 \cdot 3 \cdot x \cdot x \cdot y \cdot y \cdot y$$
$$36xy = 2 \cdot 2 \cdot 3 \cdot 3 \cdot x \cdot y$$
$$54y^2z = 2 \cdot 3 \cdot 3 \cdot 3 \cdot y \cdot y \cdot z$$

$$LCM = 3 \cdot 3 \cdot 3 \cdot x \cdot x \cdot y \cdot y \cdot y \cdot 2 \cdot 2 \cdot z$$
$$= 2^2 \cdot 3^3 \cdot x^2 \cdot y^3 \cdot z$$
$$= 108x^2y^3z$$

20.

- $\dfrac{3}{4}$, $\dfrac{-2}{3}$, $\dfrac{5}{-7}$, $-\dfrac{9}{11}$ are all fractions or rational numbers.

- $\xrightarrow{\quad} \dfrac{-5}{7} \begin{array}{l} \longrightarrow \text{Numerator} \\ \longrightarrow \text{Denominator} \end{array}$

  Fraction bar

- $\dfrac{5}{-7} = (-5) \div (7)$

- Fractions $\dfrac{5}{0}$ and $\dfrac{-7}{0}$ are not defined; therefore, they cannot be listed as rational numbers.

21. Which of the following are rational numbers?

$$-\dfrac{3}{5} \; ; \; \dfrac{7}{0} \; ; \; -\dfrac{9}{-4} \; ; \; \dfrac{15}{377} \; .$$

All ratios except $\dfrac{7}{0}$ are rational numbers.

Recall that $-3 = \dfrac{-3}{1}$

22. Graph the following fractions on a number line:

   (a) $\dfrac{13}{5}$ **(b)** $-\dfrac{10}{4}$

(a)

- Since the fraction is positive, its graph lies on the right side of 0.
- Divide each unit into 5 pieces since the denominator is 5.

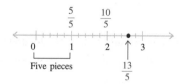

(b)

- Since the fraction is negative, its graph lies to the left of 0.

- Divide each unit into four pieces, since the denominator is 4.

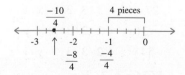

RATIONAL NUMBERS: IDENTIFYING AND GRAPHING

20. • The ratio of two integers is called a fraction or a rational number.

- A fraction has three components:
  the numerator;
  the denominator; and
  the fraction bar.

- The fraction bar separates the numerator and the denominator and also serves as a sign for division.

- A fraction or a rational number is not defined if the denominator is 0.

21. To identify rational numbers is to identify a number equal to the ratio of two integers with non-zero denominator.

22. Graphing rational numbers.

PROCESS

- Determine the sign of the rational number.

- Divide each unit on the number line into as many pieces as the number in the denominator.

- Count the number of pieces equal to the number in the numerator to the right of 0, if the fraction is positive, or to the left if the fraction is negative.

- Identify the end of that piece and mark it with a solid dot.

BUILDING AND REDUCING FRACTIONS

23. To build a fraction: multiply both the numerator and the denominator by the same non-zero number.

23. To build $\dfrac{3}{5}$ to a fraction with a denominator of 15:

Since $15 \div 5 = 3$, we multiply and divide by 3.

$$\frac{3}{5} = \frac{3 \cdot \mathbf{3}}{5 \cdot \mathbf{3}}$$

$$= \frac{\mathbf{9}}{\mathbf{15}}$$

24. To reduce a given fraction:

Step 1   Find a common factor of the numerator and the denominator by inspection or using the divisibility tests. Rewrite the numerator and denominator in factored form.

Step 2   Cancel the common factor(s).

Step 3   Repeat Steps 1 and 2, and continue until there is no common divisor in the numerator and the denominator.

24. To reduce $\dfrac{525}{1,125}$:

$$\frac{525}{1,125} = \frac{\cancel{25} \cdot 21}{\cancel{25} \cdot 45} \qquad \text{Both are divisible by 25.}$$

$$= \frac{\cancel{3} \cdot 7}{\cancel{3} \cdot 15} \qquad \text{Both are divisible by 3.}$$

$$= \frac{7}{15}$$

LEAST COMMON DENOMINATORS; COMPARING FRACTIONS

25. The Least Common Denominator (LCD) of two or more fractions is the Least Common Multiple (LCM) of the denominators.

25. Find the LCD of $\dfrac{2}{3}$, $\dfrac{4}{5}$, and $\dfrac{7}{10}$.

$$\text{LCD} = \text{LCM of } 3, 5, 10$$
$$3 = 3$$
$$5 = 5$$
$$10 = 2 \cdot 5$$
$$\text{LCM} = 2 \cdot 5 \cdot 3$$
$$= 30$$
$$\text{LCD} = 30$$

26. Procedure to change a group of fractions to equivalent fractions using the LCD:

Step 1   Find the LCD of the given fractions.

Step 2   Build each fraction to an equivalent fraction having the LCD as the denominator.

26. Change the following fractions to equivalent fractions with the LCD as the denominator:

$$\frac{5}{12}, \frac{7}{15}, \frac{-9}{10}.$$

$$\text{LCD} = \text{LCM of } 12, 15, \text{ and } 10 = 60.$$

$$\frac{5}{12} = \frac{5}{12} \cdot \frac{\mathbf{5}}{\mathbf{5}} = \frac{\mathbf{25}}{\mathbf{60}} \qquad 60 \div 12 = 5$$

$$\frac{7}{15} = \frac{7}{15} \cdot \frac{\mathbf{4}}{\mathbf{4}} = \frac{\mathbf{28}}{\mathbf{60}} \qquad 60 \div 15 = 4$$

$$\frac{-9}{10} = \frac{-9}{10} \cdot \frac{\mathbf{6}}{\mathbf{6}} = \frac{\mathbf{-54}}{\mathbf{60}} \qquad 60 \div 10 = 6$$

Thus, the equivalent fractions are:

$$\frac{25}{60}, \frac{28}{60}, \frac{-54}{60}.$$

Examples

27. $\dfrac{7}{5} > \dfrac{3}{5}$ because $7 > 3$

$\dfrac{-7}{5} < \dfrac{-4}{5}$ because $-7 < -4$

Think??

- Identify which of the following two fractions is larger:

$$\dfrac{3}{8} \text{ or } \dfrac{5}{12}$$

- LCD of 8 and 12 = 24

$$\dfrac{3}{8} \cdot \dfrac{3}{3} = \dfrac{9}{24}$$

$$\dfrac{5}{12} \cdot \dfrac{2}{2} = \dfrac{10}{24}$$

Since $\dfrac{10}{24} > \dfrac{9}{24}$, therefore $\dfrac{5}{12} > \dfrac{3}{8}$.

28. Identify if the following two fractions are equivalent:

$$\dfrac{24}{160}, \dfrac{45}{300}$$

$$\dfrac{24}{160} \underset{\diagdown}{\overset{\diagup}{\times}} \dfrac{45}{300} \longrightarrow 7200$$
$$\longrightarrow 7200$$

Since cross products are equal, fractions are equivalent.

29. Arrange the following group of fractions in descending order:

$$\dfrac{3}{4}, \dfrac{5}{12}, \dfrac{7}{8}, \dfrac{9}{16}$$

LCD = LCM of 4, 12, 8, and 16 = 48

$$\dfrac{3}{4} \cdot \dfrac{12}{12} = \dfrac{36}{48} \qquad 48 \div 4 = 12$$

$$\dfrac{5}{12} \cdot \dfrac{4}{4} = \dfrac{20}{48} \qquad 48 \div 12 = 4$$

$$\dfrac{7}{8} \cdot \dfrac{6}{6} = \dfrac{42}{48} \qquad 48 \div 8 = 6$$

$$\dfrac{9}{16} \cdot \dfrac{3}{3} = \dfrac{27}{48} \qquad 48 \div 16 = 3$$

By comparing the numerators of the equivalent fractions we arrange the fraction in descending order.

$$\dfrac{42}{48}, \dfrac{36}{48}, \dfrac{27}{48}, \dfrac{20}{48} \quad \text{OR}$$

$$\dfrac{7}{8}, \dfrac{3}{4}, \dfrac{9}{16}, \dfrac{5}{12}$$

27. Comparing two fractions:

- Two fractions having the same denominator can be compared by comparing their numerators.

- If the denominators are not the same then we use the following steps:

    ***Step* 1** Build the given fractions to equivalent fractions with LCD as the common denominator.

    ***Step* 2** Compare the new fractions.

28. To check the equivalence of two ratios or fractions:

Compute the cross products. If equivalent, the cross products will be identical.

29. To arrange a group of fractions in descending (decreasing) or ascending (increasing) order.

***Step* 1**   Find the LCD of all the fractions in the group.

***Step* 2**   Build each fraction to an equivalent fraction with the LCD as the common denominator.

***Step* 3**   Arrange the new fractions in the desired order of numerators.

***Step* 4**   Replace each new fraction by the original fraction.

Introduction to Mixed Fractions	**Examples**

30. To graph a positive mixed number, like $3\frac{3}{5}$, we move 3 units to the right of the origin on a number line, divide the 4th unit into five equal pieces, and mark the third piece of the fourth unit as the graph of $3\frac{3}{5}$.

30. Graph $2\frac{2}{3}$ on a number line.

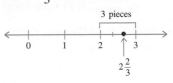

31. To graph a negative mixed number, like $-2\frac{4}{5}$, we move 2 units to the left of the origin, divide the next unit to the left in five equal pieces, and mark the 4th piece as the graph of $-2\frac{4}{5}$.

31. Graph $-3\frac{2}{5}$ on a number line.

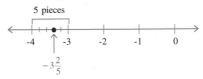

32. To change mixed number to an improper fraction:

$$a\frac{b}{c} = \frac{a \cdot c + b}{c}$$

$$5 \overset{5 \cdot 7 + 4}{\underset{5 \cdot 7}{\diagdown}} \frac{4}{7} = \frac{5 \cdot 7 + 4}{7}$$

$$= \frac{39}{7}$$

32. Change the following mixed number to an improper fraction:

(a) $5\frac{3}{4}$ **(b)** $-4\frac{3}{5}$

(a) $5\frac{3}{4} = \frac{5 \cdot 4 + 3}{4} = \frac{23}{4}$

(b) $-4\frac{3}{5} = -\left(4\frac{3}{5}\right)$

$$= -\left(\frac{4 \cdot 5 + 3}{5}\right) = -\frac{23}{4}$$

33. To convert an improper fraction to a mixed number, divide the numerator with the denominator. Find the quotient and the remainder, thus:

$$\frac{\text{Numerator}}{\text{Denominator}} = \text{Quotient}\,\frac{\text{Remainder}}{\text{Denominator}}.$$

33. Convert $\frac{35}{9}$ to a mixed number.

$$35 \div 9 = 3\,\text{R}\,8$$

$$\frac{35}{9} = 3 + \frac{8}{9}$$

$$= 3\frac{8}{9}$$

Translating English Expressions to Mathematical Expressions Involving Fractions

34. To translate an English expression to a fraction:
- Read carefully to determine what part of the total the fraction should represent:
- Write: $\dfrac{\text{Part represented}}{\text{Total amount}}$
- Reduce the fraction.

34. 15 out of 40 students in a class are overweight. What fraction of the class is overweight?

$$\frac{15}{40} = \frac{3}{10}$$

35. To find the ratio of one amount to the second amount:
- Write the fraction: $\dfrac{\text{First amount}}{\text{Second amount}}$.
- Cancel the units if they are the same.
- Reduce the fraction to lowest terms.

35. The length of a rod is 60 inches and that of another is 75 inches. Compare the length of the first rod to the second rod and express the result as a ratio.

$$\frac{60 \text{ inches}}{75 \text{ inches}} = \frac{4}{5}$$

36. (a) Linda paid $210 for 15 tickets. What is the price per ticket?

$$\frac{\$210}{15 \text{ tickets}} = \$14 \text{ per ticket}$$

(b) 52% of the children are receiving subsidized lunches.

$$52\% = \frac{52}{100} = \frac{4 \cdot 13}{4 \cdot 25} = \frac{13}{25}.$$

13 out of every 25 children are receiving subsidized lunches.

37. If 12 out of 24 students study during the weekend, what percent of students study during the weekend?

$$\frac{12}{24} = \frac{1}{2}$$

$$= \frac{1}{2} \cdot \frac{50}{50} = \frac{50}{100} = \mathbf{50}\ \%$$

36. • Ratios that involve amounts having different units are called **rates**.

• Unit rates are computed by dividing the total amount by the number of equal parts.

37. If the denominator of a fraction or a ratio is 100 then the ratio can be written as a **percent.**

• Ratios or fractions can be converted to percents by building the fraction to higher terms, with the new denominator equal to 100.

3.10   REVIEW EXERCISE

In exercises 1-6, use divisibility tests to determine whether the given integer is divisible by 2, 3, 4, 5, 9, 10, 25, 50, or 100.

1. 5,525   **2.** −8,100   **3.** 2,754   **4.** 1,193   **5.** 33,006   **6.** 4,712

In exercises 7-14, determine the divisibility of the given number as indicated:

7. −5,718 by 6 and 8   **8.** 23,970 by 3 and 9   **9.** 3,244 by 4 and 16   **10.** 7,356 by 12 and 15

11. 722,348 by 8 and 12   **12.** 76,905 by 5 and 10   **13.** 103,140 by 3 and 5   **14.** 635,025 by 6 and 15

In exercises 15-20, determine whether the given number is a multiple of 3, 7, or 13.

15. 7,707   **16.** 23,265   **17.** 3,822   **18.** 13,013   **19.** 69,433   **20.** −36,582

In exercises 21-32, determine by inspection whether the given number is even or odd, and then express it in the form $2n$ or $2n + 1$ as the case may be.

21. 7,894   **22.** 756   **23.** 87   **24.** 95   **25.** 438   **26.** 246

27. 367   **28.** 953   **29.** 173   **30.** 560   **31.** −801   **32.** 326

In exercises 33-38, determine whether the first number is a multiple of the other.

33. 235 ; 7   **34.** 1,201 ; 11   **35.** −865 ; 15   **36.** −434 ; 14   **37.** 72,936 ; 9   **38.** 24,386 ; 6

In exercises 39-42, determine whether the given number divides (is a factor of) the given product.

39. 14 ; 2·2·3·5·7   **40.** 63 ; 2·3·6·8·11   **41.** 36 ; 3·4·5·6·7·8   **42.** 54 ; 4·5·9·3·7

In exercises 43-49, determine whether the given number is prime or composite.

43. 567   **44.** 257   **45.** 407   **46.** 7,950   **47.** 109   **48.** 2,717   **49.** 89

In exercises 50-56, find the prime factorization of the given number.

50. 315   **51.** 294   **52.** 2,200   **53.** 40,320   **54.** 309   **55.** 1,080   **56.** 120

In exercises 57-64, use prime factorization to write the given number as a product of two factors in all possible ways. Then list all factors of the number.

57. 30   **58.** 22   **59.** 120   **60.** 65   **61.** 165   **62.** 24   **63.** 71   **64.** 505

In exercises 65-69, (a) find the LCM of each group of numbers, and (b) state the number of times each divides into the LCM.

65. 45, 36, 52   **66.** 12, 18, 27   **67.** 4, 14, 35   **68.** 6, 12, 24, 30   **69.** 30, 60, 90

In exercises 70-75, find the LCM of the given algebraic terms.

70. $16a, 4a^2$ **71.** $20x, 15x^2, 60$ **72.** $75ab^2, 40abc$ **73.** $12xy^2, 21yz^2, 28xyz$

74. $65x^2z^3, 55xy^2z, 25xy, 35x^3y^3$ **75.** $22x^2, 44xy^2, 121xy$

76. Which of the following numbers are not defined as a rational number?

$$-5; \ 4; \ \frac{-9}{7}; \ \frac{91}{0}; \ -\frac{-14}{-8}; \ \frac{8}{3-3}.$$

77. Which of the following expressions are not defined as a rational expression?

$$\frac{2x}{4}; \ \frac{9}{7x}; \ -\frac{4}{-5x}; \ \frac{0}{4x}; \ \frac{9x}{0}; \ \frac{14}{x-x}.$$

In exercises 78-83, graph the fraction on a number line.

78. $\dfrac{2}{3}$ **79.** $\dfrac{4}{3}$ **80.** $\dfrac{5}{4}$ **81.** $\dfrac{6}{5}$ **82.** $-\dfrac{8}{5}$ **83.** $\dfrac{11}{6}$

In exercises 84-87, graph the pair of fractions on the same number line.

84. $-\dfrac{1}{5}$ and $\dfrac{3}{5}$ **85.** $\dfrac{3}{4}$ and $\dfrac{-1}{4}$ **86.** $\dfrac{5}{8}$ and $-\dfrac{11}{8}$ **87.** $\dfrac{7}{10}$ and $\dfrac{21}{10}$

In exercises 88-93, convert the fraction to an equivalent fraction with the given number as the new denominator.

88. $\dfrac{4}{5}; 15$ **89.** $\dfrac{7}{9}; 36$ **90.** $\dfrac{-10}{13}; 65$ **91.** $\dfrac{7}{9}; 81$ **92.** $\dfrac{8}{15}; 60$ **93.** $\dfrac{13}{5}; 20x$

In exercises 94-98, reduce the given fractions to lowest terms.

94. $\dfrac{21}{28}$ **95.** $-\dfrac{15}{21}$ **96.** $\dfrac{72}{126}$ **97.** $\dfrac{4,500}{960}$ **98.** $-\dfrac{196}{210}$

In exercises 99-103, find the Least Common Denominator of the given group of fractions.

99. $\dfrac{2}{3}, \dfrac{4}{5}$ **100.** $\dfrac{1}{2}, \dfrac{4}{5}, \dfrac{9}{20}$ **101.** $\dfrac{7}{5}, \dfrac{4}{15}, \dfrac{9}{25}$ **102.** $\dfrac{7}{8}, \dfrac{3}{20}, \dfrac{4}{15}, \dfrac{8}{21}$ **103.** $\dfrac{4}{2x}, \dfrac{-5}{7x^2}, \dfrac{9}{4xy}$

In exercises 104-108, identify which of the two fractions has the larger value.

104. $\dfrac{2}{3}, \dfrac{5}{6}$ **105.** $\dfrac{7}{15}, \dfrac{8}{21}$ **106.** $\dfrac{-9}{10}, \dfrac{-7}{11}$ **107.** $\dfrac{21}{25}, \dfrac{14}{15}$ **108.** $\dfrac{17}{32}, \dfrac{35}{64}$

In exercises 109-112, arrange the group of fractions in ascending order.

109. $\dfrac{2}{5}, \dfrac{5}{4}, \dfrac{3}{10}$ **110.** $\dfrac{1}{2}, \dfrac{2}{5}, \dfrac{7}{10}, \dfrac{9}{20}$ **111.** $\dfrac{3}{4}, \dfrac{5}{12}, \dfrac{7}{16}, \dfrac{11}{24}$ **112.** $\dfrac{4}{15}, \dfrac{7}{20}, \dfrac{9}{25}, \dfrac{17}{60}$

113. Change the mixed numbers to improper fractions.

    (a) $2\dfrac{1}{5}$ **(b)** $7\dfrac{3}{5}$ **(c)** $-5\dfrac{3}{7}$ **(d)** $-7\dfrac{5}{12}$

114. Change the improper fractions to mixed numbers.

    (a) $\dfrac{7}{4}$ **(b)** $\dfrac{9}{5}$ **(c)** $\dfrac{29}{11}$ **(d)** $\dfrac{-32}{7}$

115. If 6 out of 24 students in a class received an A then;
    (a) What fraction of the class received an A?
    (b) What percent of the class received an A?

116. What fraction of the following figure is shaded?

117. Michael has completed reading 35 pages of a book. If the book has 175 pages,
    (a) What percentage of the book has he completed reading?
    (b) What fraction of the book does he still have to read?
    (c) What is the ratio of the number of pages read to the number of pages left to read?

3.11   SELF TEST

1. Is 65,576 divisible by 7?   **2.** Is 50,875 prime or composite?

3. Is 437,851 divisible by 9?

4. Write the prime factorization of: **(a)** 2,520   **(b)** 288

5. Find all possible factors of 68. Also express 68 as a product of two factors in all possible ways.

6. Find the LCM of :   **(a)** 14, 35, 130   **(b)** $5a^2x,\ 3ax^3,\ 6a^3$

7. List all the factors of 273.

8. Graph the fractions $-\dfrac{2}{5}$ and $\dfrac{3}{5}$ on the same number line.

9. Reduce $\dfrac{216}{324}$ to lowest terms.   **10.** Find the missing denominator: $\dfrac{15}{23} = \dfrac{105}{?}$

11. Raise the given fractions to equivalent fractions with the LCD as the common denominator.

$$\frac{14}{45},\ \frac{-7}{6},\ \frac{11}{10}.$$

12. Change $4\dfrac{5}{9}$ to an improper fraction.   **13.** Change $\dfrac{59}{7}$ to a mixed number.

14. Linda deposits $150 in her savings account every month from a total paycheck of $2,700.
    What fraction of her paycheck is deposited in her savings account?

Operations with Fractions

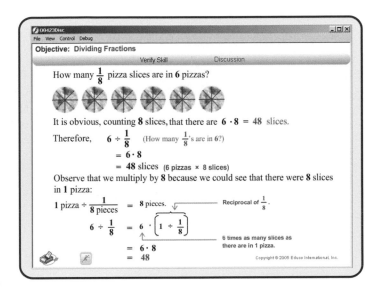

Operations with Fractions

OPERATIONS WITH FRACTIONS

Introduction

In this chapter, we shall continue our work with rational numbers (fractions). We shall review performing addition, subtraction, multiplication, and division with fractions, and discuss the properties of addition and multiplication with rational numbers.

This chapter is divided into three sections:

4.1 *Addition and Subtraction with Fractions;*

4.2 *Multiplication and Division with Fractions; and*

4.3 *Order of Operations with Fractions.*

4.1 ADDITION AND SUBTRACTION WITH FRACTIONS

4.1 A. Addition with Fractions

- **Adding Fractions with Common Denominators**

Fractions which have the same denominators are called **like fractions**. For example, $\frac{7}{5}, \frac{13}{5}, \frac{25}{5}$ are *like* fractions, while $\frac{2}{7}, \frac{3}{5}$ are *unlike* fractions. The sum of two like fractions can be obtained easily as is illustrated in Figure 4.1.

> **Objectives**
>
> After completing this section, you will be able to:
>
> A. Add fractions;
>
> B. Recognize and use the Addition Properties with fractions; and
>
> C. Subtract fractions.

Observe that in Figure 4.1, a rectangular unit is divided into 5 equal parts. Each part represents the fraction $\frac{1}{5}$. One part is shaded on the right and two parts are shaded on the left.

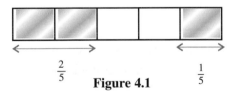

$$\frac{2}{5} \qquad \textbf{Figure 4.1} \qquad \frac{1}{5}$$

The left shaded parts represent the fraction $\frac{2}{5}$; the right shaded part represents the fraction $\frac{1}{5}$.

The total number of shaded parts is 3, together representing the fraction $\frac{3}{5}$;

therefore, $\qquad \frac{2}{5} + \frac{1}{5} = \frac{2+1}{5} = \frac{3}{5}$

Thus, we observe that

The sum of fractions with common denominators = $\dfrac{\text{sum of the numerators}}{\text{common denominator}}$, $\quad \dfrac{a}{b} + \dfrac{c}{b} = \dfrac{a+c}{b}$.

In adding, remember that we can only add fractions with common denominators.

For example:
$$\frac{3}{5} + \frac{4}{5} = \frac{3+4}{5} = \frac{7}{5}$$

$$\frac{4}{7} + \frac{2}{7} + \frac{5}{7} = \frac{4+2+5}{7} = \frac{11}{7}$$

Procedure to add two or more fractions with common denominators:

Step **1** Add the numerators.

Step **2** Write the sum over the common denominator.

Step **3** Simplify the sum.

Warm-Up

1. Add and write the sum in lowest terms.

(a) $\frac{2}{7} + \frac{1}{7} + \frac{3}{7}$

(b) $\frac{6}{15} + \frac{-3}{15} + \frac{7}{15}$

Example 1   Add the fractions and write the sum in lowest terms.

(a) $\frac{3}{5} + \frac{4}{5}$

(b) $\frac{3}{8} + \frac{7}{8} + \left(-\frac{5}{8}\right) + \frac{1}{8}$

Solutions

(a) $\frac{3}{5} + \frac{4}{5} = \frac{3+4}{5} = \frac{7}{5}$
- Add the numerators.
- Retain the common denominator.
- The sum is already in lowest terms.

(b) $\frac{3}{8} + \frac{7}{8} + \left(-\frac{5}{8}\right) + \frac{1}{8}$
- Write $-\frac{5}{8}$ as $\frac{-5}{8}$.

$= \frac{3}{8} + \frac{7}{8} + \frac{-5}{8} + \frac{1}{8}$
- Add the numerators and retain the common denominator.

$= \frac{3+7+(-5)+1}{8}$
- Simplify.

$= \frac{11-5}{8}$

$= \frac{6}{8} = \frac{3}{4}$

- **Adding Fractions with a Different Denominator** requires a little more work. Consider the shaded parts of the first two rectangles in Figure 4.2. These parts cannot be added directly because of their different sizes.

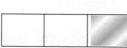   

$\frac{1}{6}$ + $\frac{1}{3}$ =   ?   Parts are not of the same size.

Figure 4.2

To add $\frac{1}{6}$ and $\frac{1}{3}$, we first make all pieces to be added the same size.

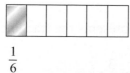   

$\frac{1}{6}$ $\frac{1}{3} = \frac{2}{6}$

Figure 4.3

$$\frac{1}{6} = \frac{1}{6} \qquad \text{and} \qquad \frac{1}{3} = \frac{1}{3} \cdot \frac{2}{2} = \frac{2}{6};$$

Observe in Figure 4.3: $\frac{1}{3} = \frac{2}{6}$.

We can add fractions only if their denominators are the same, or as in this case, if the pieces are of the same size as indicated by the common denominators.

Observe from this illustration that we converted the two fractions to equivalent fractions with 6 as the common denominator. The number 6 is the LCM of 6 and 3, or the Least Common Denominator of $\frac{1}{3}$ and $\frac{1}{6}$.

Therefore, $\quad \dfrac{1}{6} + \dfrac{1}{3} = \dfrac{1}{6} + \dfrac{2}{6} = \dfrac{1+2}{6} = \dfrac{3}{6} \qquad$ Simplify to lowest terms.

$$= \frac{1}{2}.$$

Procedure to add two or more *unlike* fractions:

Step **1**   Find the LCD of the given fractions.

Step **2**   Build the fractions to equivalent fractions with the LCD as the common denominator.

Step **3**   Write the sum of the numerators over the common denominator.

Step **4**   Simplify the sum.

Example 2   Add the following fractions:

     (a) $\dfrac{4}{5} + \dfrac{3}{10}$ **(b)** $\dfrac{2}{5} + \dfrac{-7}{15}$ **(c)** $\dfrac{2}{9} + \dfrac{5}{12} + \left(-\dfrac{13}{8} \right)$

Solutions

(a) $\dfrac{4}{5} + \dfrac{3}{10}$: LCD = 10   (By inspection)

$$\left. \begin{aligned} \frac{4}{5} &= \frac{4}{5} \cdot \frac{2}{2} = \frac{8}{10} \\[4pt] \frac{3}{10} &= \frac{3}{10}; \end{aligned} \right\}$$

Build the fractions to the common denominator of 10.

thus, $\dfrac{4}{5} + \dfrac{3}{10} = \dfrac{8}{10} + \dfrac{3}{10} = \dfrac{11}{10}$.   Add the new fractions.

(b) $\dfrac{2}{5} + \dfrac{-7}{15}$:   LCD = 15

$$\left. \begin{aligned} \frac{2}{5} &= \frac{2}{5} \cdot \frac{3}{3} = \frac{6}{15} \\[4pt] \frac{-7}{15} &= \frac{-7}{15}; \end{aligned} \right\}$$

Build the fractions to the common denominator of 15.

thus, $\dfrac{2}{5} + \dfrac{-7}{15} = \dfrac{6}{15} + \dfrac{-7}{15} = \dfrac{6 + (-7)}{15} = \dfrac{-1}{15}$.

Warm-Up

2. Find the sums.

   (a) $\dfrac{3}{4} + \dfrac{5}{6}$

   (b) $\dfrac{-3}{8} + \dfrac{1}{12}$

(c) $\dfrac{4}{3} + \dfrac{5}{12} + \dfrac{-7}{10}$

(c) $\dfrac{2}{9} + \dfrac{5}{12} + \dfrac{-13}{8}$: LCD = 72 (Verify.)

$$\dfrac{2}{9} = \dfrac{2}{9} \cdot \dfrac{8}{8} = \dfrac{16}{72} \qquad 72 \div 9 = 8$$

$$\dfrac{5}{12} = \dfrac{5}{12} \cdot \dfrac{6}{6} = \dfrac{30}{72} \qquad 72 \div 12 = 6$$

$$\dfrac{-13}{8} = \dfrac{-13}{8} \cdot \dfrac{9}{9} = \dfrac{-117}{72} \qquad 72 \div 8 = 9$$

$$\dfrac{2}{9} + \dfrac{5}{12} + \dfrac{-13}{8} = \dfrac{16}{72} + \dfrac{30}{72} + \dfrac{-117}{72}$$

$$= \dfrac{16 + 30 + (-117)}{72}$$

$$= \dfrac{46 - 117}{72} = \dfrac{-71}{72} = -\dfrac{71}{72}$$

The sum is already in lowest terms.

Adding Algebraic Fractions

3. Find the sum.

(a) $\dfrac{-2}{4a} + \dfrac{8}{4a} + \dfrac{13}{4a}$

Example 3 Find the sum.

(a) $\dfrac{7}{x} + \dfrac{5}{x} + \dfrac{-3}{x}$

(b) $\dfrac{3a}{2x} + \dfrac{5}{6}$

Solutions

(a) $\dfrac{7}{x} + \dfrac{5}{x} + \dfrac{-3}{x}$

$$= \dfrac{7 + 5 + (-3)}{x}$$

All the fractions have the same denominator. Add the numerators, and place the sum over the common denominator.

$$= \dfrac{12 - 3}{x} = \dfrac{9}{x}$$

(b) $\dfrac{5}{3x} + \dfrac{2}{9x}$

(b) $\dfrac{3a}{2x} + \dfrac{5}{6}$

$$\dfrac{3a}{2x} = \dfrac{3a}{2x} \cdot \dfrac{3}{3} = \dfrac{9a}{6x}$$

Fractions have different denominators. Build them to a common denominator, the LCD.

LCD $= 2 \cdot x \cdot 3 = 2 \cdot 3 \cdot x = 6x$

$$\dfrac{5}{6} = \dfrac{5}{6} \cdot \dfrac{x}{x} = \dfrac{5x}{6x}$$

$$\dfrac{3a}{2x} + \dfrac{5}{6} = \dfrac{9a}{6x} + \dfrac{5x}{6x}$$

$$= \dfrac{9a + 5x}{6x}$$

⚠ **Caution:**
1. The numerator can not be simplified further.
2. The fraction can not be reduced. None of the factors of the denominator (2, 3, 6, x) are factors of the numerator.

- To add mixed numbers, we first change them to improper fractions and then add.

$$15\frac{1}{2} + 7\frac{2}{3} = \frac{31}{2} + \frac{23}{3}$$ LCD = 6

$$= \frac{93}{6} + \frac{46}{6}$$ $\frac{31}{2} \cdot \frac{3}{3} = \frac{93}{6}; \quad \frac{23}{3} \cdot \frac{2}{2} = \frac{46}{6}$

$$= \frac{93 + 46}{6} = \frac{139}{6} = 23\frac{1}{6}$$

This method often involves computations with large numbers.

Alternatively, we can use the method of *vertical addition*.

The LCD is 6.

$$15\frac{1}{2} \quad = \quad 15\frac{1}{2} \cdot \frac{3}{3} \quad = \quad 15\frac{3}{6}$$

$$+ \; 7\frac{2}{3} \quad = \quad 7\frac{2}{3} \cdot \frac{2}{2} \quad = \quad 7\frac{4}{6}$$

The fraction parts now have a common denominator.

$$= \quad 22\frac{7}{6} = 22 + 1\frac{1}{6} = 23\frac{1}{6}$$

The fraction part is an improper fraction.   Change it to a mixed number.

Example 4   Add and write the sum as a mixed number.

$$-2\frac{1}{3} + 1\frac{3}{4}$$

Solution

$$-2\frac{1}{3} + 1\frac{3}{4}$$ $-2\frac{1}{3} = -\left(2\frac{1}{3}\right) = -\frac{7}{3}$

$$= -\frac{7}{3} + \frac{7}{4}$$ Change mixed numbers to improper fractions.

$$= \frac{-28}{12} + \frac{21}{12}$$ Add the fractions using LCD = 12. Build each fraction to the denominator of 12.

$$= \frac{-28 + 21}{12} = \frac{-7}{12}.$$

4.1 B.   Properties of Addition with Rational Numbers

The properties of addition that we stated earlier for integers also hold true for rational numbers. We list those properties again, now for rational numbers or fractions.

- **Properties of Addition:**

   1.   Commutative Property of Addition

   If *a* and *b* are two rational numbers, then *a* + *b* = *b* + *a*.

   Example: $\frac{3}{4} + \frac{1}{2} = \frac{1}{2} + \frac{3}{4}$

2. Associative Property of Addition

If a, b, and c are three rational numbers, then

$$(a + b) + c = a + (b + c) = a + b + c.$$

Example: $\left(\dfrac{2}{3} + \dfrac{1}{2}\right) + \dfrac{3}{4} = \dfrac{2}{3} + \left(\dfrac{1}{2} + \dfrac{3}{4}\right) = \dfrac{2}{3} + \dfrac{1}{2} + \dfrac{3}{4}$.

3. Additive Identity Property

The number 0 is the additive identity for rational numbers also.

That is, $a + 0 = a$ and $0 + a = a$, where a is any rational number.

Example: $\dfrac{2}{3} + 0 = \dfrac{2}{3}$ and $0 + \dfrac{2}{3} = \dfrac{2}{3}$.

4. Additive Inverse Property

For each rational number a, there is another rational number; namely, its opposite or additive inverse, $-a$, such that $a + (-a) = 0$ and $(-a) + a = 0$.

Example: The opposite of $-\dfrac{2}{3}$ is $\dfrac{2}{3}$.

$\left(-\dfrac{2}{3}\right) + \dfrac{2}{3} = 0$. Also, $\dfrac{2}{3} + \left(-\dfrac{2}{3}\right) = 0$.

Warm-Up

5. Identify the addition property of rational numbers used in each statement: commutative, associative, identity, or inverse.

(a) $\left(-\dfrac{4}{5}\right) + \dfrac{7}{8} = \dfrac{7}{8} + \left(-\dfrac{4}{5}\right)$

(b) $0 + \dfrac{2}{9} = \dfrac{2}{9}$

(c) $\dfrac{5}{6} + \left(-\dfrac{5}{6}\right) = 0$

(d) $\left(\dfrac{1}{2} + \dfrac{3}{4}\right) + \dfrac{7}{9} = \dfrac{1}{2} + \left(\dfrac{3}{4} + \dfrac{7}{9}\right)$

Answers:

5. (a) Commutative   (b) Identity
    (c) Inverse   (d) Associative

Example 5 Identify the addition property of rational numbers used in each statement: commutative, associative, identity, or inverse.

(a) $0 + \dfrac{x}{2} = \dfrac{x}{2}$ **(b)** $\dfrac{3}{2} + \dfrac{1}{2} = \dfrac{1}{2} + \dfrac{3}{2}$

(c) $\left(-\dfrac{3}{2}\right) + \dfrac{3}{2} = 0$ **(d)** $\left(\dfrac{3}{2} + \dfrac{1}{2}\right) + \dfrac{5}{2} = \dfrac{3}{2} + \left(\dfrac{1}{2} + \dfrac{5}{2}\right)$

Solutions

   (a) Identity   **(b)** Commutative

   (c) Inverse   **(d)** Associative

4.1 C. Subtracting with Fractions

Subtraction with fractions is similar to subtraction with integers.

Recall: $3 - 7$ is rewritten as $3 + (-7)$.

In the same way,

$\dfrac{3}{2} - \dfrac{7}{8}$ is rewritten as $\dfrac{3}{2} + \dfrac{-7}{8}$.

Note that the preferred position of the negative sign in $-\dfrac{7}{8}$ is with the numerator, $\dfrac{-7}{8}$, not in front of the fraction.

Once the subtraction is written as an addition, we follow the rules for addition.

Procedure for subtracting with fractions:

    1.   Rewrite the subtraction as addition of the additive inverse (opposite).

    2.   Follow the rules for addition:

        Step **1**   Express all numbers in fraction form (proper or improper).

        Step **2**   Convert the fractions to equivalent fractions with the LCD as the common denominator.

        Step **3**   Add the fractions.

        Step **4**   Simplify the sum.

Example 6   Simplify.

     (a) $\dfrac{15}{16} - \dfrac{3}{16}$ **(b)** $\dfrac{8}{13} - \dfrac{25}{13}$

Solutions

(a) $\dfrac{15}{16} - \dfrac{3}{16} = \dfrac{15}{16} + \dfrac{-3}{16}$ • Rewrite as addition of the opposite.

             $= \dfrac{15 + (-3)}{16}$ • Fractions have the same denominator.
                            • Add the numerators.

             $= \dfrac{12}{16}$ • Reduce.

             $= \dfrac{\cancel{2} \cdot \cancel{2} \cdot 3}{\cancel{2} \cdot \cancel{2} \cdot 2 \cdot 2}$

             $= \dfrac{3}{4}$

(b) $\dfrac{8}{13} - \dfrac{25}{13} = \dfrac{8}{13} + \dfrac{-25}{13}$ • Rewrite as addition of the opposite, and add the numerators.

             $= \dfrac{8 + (-25)}{13}$ • Simplify the numerator.

             $= \dfrac{-17}{13}$ or $-1\dfrac{4}{13}$

Warm-Up

6.   Find the difference.

     (a) $\dfrac{12}{19} - \dfrac{7}{19}$

     (b) $\dfrac{2}{5} - \dfrac{16}{5}$

Subtraction is not commutative. Order is very important. $\dfrac{3}{4} - \dfrac{7}{8}$ is not the same as $\dfrac{7}{8} - \dfrac{3}{4}$. We must read very carefully to determine which term is first, and which term is being subtracted (second in position, after "–"). Subtract $\dfrac{1}{2}$ from 8 means $8 - \dfrac{1}{2}$. $\left(\dfrac{1}{2} \text{ is being subtracted; hence, it must be after the "–".} \right)$

Warm-Up

7. Subtract:

(a) $\dfrac{2}{5}$ from $\dfrac{3}{20}$

(b) $\dfrac{5}{36}$ from $\dfrac{13}{24}$

8. Evaluate:

(a) $1 - \dfrac{5}{11}$

Example 7 Subtract:

(a) $\dfrac{3}{4}$ from $\dfrac{7}{8}$ **(b)** $\dfrac{7}{30}$ from $\dfrac{42}{45}$

Solutions

(a) Subtract $\dfrac{3}{4}$ from $\dfrac{7}{8}$ means: $\dfrac{7}{8} - \dfrac{3}{4}$

$$= \dfrac{7}{8} + \dfrac{-3}{4}$$
  • Rewrite as addition. LCD = 8.

$$= \dfrac{7}{8} + \dfrac{-3\,(2)}{4\,(2)}$$
  • Build to the LCD : 8.

$$= \dfrac{7 + (-6)}{8}$$
  • Add the numerators.

$$= \dfrac{1}{8}$$

(b) Subtract $\dfrac{7}{30}$ from $\dfrac{42}{45}$ means: $\dfrac{42}{45} - \dfrac{7}{30}$.

$$= \dfrac{42}{45} + \dfrac{-7}{30}$$
  • Rewrite as addition.
    $45 = 3 \cdot 3 \cdot 5$

$$= \dfrac{42\,(2)}{45\,(2)} + \dfrac{-7\,(3)}{30\,(3)}$$
  $30 = 2 \cdot 3 \cdot 5$
  LCD $= 2 \cdot 3 \cdot 3 \cdot 5 = 90$
  • Build to the LCD.

$$= \dfrac{84 - 21}{90}$$
  • Simplify and reduce.

$$= \dfrac{63}{90} = \dfrac{7 \cdot \cancel{9}}{10 \cdot \cancel{9}} = \dfrac{7}{10}$$

Example 8 Evaluate:

(a) $1 - \dfrac{7}{18}$ **(b)** $\dfrac{13}{15} - 4$ **(c)** $-7\dfrac{3}{8} - 5\dfrac{7}{12}$

(d) $45 - 16\dfrac{2}{3}$ **(e)** $-7\dfrac{3}{8} - \left(-4\dfrac{3}{16}\right)$

Solutions

(a) $1 - \dfrac{7}{18} = 1 + \dfrac{-7}{18}$
  • Rewrite as an addition.
    Rewrite with fractions.

$$= \dfrac{1}{1} + \dfrac{-7}{18}$$
  LCD = 18.

$$= \dfrac{1\,(18)}{1\,(18)} + \dfrac{-7}{18}$$
  • Build the fractions to the LCD (18).

$$= \dfrac{18 + (-7)}{18} = \dfrac{11}{18}$$
  • Add the numerators, and simplify.

(b) $\dfrac{13}{15} - 4 = \dfrac{13}{15} + \dfrac{-4}{1}$

- Rewrite as an addition.
  Rewrite with fractions.

$= \dfrac{13}{15} + \dfrac{-4\,(15)}{1\,(15)}$

LCD = 15.

- Build fractions to the denominator 15.

$= \dfrac{13+(-60)}{15} = \dfrac{-47}{15}$

$= -3\dfrac{2}{15}$.

- Add the numerators, and simplify.

(c) $-7\dfrac{3}{8} - 5\dfrac{7}{12} = -7\dfrac{3}{8} + \left(-5\dfrac{7}{12}\right)$

- Rewrite as addition.
  Rewrite with improper fractions.

$= \dfrac{-59}{8} + \dfrac{-67}{12}$

LCD = 24.

$= \dfrac{-59\,(3)}{8\,(3)} + \dfrac{-67(2)}{12\,(2)}$

- Build fractions to the denominator 24.

$= \dfrac{-177+(-134)}{24}$

- Add the numerators, and simplify.

$= \dfrac{-311}{24}$ or $-12\dfrac{23}{24}$

(d) $45 - 16\dfrac{2}{3} = 45 + \left(-16\dfrac{2}{3}\right)$

- Rewrite as addition.
  Rewrite with improper fractions.

$= \dfrac{45}{1} + \dfrac{-50}{3}$

LCD = 3.

$= \dfrac{45(3)}{1\,(3)} + \dfrac{-50}{3}$

- Build fractions to the LCD (3).

$= \dfrac{135+(-50)}{3}$

- Add the numerators, and simplify.

$= \dfrac{85}{3}$ or $28\dfrac{1}{3}$

(e) $-7\dfrac{3}{8} - \left(-4\dfrac{3}{16}\right) = -7\dfrac{3}{8} + \left(4\dfrac{3}{16}\right)$

- Rewrite as addition.
  Rewrite with improper fractions.

$= \dfrac{-59}{8} + \dfrac{67}{16}$

LCD = 16.

$= \dfrac{-59\,(2)}{8\,(2)} + \dfrac{67}{16}$

- Build fractions to the LCD (16).

$= \dfrac{-118+67}{16}$

- Add the numerators, and simplify.

$= \dfrac{-51}{16} = -3\dfrac{3}{16}$

(b) $\dfrac{3}{7} - 5$

(c) $-5\dfrac{2}{3} - 4\dfrac{5}{18}$

(d) $33 - 24\dfrac{1}{2}$

(e) $-5\dfrac{1}{6} - \left(-3\dfrac{11}{12}\right)$

9. Find the difference.

(a) $\dfrac{3}{y} - \dfrac{x}{4}$

(b) $\dfrac{4}{5} - 3x$

Answers:

6. (a) $\dfrac{5}{19}$ (b) $-\dfrac{14}{5}$

7. (a) $-\dfrac{1}{4}$ (b) $\dfrac{29}{72}$

8. (a) $\dfrac{6}{11}$ (b) $-4\dfrac{4}{7}$ (c) $-9\dfrac{17}{18}$

   (d) $8\dfrac{1}{2}$ (e) $-1\dfrac{1}{4}$

9. (a) $\dfrac{12 - xy}{4y}$ (b) $\dfrac{4 - 15x}{5}$

Subtracting Algebraic Fractions

Example 9   Find the difference.

(a) $\dfrac{8}{a} - \dfrac{x}{5}$ (b) $4y - \dfrac{3}{7}$

Solutions

(a)
$$\dfrac{8}{a} - \dfrac{x}{5} = \dfrac{8}{a} + \dfrac{-x}{5}$$ • Rewrite as addition.

$$= \dfrac{8}{a} \cdot \dfrac{5}{5} + \dfrac{-x}{5} \cdot \dfrac{a}{a}$$ • The LCD $= a \cdot 5 = 5a$.

$$= \dfrac{40}{5a} + \dfrac{-ax}{5a}$$ • Build the fractions to the denominator $5a$.

$$= \dfrac{40 + (-ax)}{5a} = \dfrac{40 - ax}{5a}$$ • Add the numerators.

⚠ **Caution:** We can not divide out 40 in the numerator by 5 in the denominator. (Why?)

(b)
$$4y - \dfrac{3}{7} = \dfrac{4y}{1} + \dfrac{-3}{7}$$ • Express $4y$ as a fraction with denominator 1.

$$= \dfrac{4y}{1} \cdot \dfrac{7}{7} + \dfrac{-3}{7}$$ • The LCD $= 7$.
      • Build the fractions to the LCD 7.

$$= \dfrac{28y}{7} + \dfrac{-3}{7}$$ • Add the numerators.

$$= \dfrac{28y + (-3)}{7}$$ The resulting fraction cannot be reduced since 7 is not a factor of the numerator.

$$= \dfrac{28y - 3}{7}$$

Mental Calculations for subtraction with whole numbers and fractions.

We frequently have the opportunity to subtract fractions or mixed numbers from whole numbers.

• $2\dfrac{7}{8}$ feet is cut from an 8-foot board. How long is the piece that is left?

• $\dfrac{2}{3}$ of the money has been spent. What fraction is left?

To subtract $1 - \dfrac{2}{3}$ mentally is easy.

Picture 1 whole as $\dfrac{3}{3}$ ⊘. Then it is clear that $1 - \dfrac{2}{3} = \dfrac{3}{3} - \dfrac{2}{3} = \dfrac{1}{3}$.

Do the rapid drill below before proceeding to the next part.

RAPID DRILL:

Solve the following problems:

1. $1-\dfrac{5}{9}=$ **2.** $1-\dfrac{6}{7}=$ **3.** $1-\dfrac{5}{11}=$ **4.** $1-\dfrac{8}{9}=$ **5.** $1-\dfrac{1}{4}=$

Answers:

1. $\dfrac{4}{9}$ **2.** $\dfrac{1}{7}$ **3.** $\dfrac{6}{11}$ **4.** $\dfrac{1}{9}$ **5.** $\dfrac{3}{4}$

To mentally subtract a mixed number requires forming pictures of wholes and pieces.

$$8 \;-\; 2\dfrac{7}{8}$$

Start with 8 whole objects. To subtract $2\dfrac{7}{8}$, subtract 2 wholes first. $8-2-\dfrac{7}{8}=6-\dfrac{7}{8}$

Then leave 6 wholes untouched. Break the 6th into $\dfrac{8}{8}$, so that you can take away $\dfrac{7}{8}$ leaving $\dfrac{1}{8}$.

 $=$

          6   5 $+$ $\dfrac{8}{8}-\dfrac{7}{8}=\dfrac{1}{8}$

                        $=$ $5+\dfrac{1}{8}=\mathbf{5\dfrac{1}{8}}$

RAPID DRILL:

Solve the following problems:

1. $6-2\dfrac{1}{3}$ **2.** $4-1\dfrac{5}{9}$ **3.** $11-6\dfrac{1}{2}$ **4.** $10-3\dfrac{5}{8}$ **5.** $14-10\dfrac{1}{5}$

Answers:

1. $3\dfrac{2}{3}$ **2.** $2\dfrac{4}{9}$ **3.** $4\dfrac{1}{2}$ **4.** $6\dfrac{3}{8}$ **5.** $3\dfrac{4}{5}$

Exercise 4.1

A.   **In exercises 1-12, write the sum by inspection.**

1. $\dfrac{2}{5}+\dfrac{1}{5}$ **2.** $\dfrac{2}{5}+\dfrac{3}{5}$ **3.** $\dfrac{2}{5}+\dfrac{3}{10}$ **4.** $\dfrac{4}{3}+\dfrac{2}{3}+\dfrac{1}{3}$ **5.** $\dfrac{4}{5}+\dfrac{2}{5}+\dfrac{3}{5}$ **6.** $\dfrac{4}{27}+\dfrac{5}{9}+\dfrac{1}{27}$

7. $\dfrac{7x}{6}+\dfrac{5x}{6}$ **8.** $\dfrac{3ab}{4}+\dfrac{7\,ab}{4}$ **9.** $\dfrac{5x}{2}+\dfrac{3x}{2}$ **10.** $\dfrac{2a}{7}+\dfrac{4a}{7}$ **11.** $\dfrac{3a}{8b}+\dfrac{9a}{8b}+\dfrac{a}{8b}$ **12.** $\dfrac{5}{6x}+\dfrac{1}{6x}+\dfrac{3}{6x}$

In exercises 13-37, add the given fractions and write the sum in lowest terms.

13. $\dfrac{5}{18} + \dfrac{4}{15}$ 14. $\dfrac{11}{27} + \dfrac{7}{12}$ 15. $\dfrac{2}{3} + \dfrac{7}{15}$ 16. $\dfrac{16}{39} + \dfrac{5}{3}$ 17. $\dfrac{2}{15} + \dfrac{3}{20} + \dfrac{1}{4}$

18. $\dfrac{5}{16} + \dfrac{7}{8} + \dfrac{3}{12}$ 19. $\dfrac{3}{4} + \dfrac{1}{12} + \dfrac{5}{24}$ 20. $\dfrac{1}{3} + \dfrac{1}{5} + \dfrac{2}{15}$ 21. $\dfrac{7}{8} + \dfrac{5}{12} + \dfrac{5}{6}$ 22. $\dfrac{1}{4} + \dfrac{1}{8} + \dfrac{1}{12}$

23. $\dfrac{1}{3} + \dfrac{1}{2} + \dfrac{1}{6} + \dfrac{1}{16}$ 24. $\dfrac{9}{20} + \dfrac{3}{10} + \dfrac{8}{15} + \dfrac{19}{30}$ 25. $6\dfrac{2}{3} + 8\dfrac{7}{15}$ 26. $7\dfrac{2}{5} + 4\dfrac{7}{15}$ 27. $4\dfrac{3}{8} + 11\dfrac{11}{16}$

28. $\dfrac{2a}{3} + \dfrac{2a}{5}$ 29. $\dfrac{3a}{7} + \dfrac{4a}{3}$ 30. $\dfrac{5b}{6} + \dfrac{2b}{5}$ 31. $\dfrac{9b}{7} + \dfrac{5b}{14}$ 32. $\dfrac{8b}{14} + \dfrac{4b}{21}$

33. $\dfrac{2}{5a} + \dfrac{3}{4a}$ 34. $\dfrac{7}{3a} + \dfrac{4}{2a}$ 35. $\dfrac{5}{4a} + \dfrac{2b}{6a}$ 36. $\dfrac{5}{9b} + \dfrac{2a}{6b}$ 37. $\dfrac{4a}{15b} + \dfrac{7}{10b}$

B.   **In exercises 38-45, identify the addition property of rational numbers demonstrated in the statement: Commutative, Associative, Identity, or Inverse.**

38. $\dfrac{3}{5} + 0 = \dfrac{3}{5}$ 39. $\dfrac{7}{9} + \left(-\dfrac{7}{9}\right) = 0$ 40. $\left(-\dfrac{5}{4}\right) + \dfrac{5}{4} = 0$ 41. $0 + \dfrac{7}{8} = \dfrac{7}{8}$

42. $\left\{\dfrac{1}{4} + \left(-\dfrac{3}{4}\right)\right\} + \dfrac{1}{2} = \dfrac{1}{4} + \left\{\left(-\dfrac{3}{4}\right) + \dfrac{1}{2}\right\}$ 43. $\dfrac{5}{7} + \dfrac{8}{11} = \dfrac{8}{11} + \dfrac{5}{7}$

44. $\dfrac{1}{2} + \left(\dfrac{2}{3} + \dfrac{3}{4}\right) = \left(\dfrac{1}{2} + \dfrac{2}{3}\right) + \dfrac{3}{4}$ 45. $\dfrac{5}{6} + \dfrac{6}{7} = \dfrac{6}{7} + \dfrac{5}{6}$

In exercises 46-53, fill in the blank to make the statement true. Identify the addition property used.

46. $\dfrac{2}{3} + \left(-\dfrac{1}{3}\right) = \underline{\hphantom{x}} + \dfrac{2}{3}$ 47. $\left(-\dfrac{3}{5}\right) + \left(\dfrac{2}{5}\right) = \left(\dfrac{2}{5}\right) + \underline{\hphantom{x}}$ 48. $\dfrac{7}{8} + \underline{\hphantom{x}} = \dfrac{7}{8}$ 49. $\underline{\hphantom{x}} + 0 = \dfrac{11}{13}$

50. $\dfrac{3}{7} + \underline{\hphantom{x}} = 0$ 51. $-\dfrac{5}{9} + \underline{\hphantom{x}} = 0$ 52. $\left(\dfrac{1}{2} + \dfrac{3}{4}\right) + \dfrac{5}{6} = \dfrac{1}{2} + \left(\dfrac{3}{4} + \underline{\hphantom{x}}\right)$

53. $\left(-\dfrac{4}{5}\right) + \left(\dfrac{2}{3} + \dfrac{4}{7}\right) = \left(-\dfrac{4}{5} + \underline{\hphantom{x}}\right) + \dfrac{4}{7}$

C.   **In exercises 54-90, find the difference and reduce the answer to lowest terms, wherever needed.**

54. $\dfrac{2}{3} - \dfrac{7}{8}$ 55. $\dfrac{6}{5} - \dfrac{5}{6}$ 56. $\dfrac{5}{7} + \dfrac{-3}{14}$ 57. $\dfrac{5}{6} - \dfrac{13}{16}$ 58. $\dfrac{4}{5} - \dfrac{3}{10}$ 59. $\dfrac{13}{14} - \dfrac{3}{4}$

60. $\dfrac{1}{10} - \dfrac{4}{15}$ 61. $\dfrac{39}{50} - \dfrac{8}{15}$ 62. $\dfrac{7}{12} - \dfrac{5}{16}$ 63. $\dfrac{24}{55} - \dfrac{4}{33}$ 64. $\dfrac{4}{5} - \dfrac{7}{12}$ 65. $\dfrac{15}{45} - \dfrac{9}{27}$

66. $\dfrac{3}{5} - \dfrac{7}{50}$ 67. $\dfrac{7}{10} - \dfrac{78}{100}$ 68. $1 - \dfrac{4}{13}$ 69. $\dfrac{1}{3} - \dfrac{2}{5}$ 70. $\dfrac{20}{35} - \dfrac{24}{42}$ 71. $-\dfrac{5}{14} - \dfrac{5}{7}$

72. $\dfrac{3}{7} - 1$ 73. $\dfrac{38}{45} - \dfrac{29}{35}$ 74. $\dfrac{13}{35} - \dfrac{15}{42}$ 75. $\dfrac{109}{80} - \dfrac{11}{20}$ 76. $\dfrac{5x}{2} - \dfrac{3x}{2}$ 77. $\dfrac{5x}{12} - \dfrac{x}{6}$

78. $\dfrac{3x}{10} - \dfrac{7x}{10}$ **79.** $1 - \dfrac{5x}{7}$ **80.** $4x - \dfrac{3}{8}$ **81.** $\dfrac{5x}{7} - \dfrac{12x}{21}$ **82.** $\dfrac{4x}{9} - \dfrac{9x}{27}$

83. $\dfrac{3x}{10} - \dfrac{4x}{15}$ **84.** $\dfrac{5x}{12} - \dfrac{3x}{18}$ **85.** $\dfrac{7}{6x} - \dfrac{2}{6x}$ **86.** $\dfrac{2}{5x} - \dfrac{3}{15x}$ **87.** $\dfrac{5}{9x} - \dfrac{5}{36x}$

88. $\dfrac{3}{4y} - \dfrac{5}{6y}$ **89.** $\dfrac{14}{65y} - \dfrac{3}{78y}$ **90.** $\dfrac{5x}{8y} - \dfrac{7x}{12y}$

In exercises 91-101, find the indicated sum and difference and reduce your answer to lowest terms. (*Note:* In some cases you might be able to reduce fractions before adding or subtracting, then you will be working with a smaller common denominator.)

91. $\dfrac{2}{3} + \dfrac{3}{4} - \dfrac{5}{6}$ **92.** $\dfrac{1}{8} + \dfrac{5}{12} - \dfrac{3}{4}$ **93.** $\dfrac{1}{5} - \dfrac{1}{4} + \dfrac{1}{10}$ **94.** $\dfrac{3}{4} - \dfrac{1}{2} - \dfrac{1}{18}$

95. $\dfrac{5}{8} + \dfrac{4}{5} - \dfrac{70}{80}$ **96.** $21 + 5\dfrac{5}{7} - 14\dfrac{3}{14}$ **97.** $3\dfrac{2}{9} - 2\dfrac{7}{12} + \dfrac{5}{3}$ **98.** $3\dfrac{1}{2} + 1\dfrac{3}{4} - 1\dfrac{2}{3} + \dfrac{5}{6}$

99. $\dfrac{7x}{9y} - \dfrac{4}{45y} - \dfrac{2x}{5y}$ **100.** $\dfrac{2x}{3y} + \dfrac{4y}{6x} - \dfrac{x}{2y}$ **101.** $\dfrac{3x}{4y} - \dfrac{5}{8y} + \dfrac{y}{2x} - \dfrac{2y}{3x}$

In exercises 102-116, find the indicated algebraic sum and/or difference. Assume that the variables are all non-zero numbers.

102. $\dfrac{2x}{3a} - \dfrac{5}{9b}$ **103.** $\dfrac{1}{y} - \dfrac{2}{x}$ **104.** $\dfrac{3}{8}x - \dfrac{5}{6}x$ **105.** $\dfrac{1}{3x} + \dfrac{1}{2x} - \dfrac{1}{6x}$ **106.** $\dfrac{3x}{2y} + \dfrac{3}{4y}$

107. $\dfrac{4x}{3a} - \dfrac{7}{9b}$ **108.** $\dfrac{3a}{5x} + \dfrac{2b}{7y}$ **109.** $\dfrac{3a}{7x} - \dfrac{a}{7x} + \dfrac{12a}{7x}$ **110.** $\dfrac{a}{15} - \dfrac{3a}{5} + \dfrac{a}{12}$ **111.** $\dfrac{3}{2x} + \dfrac{2}{4x} - \dfrac{4}{8x}$

112. $\dfrac{x}{5} + \dfrac{7}{2} + \dfrac{5}{3}$ **113.** $\dfrac{x}{6} - \dfrac{2}{3} - \dfrac{1}{8}$ **114.** $\dfrac{3}{4ab} + \dfrac{2}{7a} - \dfrac{4b}{14b}$ **115.** $x - \dfrac{5}{16}$ **116.** $\dfrac{2}{3y} + \dfrac{3}{4y} - \dfrac{5}{6y}$

In exercises 117-126, mentally subtract a fraction from 1.

117. $1 - \dfrac{2}{3}$ **118.** $1 - \dfrac{5}{7}$ **119.** $1 - \dfrac{3}{8}$ **120.** $1 - \dfrac{7}{10}$ **121.** $1 - \dfrac{9}{11}$

122. $1 - \dfrac{5}{12}$ **123.** $1 - \dfrac{9}{13}$ **124.** $1 - \dfrac{11}{14}$ **125.** $1 - \dfrac{13}{15}$ **126.** $1 - \dfrac{5}{16}$

In exercises 127-136, mentally subtract a mixed number from a whole number.

127. $3 - 1\dfrac{2}{3}$ **128.** $5 - 2\dfrac{4}{5}$ **129.** $6 - 3\dfrac{5}{7}$ **130.** $9 - 6\dfrac{7}{8}$ **131.** $11 - 6\dfrac{2}{9}$

132. $7 - 2\dfrac{3}{10}$ **133.** $12 - 4\dfrac{5}{11}$ **134.** $5 - 2\dfrac{7}{12}$ **135.** $4 - 1\dfrac{3}{13}$ **136.** $8 - 5\dfrac{11}{14}$

4.2 MULTIPLICATION AND DIVISION WITH FRACTIONS

Objectives

After completing this section, you will be able to:

A. Multiply fractions and mixed numbers;

B. Find reciprocals;

C. Recognize and use the multiplication properties with fractions; and

D. Divide fractions and mixed numbers.

4.2 A.   Multiplying Fractions

Recall, the area of a rectangle is given by the formula:

$$A = (\text{Length}) \cdot (\text{Width})$$

$$= L \cdot W$$

Now consider the rectangle in Figure 4.4

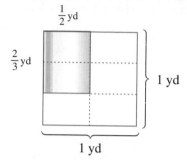

Figure 4.4

In this figure a square, of side 1 yd by 1 yd, is divided into six equal rectangles as shown above. The shaded rectangle within this square is of dimensions $\frac{2}{3}$ yd by $\frac{1}{2}$ yd. The area of this rectangle is given by:

$$A = \frac{2}{3}\text{yd} \cdot \frac{1}{2}\text{yd} \qquad (A = L \cdot W)$$

$$= \left(\frac{2}{3} \cdot \frac{1}{2}\right)\text{yd}^2$$

Notice that: $A = \dfrac{1}{3}$ (area of the square)   Two of the six parts $\left(\frac{2}{6} \text{ or } \frac{1}{3}\right)$ are shaded.

$$= \frac{1}{3} \cdot 1 \text{ yd}^2$$

$$= \frac{1}{3}\text{yd}^2 \; ;$$

therefore, $A = \left(\dfrac{2}{3} \cdot \dfrac{1}{2}\right)\text{yd}^2$ $\frac{2}{3} \cdot \frac{1}{2} = \frac{1}{3}$.

$$= \frac{1}{3}\text{yd}^2$$

Let us examine how the product of $\dfrac{2}{3}$ and $\dfrac{1}{2}$ gives us a new fraction, $\dfrac{1}{3}$.

$$\frac{2}{3} \cdot \frac{1}{2} = \frac{2 \cdot 1}{3 \cdot 2} = \frac{2}{6} = \frac{1}{3} \qquad \textbf{OR} \qquad \frac{2}{3} \cdot \frac{1}{2} = \frac{\overset{1}{2}}{3} \cdot \frac{1}{\underset{1}{2}} = \frac{1 \cdot 1}{3 \cdot 1} = \frac{1}{3}$$

This gives us the following procedure to multiply two fractions.

Procedure to multiply with fractions:

Step **1**   Express all numbers as fractions or improper fractions.

Step **2**   Cancel out the common factors (if any) between the numerators and denominators.

Step **3**   Multiply the remaining factors of the numerators to get the numerator of the product, and multiply the remaining factors of the denominators to get the denominator of the product.

Example 1   Multiply and write the product in lowest terms.

(a) $\dfrac{3}{4} \cdot \dfrac{5}{6}$ (b) $-\dfrac{15}{24} \cdot \dfrac{16}{40}$

Solutions

(a)
$$\dfrac{3}{4} \cdot \dfrac{5}{6} = \dfrac{\overset{1}{\cancel{3}}}{2 \cdot 2} \cdot \dfrac{5}{2 \cdot \underset{1}{\cancel{3}}}$$

• Cancel 3, then multiply the numerators and the denominators.

$$= \dfrac{5}{8}$$

The product of a negative and a positive number is negative.

(b)
$$-\dfrac{15}{24} \cdot \dfrac{16}{40} = -\left(\dfrac{15}{24} \cdot \dfrac{16}{40}\right)$$

$$= -\left(\dfrac{\cancel{3} \cdot \cancel{5}}{\cancel{2} \cdot \cancel{2} \cdot \cancel{2} \cdot \cancel{3}} \cdot \dfrac{\cancel{2} \cdot \cancel{2} \cdot 2 \cdot 2}{\cancel{2} \cdot 2 \cdot 2 \cdot \cancel{5}}\right)$$

Cancel the common factors between the numerators and the denominators.

$$= -\dfrac{1}{1} \cdot \dfrac{1}{4}$$

• Multiply the numerators and the denominators.

$$= \dfrac{-1 \cdot 1}{1 \cdot 4} = -\dfrac{1}{4}$$

The product of a negative and a positive number is negative.

Example 2   Multiply and write the product in lowest terms.

(a) $\dfrac{11}{2} \cdot \dfrac{3}{5} \cdot 7$ (b) $-\dfrac{7}{9} \cdot \left(-\dfrac{18}{5}\right) \cdot \left(-\dfrac{10}{21}\right) \cdot (-15)$

Solutions

(a)
$$\dfrac{11}{2} \cdot \dfrac{3}{5} \cdot 7 = \dfrac{11}{2} \cdot \dfrac{3}{5} \cdot \dfrac{7}{1}$$

• Write 7 as a fraction.

$$= \dfrac{11 \cdot 3 \cdot 7}{2 \cdot 5 \cdot 1}$$

• No common divisors. Multiply.

$$= \dfrac{231}{10}$$

(b)
$$\dfrac{-7}{9} \cdot \left(\dfrac{-18}{5}\right) \cdot \left(\dfrac{-10}{21}\right) \cdot (-15)$$

The product of an even number of negative factors is positive. Here we have 4 negative factors.

Warm-Up

1. Multiply and write the product in lowest terms.

(a) $\dfrac{12}{25} \cdot \dfrac{15}{16}$

(b) $-\dfrac{9}{64} \cdot \dfrac{80}{27}$

2. Multiply and write the product in lowest terms.

(a) $\dfrac{18}{4} \cdot (-12)$

(b) $\dfrac{3}{2} \cdot \left(-\dfrac{8}{26}\right) \cdot 13$

$$= \frac{7}{9} \cdot \frac{18}{5} \cdot \frac{10}{21} \cdot 15 = \frac{7}{9} \cdot \frac{18}{5} \cdot \frac{10}{21} \cdot \frac{15}{1}$$

Write 15 as a fraction.

$$= \frac{\overset{1}{\cancel{7}}}{\underset{1}{\cancel{9}}} \cdot \frac{\overset{1}{\cancel{9}} \cdot 2}{\cancel{5}} \cdot \frac{2 \cdot \overset{1}{\cancel{5}}}{\cancel{3} \cdot \underset{1}{\cancel{7}}} \cdot \frac{\overset{1}{\cancel{3}} \cdot 5}{1}$$

Cancel the common factors between the numerators and the denominators.

$$= \frac{2 \cdot 2 \cdot 5}{1} = \frac{20}{1} = \mathbf{20}$$

Multiply the numerators and the denominators.

3. Simplify:

$$3\frac{2}{3} \cdot \frac{5}{4}$$

Example 3   Simplify: $4\frac{2}{3} \cdot 2\frac{3}{5} \cdot \frac{5}{6}$

Solution

$$4\frac{2}{3} \cdot 2\frac{3}{5} \cdot \frac{5}{6} = \frac{14}{3} \cdot \frac{13}{5} \cdot \frac{5}{6}$$

• $4\frac{2}{3} = \frac{4 \cdot 3 + 2}{3} = \frac{14}{3}$

$2\frac{3}{5} = \frac{2 \cdot 5 + 3}{5} = \frac{13}{5}$

$$= \frac{\overset{1}{\cancel{2}} \cdot 7}{3} \cdot \frac{13}{\underset{1}{\cancel{5}}} \cdot \frac{\overset{1}{\cancel{5}}}{\underset{1}{2} \cdot 3}$$

• Cancel the common factors between the numerators and the denominators.

$$= \frac{7 \cdot 13 \cdot 1}{3 \cdot 3}$$

• Multiply.

$$= \frac{91}{9} = \mathbf{10\frac{1}{9}}$$

• $D \longleftarrow 9)\overline{\begin{array}{r} 10 \longrightarrow Q \\ 91 \\ -90 \\ \hline 01 \end{array}} \longrightarrow R$

4. Multiply and reduce the product to lowest terms.

$$\frac{3a}{10x} \cdot \frac{25}{9a} \cdot \frac{3x}{15}$$

Example 4   Multiply and reduce to lowest terms: $\frac{5a}{8x} \cdot \frac{16ax}{5} \cdot \frac{3}{4a}$

Solution $\frac{5a}{8x} \cdot \frac{16ax}{5} \cdot \frac{3}{4a}$

Answers:

1. (a) $\frac{9}{20}$ **(b)** $-\frac{5}{12}$

2. (a) -54 **(b)** -6

3. $\frac{55}{12}$ **4.** $\frac{1}{6}$

$$= \frac{\cancel{5}\cancel{a}}{8\cancel{x}} \cdot \frac{2 \cdot 8 \cdot a \cancel{x}}{\cancel{5}} \cdot \frac{3}{2 \cdot 2\cancel{a}}$$

Write factorizations, keeping in mind the factors (such as 8) that may be cancelled out easily. Cancel out the common factors.

$$= \frac{1}{1} \cdot \frac{a}{1} \cdot \frac{3}{2}$$

Write the products of the remaining factors.

$$= \frac{a \cdot 3}{2} = \mathbf{\frac{3a}{2}}$$

4.2 B.   Defining the Reciprocal or the Multiplicative Inverse of a Rational Number

• Two fractions are said to be **reciprocals** of each other if their product is 1.

For example,

$\frac{2}{5}$ and $\frac{5}{2}$ are *reciprocals* of each other because $\frac{2}{5} \cdot \frac{5}{2} = \frac{10}{10} = 1$.

$-\frac{3}{7}$ and $-\frac{7}{3}$ are *reciprocals* of each other because $\left(-\frac{3}{7}\right)\left(-\frac{7}{3}\right) = +\frac{21}{21} = 1$.

Finding the reciprocal of a fraction means inverting the fraction or swapping the numerator and the denominator. In general terms, we may define the reciprocal of a fraction as follows:

> **Definition:** The **reciprocal** (multiplicative inverse) of a non-zero rational
>
> number is the number $\dfrac{1}{a}$, such that
>
> $$a \cdot \frac{1}{a} = 1 \quad \text{and} \quad \frac{1}{a} \cdot a = 1.$$

- To find the reciprocal of an integer, we first write it as a fraction (with the denominator of 1), and then interchange the numerator and the denominator. For example,

The reciprocal of $\quad 15 \ $ or $\ \dfrac{15}{1} \ $ is $\ \dfrac{1}{15}$;

the reciprocal of $\quad -7$ (or $\dfrac{-7}{1}$ or $-\dfrac{7}{1}$) is $\ \dfrac{1}{-7}$ or $-\dfrac{1}{7}$.

We say that 15 and $\dfrac{1}{15}$ are reciprocals of each other because $15 \cdot \dfrac{1}{15} = 1.$

Similarly, -7 and $-\dfrac{1}{7}$ are also reciprocals of each other since $(-7) \cdot \left(-\dfrac{1}{7}\right) = 1.$

Note that the reciprocal of a positive number is always a positive number, and the reciprocal of a negative number is always a negative number. That is, **a number and its reciprocal always have like signs.**

The number zero "0" does not have a reciprocal because the product of 0 and any number is always 0. The product **cannot** be 1.

- The reciprocal of a (non-zero) rational number is also called its **multiplicative inverse**. The reciprocal

or the multiplicative inverse of a rational number a is denoted by $\dfrac{1}{a}$ or a^{-1}

(read : "a inverse" or "inverse of a").

$$0^{-1} \text{ is not defined.}$$

Procedure to find the multiplicative inverse (or the reciprocal) of a number:

> *Step 1*   **a.**   If the number is a fraction, find the reciprocal (or the multiplicative inverse) by inverting it (interchanging the numerator and the denominator).
>
>   **b.**   If the number is a non-zero integer, first write it as a fraction with the denominator of 1, then invert the fraction.
>
> *Step 2*   Check by showing that the product of the number and its reciprocal is 1.

Example 5   Find the reciprocals of :

    (a) 87 **(b)** $-\dfrac{8}{9}$ **(c)** $4x$ **(d)** $\dfrac{5y}{13x^2}$ **(e)** $\dfrac{0}{9}$

Warm-Up
5. Find the reciprocals of :
(a) 210

Solutions

   (a) The reciprocal of 87 is $\dfrac{1}{87}$.   First write 87 as a fraction: $87\dfrac{87}{1}$.

                                         Then, interchange the numerator and

     Check : $87 \cdot \dfrac{1}{87} = \dfrac{87}{1} \cdot \dfrac{1}{87} = 1$ the denominator to obtain $\dfrac{1}{87}$.

(b) $-\dfrac{37}{48}$

(c) $-3xy$

(d) $\dfrac{8x}{3y}$

(e) $\dfrac{0}{3x}$

(b) The reciprocal of $-\dfrac{8}{9}$ is $-\dfrac{9}{8}$ because

$$\left(-\frac{8}{9}\right)\cdot\left(-\frac{9}{8}\right)=\frac{8\cdot9}{9\cdot8}=1.$$

Since the reciprocal of a negative number is a negative number, we retain the '−' sign, and interchange the numerator and the denominator.

(c) The reciprocal of $4x$ is $\dfrac{1}{4x}$.

Write $4x=\frac{4x}{1}$.

Interchange the numerator and the denominator.

(d) The reciprocal of $\dfrac{5y}{13x^2}$ is $\dfrac{13x^2}{5y}$.

Just interchange the numerator and the denominator.

(e) $\dfrac{0}{9}$ has no reciprocal because $\dfrac{9}{0}$ is undefined.

(Alternatively, and 0 does not have a reciprocal.)

- For each multiplication problem there are two related division problems. In the case of reciprocals, this provides an interesting result.

Observe: $\dfrac{2}{5}\cdot\dfrac{5}{2}=1$

The related division facts are:

$$1\div\frac{2}{5}=\frac{5}{2}\quad\text{and}\quad1\div\frac{5}{2}=\frac{2}{5}$$

Thus, if a is any non-zero rational number then $\dfrac{1}{a}$ is its reciprocal, and $\dfrac{1}{\text{reciprocal of }a}=\text{number }a.$

Warm-Up

6. Complete the following statements:

(a) $1\div\dfrac{5}{6}=$ ___

(b) $\dfrac{1}{\frac{3}{7}}=$ ___

Answers:

5.(a) $\dfrac{1}{210}$ (b) $-\dfrac{48}{37}$ (c) $-\dfrac{1}{3xy}$

(d) $\dfrac{3y}{8x}$ (e) undefined

6.(a) $\dfrac{6}{5}$ (b) $\dfrac{7}{3}$

Example 6   Complete the following statements:

(a) $1\div\dfrac{-3}{7}=$ ___

(b) $\dfrac{1}{\frac{9}{5}}=$ ___

Solutions

(a) $1\div\dfrac{-3}{7}=$ reciprocal of $\dfrac{-3}{7}$

$=\dfrac{7}{-3}$ or $-\dfrac{7}{3}$

(b) $\dfrac{1}{\frac{9}{5}}=$ reciprocal of $\dfrac{9}{5}$

$=\dfrac{5}{9}.$

4.2 C. Properties of Multiplication with Rational Numbers

1. Commutative Property:

If a and b are two rational numbers, then $a \cdot b = b \cdot a$

Example: $\dfrac{1}{2} \cdot \dfrac{3}{4} = \dfrac{3}{4} \cdot \dfrac{1}{2}$

$$\dfrac{3}{8} = \dfrac{3}{8}$$

2. Associative Property:

If a, b, and c are three rational numbers, then $a \cdot (b \cdot c) = (a \cdot b) \cdot c$.

Example: $\dfrac{1}{2} \cdot \left(\dfrac{3}{4} \cdot \dfrac{1}{5} \right) = \left(\dfrac{1}{2} \cdot \dfrac{3}{4} \right) \dfrac{1}{5}$

$$\dfrac{1}{2} \left(\dfrac{3}{20} \right) = \left(\dfrac{3}{8} \right) \dfrac{1}{5}$$

$$\dfrac{3}{40} = \dfrac{3}{40}$$

3. Multiplicative Identity Property:

If a is any rational number, then $a \cdot 1 = a$ and $1 \cdot a = a$

Example: $-\dfrac{3}{4} \cdot 1 = -\dfrac{3}{4}$

$$1 \cdot \left(-\dfrac{3}{4} \right) = -\dfrac{3}{4}$$

4. Multiplicative Inverse Property:

For every non-zero rational number a, there is another rational number $\dfrac{1}{a}$,

called its reciprocal or **multiplicative inverse**, such that $a \cdot \dfrac{1}{a} = 1$.

The multiplicative inverse of 0 is not defined.

The multiplicative inverse of 1 is 1 itself.

Example: $\dfrac{-2}{3} \cdot \dfrac{3}{-2} = \dfrac{-6}{-6}$

$$= 1$$

5. Zero Factor Property:

For any rational number a, $a \cdot 0 = 0$; $0 \cdot a = 0$.

Example: $\dfrac{2}{3} \cdot 0 = 0$; $0 \cdot \dfrac{2}{3} = 0$

Warm-Up

7. Identify the property demonstrated: Commutative, Associative, Identity, Inverse, or Zero Factor Property.

(a) $\frac{7}{8} \cdot y = y \cdot \frac{7}{8}$

(b) $(y \cdot 5) \cdot (-2) = y \cdot (5 \cdot (-2))$

(c) $\frac{9}{5} \cdot \frac{5}{9} = 1$

(d) $Z \cdot 0 = 0$

Answers:

7.(a) Commutative Property
(b) Associative Property
(c) Multiplicative Inverse Property
(d) Zero Factor Property

Example 7   Identify the property demonstrated: Commutative, Associative, Identity, Inverse, or Zero Factor Property.

(a) $-\frac{2}{3}\left(\frac{4}{5} \cdot x\right) = \left(-\frac{2}{3} \cdot \frac{4}{5}\right) \cdot x$

(b) $x \cdot \left(-\frac{3}{5}\right) = \left(-\frac{3}{5}\right) \cdot x$

(c) $0 \cdot 2x = 0$

(d) $\frac{-2x}{3} \cdot \frac{-3}{2x} = 1$

Solutions

(a) Associative Property   (b) Commutative Property

(c) Zero Factor Property   (d) Multiplicative Inverse Property

4.2 D.   Division with Fractions

How many $\frac{1}{8}$ - pizza slices are in 6 pizzas?

It is obvious, counting 8 slices, that there are $6 \cdot 8 = 48$ slices.

Therefore, $6 \div \frac{1}{8}$ (How many $\frac{1}{8}$'s are in 6?)

$$= 6 \cdot 8$$

$$= 48$$

Observe that we multiply by 8 because we could see that there were 8 slices in 1 pizza:

$$1 \div \frac{1}{8} = 8.$$

$$6 \div \frac{1}{8} = 6 \cdot \left(1 \div \frac{1}{8}\right) \quad \longleftarrow \quad \text{Reciprocal of } \frac{1}{8}.$$

$$\longleftarrow \quad \text{6 times as many slices as there were in 1 pizza.}$$

$$= 6 \cdot 8$$

$$= 48$$

This illustrates the general procedure for division with fractions.

Procedure to divide with fractions:

Step **1**   Write the numbers as fractions.

Step **2**   Change division to multiplication. That is, change "division by a number" to "multiplication by the reciprocal of that number".

Step **3**   Perform the multiplication.

Example 8   Divide and reduce to lowest terms wherever possible.

(a) $68 \div \dfrac{12}{5}$

(b) $\dfrac{7}{8} \div (-3)$

(c) $\dfrac{-4}{13} \div \dfrac{20}{-39}$

(d) $105 \div 5\dfrac{1}{4}$

Solutions

(a) $68 \div \dfrac{12}{5} = \dfrac{68}{1} \div \dfrac{12}{5}$ • Write 68 as a fraction.

$= \dfrac{68}{1} \cdot \dfrac{5}{12}$ • Change division to multiplication by inverting the divisor.

$= \dfrac{\overset{1}{\cancel{4}} \cdot 17 \cdot 5}{\underset{1}{\cancel{4}} \cdot 3}$ • Simplify.

$= \dfrac{85}{3}$

(b) $\dfrac{7}{8} \div (-3) = \dfrac{7}{8} \div \dfrac{-3}{1}$ • Write −3 as a fraction.

$= \dfrac{7}{8} \cdot \dfrac{1}{-3}$ • Change division to multiplication.

$= \dfrac{7}{-24} = -\dfrac{7}{24}$ • Simplify.

(c) $\dfrac{-4}{13} \div \dfrac{20}{-39} = \dfrac{-4}{13} \cdot \dfrac{-39}{20}$ • Change division (÷) to multiplication by the reciprocal.

$= \dfrac{4}{13} \cdot \dfrac{39}{20}$

$= \dfrac{\overset{1}{\cancel{4}} \cdot 3 \cdot \overset{1}{\cancel{13}}}{\underset{1}{\cancel{13}} \cdot \underset{1}{\cancel{4}} \cdot 5}$ • Simplify.

$= \dfrac{3}{5}$

(d) $105 \div 5\dfrac{1}{4} = \dfrac{105}{1} \div \dfrac{21}{4}$ • Change the whole number and the mixed number to a improper fraction.

$= \dfrac{105}{1} \cdot \dfrac{4}{21}$ • Change division to multiplication by the reciprocal, $\dfrac{4}{21}$.

$= \dfrac{5 \cdot \overset{1}{\cancel{3}} \cdot \overset{1}{\cancel{7}} \cdot 4}{\underset{1}{\cancel{3}} \cdot \underset{1}{\cancel{7}}}$ • Find the prime factors of 105.

$105 = 5 \cdot 21$
$= 5 \cdot 3 \cdot 7$

$= 20$ • Simplify

Warm-Up

9. Divide and reduce to lowest terms:

(a) $\dfrac{-3x}{2y} \div \dfrac{-3x}{2y}$

(b) $\dfrac{16x^2}{5y^3} \div \dfrac{-8x}{25y^2}$

Answers:

8. (a) 35   (b) $-\dfrac{2}{3}$ (c) $\dfrac{2}{3}$ (d) 4

9. (a) 1   (b) $-\dfrac{10x}{y}$

Example 9   Divide and reduce to lowest terms.

(a) $\dfrac{4}{7x} \div \dfrac{4}{7x}$ (b) $\dfrac{-3x^2 y}{5a} \div \dfrac{9xy^3}{10ab}$

Solutions

(a) $\dfrac{4}{7x} \div \dfrac{4}{7x}$

$= \dfrac{4}{7x} \cdot \dfrac{\mathbf{7x}}{\mathbf{4}}$

      • Multiply by the reciprocal of $\dfrac{4}{7x}$.

$= \dfrac{{}^1\cancel{4} \cdot \cancel{7} \cdot \cancel{x}}{\cancel{7} \cdot \cancel{x} \cdot \cancel{4}_{\ 1}}$

      • Simplify. Since all the factors cancel out, the result is 1.

$= 1$

(b) $\dfrac{-3x^2 y}{5a} \div \dfrac{9xy^3}{10ab}$

      • Change division to multiplication by inverting the divisor.

$= \dfrac{-3x^2 y}{5a} \cdot \dfrac{\mathbf{10ab}}{\mathbf{9xy^3}}$

      • Simplify. Since the expressions have unlike signs, the sign is negative.

$= -\dfrac{\cancel{3} \cdot x \cdot x \cdot \cancel{y} \cdot 2 \cdot \cancel{5} \cdot \cancel{a} \cdot b}{\cancel{5} \cdot \cancel{a} \cdot \cancel{3} \cdot 3 \cdot \cancel{x} \cdot \cancel{y} \cdot y \cdot y}$

      • Write the prime factorizations and cancel the common factors.

$= -\dfrac{\mathbf{2bx}}{\mathbf{3y^2}}$

      • Multiply the remaining factors.

We expect the result to be 1 because we are dividing an expression by itself.

Exercise 4.2

A. In exercises 1-40, multiply the fractions and then simplify the product.

1. $\dfrac{7}{8} \cdot \dfrac{3}{5}$

2. $\dfrac{2}{5} \cdot \dfrac{2}{5}$

3. $12 \cdot \dfrac{5}{11}$

4. $\dfrac{0}{9} \cdot \dfrac{2}{6}$

5. $-4 \cdot \dfrac{4}{3}$

6. $8 \cdot \dfrac{-2}{7}$

7. $25 \cdot \dfrac{0}{-3}$

8. $\dfrac{8}{7} \cdot \left(-\dfrac{4}{15}\right)$

9. $-\dfrac{1}{2} \cdot \left(-\dfrac{3}{2}\right)$

10. $\dfrac{3}{5} \cdot 6$

11. $\dfrac{-5}{8} \cdot \dfrac{4}{15}$

12. $9 \cdot \dfrac{8}{21}$

13. $\dfrac{7}{34} \cdot 6$

14. $\dfrac{-69}{15} \cdot \dfrac{-12}{46}$

15. $\dfrac{7}{9} \cdot \dfrac{9}{7}$

16. $\dfrac{15}{16} \cdot \dfrac{12}{21}$

17. $\dfrac{7}{8} \cdot \dfrac{4}{5} \cdot \dfrac{4}{7}$

18. $\dfrac{7}{9} \cdot \dfrac{18}{5} \cdot \dfrac{-10}{21}$

19. $\dfrac{-2}{3} \cdot \dfrac{4}{15} \cdot \dfrac{-18}{7}$

20. $\dfrac{3}{4}\left(-\dfrac{8}{9}\right)$

21. $\dfrac{5}{6}(-3)$

22. $\left(-\dfrac{2}{15}\right)6$

23. $\left(-\dfrac{3}{5}\right)\left(\dfrac{10}{9}\right)$

24. $\dfrac{4}{5} \cdot \dfrac{-10}{16} \cdot \dfrac{7}{18}$

25. $\dfrac{9}{10} \cdot \dfrac{27}{135} \cdot \dfrac{40}{81}$

26. $\dfrac{-15}{42} \cdot \dfrac{-21}{12} \cdot \dfrac{-7}{30}$ **27.** $\dfrac{1}{2}\left(-\dfrac{3}{5}\right)\left(\dfrac{10}{9}\right)$ **28.** $10\left(-\dfrac{3}{15}\right)\left(\dfrac{3}{2}\right)$ **29.** $\dfrac{12}{75} \cdot \dfrac{100}{120} \cdot \dfrac{8}{9}$ **30.** $\dfrac{4}{3} \cdot (-11) \cdot \dfrac{9}{4} \cdot \dfrac{5}{66}$

31. $\dfrac{-17}{50} \cdot \dfrac{25}{35} \cdot 8$ **32.** $\left(2\dfrac{2}{5}\right)\left(12\dfrac{1}{2}\right)\left(2\dfrac{2}{3}\right)$ **33.** $2\dfrac{3}{4} \cdot \left(-\dfrac{16}{11}\right)$ **34.** $2\dfrac{3}{4} \cdot 19\dfrac{1}{5}$

35. $\left(3\dfrac{3}{4}\right)\left(2\dfrac{1}{2}\right)\left(-\dfrac{7}{25}\right)$ **36.** $\dfrac{5}{6}\left(\dfrac{1}{4}\right)\left(3\dfrac{2}{15}\right)$ **37.** $\left(4\dfrac{4}{7}\right) \cdot \left(3\dfrac{1}{2}\right)$ **38.** $2\dfrac{5}{6} \cdot \left(1\dfrac{1}{34}\right) \cdot 1\dfrac{3}{5}$

39. $\left(-7\dfrac{1}{3}\right)\left(2\dfrac{1}{4}\right)\left(-\dfrac{4}{55}\right)$ **40.** $6\dfrac{3}{8} \cdot \left(2\dfrac{2}{17}\right)$

In exercises 41-56, multiply the algebraic fractions and write the product in lowest terms.

41. $\dfrac{2u}{9v} \cdot \dfrac{27v}{u} \cdot \dfrac{u}{7}$ **42.** $\dfrac{m^2}{n} \cdot \dfrac{n}{m} \cdot \dfrac{n}{m^2}$ **43.** $10 \cdot \dfrac{3}{x^2} \cdot \dfrac{x}{5y} \cdot \dfrac{2y}{3}$ **44.** $\dfrac{5t}{4x^2} \cdot \dfrac{16x}{t^3} \cdot \dfrac{t}{20}$

45. $\dfrac{7n^2}{3m^2} \cdot \dfrac{6m}{14n} \cdot \dfrac{3m}{2}$ **46.** $\dfrac{ap^2}{q^2} \cdot \dfrac{5q}{ap} \cdot \dfrac{4q^2}{25p}$ **47.** $\dfrac{4ax}{3} \cdot \dfrac{2}{9a^2} \cdot \dfrac{a}{8}$ **48.** $\dfrac{5b^2}{6a^3} \cdot \dfrac{3a^2}{10b} \cdot \dfrac{8}{b}$

49. $\dfrac{3a^3}{4b^4} \cdot \dfrac{2ab}{9} \cdot \dfrac{2b^2}{a^2}$ **50.** $\dfrac{7t^2}{x} \cdot \dfrac{5x^2}{21t} \cdot \dfrac{3}{25}$ **51.** $\dfrac{8m^2}{x^2} \cdot \dfrac{5mx}{4} \cdot \dfrac{2x}{m^3}$ **52.** $\dfrac{4x^2}{9} \cdot \dfrac{3y}{4x^2} \cdot \dfrac{6}{y}$

53. $\dfrac{3m}{2x^3} \cdot \dfrac{x^2}{4m^2} \cdot \dfrac{8mx}{3}$ **54.** $\dfrac{2}{3}\left(-\dfrac{3c}{4x}\right)\left(-\dfrac{2x^2}{c^2}\right)$ **55.** $-\dfrac{5}{6}\left(-\dfrac{2m^2}{25x^2}\right)\left(\dfrac{3x}{m}\right)$ **56.** $-12\left(-\dfrac{5x^2}{6m}\right)\left(\dfrac{5m^2}{10x}\right)$

B. **In exercises 57-75, write the reciprocal of the given number or (expression).**

57. $\dfrac{25}{37}$ **58.** $\dfrac{1}{9}$ **59.** -13 **60.** $-\dfrac{15}{49}$ **61.** $\dfrac{0}{4}$ **62.** $-\dfrac{1}{5}$ **63.** $\dfrac{1}{27}$

64. $-\dfrac{1}{14}$ **65.** $\dfrac{2}{7x}$ **66.** $-\dfrac{2x}{5}$ **67.** $5x$ **68.** $-\dfrac{4}{13x}$ **69.** $\dfrac{11y}{18x}$ **70.** $\dfrac{2x}{5y}$

71. $\dfrac{-3ax^2}{14y}$ **72.** $15xy$ **73.** $-\dfrac{1}{8x}$ **74.** $\dfrac{3x^2}{5}$ **75.** $-\dfrac{0}{15}$

C. **In exercises 76-84, state the property of multiplication that is illustrated.**

76. $-\dfrac{5}{3}\cdot\left(\dfrac{2}{7}\cdot\dfrac{11}{9}\right) = \left(-\dfrac{5}{3}\cdot\dfrac{2}{7}\right)\cdot\dfrac{11}{9}$ **77.** $\left\{\left(-\dfrac{1}{2}\right)\cdot\dfrac{1}{11}\right\}\cdot\dfrac{2}{7} = \left(-\dfrac{1}{2}\right)\left(\dfrac{1}{11}\cdot\dfrac{2}{7}\right)$ **78.** $\dfrac{7}{11}\cdot\dfrac{11}{7} = 1$

79. $\dfrac{3}{8}\cdot\dfrac{8}{3} = 1$ **80.** $\dfrac{15}{7}\cdot 1 = \dfrac{15}{7}$ **81.** $\dfrac{a}{b}\cdot\dfrac{14}{15} = \dfrac{14}{15}\cdot\dfrac{a}{b}$

82. $\dfrac{x}{3} \cdot \dfrac{y}{4} = \dfrac{y}{4} \cdot \dfrac{x}{3}$

83. $\dfrac{11}{3} \cdot 1 = \dfrac{11}{3}$

84. $\dfrac{-11}{3} \cdot 0 = 0$

D. In exercises 85-112, divide and simplify the result to lowest terms.

85. $\dfrac{7}{2} \div 5$

86. $\dfrac{4}{5} \div \dfrac{8}{10}$

87. $\dfrac{9}{14} \div \dfrac{18}{35}$

88. $-\dfrac{3}{4} \div \dfrac{4}{3}$

89. $\dfrac{15}{14} \div \left(-\dfrac{15}{42}\right)$

90. $\dfrac{8}{5} \div -\dfrac{8}{5}$

91. $\dfrac{7}{15} \div \left(-\dfrac{7}{15}\right)$

92. $\dfrac{19}{26} \div \dfrac{19}{26}$

93. $6x \div \dfrac{1}{3x}$

94. $5y \div \dfrac{1}{10y}$

95. $\dfrac{15}{2} \div 15$

96. $0 \div \dfrac{13}{5}$

97. $(-6) \div \dfrac{12}{13}$

98. $\left(-\dfrac{8}{9}\right) \div \left(-\dfrac{24}{36}\right)$

99. $\dfrac{25}{7} \div \dfrac{25}{7}$

100. $\dfrac{8}{9} \div \dfrac{9}{8}$

101. $\dfrac{-36}{25} \div \dfrac{-24}{20}$

102. $9\dfrac{3}{4} \div 3\dfrac{1}{4}$

103. $6 \div 7\dfrac{7}{8}$

104. $3\dfrac{1}{15} \div 1\dfrac{1}{5}$

105. $-5\dfrac{1}{8} \div \dfrac{3}{4}$

106. $20\dfrac{5}{6} \div 3\dfrac{4}{7}$

107. $-33\dfrac{1}{3} \div 11\dfrac{1}{9}$

108. $15\dfrac{3}{7} \div (-14)$

109. $\dfrac{25x}{4y} \div \dfrac{15x}{16y}$

110. $\dfrac{2x^2}{7xy} \div \dfrac{10yx^2}{14xy}$

111. $\dfrac{12ab}{25} \div \dfrac{24}{15ab}$

112. $\dfrac{49pq^2}{24} \div \dfrac{35q}{16}$

113. Find the quotient when $\left(\dfrac{4}{5} \text{ of } \dfrac{15}{8}\right)$ is divided by $\left(\dfrac{15}{8} \text{ of } \dfrac{4}{5}\right)$.

114. Show that the phrases "Eighteen divided by five" and "Eighteen divided by one-fifth" do not have the same meaning.

115. The result of multiplying two numbers is $\dfrac{14}{15}$.

    (a) Is $\dfrac{14}{15}$ a product or a quotient? **(b)** If one number is $\dfrac{7}{5}$, what is the other number?

4.3 ORDER OF OPERATIONS WITH FRACTIONS

4.3 A. Performing any Combination of Operations on Fractions or Mixed Numbers

Recall the rules for order of operations on integers. The same rules are used for operations on rational numbers. The rules state that, we first evaluate the exponents, perform multiplication and division in the order in which they appear from left to right, and then addition and subtraction in the order in which they appear from left to right.

Objectives

After completing this section, you will be able to:

A. Simplify expressions involving fractions with different kinds of operations; and

B. Simplify complex fractions.

If the expression involves grouping symbols, then the operations within the grouping symbols should be carried out first following the above order of operations, starting with the innermost grouping symbol. Study the following procedure and examples carefully.

RULES FOR EVALUATING NUMERICAL EXPRESSIONS

Rule 1   Evaluate any expression(s) within *grouping symbols first*. If grouping symbols are embedded, then start first with the innermost grouping.

Rule 2   If an expression involves different operations, perform these operations in the order given below:

▸ Evaluate exponents from left to right.

▸ Evaluate multiplication and division, from left to right.

▸ Evaluate addition and subtraction from left to right.

Example 1   Simplify the expressions.

(a) $\dfrac{1}{2} + \dfrac{3}{4} \cdot \dfrac{8}{9}$

(b) $\dfrac{3}{5} \div \dfrac{27}{25} - \dfrac{4}{15}$

Solutions

(a) $\dfrac{1}{2} + \underbrace{\dfrac{\mathbf{3}}{\mathbf{4}} \cdot \dfrac{\mathbf{8}}{\mathbf{9}}}$

• Perform multiplication first.

$$\dfrac{\overset{1}{\cancel{3}}}{\underset{1}{\cancel{4}}} \cdot \dfrac{\overset{2}{\cancel{8}}}{\underset{3}{\cancel{9}}} = \dfrac{2}{3}$$

$= \dfrac{1}{2} + \dfrac{2}{3}$

• Now perform addition. LCD = 6

$= \dfrac{3}{6} + \dfrac{4}{6} = \dfrac{7}{6} = \mathbf{1\dfrac{1}{6}}$

(b) $\underbrace{\dfrac{\mathbf{3}}{\mathbf{5}} \div \dfrac{\mathbf{27}}{\mathbf{25}}} - \dfrac{4}{15}$

• Perform division first.

$$\dfrac{3}{5} \div \dfrac{27}{25} = \dfrac{\overset{1}{\cancel{3}}}{\underset{1}{\cancel{5}}} \cdot \dfrac{\overset{5}{\cancel{25}}}{\underset{9}{\cancel{27}}} = \dfrac{5}{9}$$

$= \dfrac{5}{9} - \dfrac{4}{15}$

• Now perform subtraction. LCD = 45

$= \dfrac{5}{9} + \dfrac{-4}{15} = \dfrac{5(5)}{9(5)} + \dfrac{-4(3)}{15(3)} = \dfrac{25 + (-12)}{45} = \dfrac{\mathbf{13}}{\mathbf{45}}$

Warm-Up

1. Simplify the expressions.

(a) $\dfrac{2}{3} + \dfrac{5}{6} \cdot \dfrac{9}{15}$

(b) $\dfrac{4}{9} \div \dfrac{16}{27} - \dfrac{5}{18}$

Warm-Up

2. Perform the indicated operations.

$$\frac{3}{8} \div \left(\frac{1}{4}\right)^2 - \frac{5}{7} \cdot \frac{7}{13}$$

3. Simplify:

$$\frac{13}{17} \div \left(4\frac{1}{2} + 5\frac{3}{4} \div 1\frac{1}{4}\right)$$

Example 2   Perform the indicated operations.

$$\frac{5}{8} \div \frac{1}{10} + \left(\frac{1}{3}\right)^2 \cdot \frac{3}{5}$$

Solution

$$\frac{5}{8} \div \frac{1}{10} + \left(\frac{1}{3}\right)^2 \cdot \frac{3}{5}$$
   • Simplify the exponent.

$$= \frac{5}{8} \div \frac{1}{10} + \frac{1}{9} \cdot \frac{3}{5}$$
   • Simplify the division and the multiplication.

$$\begin{array}{c|c} \frac{5}{8} \div \frac{1}{10} & \frac{1}{9} \cdot \frac{3}{5} = \frac{1}{\cancel{9}} \cdot \frac{\cancel{3}^1}{5} = \frac{1}{15} \\[6pt] = \frac{5}{8} \cdot \frac{10}{1} = \frac{5}{\cancel{8}} \cdot \frac{\cancel{10}^5}{1} = \frac{25}{4} & _3 \end{array}$$

$$= \frac{25}{4} + \frac{1}{15}$$

$$= \frac{25}{4} + \frac{1}{15} = \frac{25(15)}{4(15)} + \frac{1(4)}{15(4)}$$
   • Simplify the addition. LCD = 60

$$= \frac{375 + 4}{60} = \frac{379}{60} = 6\frac{19}{60}$$

Example 3   Simplify the numerical expression.

$$\frac{3}{4} \div \left(\frac{5}{6} \div 2 + 1\frac{1}{4}\right) + 1\frac{1}{2}$$

Solution   First change the mixed numbers to improper fractions. The given expression then becomes:

$$\frac{3}{4} \div \left(\frac{5}{6} \div \frac{2}{1} + \frac{5}{4}\right) + \frac{3}{2}$$
   • Simplify within parentheses. Rewrite the division as multiplication.

$$\frac{5}{6} \div \frac{2}{1} = \frac{5}{6} \cdot \frac{1}{2} = \frac{5}{12}$$

$$= \frac{3}{4} \div \left(\frac{5}{12} + \frac{5}{4}\right) + \frac{3}{2}$$
   • Add within the parentheses. The LCD = 12.

$$= \frac{3}{4} \div \left(\frac{5}{12} + \frac{15}{12}\right) + \frac{3}{2}$$

$$= \frac{3}{4} \div \frac{20}{12} + \frac{3}{2}$$
   $$\frac{20}{12} = \frac{\cancel{4} \cdot 5}{\cancel{4} \cdot 3} = \frac{5}{3}$$

$$= \underbrace{\frac{3}{4} \div \frac{5}{3}}_{} + \frac{3}{2}$$
   • Divide: Multiply by the reciprocal of the divisor.

$$\frac{3}{4} \div \frac{5}{3} = \frac{3}{4} \cdot \frac{3}{5} = \frac{9}{20}$$

$$= \frac{9}{20} + \frac{3}{2} = \frac{39}{20}$$
   • Finally, add. The LCD is 20.

$$\frac{9}{20} + \frac{3(10)}{2(10)} = \frac{9 + (30)}{20} = \frac{39}{20}$$

$$= 1\frac{19}{20}$$

Example 4   Divide the sum of $\dfrac{91}{12}$ and $\dfrac{11}{3}$ by their difference.

Solution   Translate.

$$\underbrace{\text{Divide the}}\ \underbrace{\text{sum of } \dfrac{91}{12} \text{ and } \dfrac{11}{3}}\ \underbrace{\text{by their difference.}}$$

$$\left(\dfrac{91}{12} + \dfrac{11}{3}\right) \div \left(\dfrac{91}{12} - \dfrac{11}{3}\right)$$

Make sure to enclose the expressions for sum and difference in parentheses.

$$\left(\dfrac{91}{12} + \dfrac{11}{3}\right) \div \left(\dfrac{91}{12} - \dfrac{11}{3}\right)$$

$$= \dfrac{135}{12} \div \dfrac{47}{12}$$

$$= \dfrac{135}{\cancel{12}} \times \dfrac{\cancel{12}^{\,1}}{47}$$

$$= \dfrac{135}{47} = \mathbf{2\dfrac{41}{47}}.$$

- Evaluate the parentheses.
  Rewrite the subtraction as addition.

$$\dfrac{91}{12} + \dfrac{11(4)}{3(4)} \qquad\Big|\qquad \dfrac{91}{12} + \dfrac{-11(4)}{3(4)}$$

$$= \dfrac{91+44}{12} \qquad\Big|\qquad = \dfrac{91+(-44)}{12}$$

$$= \dfrac{135}{12} \qquad\Big|\qquad = \dfrac{47}{12}$$

4.3 B. Simplifying Complex Fractions

A **complex fraction** is a fraction in which the numerator, denominator, or both contain one or more fractions or mixed numbers.

To simplify a complex fraction such as $\dfrac{\frac{3}{4}}{\frac{9}{10}}$, whose numerator or denominator contains a fraction, rewrite the complex fraction as a division problem.

$$\dfrac{\frac{3}{4}}{\frac{9}{10}} = \dfrac{3}{4} \div \dfrac{9}{10}$$

Divide. Rewrite the division as a multiplication, cancel factors, and multiply.

$$= \dfrac{\cancel{3}^{\,1}}{\cancel{4}_{\,2}} \cdot \dfrac{\cancel{10}^{\,5}}{\cancel{9}_{\,3}} = \dfrac{5}{6}$$

- To simplify complex fractions such as $\dfrac{4\frac{3}{5}+\frac{1}{2}}{3-\frac{2}{3}}$, rewrite the complex fraction as a division. Be sure to enclose the numerator and the denominator in parentheses, since they are expressions involving operations.

Procedure to simplify complex fractions:

Step **1** Rewrite the complex fraction as a division problem. Be sure to use parentheses to enclose the numerator and the denominator, if they contain operations.

Step **2** Use the order of operations to evaluate the expression, if several operations are indicated.

Warm-Up

5. Evaluate: $\dfrac{3\frac{3}{4}-\frac{1}{6}}{2-\frac{1}{2}}$

Answer:

5. $\frac{43}{18}$

Example 5 Evaluate: $\dfrac{4\frac{3}{5}+\frac{1}{2}}{3-\frac{2}{3}}$

Solution $\dfrac{4\frac{3}{5}+\frac{1}{2}}{3-\frac{2}{3}} = \left(4\frac{3}{5}+\frac{1}{2}\right) \div \left(3-\frac{2}{3}\right)$

- Rewrite as a division problem, using parentheses to enclose the expressions in the numerator and in the denominator.

$= \left(\dfrac{23}{5}+\dfrac{1}{2}\right) \div \left(\dfrac{3}{1}+\dfrac{-2}{3}\right)$

- Rewrite using improper fractions.
- Rewrite subtraction as addition.
- Simplify the expressions within grouping symbols.

$= \dfrac{51}{10} \div \dfrac{7}{3}$

$= \dfrac{51}{10} \cdot \dfrac{3}{7} = \dfrac{153}{70}$

$= 2\dfrac{13}{70}$

LCD = 10	LCD = 3
$\frac{23(2)}{5(2)}+\frac{1(5)}{2(5)}$	$\frac{3(3)}{1(3)}+\frac{-2}{3}$
$=\frac{46+5}{10}$	$=\frac{9+(-2)}{3}$
$=\frac{51}{10}$	$=\frac{7}{3}$

Exercise **4.3**

A. In exercises 1-34, perform the indicated operations.

1. $\dfrac{5}{9}+\dfrac{7}{3}\times\dfrac{9}{5}$

2. $\dfrac{7}{8}+\dfrac{8}{9}\times\dfrac{3}{4}$

3. $\dfrac{2}{3}+\dfrac{5}{7}\times\dfrac{14}{15}$

4. $\dfrac{5}{6}-\dfrac{11}{16}\times\dfrac{18}{22}$

5. $\dfrac{7}{12}-\dfrac{13}{30}\times\dfrac{5}{26}$

6. $\dfrac{3}{4}+\dfrac{5}{8}\div\dfrac{3}{16}$

7. $\dfrac{4}{5}-\dfrac{8}{18}\div\dfrac{20}{27}$

8. $\dfrac{5}{6}+\dfrac{7}{24}\div\dfrac{21}{8}$

9. $\dfrac{5}{8}-\dfrac{21}{6}\div\dfrac{14}{3}$

10. $\dfrac{7}{9}-\dfrac{11}{15}\div\dfrac{44}{20}$

11. $\dfrac{1}{3}\div\dfrac{1}{2}+\dfrac{5}{12}\cdot\dfrac{2}{5}-\dfrac{1}{6}$

12. $\dfrac{7}{12}-\dfrac{1}{2}\cdot\dfrac{3}{4}+\left(\dfrac{3}{4}\right)^2$

13. $\dfrac{2}{3}\div\dfrac{3}{5}\cdot\dfrac{5}{9}$

14. $\dfrac{3}{4}\div\dfrac{9}{8}\cdot\dfrac{15}{10}$

15. $\dfrac{9}{10}\div\dfrac{6}{15}\cdot\dfrac{7}{18}$

16. $\dfrac{2}{3}\cdot\dfrac{3}{5}\div\dfrac{5}{9}$

17. $\dfrac{3}{4}\cdot\dfrac{4}{5}\div\dfrac{5}{16}$

18. $\dfrac{5}{7}\cdot\dfrac{21}{20}\div\dfrac{6}{8}$

19. $\dfrac{2}{3}\div\left(\dfrac{3}{5}\cdot\dfrac{5}{9}\right)$

20. $\dfrac{5}{7}\div\left(\dfrac{2}{3}\cdot\dfrac{3}{7}\right)$

21. $\dfrac{9}{10}\div\left(\dfrac{6}{8}\cdot\dfrac{12}{5}\right)$

22. $\dfrac{1}{4}-\dfrac{2}{27}\div\dfrac{8}{3}$

23. $\dfrac{5}{6}\div\dfrac{3}{4}+\dfrac{4}{5}\cdot\dfrac{25}{16}$

24. $\dfrac{5}{6}+\dfrac{3}{4}-\dfrac{4}{5}\div\dfrac{2}{3}$

25. $\left(\dfrac{24}{35} \div \dfrac{1}{7} + \dfrac{5}{9}\right) \cdot \dfrac{3}{4}$

26. $\dfrac{3}{8} \div \dfrac{1}{16} - \dfrac{5}{17}$

27. $\dfrac{3}{4} + \left(\dfrac{1}{2}\right)^2 - \dfrac{5}{7} \cdot \dfrac{3}{8} \div \dfrac{4}{7}$

28. $\left(2\dfrac{1}{2} + 1\dfrac{1}{4}\right) \div 7\dfrac{1}{2}$

29. $\dfrac{4}{9} \div \dfrac{2}{3} - \left(\dfrac{3}{9}\right)^2 \cdot \dfrac{8}{15} + \dfrac{1}{6}$

30. $\dfrac{2}{3} + \left[3\dfrac{1}{2} - \left\{5\dfrac{1}{2} - \left(4 + \dfrac{18}{5} \cdot 1\dfrac{2}{3} - 5\right)\right\}\right]$

31. $2\dfrac{1}{2} - \left[1\dfrac{1}{3} + \left(\dfrac{1}{2} - \dfrac{1}{3}\right)\right]$

32. $\dfrac{3}{4} + \left(\dfrac{29}{12} - \dfrac{5}{4} \cdot \dfrac{3}{2}\right) \div \dfrac{5}{6}$

33. $\left[\dfrac{3}{8} - \left(\dfrac{2}{3} \div \dfrac{4}{5} - \dfrac{1}{2}\right)\right] \div \dfrac{37}{48}$

34. $\dfrac{4}{5} - \dfrac{2}{5} \cdot \dfrac{1}{2} + \left(\dfrac{3}{5} + \dfrac{7}{15}\right)\left(\dfrac{3}{2}\right)^2$

B. In exercises 35-54, simplify the complex fraction. Write the answer as a mixed number, if possible.

35. $\dfrac{\dfrac{3}{5} + \dfrac{1}{2}}{\dfrac{7}{8} - \dfrac{1}{3}}$

36. $\dfrac{\dfrac{2}{3} + \dfrac{1}{6}}{1 - \dfrac{1}{3}}$

37. $\dfrac{\dfrac{5}{8} - \dfrac{1}{2}}{\dfrac{1}{8} - \dfrac{3}{16}}$

38. $\dfrac{\dfrac{1}{4} + \dfrac{1}{3}}{2\dfrac{1}{3}}$

39. $\dfrac{\dfrac{2}{5} + \dfrac{7}{15}}{\dfrac{2}{3} - \dfrac{1}{4}}$

40. $\dfrac{3 - \dfrac{1}{2}}{1 - \dfrac{1}{3}}$

41. $\dfrac{8 - \dfrac{3}{4}}{\dfrac{3}{5} - 2}$

42. $\dfrac{\dfrac{1}{2} - \dfrac{1}{6}}{\dfrac{3}{8} + \dfrac{1}{4}}$

43. $\dfrac{\dfrac{5}{8}}{3}$

44. $\dfrac{\dfrac{2}{3}}{-5}$

45. $\dfrac{2 - \dfrac{1}{3}}{1 - \dfrac{1}{3}}$

46. $\dfrac{\dfrac{2}{3} + 4\dfrac{1}{3}}{\dfrac{11}{2} - \dfrac{7}{12}}$

47. $\dfrac{\dfrac{2}{3} - 5}{\dfrac{5}{6} - \dfrac{1}{4}}$

48. $\dfrac{\dfrac{3}{2a}}{\dfrac{6}{a}}$

49. $\dfrac{-3}{\dfrac{4}{9} - 2\dfrac{2}{3}}$

50. $\dfrac{\dfrac{1}{4} - \dfrac{7}{8}}{-15y}$

51. $\dfrac{7\dfrac{1}{3}}{-\dfrac{1}{4}}$

52. $\dfrac{-2\dfrac{1}{7}}{-2\dfrac{1}{17}}$

53. $\dfrac{7\dfrac{1}{5}}{-3}$

54. $\dfrac{6}{7\dfrac{7}{8}}$

55. The sum of $-5\dfrac{1}{10}$ and $6\dfrac{1}{2}$ is to be divided by the sum of $-1\dfrac{3}{4}$ and $-4\dfrac{1}{2}$. **(a)** Write this expression in the form of a complex fraction. **(b)** Write an equivalent expression using two pairs of parentheses and a division sign. Do not simplify the expression.

56. The sum of $1\dfrac{1}{2}$ and $\dfrac{5}{6}$ is to be divided by the difference between 4 and $2\dfrac{3}{5}$. **(a)** Write this expression in the form of a complex fraction. **(b)** Write an equivalent expression using two pairs of parentheses and a division sign. Do not simplify the expression.

57. The difference between 1 and $\dfrac{1}{5}$ is to be divided by the sum of $2\dfrac{1}{4}$ and $-\dfrac{3}{8}$. Write this expression in the form of a complex fraction, and then simplify the complex fraction.

58. The sum of $4\dfrac{2}{7}$ and $1\dfrac{3}{5}$ is to be multiplied with the difference between them. Write this expression using two pairs of parentheses.

59. The sum of $-2\dfrac{1}{5}$ and $4\dfrac{3}{10}$ is to be divided by the sum of 6 and $\dfrac{3}{7}$. Write this expression in the form of a complex fraction, then simplify the complex fraction.

60. Divide the sum of $\dfrac{1}{6}$ and $\dfrac{7}{10}$ by the sum of $\dfrac{2}{3}$ and $\dfrac{1}{12}$.

61. Multiply the difference of 15 and $8\dfrac{3}{7}$ by the sum of $2\dfrac{4}{7}$ and $3\dfrac{11}{14}$.

62. Divide $\dfrac{61}{78}$ by the sum of $3\dfrac{1}{10}$, $2\dfrac{3}{5}$, and $4\dfrac{7}{15}$.

63. Find the difference of the product of $\dfrac{5}{7}$ and $17\dfrac{1}{2}$ and the difference of $6\dfrac{3}{4}$ and $4\dfrac{7}{8}$.

64. Add the difference of $\dfrac{7}{16}$ and $\dfrac{1}{6}$ to the sum of $\dfrac{5}{8}$ and $\dfrac{1}{6}$.

4.4 CHAPTER SUMMARY

Part-I **Important Vocabulary and Symbols**

1. The sum of two or more fractions with a common denominator $= \dfrac{\text{sum of the numerators}}{\text{common denominator}}$, $\dfrac{a}{b} + \dfrac{c}{b} = \dfrac{a+c}{b}$.

2. To simplify a fraction to **lowest terms** means to write an equivalent fraction such that the numerator and the denominator have no factor in common except 1.

3. **Properties of Addition and Multiplication** used with Rational Numbers:

    (a) Commutative Properties   **(b)** Associative Properties   **(c)** Identity Properties

    (d) Inverse Properties   **(e)** Zero Factor Property

4. **Reciprocals** are a pair of numbers whose product is 1.

$\dfrac{3}{5}$ and $\dfrac{5}{3}$ are reciprocals of each other because $\dfrac{3}{5} \cdot \dfrac{5}{3} = \dfrac{15}{15}$

$$= 1.$$

5. The **reciprocal** of a (non-zero) rational number is also called its **multiplicative inverse.**

The multiplicative inverse of $\dfrac{3}{5}$ is $\dfrac{5}{3}$.

6. **Division with Fractions:** To divide one fraction by a second fraction, multiply the first (fraction) by the reciprocal of the second (fraction).

7. A **complex fraction** is a fraction in which the numerator, denominator, or both contain one or more fractions or mixed numbers.

Fractions such as $\dfrac{\frac{3}{5}}{\frac{2}{7}}$ and $\dfrac{1\frac{3}{5}+\frac{1}{2}}{3-\frac{2}{3}}$ are **complex fractions**.

Part-II Procedures and Rules

ADDITION AND SUBTRACTION WITH FRACTIONS

Examples

1. To add two or more fractions with different denominators:

    Step 1 Express all numbers in fraction form.

    Step 2 Find the LCD of the given fractions.

    Step 3 Convert the fractions to equivalent fractions with the LCD as the common denominator.

    Step 4 Add the new like fractions.

    Step 5 Simplify the sum to lowest terms.

1. Find the sum: $\dfrac{5}{6}-\dfrac{7}{8}-\dfrac{4}{15}$.

    The LCD $= 120$.

    $$\dfrac{5}{6}=\dfrac{5\cdot\mathbf{20}}{6\cdot\mathbf{20}}=\dfrac{100}{120}\,;\,\dfrac{7}{8}=\dfrac{7\cdot\mathbf{15}}{8\cdot\mathbf{15}}=\dfrac{105}{120}$$

    $$\dfrac{4}{15}=\dfrac{4\cdot\mathbf{8}}{15\cdot\mathbf{8}}=\dfrac{32}{120}\,;$$

    so,

    $$\dfrac{5}{6}-\dfrac{7}{8}-\dfrac{4}{15}=\dfrac{100-105-32}{120}=\dfrac{-37}{120}.$$

2. To subtract fractions or mixed numbers:

    i) Rewrite the subtraction as addition of the opposite.

    ii) Follow the rules for **addition**:

2. Subtract $\dfrac{5}{18}$ from $3\dfrac{1}{4}$.

    $$3\dfrac{1}{4}-\dfrac{5}{18}=\dfrac{13}{4}+\dfrac{-5}{18}\quad\text{(LCD = 36)}$$

    $$=\dfrac{117}{36}+\dfrac{-10}{36}=\dfrac{117+(-10)}{36}$$

    $$=\dfrac{107}{36}=2\dfrac{35}{36}\quad\begin{array}{l}\text{The difference is already}\\\text{in lowest terms.}\end{array}$$

MULTIPLICATION AND DIVISION WITH RATIONAL NUMBERS

3. To multiply two or more fractions:

    Step 1 Express all numbers as fractions.

    Step 2 Cancel out the common factors, if any, between the numerators and the denominators.

    Step 3 Multiply the remaining factors of the numerators, and the remaining factors of the denominators.

3. a. $\dfrac{25}{36}\cdot\dfrac{-6}{40}=\dfrac{\overset{5}{\cancel{25}}\cdot\overset{1}{\cancel{-6}}}{\underset{6}{\cancel{36}}\cdot\underset{8}{\cancel{40}}}$

    $$=-\dfrac{5}{48}$$

    b. $\left(3\dfrac{4}{7}\right)\left(6\dfrac{4}{5}\right)=\dfrac{25}{7}\cdot\dfrac{34}{5}$

    $$=\dfrac{\overset{5}{\cancel{25}}\cdot 34}{7\cdot\underset{1}{\cancel{5}}}$$

    $$=\dfrac{170}{7}\text{ or }24\dfrac{2}{7}$$

Examples

4. The reciprocal of $\dfrac{2}{11}$ is $\dfrac{11}{2}$.

The reciprocal of $55 \left(\text{or} \dfrac{55}{1}\right)$ is $\dfrac{1}{55}$.

Check: $55 \cdot \dfrac{1}{55} = \dfrac{\overset{1}{\cancel{55}}}{1} \cdot \dfrac{1}{\underset{1}{\cancel{55}}} = 1$

The reciprocal of $-2 \left(\text{or} \dfrac{-2}{1}\right)$ is $\dfrac{1}{-2}$ or $-\dfrac{1}{2}$.

Check: $(-2) \cdot \left(-\dfrac{1}{2}\right) = \dfrac{\overset{1}{\cancel{-2}}}{1} \cdot \dfrac{1}{\underset{1}{\cancel{-2}}} = 1$

5. Divide and reduce to lowest terms.

$$\dfrac{18}{35} \div \dfrac{3}{20} = \dfrac{18}{35} \cdot \dfrac{20}{3}$$

$$= \dfrac{\overset{6}{\cancel{18}}}{\underset{7}{\cancel{35}}} \cdot \dfrac{\overset{4}{\cancel{20}}}{\underset{1}{\cancel{3}}}$$

$$= \dfrac{24}{7}$$

6. Simplify:

$$\dfrac{1}{4} + \dfrac{3}{4} \div \dfrac{8}{9}$$

$$= \dfrac{1}{4} + \dfrac{3}{4} \cdot \dfrac{9}{8}$$

$$= \dfrac{1}{4} + \dfrac{27}{32}$$

$$= \dfrac{8}{32} + \dfrac{27}{32} = \dfrac{35}{32} = 1\dfrac{3}{32}$$

7. Simplify:

$$\dfrac{2\dfrac{1}{8} + \dfrac{3}{4}}{4 - \dfrac{1}{2}} = \left(2\dfrac{1}{8} + \dfrac{3}{4}\right) \div \left(4 - \dfrac{1}{2}\right)$$

$$= \left(\dfrac{17}{8} + \dfrac{3}{4}\right) \div \left(\dfrac{4}{1} + \dfrac{-1}{2}\right)$$

$$= \dfrac{23}{8} \div \dfrac{7}{2}$$

$$= \dfrac{23}{\underset{4}{\cancel{8}}} \cdot \dfrac{\overset{1}{\cancel{2}}}{7}$$

$$= \dfrac{23}{28}$$

4. To find the multiplicative inverse (or the reciprocal) of a number:

> **Step 1** **a.** If the number is a fraction, find the reciprocal (or the multiplicative inverse) by inverting it (that is, interchanging the numerator and the denominator).
>
> **b.** If the number is a non-zero integer, first write it as a fraction with a denominator of 1, then invert the fraction.
>
> **Step 2** Check to verify that the product of a number and its reciprocal is 1.

5. To divide fractions:

> **Step 1** Write the numbers as fractions.
>
> **Step 2** Change division to multiplication.
>
> That is, change "division by a number" to "multiply by the reciprocal of that number".
>
> **Step 3** Proceed with multiplication.

ORDER OF OPERATIONS WITH FRACTIONS

6. To simplify numerical expressions:

> *Rule 1* Simplify any expression(s) within *grouping symbols first*. If grouping symbols are embedded, start with the innermost grouping symbol.
>
> *Rule 2* If an expression involves different operations, perform these operations in the order given below:
>
> ▸ Simplify the exponents first, from left to right.
> ▸ Simplify multiplication and division from left to right.
> ▸ Simplify addition and subtraction from left to right.

7. To simplify complex fractions:

> **Step 1** Rewrite the complex fraction as a division problem. Be sure to use parentheses to enclose the numerator and the denominator, if they contain operations.
>
> **Step 2** Use the order of operations to simplify the expression if several operations are involved.

4.5 REVIEW EXERCISE

1. Add the given fractions and write the sum in lowest terms.

   (a) $\dfrac{6}{35}+\dfrac{5}{7}+\dfrac{4}{5}$ (b) $\dfrac{1}{3}+\dfrac{3}{5}+\dfrac{11}{15}$ (c) $\dfrac{9}{16}+\dfrac{13}{24}+\dfrac{7}{16}$ (d) $\dfrac{2}{14}+\dfrac{3}{4}-\dfrac{11}{28}$

2. Simplify:

   (a) $\dfrac{2}{3x}+\dfrac{13}{4x}+\dfrac{17}{6x}$ (b) $5\dfrac{2}{3}+2\dfrac{1}{4}+9\dfrac{5}{6}$ (c) $\dfrac{2a}{3b}-\dfrac{5}{6b}+\dfrac{a}{9b}$ (d) $1\dfrac{3}{5}-2\dfrac{1}{2}+3\dfrac{11}{15}$

3. Simplify:

   (a) $\dfrac{3}{4}-\dfrac{2}{3}$ (b) $\dfrac{14}{3}-\left(-\dfrac{15}{4}\right)$ (c) $\dfrac{3}{x}-\dfrac{9}{x}$ (d) $\dfrac{19}{y}-\dfrac{40}{7y}$

4. Simplify:

   (a) $1\dfrac{3}{4}+2\dfrac{1}{2}$ (b) $2\dfrac{1}{5}-3\dfrac{4}{5}$ (c) $-\dfrac{15}{7}+2\dfrac{6}{7}$ (d) $-3\dfrac{3}{4}-4$

5. Perform the indicated operations and reduce the answers to lowest terms.

   (a) $\dfrac{3}{5}+\dfrac{7}{15}+\dfrac{5}{6}$ (b) $\dfrac{21}{16}+\dfrac{7}{12}-\dfrac{5}{24}$ (c) $\dfrac{15}{45}-\dfrac{9}{27}+\dfrac{1}{5}$ (d) $\dfrac{1}{10}-\left(-\dfrac{3}{10}\right)-\dfrac{4}{15}$

6. Perform the indicated operations. Assume that all variables are non-zero.

   (a) $\dfrac{x}{15}-\dfrac{1}{3}-\dfrac{2}{15}$ (b) $\dfrac{7}{6x}-\dfrac{1}{8x}+\dfrac{2}{3x}$ (c) $\dfrac{3}{2x}-\dfrac{5}{4x}+\dfrac{9}{5x}$ (d) $\dfrac{2x}{3}-\dfrac{5}{2x}+\dfrac{x}{6}$

7. Multiply the given fractions and write the product in lowest terms.

   (a) $\dfrac{1}{2}\left(-\dfrac{3}{5}\right)\left(\dfrac{10}{9}\right)$ (b) $\dfrac{3}{11}\cdot\dfrac{7}{2}\cdot\dfrac{44}{5}$ (c) $\left(-\dfrac{4}{25}\right)\left(\dfrac{5}{3}\right)\left(-\dfrac{2}{3}\right)\cdot5$ (d) $\left(\dfrac{81}{100}\right)\left(\dfrac{150}{-54}\right)\cdot5$ (e) $4\dfrac{1}{5}\cdot5\dfrac{3}{5}\cdot3\dfrac{4}{7}$

8. Multiply the given algebraic fractions and write the product in lowest terms.

   (a) $\dfrac{2}{3}\left(-\dfrac{3c}{4x}\right)\left(\dfrac{2x^2}{c^2}\right)$ (b) $\dfrac{15a^2x}{4b}\cdot\dfrac{6\,ab}{5x^2}\cdot\dfrac{2}{3a}$ (c) $\dfrac{-8xy^2}{16m^3}\cdot\dfrac{-8\,m}{3y}\cdot15\,m^2$

In exercises 9-15, state the Multiplication property that is illustrated.

9. $\left(\dfrac{2x}{3}\cdot\dfrac{-5}{6}\right)\cdot\dfrac{18}{7}=\dfrac{2x}{3}\cdot\left(\dfrac{-5}{6}\cdot\dfrac{18}{7}\right)$ 10. $\dfrac{-7}{5}\cdot0=0$ 11. $\dfrac{2a}{3b}\cdot\dfrac{3b}{2a}=1$ 12. $\dfrac{15x}{y}\cdot\dfrac{-3}{4}=\dfrac{-3}{4}\cdot\dfrac{15x}{y}$

13. $-\dfrac{1}{5}\cdot\left(\dfrac{3}{7}\cdot\dfrac{4}{9}\right)=\left(-\dfrac{1}{5}\cdot\dfrac{3}{7}\right)\cdot\dfrac{4}{9}$ 14. $\dfrac{-5}{17}\cdot1=\dfrac{-5}{17}$ 15. $1\cdot\dfrac{215}{317}=\dfrac{215}{317}$

16. Write the reciprocal of the given expression, if defined.

   (a) $\dfrac{7}{5}$ (b) -14 (c) $\dfrac{1}{13x^2}$ (d) $\dfrac{0}{5}$

17. Write the multiplicative inverse of the given numbers, if defined.

(a) $\dfrac{8}{5}$ (b) 14 (c) 0 (d) $-\dfrac{37}{25}$

In exercises 18-20, divide and reduce to lowest terms.

18. $\dfrac{9}{64} \div \dfrac{-27}{80}$ **19.** $\left(-\dfrac{24}{36}\right) \div \left(-\dfrac{8}{9}\right)$ **20.** $\dfrac{25}{-7x} \div \dfrac{32x}{14}$

In exercises 21-24, perform the indicated operations.

21. $\dfrac{5}{6} \cdot \dfrac{3}{10} \div \dfrac{15}{-4}$ **22.** $\dfrac{7}{8} \cdot \dfrac{15}{4} \div \dfrac{5}{2}$ **23.** $\dfrac{8a^2x}{5y^2} \div \dfrac{4a}{15xy} \cdot \dfrac{11y^3}{2ax^2}$ **24.** $\dfrac{5ya^2}{8ay} \cdot \dfrac{24}{10a} \div \dfrac{16y^2}{9a}$

25. Use the order of operations to simplify each of the following expressions:

(a) $\dfrac{5}{6} \div \dfrac{3}{4} + \dfrac{4}{5} \cdot \dfrac{25}{16}$ (b) $2\dfrac{1}{2} \cdot 3\dfrac{1}{5} \div \dfrac{3}{4} + \dfrac{7}{10}$ (c) $\dfrac{24}{25} \div \left[3 - \left(\dfrac{3}{5} + \dfrac{7}{10} \cdot \dfrac{2}{3}\right)\left(\dfrac{3}{2}\right)^2\right]$

26. Simplify the given expressions by using the rules of order of operations.

(a) $4 - \dfrac{4}{7} \div 1\dfrac{3}{5}$ (b) $2\dfrac{7}{10} \div 5\dfrac{1}{4} - \dfrac{4}{7}$ (c) $\dfrac{2}{3} + \dfrac{8}{9} \cdot \left(2\dfrac{1}{4}\right)$

27. Simplify the following complex fractions:

(a) $\dfrac{\dfrac{3}{4} + \dfrac{1}{2}}{1 - \dfrac{1}{3}}$ (b) $\dfrac{\dfrac{5}{9} - \dfrac{4}{3}}{\dfrac{16}{21} + \dfrac{6}{7}}$ (c) $\dfrac{6\dfrac{1}{10} - 3\dfrac{1}{5}}{2\dfrac{1}{5} + 1\dfrac{1}{2}}$

28. Simplify the following complex fractions:

(a) $\dfrac{\dfrac{4}{3x}}{\dfrac{8}{9x}}$ (b) $\dfrac{\dfrac{1}{3} - 2}{\dfrac{1}{3} + 2}$ (c) $\dfrac{\dfrac{7x}{8} - \dfrac{x}{4}}{x + \dfrac{x}{4}}$ (d) $\dfrac{-3\dfrac{4}{5}}{\dfrac{3}{4} + \dfrac{1}{5}}$

29. The difference of $\dfrac{5}{7}$ and $2\dfrac{1}{3}$ is to be divided by the sum of $-2\dfrac{1}{4}$ and $\dfrac{7}{8}$; **(a)** write the expression in the form of a complex fraction, **(b)** write an equivalent expression by using two pairs of parentheses and a division sign, and **(c)** simplify the expression.

4.6 SELF TEST

1. Add: $\dfrac{5}{6} + \dfrac{7}{8}$.

2. Multiply: $4\dfrac{3}{5} \times \left(-7\dfrac{1}{2}\right)$.

3. Write the reciprocal of $\dfrac{-a}{2x}$.

4. Subtract: $\dfrac{3}{8a} - \dfrac{4}{5a}$.

5. Subtract: $7\dfrac{3}{8} - 4$.

6. Divide: $\dfrac{5x}{y^2} \div \dfrac{15x^2}{y^3}$.

7. Simplify: $\dfrac{7}{6} \div \dfrac{5}{3} \cdot \dfrac{5}{14} \div \left(\dfrac{1}{2}\right)$.

8. Perform the indicated operations: $\left(-\dfrac{5}{6} + \dfrac{1}{2}\right) \div \left[\dfrac{3}{8} - \left(-\dfrac{1}{12}\right)\right]$.

9. Simplify: $\dfrac{3}{5} + \left[1\dfrac{1}{2} \cdot \left(4\dfrac{1}{4} - 3\dfrac{1}{2}\right)\right] \div \dfrac{2}{5}$.

10. Simplify: $1\dfrac{1}{5} + \dfrac{15}{16} \div 2\dfrac{1}{2} - \dfrac{13}{10}$.

11. Simplify to a single fraction by using the order of operations: $\dfrac{x}{5} \cdot \dfrac{1}{3} - \dfrac{2}{5} \div 3$.

12. Simplify the complex fraction and express the answer as a mixed number in lowest terms: $\dfrac{1\dfrac{3}{10} + 2\dfrac{4}{5}}{2\dfrac{3}{5} - 1\dfrac{1}{3}}$.

Applications with Fractions

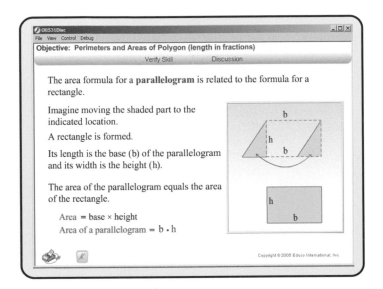

5.1 **Equations with Fractions and Proportions**

5.2 **General Applications**

5.3 **Geometric Applications**

5.4 **Chapter Summary**

5.5 **Review Exercise**

5.6 **Self Test**

Applications with Fractions

APPLICATIONS WITH FRACTIONS

Introduction

In this chapter, we shall learn to solve equations with fractions and study real-world and geometrical applications that involve the use of fractions.

This chapter is divided into the following three sections:

5.1   *Equations with Fractions and Proportions;*

5.2   *General Applications ; and*

5.3   *Geometric Applications.*

5.1   EQUATIONS WITH FRACTIONS AND PROPORTIONS

5.1 A.   Solving Linear Equations containing Fractions

Using the Addition Principle

Recall the following property:

For any rational number a,

$$a + 0 = a \qquad \text{The Identity Property for Addition.}$$

$$a + (-a) = 0 \qquad \text{The Inverse Property of Addition.}$$

A number   Additive inverse

Objectives

After completing this section, you will be able to:

A.   Use the addition or multiplication principles to solve linear one-step equations with fractions;

B.   Use the addition and multiplication principles to solve linear equations with fractions, having the variable on one side only.

C.   Solve proportions using cross products.

These properties and the addition principle of equality provide a strategy for solving equations containing fractions like $x + \dfrac{2}{3} = \dfrac{4}{3}$. Recall, the addition principle of equality: "Adding the same number to both sides of an equation yields an equivalent equation".

Study the solution below

$$x + \frac{2}{3} \;=\; \frac{4}{3}$$

$$x + \frac{2}{3} + \frac{-2}{3} \;=\; \frac{4}{3} + \frac{-2}{3} \qquad \text{Add } \tfrac{-2}{3} \text{ on both sides of the equation.}$$

$$\longrightarrow \qquad x + 0 \;=\; \frac{2}{3} \qquad \text{Inverse Property.}$$

$$\longrightarrow \qquad x \;=\; \frac{2}{3} \qquad \text{Identity Property.}$$

We can check the answer by substituting $\dfrac{2}{3}$ for x in the original equation.

$$x + \frac{2}{3} = \frac{4}{3}$$

$$\frac{2}{3} + \frac{2}{3} = \frac{4}{3}$$

$$\longrightarrow \quad \frac{4}{3} = \frac{4}{3} \qquad \text{True}$$

Therefore, $x = \dfrac{2}{3}$ is the correct answer.

The method for solving linear equations with fractions is the same as the method used when a and b are integers. Recall, that the *main* objective in solving an equation is to isolate the variable on one side of the equation (usually the left side).

Warm-Up

1. Solve and check.

 (a) $x + \dfrac{5}{7} = \dfrac{4}{5}$

 (b) $x + 4\dfrac{2}{3} = 11\dfrac{1}{2}$

Example 1   Find the value of x for the given equation and check the solution.

 (a) $x + \dfrac{2}{3} = \dfrac{4}{5}$ (b) $x + \dfrac{5}{8} = 9\dfrac{1}{6}$

Solutions

 (a)
$$x + \frac{2}{3} = \frac{4}{5}$$

$$x + \frac{2}{3} + \frac{-2}{3} = \frac{4}{5} + \frac{-2}{3} \qquad \bullet \quad \text{Add } \tfrac{-2}{3} \text{ to both sides.}$$

$$x = \frac{12}{15} + \frac{-10}{15} \qquad \bullet \quad \tfrac{4}{5} = \tfrac{12}{15}, \tfrac{-2}{3} = \tfrac{-10}{15}$$

$$x = \frac{12 - 10}{15} = \frac{2}{15}$$

The solution is $x = \dfrac{2}{15}$.

Check:
$$x + \frac{2}{3} = \frac{4}{5}$$

$$\frac{2}{15} + \frac{2}{3} = \frac{4}{5} \longrightarrow \frac{4}{5} = \frac{4}{5} \quad \text{True}$$

 (b)
$$x + \frac{5}{8} = 9\frac{1}{6} \qquad \bullet \quad \text{Given equation.}$$

$$x + \frac{5}{8} + \frac{-5}{8} = \frac{55}{6} + \frac{-5}{8} \qquad \bullet \quad \text{Add } \tfrac{-5}{8} \text{ to both sides.}$$

$$x = \frac{220}{24} + \frac{-15}{24} \qquad \bullet \quad 9\tfrac{1}{6} = \tfrac{55}{6}.$$

$$\bullet \quad \text{Build the fractions to the common denominator 24.}$$

$$= 8\frac{13}{24} \qquad \bullet \quad \tfrac{220}{24} + \tfrac{-15}{24} = \tfrac{205}{24} = 8\tfrac{13}{24}.$$

The solution is $x = 8\dfrac{13}{24}$.

(The check is left as an exercise.)

• Using the Multiplication Principle

Recall the following properties:

> For any rational number a,
>
> $$1 \cdot a = a \quad \text{The Identity Property for Multiplication.}$$
>
> and $\quad a \cdot \dfrac{1}{a} = 1 . \quad$ The Inverse Property for Multiplication.
>
> (A number times its reciprocal equals 1.)

These properties and the multiplication principle of equality provide a strategy for solving equations like $\dfrac{4}{5}x = 9$, where a fraction is the numerical coefficient. We introduce the following Multiplication Principle to solve such equations.

"Multiplying both sides of an equation by the same number results in an equivalent equation, having the same solution."

Consider the equation:

$$\frac{4}{5}x = 9.$$

We would like to have $1 \cdot x$ **or** x alone on the left side. We can do this by multiplying both sides by the reciprocal of $\dfrac{4}{5}$, which is $\dfrac{5}{4}$.

$$\frac{5}{4} \cdot \frac{4}{5}x = \frac{5}{4} \cdot \frac{9}{1} \qquad \text{Multiply both sides by } \tfrac{5}{4} \text{, the multiplicative inverse of } \tfrac{4}{5}.$$

$$\longrightarrow \quad 1 \cdot x = \frac{45}{4} \qquad \text{Inverse Property.}$$

$$\longrightarrow \quad x = \frac{45}{4} \qquad \text{Identity property.}$$

We can check the answer by substituting, $\dfrac{45}{4}$ for x in the original equation.

$$\frac{4}{5}x = 9; \qquad \frac{\cancel{4}}{\cancel{5}_1} \cdot \frac{\overset{9}{\cancel{45}}}{\cancel{4}_1} = 9 \longrightarrow 9 = 9 \; ; \; \text{True}$$

Thus, $x = \dfrac{45}{4}$ is the correct solution.

 Note $\quad \dfrac{4x}{5} = \dfrac{4}{5}x \;$ and $\; \dfrac{x}{2} = \dfrac{1}{2}x$

It is usually easier to work with the fraction written as a coefficient.

Warm-Up

2. Solve the equation.

$$-\frac{5}{6}x = 3$$

Example 2   Solve the equation: $-\dfrac{3}{7}x = -2$

Solution $-\dfrac{3}{7}x = -2$

       The coefficient of x is $\dfrac{-3}{7}$.

$$\left(\frac{-7}{3} \cdot \frac{-3}{7}\right)x = \frac{-7}{3} \cdot \frac{-2}{1}$$

       Multiply both sides by its reciprocal $\dfrac{-7}{3}$.

$$1 \cdot x = \frac{14}{3}$$

$$x = \frac{14}{3}$$

The solution is $x = \dfrac{14}{3}$.

Check: $-\dfrac{3}{7}x = -2$

$$-\frac{\overset{1}{\cancel{3}}}{\underset{1}{\cancel{7}}}\left(\frac{\overset{2}{\cancel{14}}}{\underset{1}{\cancel{3}}}\right) = -2$$

$$-2 = -2 \; ; \quad \text{True}$$

3. Solve for t.

$$\frac{4}{5} = \frac{8t}{3}$$

Example 3   Solve the equation : $\dfrac{13}{3} = \dfrac{52y}{9}$

Solution $\dfrac{13}{3} = \dfrac{52y}{9}$

       The original equation.

$$\frac{52y}{9} = \frac{13}{3}$$

       Switch the sides of the equation.

$$\frac{9}{52} \cdot \frac{52}{9}y = \frac{9}{52} \cdot \frac{13}{3}$$

       The coefficient of y is $\dfrac{52}{9}$. Multiply both

       sides by its reciprocal $\dfrac{9}{52}$.

$$1 \cdot y = \frac{3}{4}$$

       Simplify $\dfrac{9}{52} \cdot \dfrac{13}{3} = \dfrac{3}{4}$

$$y = \frac{3}{4}$$

The solution is $y = \dfrac{3}{4}$.

Check: $\dfrac{13}{3} = \dfrac{52y}{9}$

       The given equation.

$$\frac{13}{3} = \frac{52}{9} \cdot \frac{3}{4}$$

       Substitute $\dfrac{3}{4}$ for y. (*Note:* $\dfrac{52y}{9} = \dfrac{52}{9} \cdot y$)

$$= \frac{13}{3} \quad \text{True}$$

$$\frac{52}{9} \cdot \frac{3}{4} = \frac{\overset{1}{\cancel{4}} \cdot 13}{3 \cdot \cancel{3}} \cdot \frac{\overset{1}{\cancel{3}}}{\cancel{4}} = \frac{13}{3}$$

Answers:

1. (a) $\dfrac{3}{35}$ **(b)** $6\dfrac{5}{6}$

2. $x = -\dfrac{18}{5}$ **3.** $t = \dfrac{3}{10}$

5.1 B. Solving equations of type $ax + b = c$, where a, b, c may be fractions.

Consider the equation

$$\frac{3}{4}x - \frac{5}{8} = -\frac{1}{2}$$

Because of fractions, this equation looks complicated. Think of a simpler integer problem to use as a model, like $3x - 5 = 1$. Use it to help you decide which number to eliminate first as you work to get x alone on the left side. Study the example below carefully.

Procedure to solve equations of the type $ax + b = c$, where a, b, and c may be fractions:

Step 1 Switch the sides of the equation, if necessary, so the variable is on the left side.

Step 2 Use the addition property to isolate the variable term on the left side.

Step 3 Use the multiplication or division property to solve for x.

Step 4 Check your solution.

Example 4 Solve the equation: $\frac{3}{5}x - 9 = 7$

Solution $\frac{3}{5}x - 9 = 7$ Add 9 to both sides first.

$$\frac{3}{5}x - 9 + 9 = 7 + 9$$

$$\frac{3}{5}x = 16$$ Multiply both sides by $\frac{5}{3}$, the reciprocal of $\frac{3}{5}$.

$$\frac{5}{3} \cdot \frac{3}{5}x = \frac{5}{3} \cdot \frac{16}{1}$$ $\frac{\overset{1}{\cancel{5}}}{\underset{1}{\cancel{3}}} \cdot \frac{\overset{1}{\cancel{3}}}{\underset{1}{\cancel{5}}} = 1$

$$1 \cdot x = \frac{80}{3}$$

$$x = \frac{80}{3}$$ Identity property

Check: $\frac{3}{5}x - 9 = 7$

$$\frac{3}{5} \cdot \frac{80}{3} - 9 = 7$$ $\frac{\overset{1}{\cancel{3}}}{\underset{1}{\cancel{5}}} \cdot \frac{\overset{16}{\cancel{80}}}{\underset{1}{\cancel{3}}} = 16$

$$16 - 9 = 7$$

$$7 = 7; \quad \text{True}$$

The solution $x = \frac{80}{3}$ is correct.

Warm-Up

4. Solve the equation.

$$-\frac{2}{3}x + 4 = 9$$

Answer:

4. $-\frac{15}{2}$

5.1 C. Solving Proportions

The concept of proportions is used quite often in daily life, in finding distances between cities on maps, comparing prices, or comparing rates. Proportions are used in all such situations where problems translate into comparing or equating two ratios or fractions. A proportion is an equation whose left side and right side are fractions.

If $\dfrac{a}{b}$ or $\dfrac{c}{d}$ are two equivalent ratios or fractions then;

$$\frac{a}{b} = \frac{c}{d} \text{ is a proportion,}$$

where a, b, c, and d are four numbers or quantities. If we are given the value of any three of these four quantities then we can find the value of the fourth quantity. This process is called solving a proportion, or finding a missing term in a proportion.

Recall, that two fractions can be shown to be equivalent by testing their cross products.

$$\frac{2}{3} = \frac{4}{6}$$ We know this is true because $\frac{4 \div 2}{6 \div 2} = \frac{2}{3}$.

The cross products are equal. $\dfrac{2}{3} \bowtie \dfrac{4}{6}$ $\longrightarrow 3 \cdot 4 = 12$
$\longrightarrow 2 \cdot 6 = 12$

In a proportion, cross products are always equal. We can use this fact to find the value of the missing term, if any, in a proportion.

For example if $\dfrac{3x}{2} = \dfrac{15}{4}$ is a proportion then;

$\dfrac{3x}{2} \bowtie \dfrac{15}{4}$ $\longrightarrow 30$
$\longrightarrow 12x$ • Find the cross products.

or $12x = 30$ • Write an equation stating that the cross products are equal.

$\longrightarrow \quad x = \dfrac{30}{12}$ • Solve.

$= \dfrac{5}{2}$

The solution is $x = \dfrac{5}{2}$.

To check, substitute for x in the original equation, and verify that the cross products are equal.

Warm-Up	Example 5	Determine whether the proportion given below is true or false.

Warm-Up

5. Whether the proportion is true.

$$\frac{3}{16} = \frac{12}{44}$$

Example 5   Determine whether the proportion given below is true or false.

$$\frac{4}{12} = \frac{25}{75}$$

Solution

$$\frac{4}{12} = \frac{25}{75}$$ Find the cross products.

$$\frac{4}{12} \diagup\hspace{-1.2em}\diagdown \frac{25}{75} \quad\begin{array}{l}\longrightarrow 12 \cdot 25 = 300 \\ \longrightarrow 4 \cdot 75 = 300\end{array} \quad \text{equal}$$

The proportion is true.

Example 6   Find the missing term in the given proportion.

(a) $\dfrac{3\frac{1}{2}}{x} = \dfrac{14}{5}$ (b) $\dfrac{x+1}{3} = \dfrac{1}{2}$

6. Find the missing term.

(a) $\dfrac{\frac{1}{2}}{x} = \dfrac{\frac{3}{4}}{1\frac{2}{3}}$

Solutions

(a) $\dfrac{3\frac{1}{2}}{x} = \dfrac{14}{5}$ The given proportion.

$\left(3\frac{1}{2}\right)\cdot 5 = x \cdot 14$ Equate the cross products. Simplify the left side

$$3\frac{1}{2}\cdot 5 = \frac{7}{2}\cdot\frac{5}{1} = \frac{35}{2}$$

$\dfrac{35}{2} = 14x$

$\dfrac{\mathbf{1}}{\mathbf{14}}\cdot\dfrac{35}{2} = \dfrac{\mathbf{1}}{\mathbf{14}}\cdot\dfrac{14}{1}\cdot x$ Multiply both sides by the reciprocal of $\frac{14}{1} : \frac{1}{14}$.

$\dfrac{5}{4} = 1\cdot x$

or $x = \dfrac{5}{4}$ or $1\dfrac{1}{4}$

The missing term in the proportion is $1\dfrac{1}{4}$.

Check, by substituting the solution into the original equation.

(b) $\dfrac{x+1}{3} = \dfrac{1}{2}$

$2(x+1) = 3\cdot 1$ Equate the cross products.
$2x + 2 = 3$
$2x + 2 - \mathbf{2} = 3 - \mathbf{2}$ Subtract 2 from both sides.
$2x = 1$

$\dfrac{2x}{2} = \dfrac{1}{2}$ Divide by 2.

$x = \dfrac{1}{2}$

(b) $\dfrac{x+3}{5} = \dfrac{1}{4}$

The solution is $\dfrac{1}{2}$, and the value of $x + 1$ is $\dfrac{1}{2}+1$ or $\dfrac{3}{2}$.

Check the resulting cross products to verify the solution.

$2\cdot\dfrac{3}{2} = 3\cdot 1 \qquad\longrightarrow\qquad 3 = 3 \qquad\text{True}$

Answers:

5. False   **6. (a)** $1\frac{1}{9}$ **(b)** $x = -\frac{7}{4}$

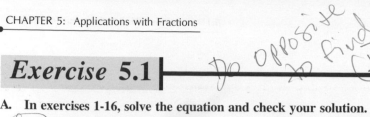

Exercise 5.1

A. In exercises 1-16, solve the equation and check your solution.

1. $x + \dfrac{1}{2} = \dfrac{3}{2}$

2. $x - \dfrac{2}{5} = \dfrac{3}{5}$

3. $3x - \dfrac{1}{9} = \dfrac{2}{9}$

4. $x + \dfrac{3}{2} = \dfrac{2}{3}$

5. $x + \dfrac{4}{5} = \dfrac{3}{2}$

6. $\dfrac{-5}{6} + a = \dfrac{3}{4}$

7. $\dfrac{3}{2} - x = \dfrac{-5}{12}$

8. $-\dfrac{5}{8} - y = \dfrac{15}{16}$

9. $\dfrac{3}{2} = x - \dfrac{4}{5}$

10. $-b + \dfrac{3}{4} = \dfrac{13}{14}$

11. $x - \dfrac{5}{7} = -\dfrac{3}{14}$

12. $x + \dfrac{3}{10} = \dfrac{7}{15}$

13. $m - 4\dfrac{4}{5} = -1\dfrac{1}{5}$

14. $1\dfrac{3}{4} - p = \dfrac{5}{8}$

15. $d + 4\dfrac{3}{4} = 7\dfrac{8}{9}$

16. $-2\dfrac{4}{5} + y = 3\dfrac{5}{8}$

B. In exercises 17-41, solve the equation and check the solution.

17. $5x = 12$

18. $-2x = 9$

19. $\dfrac{2}{5}t = \dfrac{3}{20}$

20. $\dfrac{-13q}{9} = \dfrac{78}{5}$

21. $-\dfrac{7}{9} = \dfrac{8y}{9}$

22. $\dfrac{-3}{7} \cdot t = \dfrac{27}{14}$

23. $\dfrac{51}{9} = \dfrac{3p}{2}$

24. $\dfrac{7x}{5} = -2$

25. $-\dfrac{7x}{3} = -14$

26. $8x = -36$

27. $\dfrac{12x}{7} = -8$

28. $\dfrac{9y}{4} = -15$

29. $\dfrac{4}{5}x = 6$

30. $-\dfrac{2}{3}y = 8$

31. $15y = 21$

32. $-\dfrac{23x}{15} = \dfrac{-46}{5}$

33. $\dfrac{1}{9}g = -2\dfrac{3}{5}$

34. $-x = -\dfrac{3}{4}$

35. $-x = \dfrac{7}{10}$

36. $\dfrac{7}{10}y = -28$

37. $-7p = -\dfrac{1}{2}$

38. $\dfrac{1}{3} = -2t$

39. $8b = -\dfrac{3}{2}$

40. $\dfrac{-5}{33} = -6r$

41. $\dfrac{7x}{13} = -\dfrac{14}{39}$

In exercises 42-63, use the Addition Property and the Multiplication Property to solve the equation. Write each step and remember to align the "=" signs.

42. $2z + \dfrac{7}{18} = 1\dfrac{1}{2}$

43. $\dfrac{1}{5}x + 10 = -32$

44. $\dfrac{2b}{3} - 8 = 10$

45. $\dfrac{-5x}{2} - \dfrac{3}{4} = -\dfrac{1}{4}$

46. $\dfrac{-7}{8} = \dfrac{3}{4}m - \dfrac{5}{8}$

47. $\dfrac{3}{4}x + \dfrac{1}{2}x = \dfrac{-1}{6}$

48. $\dfrac{1}{8}h - \dfrac{3}{5}h = \dfrac{7}{20}$

49. $\dfrac{t}{8} + \dfrac{1}{10} = -\dfrac{1}{6}$

50. $\dfrac{4}{5}x + \dfrac{3}{10} = \dfrac{1}{10}$

51. $\dfrac{y}{4} - \dfrac{3}{4} = -\dfrac{9}{4}$

52. $\dfrac{3x}{16} - \dfrac{5}{7} = \dfrac{5}{7}$

53. $\dfrac{8}{9}x - \dfrac{3}{19} = -\dfrac{3}{19}$

54. $\dfrac{21x}{40} - \dfrac{8}{5} = -\dfrac{8}{5}$

55. $\dfrac{2x}{7} - \dfrac{3}{5} = 4$

56. $\dfrac{5}{3} = \dfrac{1}{12}n - \dfrac{1}{4}$

57. $\dfrac{5y}{3} - \dfrac{7}{2} = \dfrac{5}{6}$

58. $5r + \dfrac{7}{2} = -\dfrac{8}{3}$

59. $x - \dfrac{1}{4}x = \dfrac{2}{5} + \dfrac{3}{2}$

60. $5\left(\dfrac{1}{3}y - 4\right) = 115$

61. $x + \dfrac{2}{5}(8 - x) = \dfrac{36}{5}$

62. $\dfrac{x}{2} + \dfrac{1}{2}(3x - 1) = \dfrac{1}{4}$

63. $\dfrac{5}{6}x - \dfrac{7}{8}x = \dfrac{5}{12}$

C. In exercises 64-68, determine whether the given proportion is true or false.

64. $\dfrac{4}{5} = \dfrac{20}{25}$

65. $\dfrac{2a}{5} = \dfrac{16a}{40}$

66. $\dfrac{12}{18} = \dfrac{28}{12}$

67. $\dfrac{6}{8} = \dfrac{15}{20}$

68. $\dfrac{25}{12} = \dfrac{19}{6}$

In exercises 69-78, solve the proportion.

69. $\dfrac{6}{15} = \dfrac{9}{x}$

70. $\dfrac{4}{x} = \dfrac{6}{14}$

71. $\dfrac{y}{6} = \dfrac{12}{21}$

72. $\dfrac{4}{5} = \dfrac{x}{\frac{5}{6}}$

73. $\dfrac{2}{2\frac{1}{4}} = \dfrac{5}{x}$

74. $\dfrac{x}{\frac{3}{8}} = \dfrac{\frac{1}{4}}{9}$

75. $\dfrac{x+1}{3} = \dfrac{4}{5}$

76. $\dfrac{x+5}{4} = \dfrac{5}{12}$

77. $\dfrac{x-7}{5} = \dfrac{13}{15}$

78. $\dfrac{2x-1}{4} = \dfrac{11}{3}$

5.2 GENERAL APPLICATIONS

5.2 A. Solving application problems by translating into equations.

In the last section, we discussed how to solve linear equations involving fractions. This skill is used extensively in solving real world application problems. Recall, the steps used in translating and solving application problems.

Procedure to formulate and solve application problems:

Step 1 Read or re-read the problem. Understand what is given and what is the unknown to be determined.

Step 2 Assign a letter, say x, to the unknown and set up the equation using the given information.

Step 3 Solve for the unknown.

Step 4 Make sure the solution makes sense.

Example 1 A concrete truck is loaded with $6\frac{1}{3}$ cubic feet of concrete. The driver delivers $2\frac{1}{12}$ cubic feet of concrete at the first stop and $2\frac{1}{12}$ cubic feet at the second stop. At the third stop he picks up 5 cubic feet of concrete not wanted by the customer. How much concrete is on the truck after the third stop?

Solution Let x represents the final amount of concrete on the truck.

$$6\frac{1}{3} - 2\frac{1}{12} - 2\frac{1}{12} + 5 = x$$

Initial amount   Taken off the truck   Loaded on the truck

$$x = \frac{19}{3} - \frac{25}{12} - \frac{25}{12} + \frac{5}{1}$$ • Rewrite as additions.

$$= \frac{76}{12} + \frac{-25}{12} + \frac{-25}{12} + \frac{60}{12}$$ • Rewrite with improper fractions.

$$= \frac{76 - 25 - 25 + 60}{12}$$ • The LCD = 12.

$$= \frac{86}{12} = 7\frac{2}{12} = 7\frac{1}{6}.$$ • Add the numerators, and simplify.

$7\frac{1}{6}$ cubic feet of concrete is left on the truck after the third stop.

Warm-Up

1. An agricultural college has four corn fields. One year the total harvest was $7\frac{2}{5}$ tons. If the harvest in three cornfields was $1\frac{3}{5}$ tons, $1\frac{9}{10}$ tons, and $1\frac{4}{9}$ tons, determine the harvest in the fourth corn fields.

2. The difference between two sides of a triangle is $3\frac{1}{2}$ inches. If the smaller side measures $1\frac{2}{3}$ inches, find the measure of the longer side.

Example 2 The sum of the sides of a triangle is $4\frac{3}{8}$ inches. If two sides measure $\frac{4}{5}$ inches and $1\frac{3}{10}$ inches, find the measure of the third side.

Solution Let the measure of the third side be represented by x.

We now translate the following sentence into symbols.

"The sum of the three sides is $4\frac{3}{8}$ inches;"

$$\frac{4}{5} + 1\frac{3}{10} + x = 4\frac{3}{8}.$$

Solve this equation for x, to find the missing side.

$$\frac{4}{5} + \frac{13}{10} + x = \frac{35}{8}$$

$$\frac{8}{10} + \frac{13}{10} + x = \frac{35}{8}$$
- Add the fractions on the left side. LCD = 10.

$$\frac{21}{10} + x = \frac{35}{8}$$

$$\frac{21}{10} + x - \mathbf{\frac{21}{10}} = \frac{35}{8} - \mathbf{\frac{21}{10}}$$
- Isolate the unknown by subtracting $\frac{21}{10}$ from both sides.

$$x = \frac{175}{40} - \frac{84}{40}$$
- The LCD is 40. Change the fractions to the common denominator (40).

$$x = \frac{175-84}{40}$$

$$x = \frac{91}{40} = 2\mathbf{\frac{11}{40}}$$

The third side is $2\frac{11}{40}$ inches.

> **Remark:** In subtraction, it is often simpler to work entirely with improper fractions.

Check:

$$\frac{4}{5} + 1\frac{3}{10} + x = \frac{35}{8}$$
- Given equation.

$$\frac{4}{5} + \frac{13}{10} + \mathbf{\frac{91}{40}} = \frac{35}{8}$$
- Substitute $\frac{91}{40}$ for x. Simplify the left side.

$$\frac{35}{8} = \frac{35}{8}$$
- True

Answers:

1. $2\frac{41}{90}$ tons   **2.** $5\frac{1}{6}$ in

5.2 B. Computing the Average of a Group of Rational numbers

Recall the procedure for finding the average of a group of whole numbers. We follow the same procedure for finding the average of a group of rational numbers. We **divide the sum** of the rational numbers **by the number of rationals in the group.**

Procedure for finding the average of a group of rational numbers:

Step **1** Find the sum of all the rational numbers in the group.

Step **2** Divide the sum by the count of rational numbers in the group.

Example 3 Find the average of the following group of rational numbers:

$$\frac{7}{8}, \quad 6\frac{1}{4}, \quad 4\frac{1}{2}, \quad \text{and} \quad \frac{5}{4}.$$

Solution

$$\text{Sum} = \frac{7}{8} + 6\frac{1}{4} + 4\frac{1}{2} + \frac{5}{4}$$

$$\text{Average} = \frac{103}{8} \div 4 = \frac{103}{8} \cdot \frac{1}{4}$$

$$= \frac{103}{32} = 3\frac{7}{32}$$

- $\text{Sum} = (6+4) + \left(\frac{7}{8} + \frac{1}{4} + \frac{1}{2} + \frac{5}{4}\right)$
- $= 10 + \left(\frac{7}{8} + \frac{2}{8} + \frac{4}{8} + \frac{10}{8}\right)$
- $= 10 + \frac{23}{8} = \frac{80}{8} + \frac{23}{8} = \frac{103}{8}$
- Divide the sum by 4.

The average of $\frac{7}{8}$, $6\frac{1}{4}$, $4\frac{1}{2}$, and $\frac{5}{4}$ is $3\frac{7}{32}$.

Example 4 The rain gauge at the water reservoir records the following rainfall during a six-month period. $3\frac{3}{4}$ in, $2\frac{1}{4}$ in, 2 in, $4\frac{1}{2}$ in, $\frac{5}{6}$ in, and $\frac{2}{3}$ in. What is the average rainfall per month during this period?

Solution To find the average rainfall per month, we first add the recorded rainfall for six months, and then divide the sum by six.

$$\text{Sum} = \left[3\frac{3}{4} + 2\frac{1}{4} + 2 + 4\frac{1}{2} + \frac{5}{6} + \frac{2}{3}\right]$$

$$\text{Average} = 14 \div 6 = \frac{\overset{7}{\cancel{14}}}{\underset{3}{\cancel{6}}} = \frac{7}{3} = 2\frac{1}{3} \text{ in.}$$

Sum of the rainfall during six month period

$$= (3+2+2+4) + \left(\frac{3}{4} + \frac{1}{4} + \frac{1}{2} + \frac{5}{6} + \frac{2}{3}\right); \text{ LCD} = 12$$

$$= 11 + \frac{9+3+6+10+8}{12}$$

$$= 11 + \frac{\overset{3}{\cancel{36}}}{\underset{1}{\cancel{12}}} = 11 + 3 = 14$$

The average rainfall per month is $2\frac{1}{3}$ in.

5.2 C. Translating "of" to "Multiply"

Very often the word "**of**" is used with fractions or percents to mean "multiply". Expressions such as:

$\dfrac{1}{4}$ **of** his earnings,

$\dfrac{2}{3}$ **of** the class, or

40% **of** the participants,

are phrases that could be translated to multiplication.

$\dfrac{1}{4}$ **of** his earnings $= \dfrac{1}{4} \cdot E$, where E represents earnings;

$\dfrac{2}{3}$ **of** the class $= \dfrac{2}{3} \cdot C$, where C represents the number of students in the class; and

40% **of** the participants $= \dfrac{40}{100} \cdot P$, where P represents the number of participants.

These "**of**" statements express a fractional part of some quantity. Usually such statements are contained in application problems.

For example, consider the following problems:

- Linda contributes one-tenth **of** her salary to different charitable organizations. Find her monthly contributions to charity if her monthly salary is $2740.

Her contributions are:

$$\dfrac{1}{10} \textbf{ of } \$2740 = \dfrac{1}{10} \cdot \$2740$$

$$= \$274$$

- Three hundred twenty-four freshman registered on the first day of registration in a college. This was $\dfrac{1}{3}$ **of** the total registration in the semester.

Let the total number of freshman $= x$.

According to the problem one-third **of** x or 324 students registered on the first day.

$$\dfrac{1}{3} \cdot x = 324 \;\; \rightarrow \;\; x = 972 \text{ students.}$$

Procedure to solve problems involving part **of** the whole:

***Step* 1**	Represent the unknown quantity by a variable.
***Step* 2**	Set up an equation by translating the sentences: (fraction) **of** (whole) = (part).
***Step* 3**	Solve for the variable.
***Step* 4**	Check the final answer.

Example 5   During the previous year, 450 out of 1,500 students received financial aid. **What fraction of the students received financial aid?**

Solution

Step 1   Let *x* represent the fraction of the students receiving financial aid.

Step 2   First re-word the English statement.

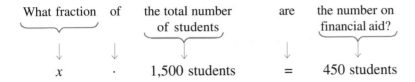

What fraction	of	the total number of students	are	the number on financial aid?
x	$\cdot$	1,500 students	$=$	450 students

Step 3   Solve:

$$x \cdot 1{,}500 \text{ students} = 450 \text{ students}$$

$$x \cdot 1{,}500 = 450$$

$$\frac{x \cdot 1{,}500}{1{,}500} = \frac{450}{1{,}500} \qquad \bullet \text{ Divide both sides by 1,500.}$$

$$x = \frac{450}{1{,}500} = \frac{50 \cdot 9}{50 \cdot 30} = \frac{3 \cdot 3}{3 \cdot 10} = \frac{3}{10}$$

$\dfrac{3}{10}$ of the students received financial aid.

Step 4   *Check:*

$\dfrac{3}{10}$ of the total number of students = Number on financial aid

$$\frac{3}{10} \cdot 1500 = 450 \qquad \Rightarrow \qquad 450 = 450 ; \quad \text{True}$$

 Recall that the above example can be interpreted also as a fraction, as discussed in Chapter 3.

$$\frac{\text{Part}}{\text{Whole}} = \frac{\text{students receiving financial aid}}{\text{total number of students}}$$

$$= \frac{450 \text{ students}}{1{,}500 \text{ students}} = \frac{3}{10}$$

Example 6   A student plans to spend $\dfrac{1}{4}$ of his earnings on his education. If he earns \$12,000 this year, how much does he plan to spend on his education?

Solution

Step 1   Let *x* represent the educational expenses.

Step 2   Re-word the sentence.

5. During a recent flu season, 140 students out of a total of 700 students were absent three or more days due to the flu. What fraction of the students were absent three or more days due to the flu?

6. A student plans to spend $\dfrac{2}{5}$ of his earnings on his education. If he earns \$8,000 this year, how much does he plan to spend on his education?

Warm-Up

The amount spent on education is $\frac{1}{4}$ of his earnings.

$$x \qquad = \frac{1}{4} \cdot \quad \$12,000$$

Step 3 Solve:

$$x = \frac{1}{4} \cdot \$12,000$$

$$x = \frac{1}{\cancel{4}} \cdot \overset{\$3,000}{\cancel{\$12,000}}$$

$$x = \mathbf{\$3,000}$$

He plans to spend $3,000 on education.

Step 4 *Check:*

$$\frac{1}{4} \text{ of earnings} = \text{educational expenses}$$

$$\frac{1}{\cancel{4}} \cdot \overset{\$3,000}{\cancel{\$12,000}} = \$3,000$$

$$\Rightarrow \qquad \mathbf{\$3,000 = \$3,000}; \quad \text{True}$$

7. The average tip is 15% of the cost of meals. One evening a waiter earned $180 in tips. Estimate the total cost of the food he served?

Example 7 The average tip is 15% of the cost of meals. One evening a waiter earned $240 in tips. Estimate the total cost of the food he served?

Solution

Step 1 Let x represent the total cost of the food he served.

Step 2 Translate the first-sentence to an equation.

The tip is 15% of the cost of the meals.

$$240 \quad = \quad \frac{3}{20} \quad \cdot \quad x \qquad 15\% = \frac{15}{100} = \frac{3 \cdot \cancel{5}}{20 \cdot \cancel{5}} = \frac{3}{20}$$

$$240 = \frac{3}{20} \cdot x$$

Step 3 Solve:

$$\frac{20}{\underset{1}{\cancel{3}}} \cdot \overset{80}{\cancel{240}} = \frac{20}{3} \cdot \frac{3}{20} x \qquad \bullet \quad \text{Multiply both sides by } \frac{20}{3}.$$

$$1,600 = x$$

The total cost of the food served was $1,600.

Step 4 *Check:*

15% of total cost of food = tip

$$\frac{15}{100} \cdot 1,600 = 240 \quad \Rightarrow \quad \mathbf{240 = 240} ; \quad \text{True}$$

Example 8   A store advertises $\frac{1}{3}$ "off" on sportswear. A pair of khaki pants is on sale for $20. What was its original price?

Solution

Step 1   Let x represent the original price.

Step 2   The discount is $\frac{1}{3}$ of x.

Sale price $=$ $\underbrace{\text{Original price}}$ $-$ $\underbrace{\text{discount}}$

$$20 = \quad x \quad - \quad \frac{1}{3} \text{ of } x$$

$$20 = x - \frac{1}{3}x$$

Step 3   Solve : $20 = x - \frac{1}{3}x$ $x - \frac{1}{3}x = 1\cdot x - \frac{1}{3}x = \left(1 - \frac{1}{3}\right)x = \frac{2}{3}x$

$$20 = \frac{2}{3}x$$ • Switch sides.

$$\frac{2}{3}x = 20$$ • Multiply by $\frac{3}{2}$ on both sides.

$$\mathbf{\frac{3}{2}} \cdot \frac{2}{3}x = \mathbf{\frac{3}{2}} \cdot \overset{10}{\cancel{20}}$$

$$x = 30$$

The original price of the khaki pants was $30.

Step 4   *Check:*

Sale price $=$ Original price $-$ discount

$$20 = 30 - \frac{1}{3} \cdot \overset{10}{\cancel{30}} \;\rightarrow\; 20 = 30 - 10 \rightarrow \mathbf{20 = 20} \;;\; \text{True}$$

5.2 D.   Rates, Unit Rates and Proportions

• Recall that rates are ratios that compare (or relate) different types of quantities. Fractions are used to make these comparisons.

$$\$17 \text{ for 2 hours} = \frac{\$17}{2\,\text{hours}}$$ Dollars are related to hours.

• Rates apply to a situation where there is the expectation that two quantities will continue to relate in the same way.

$7 for 2 hours $\longrightarrow$ $14 for 4 hours

• The word rate often compares numbers with the same unit, usually dollars, especially when rates are expressed using percents as in interest rates. Consider the following statement.

then go to Chapter 6

"The current mortgage rate is $4\frac{1}{2}$ %."

This is a ratio of $ $4\frac{1}{2}$ in annual interest for each $100 borrowed.

$$\frac{\$4\frac{1}{2}}{\$100} = \frac{4\frac{1}{2}}{100}$$

$$= \frac{9}{2} \div \frac{100}{1} = \frac{9}{2} \cdot \frac{1}{100} = \frac{9}{200}$$

or $9 for every $200 borrowed.

Note that in the ratio for mortgage rates (above), $ label cancels. In ratios or rates, labels on numbers cancel just like factors.

- **A unit rate** is a rate in which a quantity of one type of item is compared to a unit quantity of some other type of item.

$$55 \text{ m. p. h.} = \frac{55\,\text{miles}}{1\,\text{hour}}$$

The word unit has several meanings in the phrase unit rate. Unit means 1. It also means type of measure being compared or related as rates. The context determines the meaning.

It is easy to miss a unit rate when reading. There are many different ways to say "1", in the context of rates. "A" or "the" may mean "1" in context. "Per" means "for 1" or "in 1". Some of these usages are explained in the following example.

Warm-Up

9. Rewrite each of the following unit rates as fractions:

(a) 65 m.p.h.

(b) Ginger @ 89 ¢ / oz

(c) 2 liter bottles

Example 9 Rewrite each of the following unit rates as fractions:

(a) 32 mpg

(b) Bananas @ 69 ¢ / lb

(c) Shirts cost $11 **each.**

(d) 5-foot board

(e) Computers costing $599

(f) A credit, for **a** college course, costs $75.

(g) 1 foot = 12 inches

Solutions (a) 32 mpg means 32 miles **per** gallon

$$= \frac{32 \text{ miles}}{1 \text{ gallon}} \quad \text{or } 32 \text{ miles for } \mathbf{1} \text{ gallon.}$$

(b) Bananas @ 69 ¢ / lb is read as

"Bananas at 69 ¢ per pound"

$$= \frac{69\,¢}{1 \text{ pound}} \text{ , or } 69¢ \text{ for one pound.}$$

(c) Shirts cost $11 **each** or $\dfrac{\$11}{\mathbf{1\ shirt}}$ or $11 for 1 shirt.

(d) Five- foot boards means $\dfrac{5 \text{ feet}}{1 \text{ board}}$

or 5 feet **in** each board.

(e) Computers costing $599 means

$\dfrac{\$599}{1 \text{ computer}}$. We understand "1" from the context.

(f) A credit for a college course costs $75

$= \dfrac{\$75}{1 \text{ credit}}$.

(g) 1 foot $= 12$ inches or $\dfrac{12 \text{ inches}}{1 \text{ foot}}$.

(d) Shirts selling for $9.

(e) A bus holds 50 passengers

(f) Each box contains 1,000 nails.

(g) 16 ounces $= 1$ pound

- **Finding the Unit Rate**

The questions below are typical **unit rate** questions:

- Find the speed of the boat (m.p.h).
- Find the cost of 1 pound of coffee.
- How much time does **each** mile take to run?
- What was the inheritance that **each** child received?

All these questions ask that we find some number connected to "1" of some thing else. Unit rates are found using division as in the following procedure.

Procedure for finding a unit rate:

Step **1**   Set up a ratio (fraction) from the given information.

Step **2**   Change the ratio to a **unit** rate by dividing, changing the fraction to its equivalent fraction (with a denominator of 1).

Example 10   If the total airfare for a family of eight to attend a family reunion costs $2,592, what is the cost **per** person?

Solution   Let $x =$ the cost per person

$x = \dfrac{\text{cost}}{\text{person}}$

$= \dfrac{\$2,592}{8 \text{ persons}}$

$= \dfrac{\$324}{1 \text{ person}}$ $2,592 \div 8 = 324$

$= \$324 \textbf{ per person}$

The cost is $324 per person.

Warm-Up

10. If $2\frac{1}{2}$ bottles of champagne was consumed by two friends, approximately how much did each person drink?

11. If a 1,000 mile trip takes 16 hours, what is the average speed in m.p.h?

Answers:

9. (a) $\dfrac{65 \text{ miles}}{1 \text{ hour}}$ **(b)** $\dfrac{89 \text{ ¢}}{1 \text{ oz}}$ **(c)** $\dfrac{2 \text{ liters}}{1 \text{ bottle}}$

(d) $\dfrac{\$9}{1 \text{ shirt}}$ **(e)** $\dfrac{50 \text{ passengers}}{1 \text{ bus}}$

(f) $\dfrac{1,000 \text{ nails}}{1 \text{ box}}$ **(g)** $\dfrac{16 \text{ ounces}}{1 \text{ pound}}$

10. $1\frac{1}{4}$ bottles **11.** $62\frac{1}{2}$ m.p.h.

Example 11 If $6\frac{1}{2}$ pounds of ground beef are used to make 13 hamburgers, how much ground beef is in *each* hamburger?

Solution Let x = the pounds of ground beef in 1 hamburger.

$$x = \frac{6\frac{1}{2} \text{ pounds}}{13 \text{ hamburgers}} = \frac{\frac{1}{2} \text{ pound}}{1 \text{ hamburger}}$$

$$6\frac{1}{2} \div \frac{13}{1}$$
$$= \frac{\cancel{13}}{2} \cdot \frac{1}{\cancel{13}} = \frac{1}{2}$$

$$= \frac{1}{2} \text{ pound per hamburger}$$

There is $\frac{1}{2}$ pound of ground beef in *each* hamburger.

• Solving Rate Problems Using Proportions

A proportion is an equation in which both sides are fractions (or ratios). A proportion contains four quantities.

$$\frac{a}{b} = \frac{c}{d} \; ; \; a, b, c, \text{ and } d \text{ are the four quantities involved.}$$

If we are given any three of these four quantities then we can find the value of the fourth quantity by simply solving the proportion. This forms the basis of solving many real life problems. Consider for example the following situation:

A car travels 440 miles on $32 of gasoline. What gasoline expense is anticipated for a 5,000-mile trip?

Let x represent the gasoline expense for the trip.

This is a rate problem since the numbers involve different types of quantities. **Miles** are related to **dollars** spent on gasoline. Before writing the proportion, we organize the information in the following table.

	Case I	Case II
Dollars	$32	$x
miles	440 mi	5000 mi

In setting up a proportion, since the fractions are equal, the labels must be identical.

Write the proportion directly from the table.

$$\frac{\$32}{440 \text{ mi}} = \frac{\$x}{5,000 \text{ mi}}$$

Solve, setting the cross products equal to each other.

$$440 \, x = 160,000$$

$$\frac{440x}{440} = \frac{160,000}{440}$$

$32 \nearrow x \longrightarrow 440x$
$440 \searrow 5000 \longrightarrow 160,000$

Divide both sides by 440.

$$x = \$363 \frac{7}{11} \text{ or approximately } \mathbf{\$364}.$$

Approximately $364 will be spent on gasoline to travel 5,000 miles.

Procedure for using a proportion to solve a rate problem:

Step **1**   Represent the unknown quantity by a variable.

Step **2**   Organize the numbers and a variable into a table using labels.

Step **3**   Write the proportion directly from the table. Check that the labels on the two sides are the same.

Step **4**   Solve the proportion using cross products.

Example 12   A machine harvests 4 acres of beans in $1\frac{1}{2}$ hours. How long will it take to harvest 75 acres?

Solution   Let x represent the *hours* to harvest 75 acres.

This is a rate problem, because it relates *acres* and *hours*.

	Case I	Case II
acres	4 acres	75 acres
hours	$1\frac{1}{2}$ hours	x hours

$$\frac{4\ \text{acres}}{1\frac{1}{2}\ \text{hours}} \diagup\!\!\!\!\diagdown \frac{75\ \text{acres}}{x\ \text{hours}} \quad \longrightarrow \quad 1\frac{1}{2} \cdot 75$$
$$\longrightarrow \quad 4 \cdot x$$

$$4 \cdot x = 1\frac{1}{2} \cdot \frac{75}{1} \qquad \frac{3}{2} \cdot \frac{75}{1} = \frac{225}{2}$$

$$4x = \frac{225}{2}$$

$$\frac{1}{4} \cdot 4x = \frac{1}{4} \cdot \frac{225}{2} \qquad \text{Multiply both side by } \frac{1}{4}.$$

$$x = \frac{225}{8} \ \text{ or } \ 28\frac{1}{8} \ \text{ hours} \approx 28 \ \text{hours}$$

It will take approximately 28 hours to harvest 75 acres.

Example 13   If 1 oz of potato chips contains 150 calories, how many ounces would contain 2,000 calories?

Solution   Let x represent the ounces for 2,000 calories.

This is a rate problem relating ounces and calories. The unit rate is given: $\dfrac{150 \text{ calories}}{1 \text{ oz}}$.

	Case I	Case II
Calories	150 cal	2000 cal
Ounces	1 oz	x ounce

$$\frac{150 \text{ cal}}{1 \text{ oz}} = \frac{2,000 \text{ cal}}{x \text{ oz}}$$

$$150 \cdot x = 2,000 \qquad \text{Divide by 150.}$$

$$\frac{150x}{150} = \frac{2,000}{150} \rightarrow x = \frac{40}{3} \text{ or } 13\frac{1}{3} \text{ ounces.}$$

$$13\frac{1}{3} \text{ ounces contain 2,000 calories.}$$

Answers:

12. $1\frac{7}{8}$ cups   **13.** $13\frac{1}{3}$ glasses

Exercise 5.2

A. 1. A nail must reach through three levels of wood and penetrate into the fourth piece $\frac{1}{4}$ inch. If the first piece of wood is $\frac{2}{9}$ inch, the second is $\frac{5}{12}$ inch, and the third is $\frac{1}{3}$ inch, how long must the nail be?

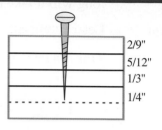

2/9"
5/12"
1/3"
1/4"

2. Three greeting cards weigh $\frac{2}{3}$ ounce, $\frac{3}{5}$ ounce, and $\frac{4}{7}$ ounce. What is the total weight of the cards?

3. The weights of three newborn babies at a maternity hospital are recorded as $7\frac{1}{8}$ lbs, $7\frac{3}{16}$ lbs, and $7\frac{1}{4}$ lbs. If all three babies are placed on the same scale, what is the expected total?

4. An irregularly shaped park is shown in the figure. How many yards does a person jog along the boundary of the park, when he goes around the park only once?

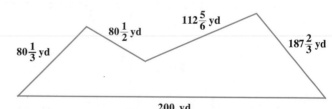

$80\frac{1}{2}$ yd $112\frac{5}{6}$ yd
$80\frac{1}{3}$ yd $187\frac{2}{3}$ yd
200 yd

B. 5. A truck is loaded with $14\frac{2}{5}$ cubic feet of concrete. The driver delivers $3\frac{2}{3}$ cubic feet of concrete at the first stop and $6\frac{3}{5}$ cubic feet at the second stop. At the third stop, he picks up $5\frac{1}{3}$ cubic feet of concrete. How much concrete is on the truck after the third stop ?

6. The science department at an undergraduate college lists the following full-time equivalent (FTE) faculty members by subject area: Physics, $5\frac{4}{5}$; Chemistry, $2\frac{3}{4}$; Mathematics, $7\frac{5}{8}$; Botany, $1\frac{1}{2}$; and Zoology, $1\frac{3}{5}$. How many FTE faculty are in the department ?

7. The sides of a pentagon measure $5\frac{1}{3}$ inches, $4\frac{2}{3}$ inches, $4\frac{3}{4}$ inches, $3\frac{1}{8}$ inches, and $2\frac{2}{3}$ inches. What is the perimeter of the pentagon?
(Recall, perimeter is the sum of all sides).

$5\frac{1}{3}$ $4\frac{2}{3}$
$2\frac{2}{3}$ $4\frac{3}{4}$
$3\frac{1}{8}$

8. The weights of four babies born in a hospital nursery are: $5\frac{1}{3}$ pounds, $4\frac{2}{3}$ pounds, $6\frac{1}{8}$ pounds, and 8 pounds. Find the total weight of the four babies.

9. There are two cubic boxes with edges of $9\frac{3}{4}$ inches and $5\frac{5}{6}$ inches. What is the difference between the lengths of their edges?

10. Carlos spends $3\frac{3}{5}$ hours studying Math, $3\frac{1}{4}$ hours on Physics, and $2\frac{1}{2}$ hours for other subjects. His sister Maria spends $8\frac{3}{8}$ hours studying all subjects. Who spends more time and by how much?

11. Two pieces of $10\frac{4}{5}$ meters and $8\frac{2}{3}$ meters are cut from a 25 meters long rope. What is the length of the remaining piece of rope?

12. Jamie weighs $138\frac{1}{2}$ pounds and decides to lose some weight. She loses a total of $5\frac{3}{4}$ pounds in one week. What is her weight after the loss?

13. From a tank containing 100 gallons of gas, William fills his Caprice using $10\frac{3}{4}$ gallons, and Larry fills his pickup using $14\frac{2}{3}$ gallons. How much gas is left in the tank?

14. In a pond containing $520\frac{3}{4}$ gallons of water in the morning at 9 AM, $45\frac{2}{5}$ gallons of water evaporated by 12 noon. How many gallons of water remained in the pond at 12 noon?

15. John makes a will that after his death $\frac{2}{7}$ of his property should go to his elder son, $\frac{1}{5}$ to his younger son, $\frac{1}{4}$ to his daughter, and the rest to his wife. What fraction of his property did John will for his wife?

    (*Hint*: Start with the whole property = 1)

In exercises 16-27, find the average of the group of numbers.

16. $\frac{15}{36}, \frac{1}{6}, \frac{5}{12}$

17. $\frac{5}{8}, \frac{9}{16}, \frac{13}{24}$

18. $\frac{3}{8}, 5, \frac{17}{4}$

19. $\frac{1}{45}, \frac{3}{75}$

20. $3\frac{3}{4}, 4\frac{1}{4}, 5\frac{1}{2}$

21. $2\frac{2}{5}, 7\frac{1}{6}, \frac{4}{15}, 3\frac{1}{10}$

22. $12\frac{5}{6}, 14\frac{5}{12}, 16\frac{3}{4}$

23. $\frac{1}{4}, \frac{5}{16}, \frac{3}{8}, \frac{9}{16}$

24. $\frac{3}{4}, 1\frac{1}{8}, 1\frac{1}{2}, 2\frac{1}{8}$

25. $3\frac{2}{3}, 4, 5\frac{2}{5}, 9\frac{7}{15}, 10\frac{4}{5}$

26. $1\frac{5}{6}, 2\frac{3}{8}, 2\frac{3}{4}, \frac{11}{12}$

27. $2\frac{2}{3}, 1\frac{8}{15}, 1\frac{4}{5}, 2\frac{5}{6}$

28. Carlos worked for $4\frac{3}{4}$ hours on Monday, $3\frac{1}{2}$ hours on Tuesday, $6\frac{3}{4}$ hours on Wednesday, $4\frac{1}{2}$ hours on both Thursday and Friday, and 5 hours on Saturday. What is the average number of hours he worked each day?

29. The rain gauge at the water reservoir records the following rainfall during a four-month period : $2\frac{7}{8}$ in; $3\frac{1}{2}$ in; $4\frac{1}{3}$ in; and $2\frac{1}{6}$ in. What is the average monthly rainfall for the four months ?

30. Robin is advised to go for a long morning walk by his doctor. He walks $1\frac{5}{6}$ miles on the first day, $1\frac{2}{3}$ miles on the second day, 2 miles on the third day, and $1\frac{1}{4}$ miles on the fourth day. What is the average number of miles that he walked per day?

31. Three friends; Louise, Ela, and Sheila are, respectively, $14\frac{1}{6}$, $13\frac{2}{3}$, and $15\frac{1}{2}$ years old. What is the average age of the girls?

32. A pilot announces that the current altitude of his plane is $31,000\frac{2}{5}$ feet. He is forced to descend $2,700\frac{3}{5}$ feet. What is the new altitude?

C. In exercises 33-38, solve by translating the word "of" in a statement.

33. Seven-fifths of 155.   **34.** Two-ninths of 36   **35.** Five-sixths of 120   **36.** Three-halves of 120

37. 65% of 40   **38.** 20% of 12

39. In a local high school, 320 out of 600 students in the junior class admit that they have used alcohol at parties. What fraction of the students admits to using alcohol? What fraction of the students does not use alcohol?

40. 800 out of 2000 calories for the day are consumed at breakfast. What fraction of the calories are eaten at breakfast? What fraction will be eaten during the rest of the day?

41. A homeowner pays $1200 each month for his mortgage payment. If his monthly expenses total $3000, what fraction of his expenses is spent on his mortgage payment?

42. Marcus is part owner of a local hardware store. $12,500 of the inventory is painting supplies. The total value of the store's inventory is $150,000. What fraction of the inventory is painting supplies?

43. Jenny spends approximately 5 hours each week filing work orders. If she works a regular 40-hour work week, what fraction of her week is spent filing work orders?

44. During the spring, the agricultural agent found that 180 out of 240 trees were infected with bagworms. What fraction of the trees was infected? What fraction of the trees did the worms not infect?

45. Three-fourths of the students in a class are male. Find the number of male students if there are 40 students in the class. Also find the number of female students.

46. A parking lot can accommodate 80 cars. If $\frac{3}{4}$ of the parking spaces are filled, how many cars are parked at that time?

47. Sharon spends half of her income on living expenses. She pays $\frac{2}{9}$ of this amount for rent. What fraction of her income goes for rent? If the rent paid per month is $150, find her monthly income.

48. Michael saves $\frac{2}{5}$ of his total earnings. What is his monthly income if his monthly saving is $100?

49. At a gift store, in a " $\frac{2}{5}$ off sale", an article is priced to sell for $275. What is its regular price?

50. Two-thirds of Mary's monthly income is spent on paying monthly bills. If the total monthly bills are $972, what is her monthly income?

51. Linda drove from her office to home in $5\frac{1}{4}$ minutes. What fraction of the trip did she complete in 1 minute?

52. Joseph earns $345 per week. He spends $\frac{7}{15}$ of his income on food, $\frac{2}{15}$ on house rent, $\frac{1}{5}$ on other items, and saves the rest. Find his savings per week. Also, express his savings as a fraction of his income.

53. A man earns $2,430 per month. He spends $\frac{2}{5}$ of his income on food, $\frac{1}{10}$ on house rent, $\frac{1}{3}$ on other items, and saves the rest. What fraction of his income does he save? Also, find his savings per month.

54. Company ABC makes a profit of \$3,395 to be distributed amongst three partners: A, B, and C. If A gets $\frac{3}{7}$ of the total profit and B gets $\frac{2}{5}$ of the total profit.

(a) what fraction of the total profit will C get?   (b) find the share of each one of them.

55. A tip is usually 15% of the amount of the purchase. If a meal is purchased for \$80, what is the amount of the tip?

56. Ninety percent of a person's body weight is water. How much water weight does a 180-lb person have?

57. If 18% of the County's residents expected to attend the county fair this year, and the county has a total of 440,000 residents, how many are expected to visit the fair?

58. In Maryland the sales tax is 5% of the total purchase. What is the sales tax on a new Toyota costing \$22,000?

59. In a certain community college, 32% of the students who enroll transfer to a 4-year college before graduating. If there are 7,250 new students this year, how many of these are expected to transfer?

60. A corporate farm plants 20% of its fields in soybeans every year. If the company farms 16,000 acres, how many acres are planted in soybeans?

D. 61. On a map, the distance 1,764 miles from City A to City B is $14\frac{1}{2}$ cm. How many miles does 1 cm on the map represent?

62. An automobile uses 45 gallons of gas to travel 1,485 miles. How many miles does it travel per gallon?

63. Derek filled his Honda's gas tank and noted that the odometer read 16,848. After the next filling, the odometer read 17,529. It took $14\frac{2}{5}$ gallon to fill the tank. How many miles per gallon did the car get?

64. Peggy filled her van's gas tank and noted that the odometer read 26,536. After the next filling, the odometer read 26,982. It took $19\frac{3}{4}$ gallons to fill the tank. How many miles per gallon did the van get?

65. A group of 15 students pays \$185 for lunch. What is each person's share of the bill?

66. A class of 40 students spends \$3,512 for a trip. What is each student's share?

67. In a recent weekly game, the lottery prize of \$225,425 was shared by 6 winners. Express each winner's share as a mixed number.

68. Katrina earned \$725 during a 40-hr week. Express her hourly wages as a mixed number.

69. Fifteen software CDs containing video instruction are purchased by a learning lab for \$95. What is the cost of each CD?

70. John's watch loses 10 min in 24 hr. At this rate, how much does it lose in 1 hr.

71. Andy's watch loses 3 minutes in 24 hr. At this rate, how much does it lose in 1 hr.?

72. A long distance telephone call between two foreign cities costs $\$6\frac{3}{4}$ for $12\frac{1}{2}$ min. What is the rate in cents per minute?

73. A medical assistant uses 1,250 ml of penicillin for 500 injections. How much penicillin is used in one injection?

74. In a dinner party, thirty pounds of salmon fish is consumed by 50 people. Determine the average consumption per person.

75. An 18 lb of ham provides 76 servings. How many servings are provided by each pound of ham?

76. A family of six members consumes 17 gallons of milk every week. Express the weekly consumption of each member of the family as a mixed number, assuming every member consumes the same amount.

77. A family of four consumes 3 gallons of orange juice every week. Express the weekly consumption of each as a fraction, assuming every member consumes the same amount.

78. To water a lawn adequately requires 645 gallons of water for every 1,544 ft^2. What is the rate in gallons per square foot?

79. Sound travels $10,773\frac{3}{4}$ feet in $9\frac{3}{4}$ seconds. What is its rate, or speed in feet per second?

80. A car covers 800 miles in $21\frac{1}{2}$ hr. What is the rate in miles per hour?

81. A train travels 544 km in $3\frac{2}{5}$ hr. What is the rate, or speed, in kilometers per hour?

82. One sheet of paper is $\frac{1}{80}$ inch thick. How thick is a stack of 500 sheets?

83. Forty-six books, each $1\frac{1}{2}$ inches thick, are piled together. What is the height of the pile?

84. A machinist takes $80\frac{1}{2}$ minutes to make seven pins. How long does it take him to make one pin?

85. A jet flies 3,345 miles in $5\frac{1}{2}$ hours. What is the speed in miles per hour?

86. Calzone State University has 1,304 faculty for 32,600 students. How many students are there in the university per teacher?

87. A car travels 108 miles on 9 liters of gas. How many miles will it travel on 21 liters?

88. A car travels 265 miles in 6 hours. How far will it travel in 4 hours?

89. A train covers a distance of 399 miles in 6 hours. How much distance will it cover in 16 hours?

90. Fifty-five yards of fabric is required to make 24 shirts of the same size. How much fabric will be required to make 36 shirts of the same size?

91. The weight of 72 books is 9 kg.

    (i) What is the weight of 80 such books?

    (ii) How many such books weigh 6 kg?

92. If 48 boxes contain 6,000 pens, how many boxes will be needed for 1,875 pens?

93. John earns $126 in 3 days. At this rate, how much will he earn in 7 days?

94. If a family of 7 people can live on $2,184 for a month, how much will be required for 9 people to live for one month?

95. If 6 oil tankers can be filled by a pipe in $4\frac{1}{2}$ hours, how long does the pipe take to fill 5 such oil tankers?

96. A pump discharges 90 gallons of water in 20 hours. How long will it take to discharge 144 gallons?

97. When Jacob earns $3,750, he puts $350 in savings. At the same rate, how much money must he earn in one month to save $490?

98. Maria is knitting a sweater. The knitting scale is 5 rows to an inch. How many rows must she knit to complete $10\frac{4}{5}$ inches of the sweater?

99. A car travels 165 miles in 3 hours.

   (a) How long does it take to travel 440 miles?   **(b)** How far does it travel in $6\frac{1}{2}$ hours?

100. Mrs. Brown saves $\$1\frac{1}{2}$ for every $20 she earns. What are her monthly savings if her monthly income is $1,236?

101. If $4\frac{1}{2}$ grams of an alloy of copper and zinc contains $3\frac{1}{2}$ grams of copper, then how much copper will there be in $18\frac{9}{10}$ grams of the alloy?

102. If a sprinter runs 100 yd in $9\frac{1}{5}$ sec, how long would it take to run 260 yd, assuming he would maintain the same speed?

103. A map uses 3 cm to represent 25 miles. If the distance between two cities on the map is $7\frac{1}{5}$ cm, how many miles apart are the cities?

104. A car travels 16 miles on a gallon of gas costing $\$1\frac{2}{5}$.

   (a) How much does it cost to travel 640 miles?   **(b)** How far can the car travel on $5 worth of gasoline?

105. The ratio of the earnings of two friends is 3 to 5. If the second friend earns $3,750 per month, find the monthly earnings of the first.

106. In a certain factory the wages of an individual for a week are proportional to the number of units he produces. In a certain week, worker *A* received gross wages of $480 for producing 200 dozen units. How much will he receive if he produces 240 dozen units the next week?

107. The circumferences of any two circles are proportional to their diameters. If the circumference of a circle is 22 inches when its diameter is 7 inches, what is the circumference of a circle that is 31 inches in diameter?

108. An electric pole casts a shadow of 20 yards when a tree 6 yds high casts a shadow of 8 yds. What is the height of the pole, if the ratio of the length of any object to its shadow is the same at a particular time.

109. A carpenter takes $80\frac{1}{2}$ minutes to make seven wood panels. How long does it take him to make one wood panel?

110. The weight of one foot of a metal bar is $2\frac{1}{5}$ pounds. What is the weight of $18\frac{3}{4}$ feet bar?

111. The water pressure during a fire was reduced to $\frac{5}{9}$ of its original pressure at the hydrant. What is the reduced pressure, if the original pressure was $70\frac{1}{5}$ pounds per square inch?

112. A man arranges to pay off $\frac{3}{7}$ of a debt of $3,150.   **(a)** How much does he pay?
   (b) What fraction of the debt is still to be paid by him?

113. An overcoat marked at $\$52\frac{4}{5}$ was sold at two-thirds of the marked price. What was the selling price of the coat?

5.3 GEOMETRIC APPLICATIONS

Objectives

After completing this section, you will be able to:

A. Find perimeters and areas of polygons;

B. Find volume and surface areas for rectangular solids; and

C. Find the missing side(s) in similar figures.

Warm-Up

1. Measure this rectangle using an inch ruler and then determine its perimeter and its area.

In this section, we will review perimeters and areas of polygons when the dimensions are measured using fractions of units. We will also introduce three dimensional figures and find surface areas and volumes of such figures. The concept of similar figures, especially similar triangles, has several applications, including enlargements of pictures and posters. This will be discussed in objective C.

5.3 A. Perimeters and the areas of Polygons

A **Polygon** is a closed geometric figure whose sides are line segments.

The perimeter of a polygon is the distance along its boundary. We have seen that perimeter of a polygon is found by adding all the sides that form its boundary.

The area of a polygon is a measure of the plane (flat) region enclosed by the polygon. It is measured in square units. We have seen that for a rectangle,

$$\text{Area} = \text{Length} \times \text{Width}$$

Example 1 Measure this rectangle using an inch ruler and then determine its perimeter and its area.

Solution Using a ruler,

the length $= 1\frac{3}{4}$ inches and the width $= \frac{7}{8}$ inches.

To find the perimeter we can add all four sides or we can use the formula:

$$P = 2L + 2W$$

$$P = 2\left(1\frac{3}{4}\,\text{inches}\right) + 2\left(\frac{7}{8}\,\text{inches}\right)$$

$$= \frac{7}{2}\,\text{inches} + \frac{7}{4}\,\text{inches}$$

$$= \frac{21}{4}\,\text{inches} = \mathbf{5\frac{1}{4}\ \text{inches}}$$

$$A = L \cdot W$$

$$= 1\frac{3}{4}\,\text{in} \cdot \frac{7}{8}\,\text{in} = \frac{7}{4} \cdot \frac{7}{8}\,\text{in}^2$$

$$= \frac{49}{32} = \mathbf{1\frac{17}{32}}\ \text{square inches}$$

$$\frac{1\cancel{2}}{1} \cdot \frac{7}{\cancel{4}} = \frac{7}{2}$$

$$\frac{1\cancel{2}}{1} \cdot \frac{7}{\cancel{8}_4} = \frac{7}{4}$$

LCD = 4

$$\frac{7}{2} + \frac{7}{4} = \frac{7}{2}\left(\frac{2}{2}\right) + \frac{7}{4}$$

$$= \frac{14}{4} + \frac{7}{4}$$

$$= \frac{21}{4} = 5\frac{1}{4}$$

The perimeter is $5\frac{1}{4}$ inches and the area is $1\frac{17}{32}$ in².

- The area formula for a parallelogram is related to the formula for a rectangle.

Imagine moving the shaded part to the indicated location. A rectangle is formed. Its length is the base (b) of the parallelogram and its width is the height (h). The area of the parallelogram equals the area of the rectangle.

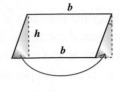

Area = base × height

Area of a parallelogram = $b \cdot h$

Example 2   The parallelogram shown in the figure has a base of $7\frac{1}{2}$ meters and an area of $22\frac{1}{2}$ m². Find its height.

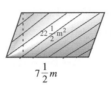

Solution   We use the formula: $A = b \cdot h$

$$22\frac{1}{2} = 7\frac{1}{2} \cdot h$$

$$\frac{45}{2} = \frac{15}{2} \cdot h$$

Multiply both sides by the reciprocal.

$$\overset{1}{\underset{1}{\frac{2}{\cancel{15}}}} \cdot \overset{3}{\underset{1}{\frac{\cancel{45}}{\cancel{2}}}} = \overset{1}{\underset{1}{\frac{2}{\cancel{15}}}} \cdot \overset{1}{\underset{1}{\frac{\cancel{15}}{\cancel{2}}}} h$$

$$3 = h \ \text{ or } \ h = 3$$

The height is 3 meters.

Example 3   Dimensions of the parallelogram are shown in the figure. Determine its perimeter and area.

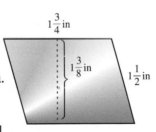

Solution $P = 1\frac{3}{4}$ in $+ 1\frac{3}{4}$ in $+ 1\frac{1}{2}$ in $+ 1\frac{1}{2}$ in

$\quad = 6\frac{1}{2}$ in

$A = b \cdot h$

$\quad = 1\frac{3}{4}$ in $\cdot 1\frac{3}{8}$ in

$\quad = \left(\frac{7}{4} \cdot \frac{11}{8}\right)$ in² $= \frac{77}{32}$ in² $= 2\frac{13}{32}$ **in²**

The perimeter is $6\frac{1}{2}$ in and the area is $2\frac{13}{32}$ **in²**.

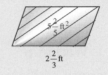
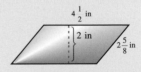

- The area formula for a triangle is related to the area formula for a parallelogram.

Imagine rotating a copy of the shaded triangle and moving it to the indicated location. A parallelogram is formed, having the same base and height as the original triangle. The area of the triangle is exactly half the area of the parallelogram.

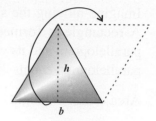

$$A = \frac{1}{2}(b \cdot h)$$

Area of a triangle $= \frac{1}{2} b \cdot h$

A side is chosen as the base. The height runs from the opposite corner perpendicularly to the line containing the base.

For triangle ABC, $\overline{BD}$ is the height for base $\overline{AC}$. $\overline{AF}$ is the height when $\overline{BC}$ is chosen as the base. $\overline{CE}$ is the height if $\overline{AB}$ is chosen as the base.

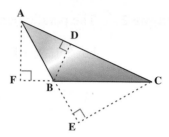

Warm-Up

4. Measure the BC and the height of the triangle shown below, in inches. Estimate the perimeter and the area.

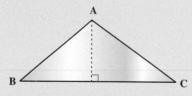

Example 4   Refer to the triangle ABC above. Measure its sides and the height BD in inches and estimate the perimeter and the area.

Solution

$$P = \overline{AB} + \overline{BC} + \overline{AC}$$

$$= \frac{5}{8} \text{ in} + 1\frac{1}{8} \text{ in} + 1\frac{1}{2} \text{ in}$$

$$= \left(\frac{5}{8} + \frac{9}{8} + \frac{3}{2}\right) \text{in}$$

$$\text{LCD} = 8$$

$$\frac{5}{8} + \frac{9}{8} + \frac{3(4)}{2(4)} = \frac{\overset{13}{26}}{\underset{4}{8}} = 3\frac{1}{4}$$

$$= 3\frac{1}{4} \text{ in} \approx \textbf{3 in}$$

The perimeter is approximately 3 inches

$$A = \frac{1}{2} b \cdot h$$

$$= \frac{1}{2} \overline{AC} \cdot \overline{BD}$$

$$= \frac{1}{2} \cdot 1\frac{1}{2} \text{ in} \cdot \frac{3}{8} \text{ in}$$

$$= \left(\frac{1}{2} \cdot \frac{3}{2} \cdot \frac{3}{8}\right) \text{in}^2 = \frac{9}{32} \text{ in}^2 \approx \textbf{\frac{1}{4} in}^2$$

The area is approximately $\frac{1}{4}$ in².

Verify that the same area results if a different base and height is used.

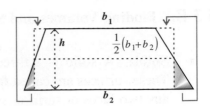

- The area formula for a trapezoid is derived using a rectangle.

A trapezoid is a four sided figure (quadrilateral) where one pair of opposite sides are parallel lines.

Imagine rotating and moving the shaded regions to the indicated locations. The resulting figure is a rectangle. It has the same height, h. But its length is the dotted line that runs midway between the two parallel bases, b_1 and b_2. Its length is equal to the average of two bases. $\dfrac{b_1+b_2}{2}$ or $\dfrac{1}{2}(b_1+b_2)$

The area of the rectangle formed is

$$A = \text{Length} \cdot \text{Width}$$

$$= \frac{1}{2}(b_1+b_2) \cdot h$$

Area of a trapezoid $= \dfrac{1}{2}(b_1+b_2) \cdot h$, where b_1 and b_2 are the lengths of the parallel bases.

Note: The height is perpendicular to both bases.

Example 5   Find the area of the side wall of the lean-to shed pictured at the right.

Solution   The wall has two sides that are parallel and two that are not. Therefore, it is a trapezoid.

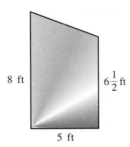

The bases are 8 ft and $6\dfrac{1}{2}$ ft.

The height is 5 ft.

$$A = \frac{1}{2}(b_1+b_2) \cdot h$$

$$= \frac{1}{2}\left(8\,\text{ft}+6\frac{1}{2}\,\text{ft}\right) \cdot 5\,\text{ft}$$

$$= \frac{1}{2}\left(14\frac{1}{2}\,\text{ft}\right) \cdot 5\,\text{ft}$$

$$= \frac{1}{2}\left(\frac{29}{2} \cdot \frac{5}{1}\right)\text{ft}^2 = \frac{145}{4}\,\text{ft}^2 = \mathbf{36\frac{1}{4}\,ft^2}$$

The area of the side of the shed is $\mathbf{36\dfrac{1}{4}\,ft^2}$

Warm-Up

5. Find the area of the side wall of the lean-to shed pictured below:

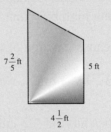

Answers:

1. $P = 8\dfrac{1}{2}$ in , $A = 4\dfrac{1}{2}$ in^2

2. $h = 2\dfrac{1}{40}$ ft

3. $P = 14\dfrac{1}{4}$ in , $A = 9$ in^2

4. $P \approx 4$, $A \approx \dfrac{1}{2}$ in^2

5. $27\dfrac{9}{10}$ ft^2

5.3 B. Finding Volumes and Surface Areas

- **Solid:** A solid is a three-dimensional figure bounded by surfaces which may be flat or curved. These surfaces are called **faces** or curved surfaces of the solid. The line (or curve) of the intersection of any two faces or surfaces of a solid is called an **edge**.

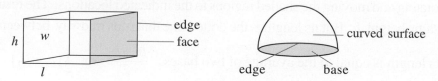

- The **volume** of any solid is the amount of space enclosed within its bounding faces. The *volume* of a solid is a *measure of its capacity*. When we say that a coca cola bottle contains 300 ml of coke we mean that the volume of the bottle is 300 ml.

- **Unit of volume:**

  Since the term 'volume' is related to three-dimensional figures, it is naturally expressed in cubic units: cubic centimeters (cm^3), cubic meters (m^3), cubic inches (in^3), and so forth. We will observe in the following discussion that in each of the formulas for the volume of a solid, three length measures are multiplied. As the length is expressed in centimeters, meters, inches, …., in computing the volume, these units get multiplied three times; hence, we get the cubic units.

- A *rectangular solid* has the shape of a box.

  A cubic unit is shaped like a cube, 1 unit wide by 1 unit high by 1 unit long.

  Because the area of the base (bottom) of the solid is $3\frac{1}{2}$ by 2 units, we are able to place a layer of cubes having $3\frac{1}{2}$ cubes in each of 2 rows on the base.

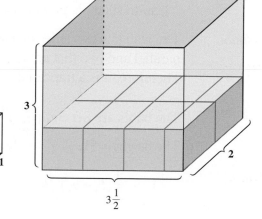

Area of the base = $3\frac{1}{2} \times 2 = 7$ square units.

Since the solid is 3 units high, we will be able to fill the solid with three layers each with the area of the bottom layer.

$$\text{Volume} = (\text{Area of bottom layer}) \times 3 \text{ layers}$$

$$= \left(3\frac{1}{2}\cdot 2\right)\cdot 3 = \left(\frac{7}{2}\cdot 2\right)\cdot 3 = 7\cdot 3 = 21 \text{ cubic units.}$$

$$\text{Volume} = (\text{Area of the base})\cdot \text{height}$$

$$= (\text{length}\cdot \text{width})\cdot \text{height}$$

$$V = l\cdot w\cdot h$$

• **The formula** $V = $ (Area of base) $\cdot\ h$ will apply to any regular *solid* which has congruent bases (top and bottom) and uniform height. The bases can be of any shape.

> For any regular solid (with congruent bases and uniform height): $V = $ (Area of base) $\cdot\ h$
>
> For a rectangular solid : $V = l \cdot w \cdot h$
>
> For a cube: $\qquad\qquad V = s \cdot s \cdot s = s^3$

• The surface area of the rectangular solid is the sum of the areas of its faces. Observe that there are six faces.

For this figure, opposite faces are congruent (match exactly). There are $2A$s (Front and back), $2B$s (top and bottom) and $2C$s (sides).

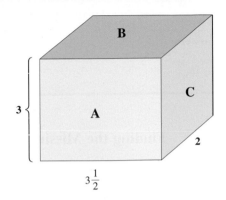

Surface Area $= 2 \cdot$ (Area of A) $+ 2 \cdot$ (Area of B) $+ 2 \cdot$ (Area of C)

$$= 2 \cdot \left(3\frac{1}{2}\cdot 3\right) + 2 \cdot \left(3\frac{1}{2}\cdot 2\right) + 2\ (3 \cdot 2)$$

$$= \frac{{}^1\cancel{2}}{1} \cdot \frac{7}{\cancel{2}_1} \cdot \frac{3}{1} + \frac{2}{1} \cdot \frac{7}{\cancel{2}_1} \cdot \frac{\cancel{2}^1}{1} + 2 \cdot 3 \cdot 2$$

$$= 21 + 14 + 12$$

$$= 47 \text{ square units.}$$

Example 6   How many cubic feet are in a cubic yd? What is the surface area of a cubic yard in square feet?

Solution $V = s^3$ Each edge $= 1\text{yd} = 3$ ft.

$\qquad\qquad = (3 \text{ ft})^3$

$\qquad\qquad = \mathbf{27 \text{ ft}^3}$

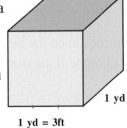

1 yd

1 yd

1 yd = 3ft

Surface Area $= 6$ (Area of each face)

$\qquad\qquad = 6 \cdot s^2$ There are 6 faces.

$\qquad\qquad = 6 \cdot (3 \text{ ft})^2$ Area of square $= s^2$

$\qquad\qquad = 6 \cdot 9 \text{ ft}^2$

$\qquad\qquad = \mathbf{54 \text{ ft}^2}$

The volume is 27 ft^3 and the surface area is 54 ft^2.

Warm-Up

6. Find the volume and surface area of the following box:

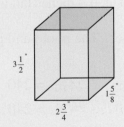

$3\frac{1}{2}"$

$1\frac{5}{8}"$

$2\frac{3}{4}"$

7. Find the volume of the figure below:

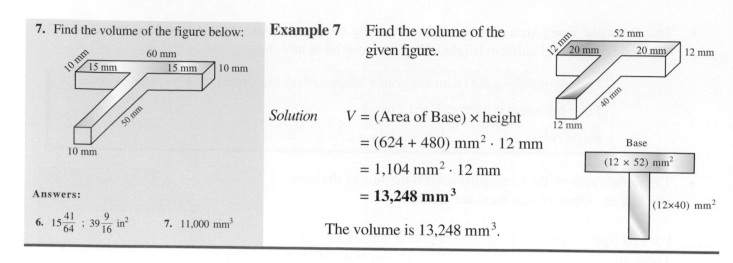

Example 7 Find the volume of the given figure.

Solution

$V = (\text{Area of Base}) \times \text{height}$

$= (624 + 480) \text{ mm}^2 \cdot 12 \text{ mm}$

$= 1{,}104 \text{ mm}^2 \cdot 12 \text{ mm}$

$= \textbf{13{,}248 mm}^3$

The volume is 13,248 mm^3.

Answers:

6. $15\frac{41}{64}$; $39\frac{9}{16}$ in^2 **7.** 11,000 mm^3

5.3 C. Finding the Missing Sides of Similar Triangles

Similar figures are figures of the same shape but different sizes corresponding linear measurements are proportional.

Suppose we consider enlarging an 8" × 10" color photograph to make a poster-sized photo.

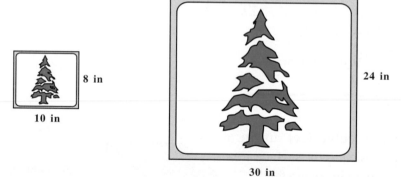

8 in

10 in

24 in

30 in

If we decide the new base will be 30 inches, then the height will need to be 24 inches. Similarly, a tree that measured 4 inches tall in the original photo will measure three times as large or 3 · 4 = 12 inches tall in the poster. The photo and poster are similar figures. Also the ratio, $\frac{\text{Width}}{\text{Length}}$, is the same for both.

$$\frac{8\text{in}}{10\text{in}} \times \frac{24\text{in}}{30\text{in}} \begin{array}{l} = 240 \\ = 240 \end{array}$$

For similar figures the ratios of corresponding measurements are proportional.

Procedure for finding a missing side with similar triangles (or other figures):

Step **1**   Represent the missing side with a variable.

Step **2**   Find the ratios of corresponding sides and construct proportions.

Step **3**   Solve the related proportion(s).

Example 8   Find the missing sides.

Solution $\dfrac{3}{4} \gtrless \dfrac{6}{x}$; $\dfrac{3}{5} \gtrless \dfrac{6}{y}$

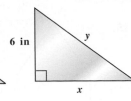

Use cross products :

$$3x = 24 \quad ; \quad 3y = 30$$

$$x = \mathbf{8} \quad ; \quad y = \mathbf{10}$$

The missing sides are **8 in** and **10 in** long.

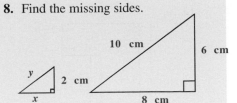
Exercise 5.3

A.   In exercises 1-4, measure the lengths of the sides of the polygons to the nearest $\dfrac{1}{8}$ of an inch and find the perimeter.

1.   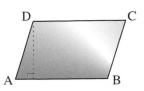   **2.**   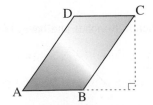   **3.** 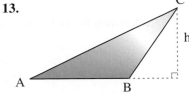   **4.**

In exercises 5-13, measure the lengths of the sides of the polygons to the nearest $\dfrac{1}{8}$ of an inch and find the area.

5.

6.

7.

8.

9.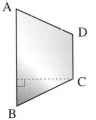

10.

11.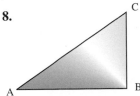

12.

13.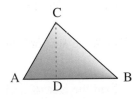

In exercises 14-18, find the area of the shaded region.

14.

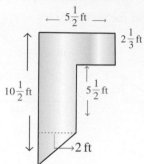

15.

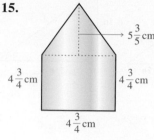

16.

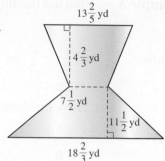

17.

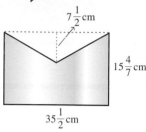

18.

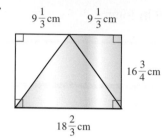

19. Find the perimeter (distance around) of a triangle with sides of length $12\frac{5}{6}$ ft, $16\frac{3}{4}$ ft, and $14\frac{5}{12}$ ft.

20. A quadrilateral (four-sided figure ▱) has sides of length $6\frac{3}{5}$ meters, $3\frac{7}{10}$ meters, $4\frac{9}{10}$ meters, and $5\frac{1}{2}$ meters. What is the perimeter of the quadrilateral in meters?

21. In exchange for a square plot of land whose side is $30\frac{2}{5}$ m, a man wants to buy a $72\frac{1}{3}$ m long rectangular plot with the same area as the square plot. Determine the width of the rectangular plot.

22. Find the area and perimeter of the unshaded triangles in

   (a) Exercise 17 ;   and   **(b)** Exercise 18

23. Find the area of a $6\frac{3}{4}$ ft by $2\frac{1}{3}$ ft rectangle.

   (For a rectangle, the area is the product of length and width.)

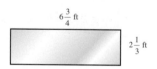

24. Find the area of a rectangle whose sides are of length $9\frac{3}{5}$ inches and $3\frac{3}{7}$ inches.

25. Find the area of a triangle whose base is $3\frac{1}{9}$ inches and whose height is $2\frac{1}{4}$ inches. Give the answer

   in square inches.   (Area of triangle = $\frac{1}{2}$ base · height)

26. Determine the area of a triangle with height 8 inches and base $12\frac{1}{2}$ inches.

27. Find the area of the triangle in the figure.

28. The base of a triangle is $8\frac{3}{4}$ inches, and its height is $2\frac{2}{5}$ times the base. Find the area of the triangle.

29. Find **(a)** the perimeter and **(b)** the area of the rectangle in the figure.

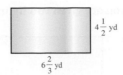

$4\frac{1}{2}$ yd

$6\frac{2}{3}$ yd

30. Find **(a)** the perimeter and **(b)** the area of the square in the figure.

$7\frac{2}{5}$ in

31. Find **(a)** the perimeter and **(b)** the area of a square with side $5\frac{7}{8}$ meters.

B. 32. Find the volume and surface area of a cube whose side is:

(a) $2\frac{3}{4}$ ft ; **(b)** $7\frac{1}{5}$ ft .

33. Find the volume of a cube whose side measure is:

(a) $\frac{31}{10}$ m ; **(b)** $\frac{7}{4}$ cm .

34. Find the volume and surface area of a rectangular box with dimensions $4\frac{3}{4}$ inches by $1\frac{1}{7}$ inches by $2\frac{1}{5}$ inches.

35. Find the volume of a room with dimensions $15\frac{1}{2}$ ft by $10\frac{1}{2}$ ft by 12 ft. Give the answer in cubic ft (ft³).

36. Find the volume and surface area of the rectangular solid pictured here.

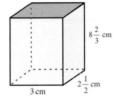

$8\frac{2}{3}$ cm

$2\frac{1}{2}$ cm

3 cm

37. What is the volume of a cube having an edge of $4\frac{2}{5}$ inches?

The formula for the volume of a cube is : $V = (\text{side})^3$

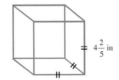

$4\frac{2}{5}$ in

38. The volume of a rectangular solid is 242 cm³. Its length and width are $7\frac{1}{3}$ cm and $6\frac{2}{7}$ cm, respectively. What is its height ?

39. How much sheet is needed to make a metal box $21\frac{1}{2}$ in by $10\frac{1}{4}$ in by $6\frac{2}{5}$ in? What is the volume of the box ?

40. Find the volume of the rectangular solid whose length is $11\frac{4}{5}$ in; width is $7\frac{3}{4}$ in; and height is $4\frac{3}{4}$ in.

41. Find the volume of the rectangular solid whose length is $3\frac{7}{8}$ yd , width is $\frac{9}{16}$ yd , and height is $1\frac{1}{3}$ yd .

42. A container is $1\frac{3}{4}$ ft by $2\frac{1}{3}$ ft by $1\frac{1}{8}$ ft . How many cubic feet of sand will this container hold?

C. In exercises 43-50, you are given two figures. One is the enlargement of the other. Find the length of the unknown side.

43.

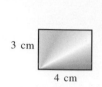 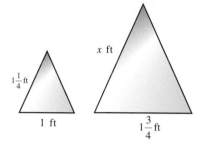

3 cm

4 cm

6 cm

x cm

44.

 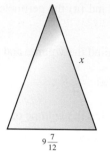

4 cm

4 cm

x cm

6 cm

45.

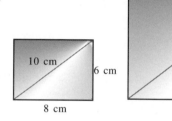

x ft

$1\frac{1}{4}$ ft

1 ft

$1\frac{3}{4}$ ft

46.

$6\frac{4}{9}$

x

$4\frac{2}{3}$

$9\frac{7}{12}$

47.

10 cm

6 cm

8 cm

x cm

12 cm

16 cm

48.

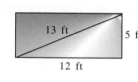 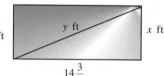

13 ft

5 ft

12 ft

y ft

x ft

$14\frac{3}{2}$

49.

$1\frac{7}{8}$ ft

$2\frac{3}{4}$ ft

x ft

$5\frac{2}{5}$ ft

50.

 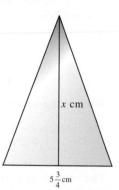

$4\frac{3}{4}$ cm

$3\frac{1}{2}$ cm

x cm

$5\frac{3}{4}$ cm

51. A photograph that measures $5\frac{1}{2}$ inches wide and $3\frac{1}{4}$ inches high is enlarged so that the height will be 13 inches.

What is the width of the enlargement?

52. A triangular photograph is enlarged as shown below.

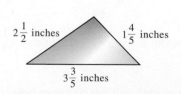

$2\frac{1}{2}$ inches

$1\frac{4}{5}$ inches

$3\frac{3}{5}$ inches

x inches

$4\frac{1}{2}$ inches

9 inches

Find the unknown side of the enlargement.

5.4 CHAPTER SUMMARY

Part I Important Vocabulary and Symbols

1. The **average** of a group of rational numbers is obtained by dividing the sum by the count of the numbers in the group.

2. **Solving a proportion** means finding the missing term that will make the proportion a true statement.

3. The word "of" means "multiply".

   For example, $\frac{1}{4}$ **of** his savings is translated to multiplication as

   $\frac{1}{4}$ **of** his savings $= \frac{1}{4} \cdot s$, where s represents savings.

4. **Rates** are ratios that compare (or relate) different types of quantities. Fractions are used to make these comparisons.

   $$\$35 \text{ for 4 shirts} = \frac{\$35}{4 \text{ shirts}}$$

5. The **perimeter** of a polygon is the distance along its boundary.

6. The **area** of a polygon is a measure of the plane (flat) region enclosed by the polygon. It is measured in square units.

7. The **volume** of any solid is the amount of space enclosed within its boundary faces, and is measured in cubic unit. The volume of a solid is a measure of its capacity.

8. The **surface area** of a solid is the sum of the areas of each of its faces.

Part II Procedures and Rules

Examples

1. **Solve linear Equations using the Addition Property and the Multiplication Property.**

   The method for solving linear equations with fractions, having the variable on one side only, is similar to the method used for integers.

   - Switch the sides of the equation, if necessary, so that the variable is on the left side.

   - Clear fractions by multiplying each term on both sides by the LCD of fractions.

   - Use the addition and multiplication properties to isolate the variables on one side.

   - Check the solution by substituting in the original equation.

1. Solve: $x + \dfrac{3}{4} = 1\dfrac{1}{8}$

   $x + \dfrac{3}{4} = \dfrac{9}{8}$ LCD = 8

   $8x + 8 \cdot \dfrac{3}{4} = 8 \cdot \dfrac{9}{8}$

   $8x + 6 = 9$

   $8x + 6 - 6 = 9 - 6$

   $8x = 3$

   $x = \dfrac{3}{8}$

Examples

2. Find the missing term:

$$\frac{x+7}{3} = \frac{5}{2}$$

$$2(x+7) = 3 \cdot 5$$

$$2x+14 = 15$$

$$2x+14-\mathbf{14} = 15-\mathbf{14}$$

$$2x = 1$$

$$x = \frac{1}{2}$$

3. Find the average of the rational numbers:

$$3\frac{1}{2}, 4\frac{1}{4}, 1\frac{3}{4}, \text{ and } 5\frac{5}{8}$$

Average: $\left(3\frac{1}{2}+4\frac{1}{4}+1\frac{3}{4}+5\frac{5}{8}\right) \div 4$

$$= \frac{121}{8} \div 4 \qquad (3+4+1+5)+\left(\frac{1}{2}+\frac{1}{4}+\frac{3}{4}+\frac{5}{8}\right)$$

$$= \frac{121}{8} \cdot \frac{1}{4} \qquad = 13+\left(\frac{4}{8}+\frac{2}{8}+\frac{6}{8}+\frac{5}{8}\right)$$

$$= \frac{121}{32} \qquad = 13+\frac{17}{8} = \frac{104}{8}+\frac{17}{8}$$

$$= 3\frac{25}{32} \qquad = \frac{121}{8}$$

4. Five-thirds of a number added to $\frac{9}{4}$ is $\frac{1}{4}$. Find the number.

Solution :

Let the number be x.

$\frac{5}{3}$ of x added to $\frac{9}{4}$ is $\frac{1}{4}$ means:

$$\frac{5}{3}x+\frac{9}{4} = \frac{1}{4}$$

Multiply both sides of this equation by the LCD of 3 and 4 = 12.

$$\mathbf{12} \cdot \frac{5}{3}x + \mathbf{12} \cdot \frac{9}{4} = \mathbf{12} \cdot \frac{1}{4}$$

$$20x + 27 = 3$$

$$20x = -24$$

$$x = \frac{-24}{20} = \frac{-6}{5}$$

5. If a car travels 35 miles on 2 gallons of gas, find the number of gallons needed to travel 80 miles.

	Case I	Case II
Miles	35	80
Gallons	2	x

---

2. Solving Proportions Using Cross Products

If one of the four quantities in a proportion include a variable and the other three are known, then we can solve the proportion obtained by equating the cross products.

3. Finding the Average of a group of Rational numbers

To find the average of a group of rational numbers:

Step 1   Find the sum of all the rational numbers in the group.

Step 2   Divide the sum by the count of rational numbers in the group.

4. Translating "of" to "multiply".

To solve problems involving part of the whole:

Step 1   Represent the unknown quantity by a variable.

Step 2   Set up an equation by translating the sentences. (Fraction) of (whole) = (Part).

Step 3   Solve for the variable.

Step 4   Check the final answer.

5. Recognizing Rates, Solving Rate Problems

To solve rate problem by using a proportion:

Step 1   Represent the unknown quantity by a variable.

Step 2   Organize the numbers into a table, using labels:

     Case I   and   **Case 2**

Step 3   Write the proportion directly from the table. Check that the labels on the two sides match.

Step 4   Solve for the unknown.

Case I   **Case II**

$$\frac{35 \text{ miles}}{2 \text{ gallons}} = \frac{80 \text{ miles}}{x \text{ gallons}} \rightarrow \frac{35}{2} \times \frac{80}{x}$$

$$\rightarrow \quad 35x = 160$$

$$x = \frac{\overset{32}{\cancel{160}}}{\underset{7}{\cancel{35}}}$$

$$= 4\frac{4}{7} \text{ gallons}$$

6.   Finding the Perimeters of Polygons

The perimeter of a polygon is the distance along its boundary.

To find the perimeter of a polygon, add all the sides that form its boundary.

6. Find the perimeter of the given polygon.

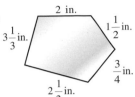

Solution:

$$P = 2\frac{1}{2} + \frac{3}{4} + 1\frac{1}{2} + 2 + 3\frac{1}{3}$$

$$= \frac{5}{2} + \frac{3}{4} + \frac{3}{2} + \frac{2}{1} + \frac{10}{3}$$

$$= \frac{30}{12} + \frac{9}{12} + \frac{18}{12} + \frac{24}{12} + \frac{40}{12}$$

$$= \frac{121}{12} = \mathbf{10\frac{1}{12}} \text{ in.}$$

7.   Finding the Areas of Polygons

The Area of a polygon is a measure of the plane (flat) region enclosed by the polygon. It is measured in square units.

Area = Length × Width $(A = L \cdot W)$.

7.

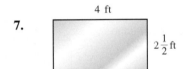

$$A = L \cdot W$$

$$= 4 \cdot 2\frac{1}{2}$$

$$= 10 \text{ ft}^2$$

8.   Finding the Volume of a Rectangular solid or Cube

The Volume of any solid is the amount of space enclosed within its boundary faces, and is measured in cubic units. The volume of a solid is a measure of its capacity.

(a)   **A rectangular solid** is bounded by six rectangular faces, and the angle between any two adjacent edges is a right angle.

Volume: $V = l \cdot w \cdot h$

8.(a) Find the volume of the rectangular solid given in the figure.

Solution:

$$V = l \cdot w \cdot h$$

$$V = \left(3\frac{3}{5} \text{ ft} \cdot 1\frac{1}{3} \text{ ft} \cdot 2\frac{1}{2} \text{ ft}\right)$$

$$V = \left(\frac{\overset{6}{\cancel{18}}}{\underset{1}{\cancel{5}}} \cdot \frac{\overset{2}{\cancel{4}}}{\underset{1}{\cancel{3}}} \cdot \frac{\overset{1}{\cancel{5}}}{\underset{1}{\cancel{2}}}\right) \text{ ft}^3$$

$$V = 12 \text{ ft}^3$$

Examples

(b) Find the volume of a cube given in the figure

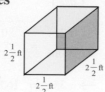

Solution: $V = s \cdot s \cdot s = s^3$

$$V = \left(2\frac{1}{2}\,\text{ft} \cdot 2\frac{1}{2}\,\text{ft} \cdot 2\frac{1}{2}\,\text{ft}\right)$$

$$= \left(\frac{5}{2} \cdot \frac{5}{2} \cdot \frac{5}{2}\right)\text{ft}^3$$

$$= \frac{125}{8}\,\text{ft}^3$$

(b) A **cube** is a special rectangular solid whose length, width, and height are all equal.

Volume: $V = s \cdot s \cdot s$

$$= s^3$$

(c) The **volume** of a regular solid with congruent bases and uniform height is:

Volume: $V = (\text{Area of the base}) \times \text{height}$

9.(a) Surface area of Rectangular solid:

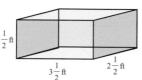

$S = 2(l \cdot w) + 2(w \cdot h) + 2(h \cdot l)$

$$S = 2\left(3\frac{1}{2} \cdot 2\frac{1}{2}\right) + 2\left(2\frac{1}{2} \cdot 1\frac{1}{2}\right) + 2\left(1\frac{1}{2} \cdot 3\frac{1}{2}\right)$$

$$= \frac{71}{2}$$

$$= 35\frac{1}{2}\,\text{ft}^2$$

9. **Surface area of a Rectangular solid or a cube**

(a) The **surface area** of a rectangular solid is the sum of the areas of its faces.

Surface area of a rectangular solid :

$$S = 2(l \cdot w) + 2(w \cdot h) + 2(h \cdot l)$$

(b) Surface area of cube:

$S = 6 \cdot s^2$

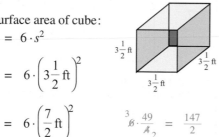

$$= 6 \cdot \left(3\frac{1}{2}\,\text{ft}\right)^2$$

$$= 6 \cdot \left(\frac{7}{2}\,\text{ft}\right)^2 \qquad \overset{3}{\cancel{6}} \cdot \frac{49}{\cancel{4}_2} = \frac{147}{2}$$

$$= 73\frac{1}{2}\,\text{ft}^2 \qquad\qquad = 73\frac{1}{2}$$

(b) The surface area of a cube is 6 times the area of one of its faces, since all faces are of the same area.

$$S = 6[s \cdot s]$$

$$= 6s^2$$

10. Find the missing sides

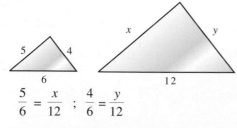

$\dfrac{5}{6} = \dfrac{x}{12}$; $\dfrac{4}{6} = \dfrac{y}{12}$

Use cross products:

$6x = 60 \qquad ; \qquad 6y = 48$

$x = 10 \qquad ; \qquad y = 8$

10. **Finding the Missing Sides of Similar Triangles**

Two triangles or any two polygons are similar if their corresponding sides are proportional.

To find a missing side with similar triangles (or other figures):

Step 1   Represent the missing side with a variable.

Step 2   Write the proportion of two pairs of corresponding sides.

Step 3   Solve the related proportion.

5.5 REVIEW EXERCISE

In exercises 1-10, solve the given equation.

1. $-\dfrac{5}{3}x = -10$ **2.** $\dfrac{4}{3}x + 3 = -5$ **3.** $-\dfrac{1}{3} + \dfrac{x}{15} = \dfrac{1}{5}$ **4.** $-\dfrac{7}{10} = \dfrac{y}{5} + \dfrac{1}{2}$ **5.** $\dfrac{2}{3}x + x = \dfrac{10}{3}$

6. $\dfrac{2x}{3} - \dfrac{x}{2} = \dfrac{5}{6}$ **7.** $2x - \dfrac{x}{4} + \dfrac{1}{5} = 3$ **8.** $\dfrac{5}{4}x - \dfrac{x}{2} = \dfrac{7}{3} - \dfrac{3}{2}$ **9.** $3x - \dfrac{3}{2} = \dfrac{5}{2}$ **10.** $\dfrac{1}{3}x + \dfrac{16}{3} = \dfrac{17}{3}$

11. Determine whether the given proportion is true or false.

(a) $\dfrac{4\frac{1}{2}}{2} = \dfrac{3\frac{1}{2}}{1\frac{5}{9}}$ (b) $\dfrac{2\frac{1}{2}}{3} = \dfrac{25}{36}$

12. Determine whether the given proportion is true or false.

(a) $\dfrac{5\,\text{dollars}}{13\,\text{grams}} = \dfrac{40\,\text{dollars}}{104\,\text{grams}}$ (b) $\dfrac{10\,\text{dollars}}{20\,\text{quarters}} = \dfrac{16\,\text{nickels}}{4\,\text{dimes}}$

13. Solve the following proportions:

(a) $\dfrac{6}{13} = \dfrac{30}{x}$ (b) $\dfrac{2}{x} = \dfrac{4}{5}$ (c) $6\dfrac{2}{5}$ is to y as 12 is to 15.

14. Find the value as indicated:

(a) Five-sevenths of 1,785 (b) Three-halves of 500 (c) 80% of 725 (d) 40% of (-135)

(e) One-seventh of $\dfrac{49}{50}$ (f) Two-thirds of $\dfrac{35}{6}$ (g) $\dfrac{4}{9}$ of $\left(-\dfrac{9}{16}\right)$

15. If $\dfrac{2}{3}$ of the selling price of a used text book is store markup, what is the markup for a book with a selling price of $63?

16. If 120 ounces of milk contains $2\dfrac{2}{5}$ ounces of fat, what fraction of the milk is fat?

17. Janelle spends 20% of her income on food. If she spends $120 each week on food, what is her weekly income?

18. A hamburger weighing $\dfrac{1}{3}$ pound is 10% fat. How much fat is in the hamburger? How much meat is in the hamburger?

19. Four-fifths of the total rainfall this year fell during the Fall. If the Fall rainfall measured 14 inches, what was the total rainfall for the year?

20. If 6 students in a class are smokers and 22 students are non-smokers, what fraction of the class are non-smokers?

21. If 12 families own a total of 32 motorized vehicles, what is the average number of vehicles per family?

22. The property tax is $1\dfrac{1}{2}$ ¢ per dollar of property value. If the taxable value of his home is $200,000, what will Luis owe for his property tax? (Recall : 100 ¢ = $1)

23. Linda is planning a trip of 240 miles and she knows that her car averages $18\frac{4}{5}$ miles per gallon of gas.

    (a) How many gallons of gas will she need for this trip?

    (b) If the gas costs $ $1\frac{1}{4}$ per gallon, how much should she plan to spend on this trip for gas?
    Write the answers as mixed numbers.

24. Thirty-five bulbs can be produced by a machine in 40 minutes. How much time will it take to produce 200 bulbs?

25. A car travels 380 miles in $8\frac{1}{2}$ hours. How many miles will it travel in 4 hours?

26. Find the average of the following group of numbers:

    (a) $2\frac{1}{4}, \frac{5}{8}$, and $1\frac{1}{2}$ **(b)** $6\frac{1}{10}, 2\frac{1}{2}, 5\frac{3}{4}$, and $3\frac{2}{5}$ **(c)** $4\frac{5}{12}, 3\frac{3}{8}$, and $10\frac{1}{3}$

In exercises 27-28, measure the lengths of the sides of the polygons to the nearest $\frac{1}{8}$ of an inch and find the area.

27.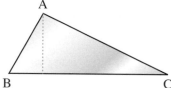
28.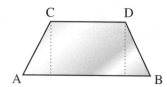

29. Find the area of a rectangle that has the length of $\frac{1}{8}$ ft and the width of $\frac{7}{9}$ ft.

30. Find the length of a rectangle if its width is $\frac{3}{4}$ ft and the area is 24 ft².

31. Find the perimeter of a square of side $\frac{1}{10}$ yd.

32. The perimeter of a rectangle is 115 ft. The width is $40\frac{1}{2}$ ft. What is the length?

33. Find the volume of a cube whose side is:

    (a) $3\frac{1}{3}$ ft   **(b)** $\frac{15}{2}$ cm

34. Find the volume of the rectangular solid whose length is $3\frac{1}{3}$ yd; width is $\frac{4}{5}$ yd; and height is $2\frac{2}{5}$ yd.

35. How much cardboard is needed to make a box $14\frac{1}{4}$ in by $18\frac{2}{5}$ in by $5\frac{1}{2}$ in. What is the volume of the box?

36. Find the missing sides in the larger triangle, if the two triangles in the figure are similar.

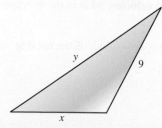

5.6 SELF TEST

In exercises 1-4, solve the equation and check your solution.

1. $3x = \dfrac{5}{4}$

2. $x + \dfrac{2}{5} = \dfrac{8}{3}$

3. $\dfrac{1}{2} - x = \dfrac{1}{4}$

4. $\dfrac{6}{5}x + \dfrac{1}{2} = \dfrac{11}{2}$

5. Find the missing term: $\dfrac{15}{23} = \dfrac{105}{?}$

6. Solve the proportion: $\dfrac{12}{35} = \dfrac{x}{21}$.

7. Is the given proportion true or false? $\dfrac{3\,\text{inches}}{1\frac{1}{2}\,\text{feet}} = \dfrac{2\,\text{feet}}{4\,\text{yds}}$.

8. Solve the proportion: $\dfrac{x-1}{4} = \dfrac{2}{7}$.

9. On a test, Alice answered 32 out of 40 questions correctly. At the same rate, how many questions would she answer correctly if there were 150 questions on a test?

10. Find the length of fence needed to fence the park shown in the figure.

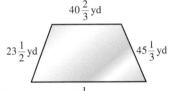

11. An airplane is carrying 180 passengers. This is 90% of its capacity. What is the capacity of the airplane?

In exercises 12-13, measure the lengths of the sides of the polygons to the nearest $\dfrac{1}{8}$ of an inch and find the perimeter and the area.

12.

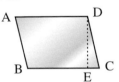

13.

14. Find the area of a rectangle whose length is $16\dfrac{1}{2}$ m and whose width is $12\dfrac{1}{3}$ m.

15. Find the volume of the solid using the information given in the figure.

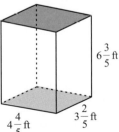

16. Find the surface area of the solid using the information given in the figure.

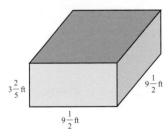

17. The figures are similar. Find the missing side.

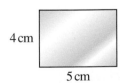

Decimal Numbers

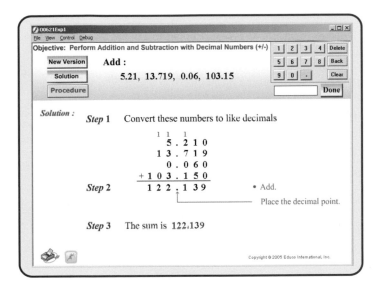

DECIMAL NUMBERS

Introduction

In this chapter, we will discuss how to read and write decimal numbers, and perform basic operations (+, −, ×, ÷) on decimal numbers. Besides discussing the order of operations and computing averages with decimal numbers, our discussion will include the concepts of 'rounding decimal numbers' and 'estimating answers'.

This chapter is divided into four sections:

6.1   *Reading and Writing Decimal Numbers, Rounding Decimal Numbers;*

6.2   *Addition and Subtraction with Decimal Numbers;*

6.3   *Multiplication and Division with Decimal Numbers;*

6.4   *Decimals and Fractions.*

6.1   READING AND WRITING DECIMAL NUMBERS, ROUNDING DECIMAL NUMBERS

IMPORTANT VOCABULARY

1. The digits and a dot, ".", called a **decimal point** are used to write place value names for decimal fractions and mixed numbers.

2. The numbers written using a **decimal point**, such as 32.715, are called decimal numbers or simply **decimals**.

3. The number of digits to the right of the decimal point are called **decimal places**; for example, 27.016 has three decimal places.

> **Objectives**
>
> After completing this section, you will be able to:
>
> A. Read and write decimal numbers;
>
> B. Round decimal numbers to a given place value; and
>
> C. Graph decimals, find absolute values, and compare decimals.

4. Decimals are either **exact** numbers or **approximate** numbers. For example, decimals that count money are usually exact. The figure $375.50 shows an exact amount. Decimals that represent measurements generally give approximations of measurements. For example, 40.6 m shows a length to the nearest tenth of a meter.

5. Like whole numbers, decimals can be rounded to any required place value. When 25.7469 is rounded to the second decimal place, we get 25.7469 ≈ 25.75.

    ↑
    approximately equal to

6.1 A. Place Value System for Decimal Numbers: The Word Names

1. Place Value System for Decimals

- The advantage of decimal fractions over other fractions is that they are based on the same number scale as whole numbers. Decimals are written by using a standard place value in the same way as whole numbers, as shown in the following chart.

PLACE VALUE CHART FOR DECIMALS

	Whole Number Part					Decimal Point	Decimal Part				
...	HUNDRED THOUSANDS	TEN THOUSANDS	THOUSANDS	HUNDREDS	TENS	ONES	•	TENTHS	HUNDREDTHS	THOUSANDTHS	TEN THOUSANDTHS	HUNDRED-THOUSANDTHS ...
... 100,000	10,000	1000	100	10	1		$\frac{1}{10}$	$\frac{1}{100}$	$\frac{1}{1000}$	$\frac{1}{10,000}$	$\frac{1}{100,000}$ ...
... 10^5	10^4	10^3	10^2	10^1	10^0		$\frac{1}{10^1}$	$\frac{1}{10^2}$	$\frac{1}{10^3}$	$\frac{1}{10^4}$	$\frac{1}{10^5}$ ...

Figure 6.1

This chart is clearly an extension of the place value chart for whole numbers. We now have place values for the digits on the right of the decimal point. For example,

the fractions such as $\dfrac{45}{1000}$ and $\dfrac{3}{1000}$, in the common decimal notation, are written as:

The digit 5 is in the thousandths position.

$$\frac{45}{1000} = 0.045 \qquad \text{(read: "forty-five thousandths")}$$

One zero must be inserted as a place holder.

and $\qquad \dfrac{3}{1000} = 0.003 \qquad$ (read: "three thousandths").

The digit 3 is in the thousandths position,

Two zeros must be inserted as place holders.

Also, a decimal number, say 45.231, in the expanded form is written as illustrated below:

$$45.231 = 40 + 5 + \frac{2}{10} + \frac{3}{100} + \frac{1}{1000}$$

SOME FACTS TO REMEMBER

1. A decimal number consists of two parts: the whole number part and the fraction part.
   In 57.629, the whole number part is 57; the fraction part .629.

2. If a decimal number does not have a whole number part, then it is recommended to place a zero to the left of the decimal point.
   For example, .73 is usually written as 0.73.

Contd..6.3

3. In the case of a whole number the decimal point is understood to be present to the right of the digit at the ones place;

thus, $75 = 75.$ $180 = 180.$ $5 = 5.$

4. The number formed by the digits in a fraction part is the numerator of the decimal fraction. The number of decimal places is equal to the number of zeros in the denominator;

thus,

$$0.23 = \frac{23}{100};$$

$$27.023 = 27 + \frac{23}{1000} \longrightarrow 27\frac{23}{1000} \text{ or } \frac{27,023}{1000}$$

$$23.0 = 23 \text{ or } 23 = 23 + \frac{0}{10}.$$

2. Reading and Writing Decimal Numbers

- In the last chapter, we learned about fractions and mixed numbers. Fractions whose denominators are 10 or powers of 10 are called **decimal fractions.**

$$\frac{3}{10}, \frac{15}{100}, \frac{47}{1,000} \text{ are examples of decimal fractions.}$$

In reading a fraction such as $\frac{52}{100}$, we read the numerator as a whole number ("fifty-two") and then attach the name of the denominator followed by *ths* ("hundred**ths**").

Note that **ths** (or **th**) is used to indicate the fraction; thus, the decimal fraction $\frac{52}{100}$ is read as "fifty-two hundred**ths**". Similarly, the fraction $\frac{1}{10}$ is read as "one ten**th**".

Usually, we write decimals without denominators. The denominator is indicated by using a dot called the "decimal point". For example,

$\frac{3}{10}$ is written as 0.3 and is read as "three tenths"; and

Decimal point

$\frac{15}{100}$ is written as 0.15 and is read as "fifteen hundredths".

Decimal point

- Improper fractions and mixed numbers whose fractional parts are decimal fractions can also be written as decimal numbers as discussed below:

$\frac{25}{10} = 2\frac{5}{10}$ is written as 2.5 and is read as "two **and** five tenths".   Read "and" in place of the decimal point.

Decimal point

$24\frac{35}{100}$ is written as 24.35 and is read as "twenty-four **and** thirty-five hundredths".

Decimal point

Whole numbers are also decimal numbers and can be written with a decimal point as illustrated below:

$$6 = 6. \quad \text{or} \quad 6.0 \quad ; \quad 15 = 15. \quad \text{or} \quad 15.0$$

Procedure to read or write a decimal number:

Step 1 Read (or write) the whole number part (that is, the whole number to the left of the decimal point).

Step 2 Read (or write) **and** for the decimal point ".".

Step 3 Read (or write) the number in the fraction part.

Step 4 Read (or write) the word name for the place value of the right most digit in the number, ending with *ths* or (th).

 Note   If the decimal has only zero or no digit to the left of the decimal point, we omit reading or writing the whole number part.

Warm-Up

1. Write the word names for the decimals.

   (a) 43.056

   (b) 0.43

   (c) 403.0

2. Write the given number in decimal notation and in words.

   (a) $16\dfrac{7}{10}$

Example 1 Write the word names for the decimals:

(a) 27.005   (b) 0.725   (c) 275.00

Solutions

(a)
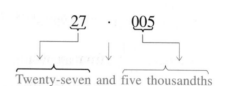

Twenty-seven and five thousandths

The word name for 27.005 is

"Twenty-seven and five thousandths."

(b) The word name for 0.725 is

"Seven hundred twenty-five thousandths".

(c) 275.00 has only zeros to the right of the decimal point; therefore, the word name of 275.00 is the same as that of 275:

"Two hundred seventy-five".

Example 2 Write the following numbers in decimal notation and in words:

(a) $27\dfrac{5}{10}$ (b) $8\dfrac{43}{1000}$

Solutions

(a) $27\dfrac{5}{10} = 27 + \dfrac{5}{10}$ • Separate the whole number part and the fraction part.

$= 27 + .5$ • Write the fraction part in decimal notation.

$= 27 \cdot 5$ (in decimal notation)   • Drop '+' sign.

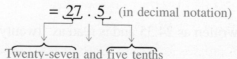

Twenty-seven and five tenths

So, the word name is: "Twenty-seven and five tenths".

(b) $8\dfrac{43}{1000} = 8 + \dfrac{43}{1000}$

$= 8 + .043$

$= \underset{\downarrow}{8} . \underset{\downarrow}{043}$ (in decimal notation);

$\underset{\text{Eight}}{} \underset{\text{and}}{} \underset{\text{forty-three thousandths}}{}$

Therefore, the word name is:

"Eight and forty-three thousandths".

(b) $34\dfrac{5}{100}$

Procedure to write the decimal number from its word name:

Step **1**   Write the number preceding "and" as the whole number part of the decimal.

Step **2**   Replace the word "and" with a decimal point.

Step **3**   Write the number for the word name after the word "and" as the fraction part such that the digit in the right-most place occupies the last decimal place as suggested by the word name.

Step **4**   Write zero(s) to fill out the vacant decimal places, if any.

Example 3   Write the decimal numbers from the word names:

     (a)   Seven hundred twelve and thirty-five hundredths.

     (b)   Forty-nine and twenty-five thousandths.

     (c)   Five hundred-thousandths.

Solutions

   (a)   Seven hundred twelve   and   thirty-five   hundredths

          712   .   35   two decimal places;

thus, "Seven hundred twelve and thirty-five hundredths" when written as a decimal number $= 712.35$.

   (b)   Forty-nine   and   twenty-five   thousandths

         49   .   25   three decimal places;

     $= 49.025$.

   (c)   Five hundred-thousandths

     The whole number part is zero.

     The number to the right of the decimal point is 5.

     The place of 5 is hundred-thousandths (five decimal places).

     Therefore, "five hundred-thousandths" $= 0.00005$.

Warm-Up

3. Write the decimal numbers from the word names.

     (a)   Four hundred five and fifteen hundred-thousandths.

     (b)   Seventy-two and four thousandths.

     (c)   Twenty thousandths

Answers:

1. (a)   Forty-three and fifty-six thousandths.

    (b)   Forty-three hundredths.

    (c)   Four-hundred three.

2. (a)   16.7 ; Sixteen and seven tenths.

    (b)   34.05 ; Thirty-four and five hundredths.

3. (a)   405.00015   **(b)**   72.004   **(c)**   .020

6.1 B.   Rounding Decimals to a Given Place of Accuracy

Recall that in rounding we identify the two numbers closest to a number that have the desired precision (place value). We determine which of the two numbers is closer and use that number as an approximation. When we work with decimals we frequently get results that have many more place values that we need. When this happens we round to a desired place value (precision).

For instance, suppose you own a business and calculate your employee's weekly pay to be 30.75 hr × $9.85/hr = $302.8875. You cannot pay this amount exactly. The smallest unit of money is the penny, which is hundredths of a dollar, the second decimal place. The number already shows $302.88. By rounding, we determine whether the employee should be paid $302.88 or $302.**89**.

We discussed earlier in Chapter 1 how whole numbers can be rounded to a particular place value. We round decimal numbers the same way, using the following rules:

RULES FOR ROUNDING

Rule **1**   If the digit to the right of the rounding place is 5 or greater, **round up** by adding 1 to the *digit* at the rounding place and change the remaining digits to its right to zeros.

Rule **2**   If the digit to the right of the rounding place is less than 5, **round down** by changing the digits to the right of the rounding place to zeros. Leave the digit in the rounding place as it is.

Rule **3**   Drop zeros in the decimal places to the right of the rounding place.

To round 235.6473 to the **nearest tenths**, draw an arrow under the digit in the **tenths place**.

$$235.6473$$
$$\uparrow$$

Since the digit to the right of the arrow is 4, we *round down* by replacing each digit to the right of the arrow with zeros.

235.6473 is rounded to 235.6000, or to 235.6 after dropping extra zeros.

We say 235.**6473** ≈ 235.**6**   rounded to the nearest tenths.

      ↑_____ "is approximately equal to"

Similarly, if we want to round the same number to the nearest hundredths, we draw an arrow under 4, the digit in the hundredths place.

$$235.6473 \longrightarrow 235.6500$$
$$\uparrow$$

Since the digit to right of the arrow is 7, we *round up* by adding 1 to hundredths place and replacing each digit to the right of the hundredths place by zeros. We then drop the additional zeros in the decimal places to the right of the 5.

235.**6473** ≈ 235.**65** to the nearest hundredths.

Procedure to round a decimal to a given place of accuracy:

Step **1**   Draw an arrow under the digit in the rounding place.

Step **2**   Round up or round down.

Step **3**   Drop the unnecessary zeros to the right of the arrow.

Example 4   Round the following decimals to the nearest thousandths:

(a) 15.43281   (b) 0.084413   (c) 251.629601

Solutions

(a)   *Step* 1   15.43281
                        ↑

- Draw an arrow under the digit at the thousandths place.

Step 2   15.43300
                    ↑

- Since the first digit to the right of the arrow is 8, round up.

Step 3   15.433

- Drop the unnecessary zeros.

15.43281 ≈ 15.433 to the nearest thousandths.

(b)   0.084413
              ↑

- Draw an arrow under the digit at the thousandths place.

0.084000 = **0.084**

- Since the first digit to the right of the arrow is 4 (less than 5), round down.

0.084413 ≈ 0.084 to the nearest thousandths.

(c)   251.629601
                  ↑

- Draw an arrow under the digit at the thousandths place.

251.630000 = 251.630

- Since the first digit to the right of the arrow is 6, round up by adding 1 to 9 in 251.629 to get 251.630.

251.629601 ≈ 251.630
to the nearest thousandths.

⚠ **Caution:**   Do not drop a zero in the rounding place. It is required to display the place of accuracy.

Example 5   Round the following numbers as indicated:

(a)   4,065.23   to the nearest tens.

(b)   239.8059   to the nearest whole number

Solutions

(a)   4,065.23
              ↑

- Draw an arrow under the digit 6, at the tens place.

4,070.00
      ↑

- Round up, since the digit to the right of the arrow is 5.

4,070.
    ↑

- Drop the unnecessary zeros.

4,065.23 ≈ 4,070 to the nearest tens.

4. Round the following decimals to the nearest hundredths:

(a) 537.4139

(b) 21.72564

(c) 0.29985

5. Round the following numbers as indicated:

(a) 23501.9 to the nearest thousands.

(b) 47.399 to the nearest whole number.

(b)   239.8059
           ↑
        240.0000 = 240.

- Round the number to the nearest whole number means round to the nearest ones.
- Round up by adding 1 to 239.
- Drop the **unnecessary** zeros.

239.8059 ≈ 240 to the nearest whole number.

⚠ **Caution:** Do not drop the zero from the whole number part.

Answers:

4. (a) 537.41   **(b)** 21.73   **(c)** 0.30

5. (a) 24,000   **(b)** 47

Example 6   Application

Charles plans to deduct $385.65 for union dues when he files his tax return. If the instructions are that the amount should be rounded to the nearest dollar, how much can he deduct?

Solution

Since 385.65 ≈ 386 rounded to the nearest whole dollar, Charles can deduct $386 for union dues.
              ↑

6.1 C Graphing Decimals, Measuring using Decimals, Absolute Values, and Comparing Decimals

- **Graphing Decimals**

To graph decimal numbers, we identify the nearest tenth and locate the decimal number close to that point on the number line.

Warm-Up

7. Graph on a number line.

(a) 0.87

Example 7   Graph each of the following on a number line.

(a) –2.583   **(b)** 0.31   **(c)** 4.99

Solution

(a)   –2.583

Sketch a number line, with units broken into tenths.

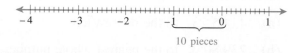

−2.583 ≈ −2.6

Start at zero. Move 2 units to the left and then 6 tenths further to the left.

Mark a dot for −2.583.

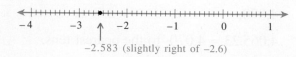

−2.583 (slightly right of −2.6)

(b) **0.31**

$0.31 \approx 0.3$

Move 3 tenths to the right of zero and place a point for 0.31.

0.31 (slightly right of 0.3)

(c) **4.99**

$4.99 \approx 5.0$

Move 5 units to the right of zero. Place a point for 4.99.

4.99 ≈ 5.0
(slightly left of 5.0)

(b) −1.562

(c) 0.3333

- **Measuring Using Decimals**

In chapter 3, we learned to read a centimeter ruler using tenths. The tenths $\left(\frac{1}{10}\text{'s}\right)$ can more easily be expressed

and calculated using decimals. For example, $3\frac{7}{10}$ cm (centimeter) = 3.7 cm.

$\frac{1}{10}$ **cm** is also called a **millimeter** (mm) and 1 cm = 10 mm.

Example 8 **(a)** Determine the diameter of a quarter in centimeters and millimeters.

(b) Determine the length of the key using both **cm** and **mm**.

Solution **(a)** Position the quarter so that the left edge corresponds to 0 as illustrated in the figure 6.2. Then read its measurements in

$\frac{1}{10}$'s of a centimeter.

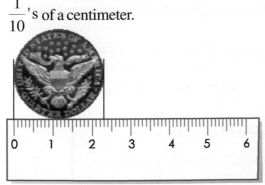

Figure 6.2

$$\text{Diameter} \approx 2\frac{3}{10} \text{ cm} = 20 \text{ mm} + 3 \text{ mm}$$

$$\approx 2.3 \text{ cm} \qquad = 23 \text{ mm}$$

The diameter is approximately 2.3 cm or 23 mm.

8. Use ruler to measure the line segment, in cm and in mm.

(b) _____

(b) Position the key so that the left edge corresponds to 0 as illustrated in the figure 6.3. Read its measurements in $\frac{1}{10}$'s of a centimeter.

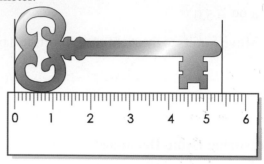

Figure 6.3

$$\text{Length} \approx 5\frac{4}{10} \text{ cm} = 50 \text{ mm} + 4 \text{ mm}$$

Answers:

7. (a)
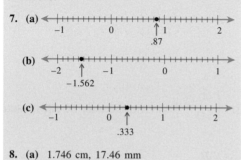

(b)

(c)

8. (a) 1.746 cm, 17.46 mm

(b) 3.353 cm, 33.53 mm

$$\approx 5.4 \text{ cm} = 54 \text{ mm}$$

The length is approximately 5.4 cm or 54 mm.

• **Finding the Absolute Value**

The absolute value of a decimal number, as in the case of integers, fractions, and mixed numbers, is its distance from 0 on the number line. The absolute value of a number is never negative. We use vertical bars | | to indicate the absolute value of all kinds of numbers, whether integers, fractions, or decimal numbers, or any other kind of numbers used in mathematics.

$$\text{Absolute value of} \quad -3.75 = |-3.75|$$

$$= 3.75 \; ;$$

$$|1.25| = 1.25 \; ;$$

$$|-0.9| = 0.9;$$

$$|0| = 0$$

The definition of absolute value was given in Section 2.1 in terms of integers, and then in Section 3.4 for fractions. This definition is also valid for decimal numbers. We can express the definition symbolically, for any decimal number 'a' as follows:

Definition:

The absolute value of a decimal number a is denoted by the symbol $|a|$, and is defined as follows:

If a is positive or 0, then $|a| = a$.   For example, $|3.6| = 3.6$, $|0| = 0$.

If a is negative, then $-|-a| = a$.   For example, $|-25| = 2.5 = -(-2.5)$.

Example 9   Find the absolute values indicated below:

(a) $|-2.9|$ (b) $|13.58|$

Solutions (a) $|-2.9| = 2.9$

(b) $|13.58| = 13.58$

Warm-Up

9. Find the absolute values indicated below:

(a) $|0.92|$ (b) $|-4.5|$

- **Comparing Decimals**

Two or more decimal numbers are called **like decimals** if they have the same number of decimal places. Otherwise, they are called **unlike decimals**.

Comparing two Decimals is very simple. To compare *like* decimals, we compare the integers obtained by dropping the decimal point. For example, $8.67 < 9.34$ because $867 < 934$. To compare *unlike* decimals, we first convert them to like decimals and then compare. For example, to compare 3.7 and 3.69, we write $3.7 = 3.70$ and then compare the like decimals 3.69 and 3.70. Since $3.70 > 3.69$, therefore, $3.7 > 3.69$. Recall, when comparing numbers, we use their positions on the number line. The number on the left is smaller.

Example 10   Insert the appropriate inequality symbol in the given pair of decimals:

(a) 3.45 ☐ 34.5   (b) 2.47 ☐ 2.097

(c) −4.5 ☐ −9.05   (d) −2.05 ☐ 2.04

Warm-Up

10. Insert the appropriate inequality symbol in the given pair of decimals:

(a) 2.79 ☐ 2.097

(b) 34.4 ☐ 9.75

(c) −15.2 ☐ −7.04

(d) −9.47 ☐ 4.59

Solution (a) 3.45 ☐ 34.5

3.45 ☐ 34.50   Convert to like decimals.

345 ☐ 3450   Drop decimal point.

Since $345 < 3,450$; therefore, $3.45 < 34.5$.

(b) 2.47 ☐ 2.097

2.470 ☐ 2.097   Convert to like decimals.

2470 ☐ 2097   Drop decimal point.

Since $2470 > 2097$; therefore, $2.47 > 2.097$.

(c) −4.5 ☐ −9.05

−4.50 ☐ −9.05   Convert to like decimals.

−450 ☐ −905   Drop decimal point.

Since $450 < 905$, $\longrightarrow$ $-450 > -905$; therefore, $-4.5 > -9.05$.

(d) −2.05 is to the left of 2.04 on the number line.

Therefore, $-2.05 < 2.04$.

Warm-Up

11. Write the numbers below in ascending order:

-2.1   -2.141   -1.52

Answers:

9. (a) 0.92 (b) 4.5

10. (a) >   (b) >   (c) <   (d) <

11. -2.141, -2.1, -1.52

Example 11   Write the numbers below in ascending order:

0.5,   0.412,   0.4025

Solution   Attach zeros so that each extends to 4 decimal places.

0.5 is rewritten as 0.5000.

0.412 is rewritten as 0.4120.

Compare 0.5000, 0.4120, and 0.4025.

4025 < 4120 < 5000

Therefore, the numbers in ascending order are :

0.4025, 0.412, 0.5.

when dividing move decimal From Right to left

Exercise 6.1

A.   **In exercises 1-10, write the given number in decimal notation.**

1. $12\frac{9}{10}$ **2.** $43\frac{15}{100}$ **3.** $9\frac{24}{1,000}$ *9.024*   **4.** $\frac{485}{1,000}$ **5.** $72\frac{56}{100}$

6. $4{,}312\frac{6}{100}$ **7.** $4\frac{8}{10}$ **8.** $5\frac{3}{100}$ **9.** $35\frac{246}{1,000}$ **10.** $\frac{45}{10,000}$

In exercises 11-20, write the decimal number as a fraction or a mixed number. Do not reduce.

11. 2.73 $2\frac{73}{100}$ **12.** 295.84   **13.** 35.432 $35\frac{432}{100}$ **14.** 47.08   **15.** 19.5 $19\frac{5}{10}$

16. 52.001   **17.** 27.005   **18.** 14.09   **19.** 3.815   **20.** 729.025

In exercises 21-30, write the word name for the given decimal number. *in words*

21. 4,005.083   **22.** 21.002   **23.** 491.283   **24.** 4.1   **25.** 842.0049

26. 15.01   **27.** 29.605   **28.** 6.05   **29.** 0.805   **30.** 24.5483

In exercises 31-40, write the decimal number from the given word name.

31. Two hundred seventeen and three hundredths   **32.** Twenty-nine and five tenths

217.030

33. Three hundred forty-nine thousandths   **34.** Five and twenty-five hundredths

35. Four thousand, five hundred thirty-two and ninety-two thousandths   **36.** Eight and eight ten-thousandths

37. One million, ninety-two and twelve hundredths   **38.** Eight and eight tenths

39. Seventy-three and five hundred forty-nine thousandths   **40.** Twenty-three hundredths

B.   **In exercises 41-48, round the decimal number to the nearest tenth.**

41. 275.57 *275.60*   **42.** 6.555   **43.** 0.067 *0.1*   **44.** 23.498

45. 45.039   **46.** 1,235.86   **47.** 4.0398   **48.** 17.4601

See chart in Pg 298 or review

In exercises 49-52, round the decimal number to the nearest hundredth.

49. 5.2764   **50.** 25.4538   **51.** 5.042   **52.** 6.602

In exercises 53-56, round the decimal number to the nearest thousandth.

53. 23.5482   **54.** 0.8095   **55.** 7.2974   **56.** 145.3156

In exercises 57-60, round the decimal number to the nearest whole number.

57. 256.89   **58.** 58.542   **59.** 420.495   **60.** 79.998

In exercises 61-69, round the number as indicated.

61. 275.57 to the tenths place   **62.** 17.036 to the nearest hundredth

63. 569.692 to the nearest whole number   **64.** 43.0091 to three decimal places

65. 0.9521 to one decimal place   **66.** 15.0049 to two decimal places

67. 2,564.99 to the nearest tenth   **68.** 0.05962 to the nearest thousandth

69. 754.93102 to the nearest hundredth

70. Complete the following chart by rounding the numbers as indicated.

Number	Round to nearest Tens	Ones	Tenths	Hundredths
26.1095				
399.563				

$2\dfrac{73}{100}$

In exercises 71-74, graph the numbers on a number line.

71. 2.5   **72.** 3.457   **73.** −2.487   **74.** 0.472

In exercises 75-78, find the absolute value of the number.

75. $\left|-3.98\right|$ **76.** $\left|0.49\right|$ **77.** $\left|-1.457\right|$ **78.** $\left|2.47\right|$

In exercises 79-82, compare each pair of numbers using < or > symbols.

79. 1.4 and 1.352   **80.** −7.8 and 7.92   **81.** −6.2 and −6   **82.** 4.325 and 4.0928

In exercises 83-86, write the given numbers in ascending order.

83. −4, 2.75, and 0.845   **84.** 0.75, 4.72, and −9.82   **85.** 2, −4, 0.79, and −7.2   **86.** 2.9, −7.4, 0.23, and 4.14

In exercise 87-90, measure the indicated distances for the items below, as indicated, using decimal notation, in cm and mm.

87. The length of the pen.

88. The length of the paper clip.

89. The diameter of the dime.

90. The diameter of the nickel.

Applications

91. Maria buys a battery for $95.35. How would she write this amount in word form on her check?

92. Mr. Stephen wants to write a check for $58.06 to pay for groceries. How would he write this amount in word form on his check?

93. Heather wants to write a check for $322.17 for purchases from a store. How would she write this amount in word form on the check?

94. Roza has five hundred sixty-four and twenty-eight hundredths dollars to spend on holiday gifts this year. Write the amount she has to spend using decimal notation.

95. Joan's savings record on the computer shows that the balance in her account is $ 2,073.50433391. What is the value of the account to the nearest cent?

96. Elizabeth worked for 162 days in a fashion designer's company and received a paycheck for $8,654. To find the average pay per day, she divided the amount $8,654 by 162 on her calculator and found 53.419753 as the answer. Round the average pay per day to the nearest dollar.

97. Round the number 5,499.999 to the nearest hundredth, tenth, one, and ten. What do you observe?

88. One basket of oranges weighs 14.059 pounds and another weighs 14.0589 pounds. Which of the two baskets is heavier?

99. One quart of water weighs approximately 2.0825 pounds. What is the weight of one quart of water rounded to two decimal places?

6.2 ADDITION AND SUBTRACTION WITH DECIMAL NUMBERS

Objectives

After completing this section, you will be able to:

A. Perform addition and subtraction with decimal numbers; and

B. Estimate decimal sums and differences.

6.2 A. Performing Addition and Subtraction with Decimal Numbers

(a) *Adding decimals:* To add **decimals**, we first attach zeros if necessary so that all decimal numbers have the same number of decimal places, and then add. We can do this because of the fact that the value of a decimal number does not change if we attach zeros to the right of the last decimal place.

28.5 = 28.50 = 28.500 = 28.5000, and so on.

Similarly, we observe that dropping the zero(s) at the right end of the decimal part does not change the value of the decimal number.

To add decimals like 2.4, 15, 0.05, and 1.215, we change the numbers by attaching zeros so that each decimal number has the same number of decimal places and then add. For example:

$$
\begin{array}{r}
2.400 \\
+\ 15.000 \\
+\ 0.050 \\
+\ 1.215 \\
\hline
18.665
\end{array}
$$

$\leftarrow \quad 2.4 \ =\ 2.400$

$\leftarrow \quad 15\ =\ 15.\ =\ 15.000$

$\leftarrow \quad 0.05\ =\ 0.050$

Change each decimal to three decimal places since the largest number of decimal places is three.

With practice, we may not even need to attach the zeros. It is necessary only to align the decimal points and write each digit in its proper place, as shown below.

$$
\begin{array}{r}
2.4 \\
15. \\
0.05 \\
1.215 \\
\hline
18.665
\end{array}
$$

Procedure to add a group of decimals:

Step 1   Write the decimals in columns so that the decimal points and the corresponding place values on either side of the decimal are lined up, attaching zeros so that each number has the same number of places.

Step 2   Add the decimals as if they were whole numbers.

Step 3   Place the decimal point in the sum just below those in the addends.

Example 1   Add: 5.21, 13.719, 0.06, 103.15

Solution

Step 1
$$
\begin{array}{r}
\overset{1\ \ 1\ \ \ 1}{} \\
5.210 \\
13.719 \\
0.060 \\
103.150 \\
\end{array}
$$

5.21   =   5.210

0.06   =   0.060

103.15   =   103.150

Step 2   122.139   Add

Step 3   Place the decimal point.

The sum is 122.139.

Example 2   Add the following numbers and round the sum to the nearest tenth:

824.6,   53.0484,   17.9736,   275

Solution

$$
\begin{array}{r}
\overset{1\ 2\ 1\ \ \ \ 1\ 1\ 1}{} \\
824.6000 \\
53.0484 \\
17.9736 \\
275.0000 \\
\hline
1{,}170.6220
\end{array}
$$

$\leftarrow$ Note this step.

$\leftarrow$ Note this step.

Add.

The sum of the given numbers is 1,170.6220 or 1,170.622.

1,170.622 ≈ 1,170.6 rounded **to the nearest tenth.**

Warm-Up

1. Add.

2.7, 17.45, 0.034, and 24.5

2. Find the sum of 43.55, 9.005, 215.25, and 5.085, and round it to the nearest whole number.

3. Add.

$25.3 + 17 + 1.952 + 0.5$

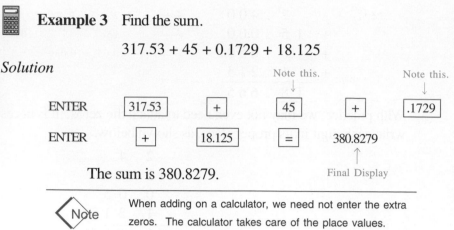

Example 3   Find the sum.

$$317.53 + 45 + 0.1729 + 18.125$$

Solution

ENTER $\boxed{317.53}$ $\boxed{+}$ $\boxed{45}$ $\boxed{+}$ $\boxed{.1729}$

ENTER $\boxed{+}$ $\boxed{18.125}$ $\boxed{=}$ 380.8279

The sum is 380.8279.   Final Display

> **Note** When adding on a calculator, we need not enter the extra zeros. The calculator takes care of the place values.

(b)   *Subtracting decimals:*   To subtract decimals, we first attach zeros if necessary so that all decimals have the same number of decimal places and then subtract. For example, to subtract 19.249 from 75.46, we write 75.46 = 75.460 and then subtract. We use the same process for borrowing that we use with whole numbers.

$$
\begin{array}{r}
7\ 5\ .\ 4\ 6 \\
-\ 1\ 9\ .\ 2\ 4\ 9 \\
\end{array}
\longrightarrow
\begin{array}{r}
7\ 5\ .\ 4\ 6\ 0 \\
-\ 1\ 9\ .\ 2\ 4\ 9 \\
\hline
5\ 6\ .\ 2\ 1\ 1 \\
\end{array}
$$

• Change to like decimals.
• Subtract.

We can **check** the answer by addition.

$$
\begin{array}{r}
1\ 9\ .\ 2\ 4\ 9 \\
+\ 5\ 6\ .\ 2\ 1\ 1 \\
\hline
7\ 5\ .\ 4\ 6\ 0 \\
\end{array}
= 75.46
$$

Procedure   to subtract decimals:

Step **1**   Write the decimals in columns so that the decimal points and the corresponding place values on either side of the decimals are lined up. Attach zeros, if necessary, to have same number of decimal places in each number.

Step **2**   Subtract the decimals as if they were whole numbers.

Step **3**   The difference should have the same number of decimal places as the other two decimal numbers in step 2.

Warm-Up

4.   Find the difference.

(a) $13.55 - 2.34$

Example 4   Find the difference.

(a) $32.189 - 5.069$ (b) $268.15 - 53.1467$

Solutions

(a)
$$
\begin{array}{r}
3\ 2\ .\ 1\ 8\ 9 \\
-\ 5\ .\ 0\ 6\ 9 \\
\hline
2\ 7\ .\ 1\ 2\ 0 \\
\end{array}
$$

• Write the numbers lining up the decimal points and the corresponding place values.
• Subtract.
• Place the decimal point.

The difference is 27.120 or 27.12.

Check:
$$\begin{array}{r} 5\;.\;069 \\ +\;\;27\;.\;120 \\ \hline 32\;.\;189 \end{array}$$

The difference 27.120 or 27.12 is correct.

(b)   *Step* 1 $\begin{array}{r} 268\;.\;1500 \\ -\;\;53\;.\;1467 \\ \hline \end{array}$ ⟵   Note this step, we added two extra 0s.

Step 2

$$\begin{array}{r} 268\;.\;1500 \\ -\;\;53\;.\;1467 \\ \hline 215\;.\;0033 \end{array}$$ ⟵   Subtract.

The difference is 215.0033.

 Example 5   Subtract 59.6758 from 263.

Solution

ENTER | 263 | | – | | 59.6758 | | = | 203.3242

Final Display

The difference is 203.3242.

- The rules for addition with positive and negative decimal numbers are the same as those for addition with integers, fractions and mixed numbers. These rules are revisited below.

> ### RULES FOR ADDITION AND SUBTRACTION WITH SIGNED NUMBERS:
>
> *Rule* **1:**   To add two or more numbers with *like* signs, add their absolute values and use the common sign with the sum obtained.
>
>   For example, $(-3.5) + (-4.3) = -(3.5 + 4.3)$
> $$= -7.8$$
>
> *Rule* **2:**   To add two numbers with *unlike* signs, subtract their absolute values (the smaller from the larger) and attach the sign of the number that has the larger absolute value.
>
>   For example, $12.5 + (-8.2) = +(12.5 - 8.2) = 4.3$;
> $$(-23.4) + 6.9 = -(23.4 - 6.9)$$
> $$= -16.5$$
>
> *Rule* **3:**   Change subtraction (of second term) to addition of the opposite. Then follow the addition rule.
>
>   For example, $-15.6 - 4.2 = -15.6 + (-4.2)$
> $$= -(15.6 + 4.2) = -19.8 ;$$
>   and $7.8 - (-8.5) = 7.8 + (8.5)$
> $$= 16.3$$

Warm-Up

6. Find the sum.

(a) $-4.5 + 1.23$

(b) $8.3 + (-5.2)$

Example 6 Find the indicated sums.

(a) $-7.5 + 9.25$ (b) $41.39 + (-62.14)$

Solutions

The absolute value of 9.25.
The absolute value of -7.5.

(a) $-7.5 + 9.25 = + (9.25 - 7.5) = \mathbf{1.75}$

$$\begin{array}{r} 9.25 \\ -7.50 \\ \hline 1.75 \end{array}$$

The sign of the number having the larger absolute value.

The absolute value of (-62.14).

(b) $41.39 + (-62.14) = - (62.14 - 41.39) = \mathbf{-20.75}$

The absolute value of 41.39.

The sign of the number having the larger absolute value (-62.14).

7. Find the difference.

$-14.823 - (-21.715)$

Example 7 Find the difference: $-212.69 - (-195.84)$.

Solution

$$-212.69 - (-195.84) = -212.69 + (195.84)$$

Change subtraction to addition of the opposite.

$$= -(212.69 - 195.84)$$

$$= \mathbf{-16.85}$$

8. Simplify by combining like terms.

$-56.3x + 77.5x - 34.1x$

Example 8 Simplify by combining like terms:

$$56.25\,x + (-72.13\,x) + 21.98\,x$$

Solution

$$56.25\,x + (-72.13x) + 21.98\,x$$

$$= (56.25\,x + 21.98\,x) + (-72.13x) \bullet$$ Group the like terms having like signs.

$$= (56.25 + 21.98)\,x + (-72.13x) \bullet$$ Add the like terms in each group.

$$= 78.23\,x + (-72.13\,x)$$

$$= [78.23 + (-72.13)]\,x$$

$$= + (78.23 - 72.13)\,x \qquad \bullet$$ Add the coefficients of x.

$$= \mathbf{6.10\,x}$$

9. Find the sum using a calculator.

$26 + (-34.8) + (-15.2) + 19.3$

Example 9 Compute the sum using a calculator.

$$-45 + 7.32 + (-12.6) + (-6.5)$$

Solution   Enter the expression exactly as it is written

ENTER   [(−)] [45] [+] [7.32] [+] [(] [(−)] [12.6] [)]

ENTER   [+] [(] [(−)] [6.5] [)] [=] -56.78 ;

↑
Sum

Thus, $-45 + 7.32 + (-12.6) + (-6.5) = -56.78$.

Example 10 Find the difference using a calculator:
$$-212.69 - (-195.84).$$

Solution

ENTER [(−)] [212.69] [(] [−] [(−)] [195.84] [)] [=] −16.85

Thus, $-212.69 - (-195.84) = -16.85$

6.2 B. Estimating Decimal Sums or Differences

Estimates are made with decimal numbers in a similar way as they are made with integers and whole numbers. For addition or subtraction all numbers must be rounded to the same place value: either the largest or second largest (zeros have no place value).

Example 11 Estimate the following. Compare the estimate to the actual answer found using a calculator.

    (a) $-0.0526 + 0.06758$ **(b)** $-73.48 - 8.593$

Solution

(a) The largest place value occupied by a non-zero digit is the hundredths place for both numbers. We will round both numbers to the same place value, hundredths and then add.

$$
\begin{array}{rcr}
-0.0526 & \approx & -0.05 \\
+0.06728 & \approx & +0.07 \\
\hline
& & 0.02 \quad \leftarrow \text{Estimate}
\end{array}
$$

The estimate, 0.02, is very close to the actual answer, 0.01468, which rounds to 0.01.

(b) The largest place value is tens. The second largest place value is ones. We can use either for estimating. Both are shown below.

    Rounding to tens place: *Rounding to ones place:*

$$
\begin{array}{rclcrcl}
-73.48 & \approx & -70 & \text{or} & -73.48 & \approx & -73 \\
+08.593 & \approx & -10 & & -8.593 & \approx & -9 \\
\cline{3-3}\cline{7-7}
& & -80 & & & & -82
\end{array}
$$

Both estimates, −80 and −82, are very close to the actual difference, −82.073.

Example 12 Application

George writes four checks in the amounts of $774.94, $2,150.35, $1,379.75, and $155.80. He has $4,450.00 in his checking account. Does he have enough money to cover the four checks? If not, how much more, to the nearest dollar, must he deposit in order to cover the four checks? As per bank requirements, he must always have a minimum balance of $100 in his account. (First estimate the answer mentally before actually calculating.)

CHAPTER 6: Decimal Numbers

Solution

The money in the bank must equal the amount of the four checks plus $100, the minimum balance required.

(**Estimate**: The sum of the amounts of the four checks and the minimum balance requirement $\approx 800 + 2,200 + 1,400 + 200 + 100 = \$4,700$, when all figures are rounded to hundred's place.)

He does not *seem* to have enough money to cover the four checks and the minimum balance required).

Sum of the amounts of checks:

$$
\begin{array}{r}
774 \ . \ 94 \\
2,150 \ . \ 35 \\
1,379 \ . \ 75 \\
+ \ \ 155 \ . \ 80 \\
\hline
4,460 \ . \ 84
\end{array}
\qquad
\begin{array}{r}
\rightarrow \quad 4,460 \ . \ 84 \\
+ \ 100 \ . \ 00 \\
\hline
\mathbf{4,560 \ . \ 84} \ \leftarrow
\end{array}
$$

The minimum required amount
(This sum is more than $4,450.00, the amount in the account).

He does not have enough money in his account to cover the four checks.

$$
\begin{array}{r}
4,560 \ . \ 84 \\
- \ 4,450 \ . \ 00 \\
\hline
110 \ . \ 84 \\
\hline
\approx \ \ 111 \ . \ 00
\end{array}
$$

The minimum required amount.

The amount available in the account.

The money George must deposit.

To the nearest dollar.

George must deposit at least $111 more in order to cover the four checks and meet the minimum bank requirement.

Exercise 6.2

A. In exercises 1-7, add the decimals. Check answers using a calculator.

1. 24.4 + 16.6 + 8.7

2. 3.05 + 12.86 + 17.29

3. 123.043 + 72.006 + 9.104

4.
$$
\begin{array}{r}
3.410 \\
6.3975 \\
+ \ 23.251 \\
\hline
\end{array}
$$

5.
$$
\begin{array}{r}
1.4003 \\
13.5 \\
+ \ 27.251 \\
\hline
\end{array}
$$

6.
$$
\begin{array}{r}
28.92 \\
3.49 \\
45.788 \\
+ \ 36.066 \\
\hline
\end{array}
$$

7.
$$
\begin{array}{rl}
68.39 & \text{lb} \\
141.45 & \text{lb} \\
87.3 & \text{lb} \\
+ \ 213.09 & \text{lb} \\
\hline
\end{array}
$$

In exercises 8-10, add the numbers on a calculator.

8. 441.03 + 2.59 + 73.123 + 0.9925

9. 13.715 + 25.25 + 75.025 + 105.05

10. 18.624 + 0.0116 + 3.410 + 6.3975

In exercises 11-26, find the difference. Check your answer using a calculator.

11. 85.294 − 36.079

12. 191.05 − 71.02

13. 8.201 − 7.091

14. 17.946 − 0.378

15. 5.831 − 0.287

16. 6.271 − 3.845

17. 86.236 − 49.547

18. 93.782 − 56.896

19.
$$
\begin{array}{r}
39.502 \\
- \ 15.400 \\
\hline
\end{array}
$$

20.
$$
\begin{array}{r}
27.216 \\
- \ 26.8383 \\
\hline
\end{array}
$$

21.
$$
\begin{array}{r}
72.53 \\
- \ 24.642 \\
\hline
\end{array}
$$

22.
$$
\begin{array}{r}
603.042 \\
- \ 246.3 \\
\hline
\end{array}
$$

23.
$$
\begin{array}{r}
0.3 \\
- \ 0.1350 \\
\hline
\end{array}
$$

24.
$$
\begin{array}{r}
102.578 \\
- \ 73.678 \\
\hline
\end{array}
$$

25.
$$
\begin{array}{r}
\$979.84 \\
- \ \$425.69 \\
\hline
\end{array}
$$

26.
$$
\begin{array}{r}
254.345 \\
- \ 129.4 \\
\hline
\end{array}
$$

27. Subtract 218.765 from 300.

28. Subtract 573.0958 from 1,069.75 and round the difference to the nearest hundredth.

29. Subtract 14.962 from 21.

In exercises 30-38, find the indicated sum. Check using a calculator.

30. $-8.9 + 17.82$ **31.** $-29.6 + 13.71$ **32.** $0.543 + (-31.007)$ **33.** $-17.526 + 132.418$ **34.** $14.823 + (-21.715)$

35. $100 + (-82.89)$ **36.** $23.175 + (-18.627)$ **37.** $25.264 + (-19.837)$ **38.** $27.893 + (-22.934)$

In exercises 39-48, find the indicated difference. Check using a calculator.

39. $-8.3 - (-7.265)$ **40.** $-4.7 - (-3.92)$ **41.** $-3.75 - (-5.3)$ **42.** $-13.71 - (-29.6)$ **43.** $6 - 2.94$

44. $-3.845 - (-6.271)$ **45.** $-200.36 - (-45.87)$ **46.** $350.42 - (-51.63)$ **47.** $203.13 - (-19.25)$

48. $-419.234 - (-412.479)$

B. **In exercises 49-56, simplify by combining like terms.**

49. $6x + 5.1x - 11.9x$ **50.** $5.65y - 4.91y - 0.05y$ **51.** $1.3x + 21.41x + 32.05x$ **52.** $4.31t - 9.74t + 3.21t$

53. $85.7x - 22.3x - 17.9x$ **54.** $13.7x - 7.29y + 2.89y - 2.6x$ **55.** $2.5x + 16.37 - 5.8x$ **56.** $1.254x + 1.425x - 3.203x$

C. **In exercises 57-72, first estimate the answer, then perform the actual calculation. Check to see that your answer is close to the estimated value.**

57. $0.0125 + 0.8235$ **58.** $0.3691 - 0.2798$ **59.** $-0.5913 - 0.3617$ **60.** $0.0673 - (-0.7981)$

61. $-0.0081 + (-0.0963)$ **62.** $0.8571 - (-0.0689)$ **63.** $-0.0897 + (-0.8973)$ **64.** $-0.0719 - (-0.8397)$

65. $47.0987 - 23.601$ **66.** $2,759.543 - 874.099$ **67.** $2.79 + 19.23 + 15.8$ **68.** $77.9 + 18.42 - 9.89$

69. $1,099.9 + 2,154.23 - 819.72$ **70.** $\$79.82 + \$26.70 + \$43.39$ **71.** $678.49\,\text{lb} - 57.61\,\text{lb}$ **72.** $6.271 - 3.845$

Applications

73. Subtract the difference of 111.051 and 72.63 from the sum of 135.065 and 205.

74. Subtract the difference of 235.231 and 57.7 from the sum of 342.159 and 132.6.

75. Add the difference of 2.0593 and 0.655 to the difference of 0.555 and 0.55.

76. Add the sum of 5.169 and 9.254 to the difference of 23.456 and 7.981.

6.3 MULTIPLICATION AND DIVISION WITH DECIMAL NUMBERS

Objectives 📖

After completing this section, you will be able to:

A. Perform multiplication with decimal numbers;

B. Perform division with decimal numbers; and

C. Estimate products and quotients.

IMPORTANT VOCABULARY 💾

1. A **power of ten** is a number of the type 10^n, where n is an integer.

   For example: $10^1 = 10$, $10^2 = 10 \times 10 = 100$,
   $10^3 = 10 \times 10 \times 10 = 1,000$ and so forth.

2. Decimals such as 2.8753 or 46.009536 are called **terminating** decimals. Terminating decimals have a fixed number of non-zero decimal places.

3. Decimal numbers having an unlimited number of significant decimal places are called **non-terminating** decimals.

$$4.026666 \ldots , \text{ and } 23.101001000100001 \ldots$$

   are examples of non-terminating decimals.

4. Non-terminating decimals can be **repeating** or **non-repeating.**

   A **non-terminating repeating decimal** has a repeating pattern to its digits. For example, 4.02666... and 325.8316316316 ... are non-terminating repeating decimals. It is usual to write non-terminating repeating decimals in a compact form:

$$4.026666 \ldots = 4.02\overline{6}$$

$$325.8316316316 \ldots = 325.8\overline{316}$$

   The bar indicates that these digits are repeated indefinitely.

   Non-terminating, non-repeating decimals are called **irrational numbers**.

6.3 A.   Multiplication with Decimal Numbers

- **Multiplying decimal numbers:**   The multiplication of two positive decimals is performed almost in the same way as the multiplication of whole numbers. The only additional step is to place the decimal point in the product. To understand how to locate the decimal point in 0.06×0.8, let us change the decimals to fractions:

$$0.06 \times 0.8 = \frac{6}{100} \times \frac{8}{10} = \frac{6 \times 8}{1000} = \frac{48}{1000} = 0.048$$

Observe that the factor 0.06 has *two* decimal places and the factor 0.8 has *one* decimal place.

Note the relationship of the zeros in the denominators.

The product 0.06×0.8 has *three* (2 + 1) decimal places.

Similarly, to multiply 2.3 and 0.04:

$$2.3 \times 0.04 = \frac{23}{10} \times \frac{4}{100} = \frac{23 \times 4}{1000} = \frac{92}{1000}$$

$$= 0.0092$$

The short cut is: multiply 2.3×0.04 ignoring the decimal points: $23 \times 4 = 92$; then locate the decimal point in the product by counting the number of decimal places in both the factors. In this case, the count (or sum) of the number of decimal places in both the factors is 3, and the product of the factors is 92. As the product must have *three* decimal places, we insert a zero to the left of 92 to have three decimal places;

thus, $2.3 \times 0.04 = 0.092$.

The **usual method** to find the product of 2.738×13.5 is shown below:

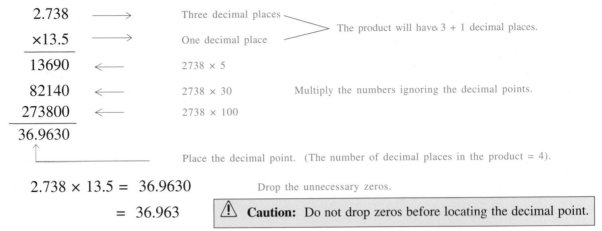

$$2.738 \times 13.5 = 36.9630 \qquad \text{Drop the unnecessary zeros.}$$
$$= 36.963$$

⚠ **Caution:** Do not drop zeros before locating the decimal point.

It should be noted, as is illustrated in the above example, that while multiplying two decimal numbers using the usual method, **there is no need to line up the decimal points**.

- Products involving *negative* decimals are also obtained exactly the same way as explained above, except for the determination of the sign. Remember that if there is an *even* number of negative factors, the product will be *positive* and if there is an *odd* number of negative factors, the product will be negative.

$$-0.2 \times 0.003 = -0.0006 \quad ; \quad (0.4)(-0.06)(-0.02) = 0.00048$$

Product is negative.   Product is positive.

Procedure to multiply two or more decimals:

Step 1   Multiply the numbers as if they were whole numbers ignoring the decimal point.

Step 2   Count the number of decimal places in each of the factors and take the **sum** of these counts. This sum is the number of decimal places in the product.

Step 3   Place the decimal point in the product so that the number of places to its right is equal to the **sum** found in step 2. Insert zeros to the left of the product, if necessary, to have enough digits for decimal places.

Step 4   Drop the unnecessary zeros, if any.

Example 1   Compute the indicated products.

     (a) 0.005×0.03 (b) 75.34×9.4

     (c) $(-0.0312)(0.065)$

Warm-Up

1. Compute the indicated products.

     (a) 0.04×0.0007

Solutions

(a)
$$
\begin{array}{r}
0.005 \\
\times \quad 0.03 \\
\hline
0.00015
\end{array}
$$

0.005 → 3 decimal places ⎫
× 0.03 → 2 decimal places ⎬ Total of 5 decimal places.
0.00015 → 5 decimal places

Note that three zeros have been inserted between 1 and the decimal point to have 5 decimal places.

(b) 503.18×2.7

(b)
$$
\begin{array}{r}
75.34 \\
\times \quad 9.4 \\
\hline
30136 \\
678060 \\
\hline
708.196
\end{array}
$$

75.34 → 2 decimal places ⎫
× 9.4 → 1 decimal place ⎬ Total of 3 decimal places.

30136 ⎫ Multiply as whole numbers
678060 ⎬ ignoring the decimal points.

708.196 → The product must have 3 decimal places.

So,   75.34 × 9.4 = 708.196.

(c) (–0.045)(0.008)

(c) Since *one* factor is negative, the product will be negative.

$$
\begin{array}{r}
-0.0312 \\
\times \quad 0.065 \\
\hline
1560 \\
18720 \\
\hline
-0.0020280
\end{array}
$$

– 0.0312 → 4 decimal places ⎫ Total of 7 places, so,
× 0.065 → 3 decimal places ⎬ the product will have 7 decimal places.

1560 ⎫
18720 ⎬ → Multiply as whole numbers.

$$
\begin{array}{r}
312 \\
\times \quad 65
\end{array}
$$

–0.0020280 → 7 decimal places in the product. The product is negative.

Note that *two* zeros have been inserted to the right of the decimal point in the product to get a total of 7 decimal places;

so,   (– 0.0312) (0.065) = – 0.0020280   Drop the unnecessary zeros.
                        = – 0.002028

2. Multiply:
0.045 × 0.008 on a calculator and verify your answer.

 Example 2   Multiply – 0.0312 and 0.065 on a calculator and verify the answer in Example 1 (c).

Solution

ENTER   (–)   .0312   ×   .065   =   –0.002028

↑ The product is the same as obtained in Example 1 (c).

- **Multiplication by powers of 10:**   Multiplying a decimal by 10 or by a power of 10 is equivalent to moving the decimal point to the right by one or more places.

This can be generalized in the following rule:

> ### Rule 1:
> To multiply a decimal number by a power of 10, we move the decimal point to the right by as many places as is the exponent of 10.

Examples: $2.735 \times 10^2 = 273.5$, $154.739 \times 10^3 = 154739$.

Procedure to multiply a decimal by a power of 10:

> **Step 1** Move the decimal point to the right by as many places as is the exponent of 10. (Insert zeros, if necessary).
>
> **Step 2** Drop the unnecessary zeros, if any.

Example 3 Multiply mentally by moving the decimal point.

(a) 0.0054×10^3 (b) 127.03×10^5 (c) 100×265

Solutions

(a) $0.0054 \times 10^3 = 0\,0\,0\,5\,.4$

                $= \mathbf{5.4}$

Step 1 Multiply: Move the decimal point to the right 3 places since the exponent of 10 is 3.

Step 2 Drop the unnecessary zeros.

(b) $127.03 \times 10^5 = 127\,0\,3\,0\,0\,0.$

   $127.03 \times 10^5 = \mathbf{12{,}703{,}000}$

Step 1 The exponent of 10 is 5. Move the decimal point to the right 5 places.

Insert three zeros to make 5 moves possible.

Step 2 There are no unnecessary zeros.

(c) $100 \times 265 = 26500.$

               $= \mathbf{26{,}500}$

Recall: $100 = 10^2$; $265 = 265.$

Move the decimal point two places to the right. Insert two zeros to make 2 moves possible.

Warm-Up

3. Multiply mentally by moving the decimal point.

(a) 0.0069×10^3

(b) $(45.09)(10^4)$

(c) 3.52×10

(d) $1000(0.8723)$

Answers:
1. (a) 0.000028   (b) 1358.586   (c) −0.00036
2. (a) 0.00036
3. (a) 6.9   (b) 450,900
   (c) 35.2   (d) 872.3

6.3 B. Division with Decimal Numbers.

1. **Dividing a decimal by a whole number:** We use three different **notations for division**. For example, we may write the division of 31.2 by 40 as $31.2 \div 40$, or $\dfrac{31.2}{40}$, or $40\overline{)31.2}$. The division of a decimal by a whole number is performed in almost the same way as the division of whole numbers. The only additional step is to place the decimal point in the quotient.

Compare the following two divisions:

Whole numbers	Decimal numbers

$$
\begin{array}{r}
258 \\
6\,)\overline{1548} \\
-12 \\
\hline
34 \\
-30 \\
\hline
48 \\
-48 \\
\hline
0
\end{array}
\qquad\qquad
\begin{array}{r}
2.58 \quad\longrightarrow\ \text{Quotient}\\
\text{Divisor} \longrightarrow\ 6\,)\overline{15.48} \quad\longrightarrow\ \text{Dividend}\\
-12 \\
\hline
34 \\
-30 \\
\hline
48 \\
-48 \\
\hline
0 \quad\longrightarrow\ \text{Remainder}
\end{array}
$$

We place the decimal point in the quotient just above the decimal point in the dividend.

We can check the answer by multiplication. $6 \times 2.58 = 15.48$

This verifies that the decimal point is correctly placed in the quotient.

- In a division problem, the division process may not leave a remainder of zero.
  Example: 14.527 ÷ 25.

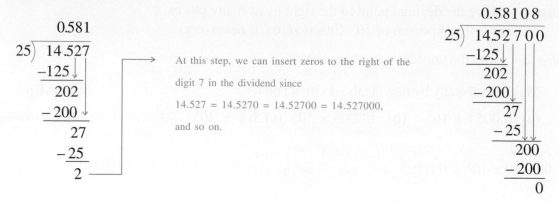

At this step, we can insert zeros to the right of the digit 7 in the dividend since

14.527 = 14.5270 = 14.52700 = 14.527000,

and so on.

We are able to obtain the remainder zero by inserting two zeros in the dividend, and we write

14.527 ÷ 25 = 0.58108.

In both the above examples, we say that the quotient is a **terminating decimal.**

- At times, the process of inserting zeros and dividing may continue endlessly.
  Example: 3.29 ÷ 13.

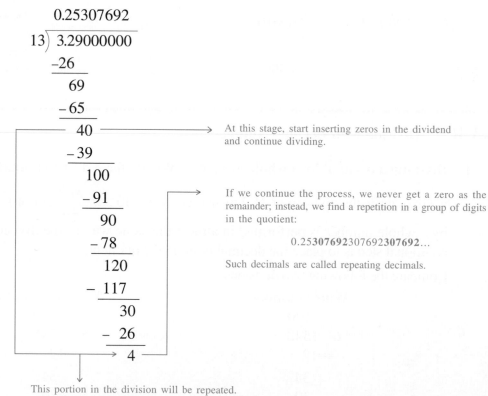

At this stage, start inserting zeros in the dividend and continue dividing.

If we continue the process, we never get a zero as the remainder; instead, we find a repetition in a group of digits in the quotient:

0.25**307692**307692**307692**...

Such decimals are called repeating decimals.

This portion in the division will be repeated.

We usually write such decimals in a more compact form by grouping the digits that repeat. For example, the above decimal is written as:

$$0.25\overline{307692}$$

The bar written above the group of digits, 307692, indicates that these digits are repeated. In such cases we say that the quotient is a **non-terminating repeating decimal.**

- Usually we need to find the quotient to a given place only. In that case, we stop the division process one place value beyond the required place , and then round the decimal number to the place.

We have seen that $3.29 \div 13 = 0.25\overline{307692}$; therefore,

$3.29 \div 13$	$\approx$	0.3	rounded to the nearest tenth;
$3.29 \div 13$	$\approx$	0.25	rounded to the nearest hundredth;
$3.29 \div 13$	$\approx$	0.2531	rounded to the nearest ten-thousandth.

Procedure to divide a decimal by a whole number:

Step **1** Use long division. Place the decimal point in the quotient just above the decimal point in the dividend.

Step **2** Divide as if both numbers were whole numbers.

Step **3** Round to the given place. If no rounding place is given, divide until the remainder is zero, or continue until some digits in the quotient start repeating. Otherwise, choose a common place value for rounding, such as tenths or hundredths.

Example 4   Divide.

(a) $6.846 \div 21$ (b) $1.664 \div 32$

Warm-Up

4. Divide.

(a) $13.28 \div 64$

Solutions   (a) **$6.846 \div 21$**

$$21\overline{)6.846}$$

$$\begin{array}{r} 0.326 \\ 21\overline{)\,6.846} \\ -63 \\ \hline 54 \\ -42 \\ \hline 126 \\ -126 \\ \hline 0 \end{array}$$

← *Step* 1 Place the decimal point in the quotient just above the decimal point in the dividend.

Step 2 Divide as whole numbers. The whole number part, 6, is less than 21; so, write a zero above 6 in the quotient. Include the next digit, 8, in the group to be divided first, and continue.

Remainder is 0 ;
therefore, $6.846 \div 21 = 0.326$.

(b) **$1.664 \div 32$**

$$32\overline{)1.664}$$

$$\begin{array}{r} 0.052 \\ 32\overline{)\,1.664} \\ -160 \\ \hline 64 \\ -64 \\ \hline 0 \end{array}$$

← • Write the decimal point in the quotient just above the decimal in the dividend.

• Start dividing. As the whole number part, 1, is less than 32, write a zero in the quotient above 1. Now consider the group 16. This is also less than 32, so write a zero in the quotient above 6.

Include the next digit in the group to get 166. Divide 166 by 32 and continue dividing until the remainder is zero.

(b) $0.48 \div 75$

Remainder is 0; therefore, $1.664 \div 32 = 0.052$.

Warm-Up

5. Divide and round the quotient to the nearest thousandth.

$$13.2 \div 7$$

Example 5   Divide and round the quotient to the nearest hundredth.

$$68.9 \div 35$$

Solution

```
        1.968
   35) 68.900
       -35
        339
       -315
         240
        -210
          300
         -280
           20    Stop
```

At this stage, start inserting zeros in the dividend and continue dividing. Since we have to divide to the nearest hundredth, stop the division process one place value beyond the hundredths place. This last digit will be used to round the quotient to the desired place of accuracy.

Therefore, $68.9 \div 35 \approx 1.968 \approx 1.97$ to the nearest hundredth.

2. Dividing a decimal by another decimal

Consider the division:

$$2.53 \div 1.2 = \frac{2.53}{1.2} = \frac{2.53}{1.2} \times \frac{10}{10}$$

Note this step. The **divisor** has one decimal place; so, multiply by $\frac{10}{10}$.

$$= \frac{25.3}{12} ;$$

To multiply by 10 means to move the decimal point to the right by one place.

$$\frac{2.53}{1.2} = \frac{25.3}{12}.$$ This means that $1.2\overline{)2.53}$ is the same as $12\overline{)25.3}$.

Similarly :

$$\frac{15.753}{2.54} = \frac{15.753}{2.54} \times \frac{100}{100}$$

The divisor has **two** decimal places; so, we multiply by $\frac{100}{100}$.

$$= \frac{1575.3}{254.} = \frac{1575.3}{254}$$

Shift the decimal point two places to the right, both in the numerator and in the denominator.

$$\frac{1.7354}{.034} = \frac{1.7354}{.034} \times \frac{1000}{1000}$$

The divisor has **three** decimal places; so, we multiply by $\frac{1000}{1000}$.

$$= \frac{1735.4}{034.} = \frac{1735.4}{34}$$

Shift the decimal by three places to the right, both in the numerator and in the denominator.

Generalizing these observations we may conclude that :

To change the divisor to a whole number, we shift the decimal point both in the divisor and the dividend to the right as many places as is necessary to make the **divisor a whole number**.

For example:

$$\frac{47.375}{3.82} = \frac{4737.5}{382} \implies 3.82\overline{)47.375} = 382\overline{)4737.5}$$

$$\frac{23.45}{0.043} = \frac{23450}{43} \implies .043\overline{)23.45} = 43\overline{)23450}$$

In each of the previous examples, **to divide a decimal by another decimal, we first change the divisor to a whole number by shifting the decimal point both in the divisor and the dividend by the number of decimal places in the divisor.**

Procedure to divide a number by a decimal:

Step 1 Change the divisor to a whole number by shifting the decimal point both in the divisor and the dividend. Place the decimal point in the quotient directly above its final position in the dividend.

Step 2 Divide the resulting numbers.

Example 6 Divide and round the quotient as indicated.

(a) $0.08919 \div 0.0046$; to the nearest hundredth.

(b) $6.475 \div (-0.03)$; to the nearest tenth.

Solutions

(a) $0.0046 \overline{)0.08919}$

- Move the decimal point in both the numbers to the right by 4 places so that the divisor is a whole number.

$= 0\,0046.\,\overline{)0\,0891\,.\,9}$

$$= 46\overline{)891.900} \quad \begin{array}{r} 19.389 \\ \end{array}$$

$$\begin{array}{r}
19.389 \\
46\overline{)891.900} \\
-46 \\
\hline
431 \\
-414 \\
\hline
179 \\
-138 \\
\hline
410 \\
-368 \\
\hline
\boxed{420} \\
-414 \\
\hline
6
\end{array}$$

- Divide the resulting numbers.

  Recall, division is easier if we list the first 9 multiples of the divisor.

  Multiples of 46
1st	46
2nd	92
3rd	138
4th	184
5th	230
6th	276
7th	322
8th	368
9th	414

- Start inserting zeros in the dividend.

  Stop: We need to have the quotient only to the thousandths place.

Thus, $0.08919 \div 0.0046 \approx 19.389$

≈ 19.39 to the nearest hundredth.

(b) Divide the absolute values. Remember that the quotient of a positive and a negative number is negative.

$-0.03\overline{)6.475} \quad =$

The quotient is negative. Write down the sign first.

$$\begin{array}{r}
-215.83 \approx -215.8 \\
-03\overline{)647.50} \\
-6 \\
\hline
04 \\
-03 \\
\hline
17 \\
-15 \\
\hline
25 \\
-24 \\
\hline
10 \\
-9 \\
\hline
1
\end{array}$$

Insert 0 in the dividend.

Since the quotient is to be rounded to the nearest tenth, we may stop here.

So, $6.475 \div (-0.03) \approx -215.83$

≈ -215.8 to the nearest tenth.

7. Verify the answers in Warm-up 6 with a calculator.

Example 7   Verify the answer in Example 6(a) with a calculator.

Solution

ENTER | .08919 | | ÷ | | .0046 | | = | 19.38913

$0.08919 \div 0.0046 \approx 19.38913$,

≈ 19.39 to the nearest hundredth.

3. Dividing a decimal by a power of 10

- **Dividing** a decimal by 10 or by a power of 10 is equivalent to moving the decimal point **to the left**.

  This statement can be generalized in the following rule:

> **Rule 2**
>
> To divide a decimal number by a power of 10, the quotient is obtained by moving the decimal point in the dividend to the left by as many places as is the exponent of 10.

Examples: $43.473 \div 10^2 = .43473$, $2.42 \div 10^3 = 0.00242$
                              2 1   3 2 1

Procedure to divide a decimal by a power of 10:

Step 1   Move the decimal point to the left by as many places as is the exponent of 10. (Insert zeros, if necessary.)

Step 2   Drop the unnecessary zeros, if any.

Warm-Up

8. Divide mentally by moving the decimal point.

(a) $3495.25 \div 10^3$

(b) $0.8 \div 10^2$

(c) $0.4 \div 10$

Answers:

4. (a) 0.2075   (b) 0.0064

5. 1.886   6. (a) 4.0   (b) −81.2

7. (a) 3.960833333 ≈ 4.0

  (b) −81.17142857 ≈ −81.2

8. (a) 3.49525   (b) 0.008   (c) 0.04

Example 8   Divide mentally by moving the decimal point.

(a) $2,458.1 \div 10^2$ (b) $71.5 \div 10^3$ (c) $0.5 \div 10$

Solutions

(a) $2,458.1 \div 10^2$

$= 24.581$;
        2 1

$2,458.1 \div 10^2 = 24.581.$

Step 1 Move the decimal point to the *left* 2 places since the exponent of 10 is 2.

Step 2 No unnecessary zeros.

(b) $71.5 \div 10^3$

$= 0.0715$;
      3 2 1

$71.5 \div 10^3 = 0.0715.$

Step 1 The exponent of 10 is 3. Move the decimal point to the *left* 3 places.

Insert zeros to make 3 moves possible.

(c) $0.5 \div 10 = 0.05$

Move the decimal point to the left one place.

- **Mental Calculations with Powers of 10**

$3.45 \div 0.01$ means the same as $3.45 \div \dfrac{1}{100}$. $0.01 = \dfrac{1}{100}$

By the rules of fractions, $3.45 \div \dfrac{1}{100} = 3.45 \cdot 100$ (since 100 is the reciprocal of $\dfrac{1}{100}$).

Similarly, division by 100 is the equivalent of multiplying by $\dfrac{1}{100}$ or 0.01.

Division by 0.01 is equivalent to multiplying by 100. Multiplying by 0.01 is equivalent to dividing by 100. Multiplying or dividing by numbers such as 0.1, 0.01, 0.001, is equivalent to the inverse operation using the reciprocals, 10, 100, 1000, *etc.*

Example 9   Evaluate the following mentally.

  a. -0.624×0.001 **b.** $42.5 \div 0.1$

  c. $72 \cdot (0.01)$

Solution

  a. -0.624×0.001 $0.001 = \dfrac{1}{1000}$

        $= -000.624$ Divide by 1000

        $= -0.000624$ Move the decimal 3 places to the left.

  b. $42.5 \div 0.1$ $0.1 = \dfrac{1}{10}$

        $= 42.5$ Multiply by 10. Move the decimal 1 place to the right.

        $= 425.$

  c. $72 \cdot (0.01)$ $0.01 = \dfrac{1}{100}$

        $= 72.$ Divide by 100. Move the decimal 2 places to the left.

        $= 0.72$

Warm-Up

9. Evaluate the following mentally.

(a) -2.74×0.01

(b) $21.9 \div 0.001$

(c) $12.4 \times (0.001)$

6.3 C.   Estimating Products and Quotients

- **Estimating a Product**

It is very important to have an estimate of the product or quotient in mind before actually performing multiplication or division. The estimate can be used to keep a check on placing the decimal point in the product and in the quotient. To estimate a product, **front end round each number using the first non-zero digit and then multiply using these rounded numbers.** For example, let us first estimate and then compute the actual product (0.463) (7.2):

	Estimate		*Actual Product*

$$
\begin{array}{rl}
0.463 \approx & 0.5 \\
7.2 \approx & \underline{\times\ 7} \\
& 3.5 \longrightarrow \text{Estimate.}
\end{array}
\qquad
\begin{array}{r}
0.463 \\
\underline{\times\ 7.2} \\
926 \\
\underline{32410} \\
3.3336 \longrightarrow \text{The actual product.}
\end{array}
$$

Multiply ignoring the decimal points.

The estimated product 3.5 helps us place the decimal point correctly in the product 3.3336. Thus, an answer of 33.336 or 0.33336 would indicate an error in the placement of the decimal point, since the answer should be close to 3.5 (or between 3 and 4).

 Note   Estimates in multiplication/division are not always as close as they are in addition or subtraction. A small change in rounding can make a big change in the estimate.

Procedure to estimate a product involving decimals

    Step **1**   Front-end round each factor using the first non-zero digit.

    Step **2**   Multiply the rounded factors.

Warm-Up

10. First estimate the product and then find the actual product on a calculator.

 (a) 5.973×3.45

(b) 0.128×0.036

Example 10   First estimate the product and then find the actual product on a calculator.

    (a)   (2.579) (4.978)   **(b)**   421 × 0.0542

    (c)   (–0.008956) (201.67)

Solutions

    (a)   **(2.579) (4.978)**

         i)   *Estimate:*

    Step 1   **2**.579   ≈ 3.0 or **3**
              ↑

             4.978   ≈ 5.0 or **5**
              ↑

    Step 2   The estimate of the product (2.579) (4.978) is 3 × 5 = 15.

 Note   This is a high estimate, since both factors were rounded up. But it serves our purpose for placement of the decimal in the actual product.

         ii)   *Actual Product:*   (2.579) (4.978) = 12.838262

            The actual product, 12.838262, is close to 15.

    (b)   **421 × 0.0542**

         i)   *Estimate:*

                 421   ≈   400   • Front-end round
                 ↑   each factor.

               0.0542   ≈   0.05
                  ↑

            421 × 0.0542   ≈   400 × 0.05   =   20   • Multiply: 400
            The estimate of the product is 20.   0.05
                                                    $\overline{}$
                                                     20.00

         ii)   *The Actual Product:*   421 × 0.0542 = **22.8182**.

            22.8182 is close to 20.

(c) $(-0.008956)(201.67)$

Estimate :

$$-0.008956 \approx -.009$$

$$201.67 \approx \quad 200$$

Estimate $\quad = -1.800$

The actual product is -1.80615652.

(c) $(-0.00078234)(4907.72)$

- **Estimating a Quotient**

  Estimating a quotient of rational numbers in decimal form is similar to estimating a quotient of integers. No rounding is necessary in finding a good estimate.

  To estimate a quotient, carefully position the decimal point in the quotient. Locate and place the first non-zero digit in the quotient. Enter zeros for any remaining places between the digit and the decimal point.

  Estimate the quotient $2.055 \div 0.047$.

  - Move the decimal point in the divisor and the dividend to make the divisor a whole number.

    $$\frac{2.055}{0.047} = \frac{2\,0\,5\,5.}{0\,4\,7} = \frac{2055.}{47}$$

  - Position the decimal point in the quotient.

    $$47\overline{)2055.}$$

  - Divide and identify the first non-zero digit of the quotient.

    $$47\overline{)\overset{4\ \ \ .}{2055.}}$$

  - Insert zeros between the digit in the quotient and the decimal point

    $$47\overline{)\overset{40.}{2055.}} \quad \longleftarrow \quad \text{Estimate of the quotients.}$$

  - The quotient thus obtained is the estimate.

    Thus, $2.055 \div 0.047 \approx 40$.

  - The exact value is 43.7234, which is quite close to the estimate.

  The process discussed in this illustration leads us to the following procedure.

Procedure to estimate a quotient involving decimals:

Step **1** Move the decimal point in the divisor and the dividend to make the divisor a whole number.

Step **2** Position the decimal in the quotient

Step **3** Divide and identify the first non-zero digit of the quotient and its correct place.

Step **4** Insert zeros between that digit and the decimal point.

Warm-Up

11. Estimate the quotient. Compare to the actual quotients.

   (a) $0.031765 \div 8.36$

   (b) $5.47123 \div 0.349$

Answers:

9. (a) -0.0274 **(b)** 21900 **(b)** 0.0124

10. (a) $18 \; ; \; 20.60685$ **(b)** $0.004 \; ; \; 0.004608$

   (c) $-4.0; \; -3.8393093$

11. (a) $0.004 \; ; \; 0.0037996$

   (b) $20 \; ; \; 15.676876$

Example 11   Estimate the quotient. Compare to the actual quotients.

   (a) $-0.00284 \div 9.12$ **(b)** $2.0863 \div 0.193$

Solution

(a)

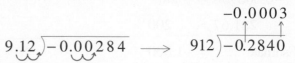

$$9.12\overline{)-0.00284} \longrightarrow 912\overline{)-0.2840} \qquad -0.0003$$

Position the decimal point in the quotient. The first digit in the quotient is 3, which is positioned above the 0 in the dividend. Zeros are inserted in the three places in the quotient between the decimal point and the digit 3. The estimate is -0.0003.

The actual quotient is obtained with calculator.

 ENTER $\boxed{(-)}$ $\boxed{.00284}$ $\boxed{\div}$ $\boxed{9.12}$ $\boxed{=}$ **-0.000311404**

The estimate, -0.0003, is very close to the actual quotient -0.000311404.

(b) 

$$0.193\overline{)2.0863} \rightarrow 0.193\overline{)2.0863} \rightarrow 193\overline{)2086.3} \qquad \overset{\text{Estimate}}{10.}$$

Position the decimal point in the quotient. Dividing 193 into 208 give us 1 in the quotient placed above 8 in the dividend. Insert zero between 1 and the decimal point. The estimate, 10, is very close to the actual quotient 10.80984.

Exercise 6.3

A.   **In exercises 1-10, multiply mentally.**

  1. 0.2×0.4 **2.** 0.02×0.4 **3.** 0.03×0.05 **4.** 4.5×0.6 **5.** 12.35×0.03

  6. 0.8×7 **7.** -4.9×5 **8.** 0.013×0.5 **9.** 8.3×5 **10.** $27.14 \times (-0.06)$

In exercises 11-28, compute the indicated product.

  11. $0.2 \times 0.3 \times 0.8$ **12.** $-1.2 \times 0.4 \times 0.07$ **13.** $(-11.23)\,(0.5)\,(-1.1)$ **14.** $8.3 \times 5 \times 0.6$

15.	**16.**	**17.**	**18.**	**19.**
36.8	0.456	34.5	28.65	$4,739$
$\times 5.7$	$\times 0.23$	$\times 0.37$	$\times 25$	$\times 0.27$

20.	**21.**	**22.**	**23.**	**24.**
1.45	8.97	6.005	0.011	3.207
$\times 2.1$	$\times 0.61$	$\times 75$	$\times .32$	$\times 29$

25.	**26.**	**27.**	**28.**
6.23	4.01	14.25	6.04
$\times 1.7$	$\times 2.02$	$\times 6.4$	$\times 5.05$

29.   **In exercises 11-28, multiply the numbers on a calculator and verify your answer.**

In exercises 30-41, find each product mentally by moving the decimal point.

30. 0.3257×10^4 **31.** $1.758\,(100)$ **32.** $0.0421\,(10^3)$ **33.** 0.534×10^5 **34.** 0.005×100 **35.** 75.235×10

36. 2.851×10^5 **37.** 2.3781×10^3 **38.** $0.00123\,(10)$ **39.** 0.0052×10^6 **40.** $264.3 \times (10^3)$ **41.** $31.45 \times (10^2)$

B. In exercises 42-54, find the quotient.

42. $6.8 \div 4$ **43.** $3.2 \div 2$ **44.** $72.5 \div 5$ **45.** $4.8 \div 12$ **46.** $13.026 \div 13$ **47.** $15\overline{)45.105}$ **48.** $7\overline{)1.26}$

49. $4\overline{)0.068}$ **50.** $12\overline{)242.2}$ **51.** $337.7 \div 11$ **52.** $-51.6 \div 24$ **53.** $-34.56 \div 3$ **54.** $14.2 \div (-3)$

In exercises 55-64, divide and round the quotient to the nearest hundredth.

55. $35.836 \div 62$ **56.** $25.24 \div 12$ **57.** $29.47 \div 11$ **58.** $212.49 \div 31$ **59.** $36\overline{)2.8872}$

60. $18\overline{)231.14}$ **61.** $64\overline{)6,211.84}$ **62.** $13\overline{)0.234}$ **63.** $125\overline{)1,562.3}$ **64.** $34\overline{)375.42}$

In exercises 65-79, find the quotient.

65. $316.96 \div 2.8$ **66.** $21.04 \div 0.4$ **67.** $28 \div 5.6$ **68.** $43.5 \div 1.5$ **69.** $27.12 \div 0.06$

70. $63.86 \div 0.2$ **71.** $-80.24 \div 0.04$ **72.** $-0.054 \div 9$ **73.** $4.6125 \div .012$ **74.** $4.8 \div 0.25$

75. $2.036 \div 0.004$ **76.** $29.82 \div 0.006$ **77.** $0.31696 \div 0.0002$ **78.** $19.843 \div 0.005$ **79.** $21.512 \div 0.007$

In exercises 80-91, find the quotient mentally by moving the decimal point.

80. $0.5 \div 10^2$ **81.** $0.7 \div 10$ **82.** $473.5 \div 100$ **83.** $27 \div 10^3$ **84.** $322.56 \div 10^3$ **85.** $198,345 \div 10^4$

86. $65.4 \div 10$ **87.** $7.4 \div 10^2$ **88.** $5.5 \div 10^6$ **89.** $35.35 \div 100$ **90.** $456 \div 10^2$ **91.** $0.832 \div 10^3$

In exercises 92-93, evaluate the division or product mentally.

92. (a) $-53.8 \div 0.001$ (b) $0.015 \cdot (0.1)$ (c) $-56 \div (0.01)$

93. (a) $1.065 \div 0.1$ (b) $-49.28 \cdot (0.001)$ (c) $0.0463 \cdot (0.01)$

C. In exercises 94-127, first estimate the product or quotient, then compute the actual product or quotient on a calculator.

94. 5.414×2.8 **95.** 8.28×7.12 **96.** 6.07×21.52 **97.** 7.05×145 **98.** 67.3×42.44

99. 0.64×9.71 **100.** 34.6×3.577 **101.** $0.03\overline{)6.275}$ **102.** $0.3\overline{)0.6275}$ **103.** $3.1\overline{)0.0636}$

104. $3.6\overline{)282.4}$ **105.** $3.1\overline{)6.36}$ **106.** $18.2\overline{)132.9}$ **107.** $3.8\overline{)0.0676}$ **108.** 8.2×9.75

109. 1.62×0.03 **110.** $0.1\overline{)211.5}$ **111.** $162\,(-0.03)$ **112.** $17.3 \times (-0.67)$ **113.** -19.4×0.897

114. $15.6 \div (-0.78)$ **115.** $0.08\overline{)18.346}$ **116.** $-13.8 \times (-7.91)$ **117.** $-16.8 \div (-0.79)$ **118.** $1.2\overline{)0.985}$

119. $-18.7 \times (9.67)$ **120.** $-21.7 \times (-19.79)$ **121.** $23.8 \times (-14.567)$ **122.** $2.89\overline{)0.0867}$ **123.** $-31.7 \div (-1.98)$

124. $28.8 \times (-0.0094)$ **125.** $-35.8 \times (-0.0379)$ **126.** $-34.8 \div (-4.879)$ **127.** $11.65\overline{)34.569}$

6.4 DECIMALS AND FRACTIONS

Objectives 📚

After completing this section, you will be able to:

A. Change numbers in fraction form to decimal form and vice versa ;

B. Evaluate numerical and algebraic expressions containing decimals or fractions ;

C. Use decimal number estimates for fractional expressions; and

D. Compute averages.

IMPORTANT VOCABULARY 💾

We have discussed, so far, only three different forms of rational numbers in an expression; fractions, mixed numbers, and decimals. We simplified expressions involving one of these types. The main purpose of this section is to understand that we can change rational numbers from any one of these forms into the other two forms. A single numerical expression may contain two or more forms of rational numbers and it can be simplified by converting each number to any one of the forms.

6.4 A. Changing numbers in Fractional Form to Decimal Form and Vice versa.

1. Changing Fractions to Decimals

- Every fraction can be thought of as a division problem $\left(\dfrac{3}{5} = 3 \div 5\right)$. Division is the common method of changing fractions to decimals. Divide the numerator by the denominator to convert the fraction to a decimal.

For example, let us convert $\dfrac{21}{8}$ and $\dfrac{11}{6}$ to decimals.

Change $\dfrac{21}{8}$ to a decimal:

$$
\begin{array}{r}
2.625 \\
8\,)\overline{21.000} \\
-16 \\
\hline
50 \\
-48 \\
\hline
20 \\
-16 \\
\hline
40 \\
-40 \\
\hline
0
\end{array}
$$

21 = 21.0
   = 21.00

⟶ Start inserting zero in the dividend at this stage.

Remainder is zero.

Therefore, $\dfrac{21}{8} = \mathbf{2.625}$ (a terminating decimal).

Change $\dfrac{11}{6}$ to a decimal:

$$
\begin{array}{r}
1.833 \\
6\,)\overline{11.000} \\
-6 \\
\hline
50 \\
-48 \\
\hline
20 \\
-18 \\
\hline
20 \\
-18 \\
\hline
2
\end{array}
$$

11 = 11. = 11.0
   = 11.00, and so on.

⟶ Insert zeros in the dividend at this stage.

⟶ Stop. The remainder 2 is repeating.

Therefore, $\dfrac{11}{6} = 1.833\ldots = \mathbf{1.8\overline{3}}$ (a non-terminating repeating decimal).

or ≈ 1.8 to the nearest tenths.

or ≈ 1.83 to the nearest hundredths.

It is important to observe here that the division process terminates at some stage when denominators have only 2 or 5 as prime factors. Verify the following by actual division:

$$
\left.
\begin{array}{ll}
\dfrac{13}{4} = 3.25, & \dfrac{14}{25} = 0.56 \\[2mm]
\dfrac{17}{40} = 0.425, & \dfrac{51}{16} = 3.1875
\end{array}
\right\}
$$

In such cases, the fractions are converted to terminating decimals.

The remainder is never zero when denominators have prime factors other than 2 or 5. Verify the following by actual division:

$$\left. \begin{array}{l} \dfrac{5}{3} = 1.6666\ldots \\[2mm] \phantom{\dfrac{5}{3}} = 1.\overline{6} \\[3mm] \dfrac{23}{7} = 3.28571428571\ldots \\[2mm] \phantom{\dfrac{23}{7}} = 3.\overline{285714} \end{array} \right\}$$

In such cases, the fractions are converted to non-terminating repeating decimals.

Procedure to express fractions as decimals:

Write the numerator (dividend) as a decimal and divide by the denominator.

Continue dividing until either

    (a) the remainder is zero, or some digit(s) in the quotient start getting repeated;

or   **(b)** there are enough decimal places to attain the required accuracy by rounding.

Example 1   Express $\dfrac{37}{40}$ as a decimal to the nearest hundredths.

Solution

```
        0.925
40 ) 37.000
     − 360
       100
      − 80
       200
     − 200
         0
```

• Carry out division to three decimal places and round to the nearest hundredths.

The remainder is zero.

$$\dfrac{37}{40} = 0.925 \approx 0.93.$$

 Alternatively,

ENTER $\boxed{37}$ $\boxed{\div}$ $\boxed{40}$ $\boxed{=}$ 0.925   (Final display)

Example 2   Express $\dfrac{123}{160}$ as an exact decimal.

Solution

```
         0.76875
160 ) 123.00000
      −1120
        1100
       − 960
        1400
       −1280
         1200
        −1120
           800
          −800
             0
```

160 does not divide into 123, Start inserting zeros after the decimal point.

OR

The remainder is 0.

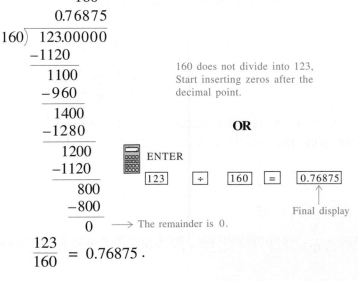

ENTER $\boxed{123}$ $\boxed{\div}$ $\boxed{160}$ $\boxed{=}$ $\boxed{0.76875}$

Final display

$$\dfrac{123}{160} = 0.76875 .$$

Warm-Up

1.   Express $\dfrac{29}{4}$ as a decimal to the nearest tenths.

2.   Express $\dfrac{8}{5}$ as an exact decimal.

Example 3   Change $\dfrac{-42}{11}$ to a decimal and

    (a)   express it as a repeating decimal.

    (b)   round it to the nearest hundredths.

Solutions

  (a)   Since $\dfrac{-42}{11} = -\dfrac{42}{11}$

$= -(42 \div 11)$, we simply divide 42 by 11, and then attach the negative sign to the quotient.

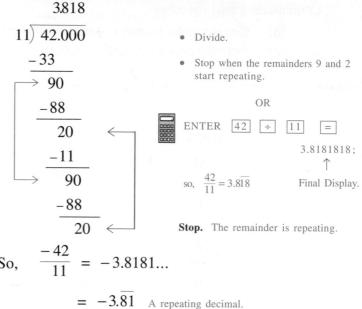

- Divide.
- Stop when the remainders 9 and 2 start repeating.

OR

ENTER $\boxed{42}$ $\boxed{\div}$ $\boxed{11}$ $\boxed{=}$

3.8181818;

↑

so, $\dfrac{42}{11} = 3.8\overline{18}$ Final Display.

Stop. The remainder is repeating.

So, $\dfrac{-42}{11} = -3.8181...$

$= -3.\overline{81}$ A repeating decimal.

  (b)   To round to the nearest hundredths, we write

$\dfrac{-42}{11} \approx -3.818 \approx -\mathbf{3.82}$ rounded to the hundredths place.

- To change a mixed number to a decimal, we may first convert the number into an improper fraction and then divide. It is often easier to change the fraction part to a decimal and attach it to the whole-number part. To change $15\dfrac{3}{5}$ to a decimal, we may use any of the following two methods:

Method 1

First we express $\dfrac{3}{5}$ as a decimal:

$$\dfrac{3}{5} = \dfrac{3}{5} \times \dfrac{2}{2} = \dfrac{6}{10} = 0.6$$

Add this decimal to the whole-number part, 15.

$$15\dfrac{3}{5} = 15 + 0.6$$

$$= \mathbf{15.6.}$$

Method 2

$$15\dfrac{3}{5} = \dfrac{78}{5} \qquad \text{Divide.}$$

$$= 78 \div 5$$

$$= \mathbf{15.6}$$

- To change a negative number such as $-\dfrac{3}{4}$, we simply divide 3 by 4, and then attach the negative sign to the quotient, as shown below.

$$\frac{3}{4}: \quad \begin{array}{r} 0.75 \\ 4\overline{)3.00} \\ -2\ 8 \\ \hline 20 \\ -20 \\ \hline 0 \end{array}$$

so, $-\dfrac{3}{4} = -0.75.$

Recall that $-\dfrac{3}{4}$ can also be written as $\dfrac{-3}{4}$ or $\dfrac{3}{-4}$. In any case, the quotient will be negative.

Any rational number in fraction form with an integer numerator and non-zero integer denominator converts either to a terminating decimal or to a non-terminating repeating decimal.

Example 4   Change $5\dfrac{6}{13}$ to decimal form and round the answer to two decimal places.

Solution   Convert $\dfrac{6}{13}$ to a decimal.

$$\frac{6}{13}: \quad \begin{array}{r} 0.461 \\ 13\overline{)6.000} \\ -52 \\ \hline 80 \\ -78 \\ \hline 20 \\ -13 \\ \hline 7 \end{array}$$

Express $\dfrac{6}{13}$ as a decimal.

$\longrightarrow$ Stop here to round to two places.

So, $\dfrac{6}{13} \approx 0.46$; hence, $5\dfrac{6}{13} \approx 5 + 0.46.$

$\approx 5.46.$

Warm-Up

4.   Change $15\dfrac{2}{3}$ to decimal form and round to three decimal places. Check your answer using a calculator.

2.   Changing Decimals to Fractions

- The following fractions and their equivalent decimal forms are commonly used in everyday life.

$$\frac{1}{4} = 0.25 \qquad \frac{1}{2} = 0.5 \qquad \frac{3}{4} = 0.75 \qquad \frac{1}{3} = 0.\overline{3} \qquad \frac{2}{3} = 0.\overline{6}$$

$$\frac{1}{10} = 0.1 \qquad \frac{2}{10} = 0.2 \; etc\ldots \qquad \frac{1}{100} = 0.01 \qquad \frac{2}{100} = 0.02, \; etc\ldots$$

- As discussed earlier, decimal numbers (terminating) can be written in fraction form with denominators that are powers of 10. For example,

$$0.25 = \frac{25}{100} \quad \begin{array}{l} \longrightarrow \\ \longrightarrow \end{array}$$

   The number without the decimal point.
   10^2, since there are 2 decimal places.

$$0.036 = \frac{36}{1000} \quad \begin{array}{l} \longrightarrow \\ \longrightarrow \end{array}$$

   The number without the decimal point.
   10^2, since there are 2 decimal places.

$$23.15 = 23 + .15 = 23 + \frac{15}{100} = 23\frac{15}{100} = \frac{2315}{100} \; ;$$

$$23.15 = \frac{2315}{100} \quad \longrightarrow \quad \text{The number without the decimal point.}$$
$$\qquad\qquad\qquad \longrightarrow \quad 10^2, \text{ since there are 2 decimal places.}$$

In each of the above cases, we observe that to change a decimal fraction to a common fraction, we drop the decimal point and write the resulting number as the numerator of the fraction; the denominator is 10 or 100 or 1000... if the number of decimal places are 1 or 2 or 3..., respectively. We may then simplify the fraction to its lowest terms.

$$0.25 = \frac{25}{100} = \frac{1}{4}; \; 0.036 = \frac{36}{1000} = \frac{9}{250}; \; 23.15 = \frac{2315}{100} = \frac{463}{20} \text{ or } 23\frac{3}{20}.$$

For decimals whose whole number part is a non-zero number, as in the case of 23.15, it is convenient to change only the decimal part to a common fraction, and leave the whole number part unchanged. That is, to change 23.15 to a common fraction, we may write:

$$23.15 = 23\frac{\overset{3}{\cancel{15}}}{\underset{20}{\cancel{100}}} = 23\frac{3}{20}.$$

Procedure to convert terminating decimals to fractions:

Step **1**   Drop the decimal point and write the resulting number as the numerator of the fraction.

Step **2**   The denominator is 10, 10^2, or 10^3,..., if the number of decimal places are 1, 2 or 3, respectively.

Step **3**   Simplify the resulting fraction, if possible.

<table>
<tr><td>

Warm-Up

5. Convert the following decimals to common fractions or mixed numbers:

   (a) 0.35

   (b) 421.6

Answers:

1. 7.3   2. 1.6

3. $-3.833... = -3.8\overline{3} \approx -3.8$ 4. 15.667

5. a) $\frac{7}{20}$ b) $\frac{2108}{5}$ or $421\frac{3}{5}$

</td><td>

Example 5   Change the given decimals to common fractions or mixed numbers.

   (a) 0.065   **(b)** 21.14

Solutions

   (a) $0.065 = \dfrac{65}{1000}$

   $ = \dfrac{13}{200}$

   (b) $21.14 = \dfrac{2114}{100}$

   $ = \dfrac{1057}{50}$ or $21\dfrac{7}{50}.$

Alternatively,

   $21.14 = 21\dfrac{\overset{7}{\cancel{14}}}{\underset{50}{\cancel{100}}}$

   $ = 21\dfrac{7}{50}.$

</td><td>

• Drop the decimal point. The numerator is 65.

• Three decimal places; therefore, the denominator is 10^3 or 1,000.

• Simplify the fraction.

• Drop the decimal point. The numerator is 2,114. The denominator is 100, since there are two decimal places. Reduce and change to a mixed number.

</td></tr>
</table>

6.4 B.   Evaluating Numerical or Algebraic Expressions containing Decimals or Fractions

- To simplify expressions that contain both decimals and fractions, we can change all fractions to decimal form or change all decimals to fraction form. In cases where the decimal form of a fraction involves several decimal places or is a non-terminating decimal, we will use the fraction form, since rounding introduces error into the calculation. It is always best to round only final answers, unless we are finding an estimate. If a calculator is available, fractions that convert as non-terminating decimals should be entered in their fraction form to avoid error.

Example 6   Find the sum $8\frac{3}{5} + 0.03 + 1\frac{3}{4}$

  (a) in decimal form   **(b)** in fraction form

Solutions

  (a)   Change each number to decimal form and then add.

$$8\frac{3}{5} = 8.6$$
$$0.03 = 0.03$$
$$+\ 1\frac{3}{4} = \underline{1.75}$$
$$\mathbf{10.38}$$

  (b)   Change the decimal to a fraction, find a common denominator (the LCD), and add.

$$8\frac{3}{5} + 0.03 + 1\frac{3}{4} = 8\frac{3}{5} + \frac{3}{100} + 1\frac{3}{4}$$

$0.03 = \frac{3}{100}$

$$= (8+1) + \left(\frac{3}{5} + \frac{3}{100} + \frac{3}{4}\right)$$

LCD = 100
    = 5 × 20
    = 4 × 25

$$= 9 + \left(\frac{60+3+75}{100}\right)$$

Add fractions.

$$= 9 + \frac{138}{100}$$

Reduce.

$$= 9 + \frac{69}{50}$$

Change $\frac{69}{50}$ to a mixed number.

$$= 9 + \left(1 + \frac{19}{50}\right) = \mathbf{10\frac{19}{50}}$$

The answers for parts (a) and (b) must be equal; thus,

$$\mathbf{10\frac{19}{50}} = 10\frac{38}{100} = \mathbf{10.38.}$$

Example 7   Find the product $\left(2\frac{1}{4}\right)\left(-3\frac{1}{2}\right)(4.1)$ and write the answer in decimal form.

Warm-Up

6.   Find the sum $3.45 + \frac{2}{5} + \frac{1}{4}$

  (a)   in decimal form; and

  (b)   in fraction form.

7.   Find the quotient $6\frac{3}{8} \div \left(-\frac{1}{4}\right)$ in decimal form.

Solution   Since there is one negative factor, the product is negative. First change each number to decimal form. Find the product.

$$\left(2\frac{1}{4}\right)\left(-3\frac{1}{2}\right)(4.1) = -(2.25 \times 3.5 \times 4.1) \quad \frac{1}{4} = .25, \frac{1}{2} = 0.5$$

$$= -32.2875 \qquad \text{Using a calculator.}$$

• The various combinations of operations on decimals and fractions are to be carried out exactly in the same order as on integers and fractions. That is, first evaluate all exponent expressions; then perform all multiplications and divisions from left to right in the order they appear; and lastly perform all additions and subtractions from left to right in the order they appear.

If the expression involves any grouping symbols then first perform the operations within the grouping symbols, starting at the innermost grouping symbol until all the grouping symbols are simplified.

Warm-Up	**Example 8** Simplify the numerical expression.

Warm-Up

8. Simplify the numerical expression.

(a) $0.5 \div 0.25 + (1.5)(0.2)^2$

Example 8   Simplify the numerical expression.

(a) $(0.6)(0.02) + 3.75 \div (0.5)^2$

(b) $14.6 \div \left[(0.5)^2 + 0.3 \times 1.6\right] - 5.4$

Solutions

(a) $(0.6)(0.02) + 3.75 \div \underline{(0.5)^2}$ • Evaluate exponents.

$= \underline{(0.6)(0.02)} + 3.75 \div (0.25)$ • Multiply and divide from left to right.

$=\quad 0.012 \quad + \underline{3.75 \div 0.25}$

$=\quad \underline{0.012 \quad + \quad 15}$ • Add

$=\quad \mathbf{15.012}$

(b) $1.2 - [2.5 - 0.3 \times 1.4] \div (0.5)^2$

(b) $14.6 \div \left[\underline{(0.5)^2} + 0.3 \times 1.6\right] - 5.4$ • First perform operations within brackets.

$= 14.6 \div [0.25 + \underline{0.3 \times 1.6}] - 5.4$ i)   Evaluate the exponent.

$= 14.6 \div [\underline{0.25 + 0.48}] - 5.4$ ii)   Multiply.

$= \mathbf{14.6} \div \quad \mathbf{0.73} \quad - 5.4$ iii) Add.

$= \dfrac{14.6}{0.73} - 5.4$ • Divide.

$= 20 - 5.4$ • Subtract.

$= \mathbf{14.6}$

- Recall that an algebraic expression contains letters of the alphabet called variables, that can take any numerical value. If we assign specific numerical values to the variables we can calculate the numerical value of the algebraic expression. This process is called evaluating the expression for specific values of the variables.

For example:

(a) The value of $2x + 4$ for $x = 2$ is: $\quad$ $\mathbf{2(2) + 4 = 4 + 4 = 8}$.

(b) The value of $2ab + 5b$ for $a = -1$ and $b = 3$ is: $2(-1)(3) + 5(3)$

$$= -6 + 15 = \mathbf{9}.$$

Example 9 $\quad$ Evaluate the expression $5x^2 - 5x + 4y$ for $x = \dfrac{3}{4}$ and $y = 1.5$.

Solution

$$
\begin{aligned}
5x^2 - 5x + 4y &= 5(0.75)^2 - 5(0.75) + 4(1.5) \\
&= 5(0.5625) - 5(0.75) + 4(1.5) \\
&= \quad 2.8125 \quad - \quad 3.75 \quad + 6 \\
&= 2.8125 + (-3.75) + 6 \\
&= 8.8125 + (-3.75) \\
&= 5.0625
\end{aligned}
$$

Substitute $x = \dfrac{3}{4} = 0.75$ and $y = 1.5$.

Evaluate the exponent.

Multiply from left to right.

Combine numbers with like sign.

Add

$5.0625 = 5\dfrac{625}{10,000}$

The value of the expression is 5.0625 or $5\dfrac{1}{16}$. $\quad = 5\dfrac{1}{16}$.

Warm-Up

9. Evaluate the following expression for $m = 1.5$ and $n = \dfrac{2}{3}$:

$$m^2 + 6mn + 9n^2$$

Answers:

6.(a) 4.10 $\qquad$ (b) $4\dfrac{1}{10}$

7. -25.5 $\qquad$ 8. (a) 2.06 $\quad$ (b) -7.12

9. $12\dfrac{1}{4}$ or 12.25

6.4 C. Using Decimal Number Estimates for Fractional Expressions

1. Expressions using decimal number approximations

Since it is easier to simplify operations on decimal numbers as compared to fractions or mixed numbers, we can estimate answers to problems involving fractions by using decimal approximations for the fractions.

For example, for $6\dfrac{1}{3}$, we can use 6.3, since $\dfrac{1}{3} = 0.333\ldots \approx 0.3$

For $-2\dfrac{7}{9}$, we can use -2.8, since $\dfrac{7}{9} = 0.777\ldots \approx 0.8$

The process of estimating the value of a rational number expression using decimal number approximations is given below.

Step 1 $\quad$ Use a calculator to find the decimal equivalent of the fractions, and round each decimal to only one decimal place.

Step 2 $\quad$ Compute the decimal expression, thus formed, and round the answer again to a single significant digit.

Warm-Up

10. Find the decimal approximation of the following rational numbers expressions.

(a) $-1\dfrac{2}{5}+3\dfrac{2}{9}$

(b) $-\dfrac{5}{19}\left(-2\dfrac{3}{16}\right)$

(c) $-\dfrac{4}{19}\div3\dfrac{4}{9}$

Answers:

10. (a) 1.8   (b) 0.7   (c) −0.06

Example 10 Find the decimal approximation of the following rational number expressions.

(a) $-3\dfrac{5}{8}+2\dfrac{8}{9}$ **(b)** $-\dfrac{1}{90}\left(-3\dfrac{5}{6}\right)$ **c)** $-\dfrac{3}{16}\div2\dfrac{3}{11}$

Solutions

(a) Using the calculator and front-end rounding,

$$\dfrac{5}{8}\approx0.6\quad\text{and}\quad\dfrac{8}{9}\approx0.9$$

$$-3\dfrac{5}{8}\approx\quad-3.6\qquad\text{Rounded to tenths.}$$

$$+2\dfrac{8}{9}\approx\quad\underline{+2.9}\qquad\text{Rounded to tenths.}$$

$$-0.7$$

$$-3\dfrac{5}{8}+2\dfrac{8}{9}\approx-0.7.$$

The estimate -0.7 is close to the actual sum $\dfrac{-53}{72}=-0.736\overline{1}$.

(b) $\left(-\dfrac{1}{90}\right)\left(-3\dfrac{5}{6}\right)$

Using the calculator and front-end rounding, we find the decimal equivalent of $\dfrac{1}{90}$ and $\dfrac{5}{6}$. $\dfrac{1}{90}\approx0.01$, and $\dfrac{5}{6}\approx0.8.$

$$-\dfrac{1}{90}\left(-3\dfrac{5}{6}\right)\approx-0.01\,(-3.8)$$

$$=0.038\approx0.04$$

The estimate 0.04 is close to the actual product, $\dfrac{23}{540}=0.0426$.

(c) $-\dfrac{3}{16}\div2\dfrac{3}{11}$

Using the calculator and front-end rounding, we find the decimal equivalent of $\dfrac{3}{16}$ and $\dfrac{3}{11}$. $\dfrac{3}{16}\approx0.2$, and $\dfrac{3}{11}\approx0.3.$

$$-\dfrac{3}{16}\div2\dfrac{3}{11}\approx-0.2\div2.3$$

$$\approx-0.2\div2$$

$$=-0.1$$

The estimate $-.1$ is close to the actual quotient, $-\dfrac{33}{400}=-0.08$

6.4 D. Computing Averages

The method of finding the average of a group of any kind of numbers is the same as that for whole numbers and fractions. That is, the average is the sum of the given numbers divided by the count of the numbers in the group.

Example 11   Find the average of the following group of numbers and round to the largest decimal place in the group:

$$3\frac{4}{5}, \ 1.2, \ 2.75, \ 3.5, \ 2.6, \ \text{and} \ 2.2$$

Solution

First, we express all the numbers in the same form. Here it is convenient to change $3\frac{4}{5}$ to decimal form:

$$3\frac{4}{5} = 3\frac{8}{10} = \mathbf{3.8}$$

The average $= \dfrac{(3.8 + 1.2 + 2.75 + 3.5 + 2.6 + 2.2)}{6}$

$= \dfrac{16.05}{6}$ Add all the numbers.

$= 2.675$ Divide the sum by 6 as there are six numbers.

≈ 2.68 Round to two decimal places.

The average, rounded to the second decimal place in the group, is 2.68.

Warm-Up

11. Find the average of 2.5, $\frac{3}{10}$, 1.6, 1.4, and $1\frac{2}{5}$.

Answer:

11. 1.44

Exercise 6.4

A. In exercises 1-23, change the fraction or mixed number to decimal form. If the decimal is non-terminating. Place a bar over the repeating digit.

1. $\dfrac{8}{15}$ 2. $-\dfrac{5}{8}$ 3. $\dfrac{11}{5}$ 4. $-\dfrac{2}{3}$ 5. $2\dfrac{1}{7}$ 6. $3\dfrac{5}{8}$ 7. $\dfrac{5}{11}$ 8. $\dfrac{2}{9}$

9. $-4\dfrac{8}{15}$ 10. $-\dfrac{5}{16}$ 11. $\dfrac{27}{40}$ 12. $\dfrac{19}{-25}$ 13. $-\dfrac{11}{16}$ 14. $4\dfrac{5}{6}$ 15. $\dfrac{15}{33}$ 16. $-5\dfrac{2}{7}$

17. $\dfrac{28}{33}$ 18. $2\dfrac{28}{33}$ 19. $3\dfrac{9}{20}$ 20. $\dfrac{7}{12}$ 21. $\dfrac{7}{11}$ 22. $\dfrac{9}{20}$ 23. $1\dfrac{23}{40}$

In exercises 24-33, express the fraction or mixed number using decimal notation. Round to the nearest tenth.

24. $\dfrac{27}{40}$ 25. $\dfrac{105}{128}$ 26. $\dfrac{19}{25}$ 27. $\dfrac{93}{125}$ 28. $\dfrac{-53}{24}$

29. $\dfrac{13}{16}$ 30. $\dfrac{7}{12}$ 31. $\dfrac{2}{7}$ 32. $3\dfrac{5}{8}$ 33. $2\dfrac{7}{9}$

341

In exercises 34-56, change the fraction to a decimal number. Round as indicated. (Use a calculator wherever necessary).

34. $\frac{2}{9}$, tenth

35. $\frac{24}{11}$; tenth

36. $\frac{5}{11}$; hundredth

37. $3\frac{5}{12}$; hundredth

38. $\frac{5}{16}$; thousandth

39. $\frac{4}{7}$; hundredth

40. $2\frac{4}{7}$; thousandth

41. $-\frac{22}{7}$; thousandth

42. $\frac{5}{12}$; tenth

43. $13\frac{17}{40}$; tenth

44. $\frac{7}{16}$; tenth

45. $\frac{16}{7}$; thousandth

46. $\frac{99}{125}$; hundredth

47. $\frac{32}{35}$; hundredth

48. $\frac{4,375}{135}$; thousandth

49. $-4\frac{17}{20}$; hundredth

50. $12\frac{8}{9}$; thousandth

51. $\frac{135}{42}$; ten−thousandth

52. $\frac{7}{9}$; tenth

53. $4\frac{7}{9}$; tenth

54. $-\frac{18}{23}$; hundredth

55. $8\frac{7}{15}$; thousandth

56. $17\frac{5}{6}$; tenth

In exercises 57-79, change the number from decimal form to fraction form (or mixed number form), and reduce to lowest terms, wherever possible.

57. 12.075   **58.** 0.15   **59.** −17.28   **60.** 0.125   **61.** 0.54   **62.** 0.85   **63.** 0.0125   **64.** −1256.003

65. 6.736   **66.** −7.305   **67.** 0.875   **68.** 3.875   **69.** 0.007   **70.** 542.0008   **71.** 67.034   **72.** 15.135

73. 5.075   **74.** 0.0075   **75.** −0.95   **76.** 417.15   **77.** 0.004   **78.** 0.625   **79.** −3.125

B. **In exercises 80-104, perform the indicated operations by writing all the numbers in decimal form. Round to the nearest thousandth if the decimal is non-terminating.**

80. $0.824 - 1$

81. $\frac{2}{5} + 0.39 + \frac{9}{4}$

82. $\frac{3}{8} + 0.25 + \frac{13}{12}$

83. $6\frac{4}{5} + \frac{7}{8} + 9.5$

84. $0.63 - 0.52 + 3.1$

85. $0.97 + 0.78 - 3$

86. $\frac{9}{4} - 0.34 - \frac{6}{4}$

87. $0.35 + 8\frac{3}{5} - \frac{7}{8}$

88. $-0.73 - 3\frac{3}{4} + \frac{9}{5}$

89. $0.85 - 7\frac{2}{3} + \frac{7}{4}$

90. $8.75 - 1\frac{5}{6} + 2\frac{2}{3}$

91. $10\frac{1}{2} + 3\frac{4}{5} + 7.64$

92. $5\frac{1}{4} + 2\frac{3}{4} - 4.75$

93. $35.276 \div \frac{3}{5}$

94. $-23.548 \div \frac{7}{2}$

95. $(3.6)\left(-1\frac{3}{8}\right)(2.1)$

96. $(2.4)\left(3\frac{1}{2}\right)(-5.2)$

97. $(8.4)\left(-4\frac{2}{3}\right)(-5.1)$

98. $\left(4\frac{3}{4}\right)(-2.5) \div \frac{4}{5}$

99. $\left(\frac{5}{8}\right)\left(-3\frac{4}{5}\right) \div 1\frac{1}{4}$

100. $\left(-2\frac{3}{5}\right)(-0.78)(5.8)$

101. $\left(4\frac{4}{5}\right)\left(-5\frac{2}{5}\right) \div 3\frac{2}{3}$

102. $\left(-5\frac{1}{4}\right)(-2.39)(1.42)$ **103.** $\left(-1\frac{1}{2}\right) \div 1\frac{1}{6} \div 0.684$

104. $3.45 \div 1.15\left(1\frac{3}{9}\right)$

In exercises 105-124, simplify the numerical expression.

105. $0.67 - 0.26(0.5)$

106. $4.56 \div 0.6(1.03) + 7.5$

107. $3.48 \div 0.4(7.01) - 2.34$

108. $(0.4)(1.13) - 6.25 \div (0.5)^2$

109. $-0.8(2.55) + 25.6 \div (0.8)^2$

110. $0.54(0.05) + 12.8 \div (2.8 - 2)$

111. $3.5(0.8) - (10.4 - 7.2) \div (3.9 - 2.3)$ **112.** $3.5 + [5.8 + 4(4.9 - 3.2) - 1.2]$ **113.** $0.9[(0.55 - 1.05) \div 0.5] + 2.1$

114. $0.8[0.75 \div (1.35 - 0.6)] - 0.8$ **115.** $2.6 - [7.4 - 3(3.8 - 1.5) + 2.5]$ **116.** $1 - [0.8 - \{0.4 - (0.6 - 0.3)\}]$

117. $2.9[9.3 - 3(6.7 - 4.2 + 2.3) + 8.9]$ **118.** $5.3 - 2.5[8.4 - 4(5.6 - 1.3) + 3.4]$ **119.** $2.3 - [9.5 - 2\{1.3 - (0.7 - 0.4)\}]$

120. $4.9 - [5.3 - 5\{3.4 - (0.7 - 1.3)\}]$ **121.** $5.1 - [10.2 - 4\{6.42 - (5.6 - 5.4)\}]$ **122.** $3.7 + [-7.4 + 8\{(3.9 \div 0.3 - 0.3)\}]$

123. $0.7[-4.6 \div 2.3 + 0.4(7.2 \div 4 - 17.6)]$ **124.** $-7.6 + [0.4 \{2.5 \div 5(2.2 + 3.8) - 1\}]$

In exercises 125-134, evaluate the expression for $x = 2.5$ and $y = \dfrac{3}{4}$. Leave the answer in fraction or mixed number form.

125. $2x - y^2$ **126.** $3x^2 - 5y + 4$ **127.** $4.5 - 7x + y$ **128.** $5x^2 - 3xy + 1$ **129.** $2x^2 - x - 3$

130. $2y - 3x - x^2$ **131.** $2x + 3y$ **132.** $6 - 3x + y$ **133.** $4 - 7.6y$ **134.** $2x^2 - y^2 + xy - 4$

C. In exercises 135-150, estimate the value of the fractional expressions using decimals. Compare the estimate with the actual value (Use a calculator for computations, wherever necessary).

135. $-2\dfrac{3}{7} + 3\dfrac{4}{6}$ **136.** $2\dfrac{3}{8} + 1\dfrac{5}{9}$ **137.** $3\dfrac{5}{6} - 2\dfrac{3}{7}$ **138.** $2\dfrac{5}{11} - 1\dfrac{7}{12}$

139. $1\dfrac{3}{13}\left(5\dfrac{7}{11}\right)$ **140.** $-\dfrac{3}{70}\left(-5\dfrac{4}{9}\right)$ **141.** $4\dfrac{6}{11}\left(-3\dfrac{5}{9}\right)$ **142.** $2\dfrac{7}{15}\left(4\dfrac{6}{7}\right)$

143. $11\dfrac{1}{3} - 3\dfrac{1}{6} + 5\dfrac{4}{5}$ **144.** $7\dfrac{1}{5} + 2\dfrac{3}{7} - 4\dfrac{1}{6}$ **145.** $3\dfrac{1}{7} + 5\dfrac{2}{9} - 7\dfrac{6}{11}$ **146.** $5\dfrac{2}{7} \div \left(-3\dfrac{1}{5}\right)\left(-4\dfrac{2}{9}\right)$

147. $4\dfrac{3}{7}\left(-2\dfrac{5}{8}\right)\left(-4\dfrac{3}{5}\right)$ **148.** $7\dfrac{2}{5} \div 6\dfrac{3}{11}\left(-2\dfrac{7}{13}\right)$ **149.** $5\dfrac{8}{15}\left(-3\dfrac{9}{11}\right) \div 4\dfrac{3}{51}$ **150.** $\left(-2\dfrac{9}{13}\right)\left(-4\dfrac{3}{11}\right) \div \left(3\dfrac{7}{9}\right)$

D. In exercises 151-158, find the average and check your answer with a calculator.

151. 4.3, 3.9, 6.51, 3.72, 5.35   **152.** 1.06, 2.14, 3.5, 2.15, 3   **153.** 6.05, 5.08, 9.06, 1.6, 0.035

154. 1.6, 0.85, 3.06, 0.91, 4, 1.1   **155.** 2.5, 1.26, 3.75, 4.34   **156.** 2.1, 4.6, 2.8, 3.12, 3.05, 2.01

157. 2.05, 1.42, 3.9, 4.2, 7.9, 5.4, 1.9   **158.** 0.1, 0.27, 0.48, 0.03

6.5 CHAPTER SUMMARY

Part I Definitions, Important Vocabulary, and Symbols

1. A **decimal** is a number written using a *decimal point*.
   For example, 2,345.69 is a *decimal number*.

$$2345.69 = \overbrace{2345}^{\text{Whole number part}} + \underbrace{.69}_{\substack{\text{Decimal Part, or} \\ \text{fraction part.}}}$$

   Decimal Point

2. The decimal number 24.035 has three **decimal places**.

3. $17.483 \approx 17.5$ rounded to the nearest tenths. $17.483 \approx 17.48$ rounded to the nearest hundredths.

4. **Powers of 10** are: $10^1, 10^2, 10^3, 10^4, \ldots$

   or   10, 100, 1000, 10000, ...

5. Decimals such as 2.5, 4.52, 7.4324 are **terminating decimals**.

6. Non-terminating decimals, such as 23.05262626 ... or $23.05\overline{26}$ are called **repeating decimals**.

Part II Procedure and Rules

DECIMAL NUMBERS

1. **Place Value Chart for Decimals:**

	Whole Number Part					Decimal Point	Decimal Part				
...	HUNDRED THOUSANDS	TEN THOUSANDS	THOUSANDS	HUNDREDS	TENS	ONES	TENTHS	HUNDREDTHS	THOUSANDTHS	TEN - THOUSANDTHS	HUNDRED - THOUSANDTHS ...
... 100,000	10,000	1000	100	10	1	$\frac{1}{10}$	$\frac{1}{100}$	$\frac{1}{1000}$	$\frac{1}{10,000}$	$\frac{1}{100,000}$ ...
... 10^5	10^4	10^3	10^2	10^1	10^0	$\frac{1}{10^1}$	$\frac{1}{10^2}$	$\frac{1}{10^3}$	$\frac{1}{10^4}$	$\frac{1}{10^5}$ ...

2. **To read or write a decimal number:**

Step 1 Read (or write) the whole number part (that is, the whole number to the left of the decimal point).

Step 2 Read (or write) **and** for the decimal point.

Step 3 Read (or write) the number in the fraction part (that is, the whole number to the right of the decimal point) as a whole number.

Step 4 Read (or write) the word name for the place value of the right-most digit in the number.

 Note If the decimal has only zero or no digit to the left of the decimal point, we omit reading or writing the whole number part. If the decimal has only zero(s) to the right of the decimal point, we read or write only the whole number part.

3. **To write a decimal number from its word name:**

Step 1 Write the number preceding "and" as the whole number part of the decimal.

Step 2 Replace the word "and" with a decimal point.

Step 3 Write the number for the word name after the word "and" as the fraction part, such that the digit in the ones place occupies the last decimal place as suggested by the word name.

Step 4 Write zero(s) to fill out the vacant decimal places if any.

4. **To round a decimal to a given place of accuracy:**

Step 1 Draw an arrow under the digit in the rounding place.

Step 2 Round up or round down as we do with whole numbers.

Step 3 Drop the unnecessary zeros (on the right of the arrow), if any.

OPERATIONS WITH DECIMALS

5. **To add a group of decimals or to subtract two decimals:**

Step 1 Write the decimals in columns so that the decimal points and the corresponding place values on either side of the decimals are lined up.

Step 2 Attach zero(s) if required so that all have the same number of decimal places.

Step 3 Add or subtract as whole numbers.

Examples

2. The word name of 123.046 is:

One hundred twenty-three **and** forty-six thousandths.

The word name for 0.37 is: Thirty-seven hundredths.

The word name for 759.0 is: Seven hundred fifty-nine.

3. The numeral corresponding to the word name:

"One thousand three hundred twenty-five and forty-six hundred thousandths" is:
1325.00046.

4. Round the number 246.3471 to the nearest hundredths.
246.3471
$\uparrow$

Round up as in whole numbers. Hence,
$246.3471 \approx 246.3500$

Thus $246.3471 \approx 246.35$ to the nearest hundredths.

5. (a) Add 12.05, 3.146, and 209.6.

$$\begin{array}{r} 12.050 \\ 3.146 \\ +\ 209.600 \\ \hline 224.796 \end{array}$$

(b) Subtract 27.16 from 143.56.

$$\begin{array}{r} 143.56 \\ -\ 27.16 \\ \hline 116.40 \end{array}$$

The difference is 116.4.

Examples

6. (a) Estimate the sum of 293.74 and 16.095.

Round both numbers to tens.

$$\begin{array}{rcr} 293.74 & \approx & 290 \\ 16.095 & \approx & +20 \\ \hline & & 310 \end{array}$$

(b) The estimated difference of the above numbers is $290 - 20 = 270$.

7. Multiply 2.35 and 0.012.

$$\begin{array}{rl} 2.35 & \longrightarrow \text{2 decimal places} \\ \times\ \underline{0.012} & \longrightarrow \text{3 decimal places} \\ 470 & \longleftarrow 235 \times 2 \\ +\ \underline{2350} & \longleftarrow 235 \times 10 \\ 2820 & \end{array}$$

The product should have 5 decimal places;

hence, $2.35 \times 0.012 = 0.0282$

8. To compute the quotient $17.5 \div 3$ to the nearest tenths:

$$\begin{array}{r} 5.83 \\ 3\overline{)17.50} \\ \underline{-15} \\ 25 \\ \underline{-24} \\ 10 \\ \underline{-\ 9} \\ 1 \end{array}$$

10 ⟵ Start inserting zeros at this stage.

STOP here.

So, $17.5 \div 3 \approx 5.8$ to the nearest tenths.

9. To divide 3.5 by 0.03:

$$0.03\overline{)3.5}$$

$$003.\overline{)350.}$$

$$3.5 \div 0.03 \rightarrow 350 \div 3 = 116.\overline{6}$$

$$3.5 \div 0.03 = 116.\overline{6}$$
$$\approx 116.7 \text{ to the nearest tenths.}$$

Step 4 Place the decimal point in the result just below those above.

Step 5 Drop unnecessary zeros, if any.

6. **To estimate the sum (or difference) of decimals:**

Step 1 Round each number to the same place, largest or second largest place.

Step 2 Add or subtract the rounded numbers.

7. **To multiply two or more decimals:**

Step 1 Multiply the numbers as if they were whole numbers ignoring the decimal point.

Step 2 Count the number of decimal places in each of the factors and take the sum of these counts. This sum is the number of decimal places in the product.

Step 3 Locate the decimal point in the product by counting from the right the number of decimal places obtained. Insert zeros to the left of the product, if necessary, to have enough digits for decimal places.

Step 4 Drop the unnecessary zeros, if any.

8. **To divide a decimal by a whole number:**

Step 1 Use long division. Place the decimal point in the quotient just above the decimal point in the dividend.

Step 2 Divide as if both numbers were whole numbers.

Step 3 Round to the given place. If no rounding place is given, divide until the remainder is zero, or continue until some digits in the quotient repeat. Otherwise, choose a common place value for rounding, such as tenths or hundredths.

9. **To divide a decimal by a decimal:**

Step 1 Change the divisor to a whole number by shifting the decimal point after the right most digit.

Simultaneously, shift the decimal point in the dividend to the right by an equal number of decimal places.

Step 2 Place the decimal point in the quotient just above its new position in the dividend. Insert zeros, if necessary, to have enough decimal places in the dividend, one beyond the rounding place for the quotient.

Step 3 Divide the resulting numbers.

10. Procedure to estimate a product involving decimals:

Step 1 Front-end round each factor using the first non-zero digit.

Step 2 Multiply the rounded factors.

11. Procedure to estimate a quotient involving decimals:

Step 1 Move the decimal point in the divisor and the dividend to make the divisor a whole number.

Step 2 Position the decimal in the quotient

Step 3 Divide and identify the first non-zero digit of the quotient and its correct place.

Step 4 Insert zeros between that digit and the decimal point.

Multiplication and Division by a power of 10

12. To multiply a decimal by a power of 10, we move the decimal point to the *right* by as many places as is the exponent of 10. (Insert zeros, if necessary.)

13. To divide a decimal by a power of 10, move the decimal point in the dividend to the *left* by as many places as is the exponent of 10. (Insert zeros, if necessary.)

Decimals and fractions

14. To express fractions as decimals:

Step 1 Divide the numerator by the denominator.

Step 2 Continue dividing until

   (i) the remainder is zero; **or**

   (ii) there are enough decimal places to attain the required accuracy by rounding; **or**

   (iii) we find a repetition of a group of digits in the quotient.

 Note If the number is a mixed number, change the fraction part to a decimal and add it to the whole number part.

15. To convert terminating decimals to fraction form:

Step 1 Drop the decimal point and write the resulting number as the numerator of the fraction.

Examples

10. Estimate the product $(3.521)(12.219)$.

$$3.521 \approx 4$$
$$12.219 \approx 10$$

The estimate of
$$3.521 \times 12.219 \approx 4 \times 10 = 40.$$

11. Estimate the quotient $7.2 \div 0.23$:

$$0.23\overline{)7.20}\quad \overset{30.}{}$$

$$\frac{7.2}{.23} \approx 30 \quad \text{(estimate)}$$

12. 0.035×10^4
$$= 0\,0\,3\,5\,0.$$
$$= \mathbf{350} \quad \text{(Drop unnecessary zeros.)}$$

13. $54.6 \div 10^3$
$$= .0\,5\,4\,6$$
$$= 0.0546$$

14. To express $\dfrac{235}{6}$ as a decimal:

$$
\begin{array}{r}
39.166 \\
6\overline{)235.000} \\
-18 \\
\hline
55 \\
-54 \\
\hline
10 \\
-6 \\
\hline
40 \\
-36 \\
\hline
40 \\
-36 \\
\hline
4
\end{array}
$$

Stop, since the digit 6 has started repeating in the quotient.

$$\frac{235}{6} = 39.1666\ldots$$
$$= 39.1\overline{6}$$

15. To express 21.14 as a fraction (or a mixed number):

$$21.14 = \frac{\cancel{2114}^{\,1057}}{\cancel{100}_{\,50}}$$

347

$$= \frac{1057}{50}$$

$$= 21\frac{7}{50}$$

Alternatively,

$$21.14 = 21\frac{14}{100} = 21\frac{7}{50}$$

Step 2 The denominator is 10, 10^2, or 10^3, and so on, if the number of decimal places are 1, 2 or 3, respectively.

Step 3 Simplify the resulting fraction, if possible.

ORDER OF OPERATIONS

16. To evaluate:

$$2.5 + 1.5 \times 3 \div 0.05 - 75.3$$
$$2.5 + 4.5 \div 0.05 - 75.3$$
$$2.5 + 90 - 75.3 = 92.5 - 75.3 = 17.2.$$

16. **To perform various combinations of operations on decimals, we follow the same oder of operations that we used for integers and fractions.**

17. Evaluate

$-2x^2 + 7xy$, for $x = 1.05$ and $y = -0.3$

$$= -2(1.05)^2 + 7(1.05)(-0.3)$$
$$= -2(1.1025) + 7(1.05)(-0.3)$$
$$= -2.205 + (-2.205)$$
$$= -4.41$$

17. **To evaluate expressions with variables :**

Step 1 Replace each variable by the value assigned to it, using parentheses.

Step 2 Evaluate, using order of operations.

ESTIMATION

 18. Estimate the value using decimal approximation.

(a) $\dfrac{3}{7} + \dfrac{9}{11} \approx 0.4 + 0.8$

$$= 1.2$$

(b) $\left(-4\dfrac{7}{21}\right)\left(-7\dfrac{2}{41}\right) \approx (-4) \cdot (-7)$

$$= 28$$

18. We can estimate the value of a rational number expression using decimal number estimates of rational numbers.

Step 1 Use a calculator to find the decimal equivalent of the fractions, and round each decimal to only one significant digit.

Step 2 Compute the decimal expression, thus formed, and round the answer again to a single significant digit.

6.6 REVIEW EXERCISE

1. Write the following mixed numbers in decimal notation:

(a) $65\dfrac{4}{100}$ (b) $\dfrac{75}{1,000}$ (c) $6\dfrac{2}{25}$ (d) $25\dfrac{3}{20}$ (e) $9\dfrac{7}{500}$

2. Write the following decimal numbers in mixed number form:

(a) 425.36 (b) 12.3 (c) 17.005 (d) 2.59 (e) 0.375

3. Write the following decimal numbers in word form.

(a) 26.405   (b) 6.72   (c) 200.033   (d) 0.0082   (e) 0.444

4. Write the following numbers in decimal form:

(a) Five and twenty-eight hundredths

(b) Seven thousand five hundred and sixty-five ten-thousandths

5. Round the following numbers as indicated.

(a) 569.84 to the nearest whole number.   (b) 6.55321 to the nearest tenth.

(c) 8.0049 to the nearest hundredth.   (d) 37.2828 to the nearest thousandth.

6. Find the indicated sum or difference.

(a) $-310.5 - (-275.32)$ (b) $-5.736 + (-9.382)$ (c) $7.6 + 6 + 5.06$

7. Simplify by combining like terms.

(a) $15.6x - 22.7x + 13.4x$ (b) $-34.1t + 77.5t - 56.3t$ (c) $6y - 2.94y + y$

8. First estimate the answer, then perform the actual calculation.

(a) $187.9635 - 96.938$ (b) $62.71 + 3.53 + 84$ (c) $3.577 + 16.563 - 6.425$

9. Micky buys a small radio for $13.89. She gives $20 to pay for the radio. How much change does she get back?

10. Alice and Allen went on a trip with their school. Alice spent $125.75 on food and $230.86 in buying gifts, while Allen spent $147.25 on food and $215.67 on gifts. Whose expenditure was more and by what amount?

11. Find the indicated products:

(a) 24.5×0.03 (b) 127.02×5.05 (c) $(0.7)(0.3)(0.4)$ (d) $(5.06)(3)(2.06)$

12. Divide and round the quotient to two decimal places:

(a) $45.3 \div 0.011$ (b) $279.45 \div 2.450$ (c) $32\overline{)201.824}$ (d) $29 \div 0.081$

13. First estimate the product, then find the actual product.

(a) 12.05×6.9 (b) 93.1×0.57 (c) $(99.63)(30.07)$ (d) $(89.6)(5.37)$

14. First estimate the quotient, then perform actual division to find the quotient to the nearest thousandth.

(a) $31\overline{)91}$ (b) $60.363 \div 24.9$ (c) $0.03\overline{)6.275}$ (d) $1.975 \div 36$

15. Find the indicated product or quotient just by inspection.

(a) $10^5 \times 0.0735$ (b) 3.492×10^3 (c) $398.5 \div 100$ (d) 3.492×10^2

(e) 2.492×0.001 (f) $-14.7 \div 0.01$ (g) $-0.023 \div 0.1$ (h) 59×0.01

16. Change each number to decimal form. If the decimal is non-terminating, write it using bar notation over the repeating digit(s).

(a) $15\dfrac{5}{8}$ (b) $\dfrac{31}{36}$ (c) $-\dfrac{712}{15}$ (d) $\dfrac{9}{2,000}$ (e) $\dfrac{15}{16}$

17. Change each decimal to a fraction or a mixed number and reduce the fraction, if possible.

    (a) -2.75 **(b)** 0.35 **(c)** 0.375 **(d)** 2.78 **(e)** -24.90

18. Perform the indicated operations by writing all the numbers in decimal form. Round to the nearest thousandth if the decimal is non-terminating.

    (a) $(2.1)\left(-1\dfrac{3}{8}\right)(3.6)$ **(b)** $\dfrac{13}{12} - 0.78 - 1\dfrac{1}{4}$ **(c)** $3.62 \div (0.02 + 72.3 \times 0.2)$

19. Simplify the following expressions:

    (a) $0.6\,[9.4 - 3(5.8 - 4.6 + 2.3) + 8.7]$ **(b)** $3x^2 - 5x + 2y$ for $x = 1.5$ and $y = \dfrac{3}{4}$

20. Evaluate the following expression:

$$4x^2y - 3xy \text{ for } x = -2.5 \text{ and } y = \frac{3}{5}$$

In exercises 21-24, estimate the value of the mixed number expression using decimal approximation correct to one decimal place.

21. $\dfrac{4}{5} + \dfrac{8}{9}$ **22.** $5\dfrac{3}{4} - 8\dfrac{3}{7}$ **23.** $\dfrac{4}{9}\left(-\dfrac{6}{7}\right)$ **24.** $\left(-\dfrac{3}{11}\right)\left(-5\dfrac{1}{13}\right) \div \left(4\dfrac{3}{7}\right)$

In exercises 25-27, find the average of the group of numbers. Round your answer to the nearest tenth.

25. 2.5, 7.4, and 2.9 **26.** 14.92, 17.2, 25.74, and 21.43 **27.** 172.4, 294.72, 395.37, and 712.42

6.7   SELF TEST

1. Add: $0.06 + 1.385 + 432.8$ **2.**   Subtract: 102.58 from 541.6215

3. Multiply: 269.83106×10^4 **4.**   Find the sum: $-17.538 + 22.426$

5. Simplify by combining like terms: $2x - 3.7x - 0.1x - 8.4x$

6. First estimate the quotient and then find its exact value: $2.065 \div 0.007$

7. Simplify: $2.49 + 50.4 \div 0.01$

8. Perform the indicated operations:

$$4.9 \div 0.7 + 3.0 \times 8.0 - 1.6 \times \frac{1}{2} \div \frac{1}{5}$$

9. Evaluate the expression $y^2 + 3y - 2x$ for $x = 4.2$ and $y = \dfrac{3}{4}$. Express the answer as a decimal.

10. Find the dividend if the divisor is 2.5; the quotient is 0.08; and the remainder, 1.7.

11. Find the difference: $4.8 - 7.25$.

12. Write the numeral for:

    4 thousands + 0 hundreds + 6 tens + 3 ones + 9 tenths + 5 hundredths + 2 thousandths.

13. Find the difference: $-43.008 - (-45.002)$.

14. The sale price of a Tomaya VCR is $239.95. If the discount was $49.85, what was the original price?

15. Change $\dfrac{3}{7}$ to a decimal and write the decimal using bar notation over the repeating digits.

16. Mentally calculate the value of :   **(a)** 1.24×0.0001 **(b)** $-4.6 \div 10$

17. Find the quotient $4\dfrac{3}{8} \div (-10)$ in decimal form.

18. Multiply 43.15 by 2.03 and round the answer to two decimal places.

In exercises 19-20, estimate the value of the mixed number expression using decimal approximation *correct to one decimal place.*

19. $\dfrac{5}{8} - \dfrac{4}{7} + \dfrac{5}{9}$ 20. $\left(-4\dfrac{5}{6}\right)\left(3\dfrac{2}{7}\right) \div \left(-2\dfrac{8}{11}\right)$

21. Compute the average of :   3.72 ; 17.953 ; 21.72 ; and 19.42.

7

Applications with Decimals

```
00711Disc                                                    _ □ ×
File  View  Control  Debug

Objective:  Solve Equations involving decimals : Variable on one side
                  Verify Skill          Discussion
            Procedure                             Example
To solve an equation with x on one side only.    30 - 15.2  =  16.5 + x

Step 1   If x is on the right side, rewrite the   16.5 + x  =  30 - 15.2
         equation, switching the two sides.

Step 2   Simplify each side separately if         16.5 + x  =  14.8
         possible, using the distributive property
         and combining like terms.

Step 3   Eliminate any constant on the side       16.5 + ( - 16.5 ) + x  =  14.8 + ( - 16.5 )
         with x by adding its opposite to                    x  =  - 1.7
         both sides.

Step 4   Eliminate any numerical coefficient      Check :
         of x by dividing both sides by that        16.5 + x  =  30 - 15.2
         number (or multiplying both sides
         by its reciprocal).                       16.5 + ( - 1.7 )  =  30 - 15.2

Step 5   Check the resulting solution.                  14.8  =  14.8
              The solution x = - 1.7 is correct.
                                                   Copyright © 2005 Educo International, Inc.
```

APPLICATIONS OF DECIMALS

Introduction

In this chapter, we shall discuss the solution of linear equations involving decimals. We will solve general application problems using decimals, ratios, rates, and unit rates. We will also discuss geometric applications including applications of the Pythagorean theorem, perimeters, areas, and volumes.

The discussion in this chapter is divided into four sections:

7.1 *Solving linear equations with Decimals Numbers;*

7.2 *Applications using decimals;*

7.3 *Square Roots and the Pythagorean Theorem; and*

7.4 *Applications to Geometry.*

7.1 SOLVING LINEAR EQUATIONS WITH DECIMAL NUMBERS

7.1A. Solving equations with the variable on one side only.

We solve equations with decimals in the same way that we solve equations with other rational numbers (fractions or integers). The Addition, Multiplication, and Division Principles of Equality still are the primary tools for solving. Recall, **the main objective in solving an equation is to isolate the variable with a coefficient of 1 on the left side of the equation** using the following procedure.

Objectives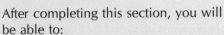

After completing this section, you will be able to:

A. Solve equations with the variable on one side only;

B. Solve equations with the variable on both sides ; and

C. Solve equations in several variables where values of all except one are known.

> **The Addition Principle of Equality :** Adding the same number to both sides of an equation yields an equivalent equation.
>
> **The Multiplication Principle of Equality :** Multiplying both sides of an equation by the same number yields an equivalent equation.
>
> **The Division Principle of Equality :** Dividing both sides of an equation by the same non-zero number yields an equivalent equation.

Procedure to solve an equation with x on one side only.

Step 1 If x is on the right side, rewrite the equation, switching the two sides.

Step 2 Simplify each side separately if possible, using the distributive property and combining like terms.

Step 3 Eliminate any constant on the side with x by adding its opposite to both sides.

Step 4 Eliminate any numerical coefficient of x by dividing both sides by that number (or multiplying both sides by its reciprocal).

Step 5 Check the resulting solution.

Warm-Up

1. Solve for the unknown.

   (a) $x - 0.15 = 3.85$

   (b) $-11.22 + x = 13.4$

2. Solve and check.

   $\dfrac{w}{0.02} - 7.13 = 1.6$

3. Solve: $\dfrac{2}{3} + 4x = 0.6$.

Example 1 Solve the following equations:

   (a) $14.63 = y - 2.37$ (b) $16.5 + x = 30 - 15.2$

Solutions

(a)

$$14.63 = y - 2.37$$
$$y + (-2.37) = 14.63 \qquad \text{• Switch sides}$$
$$y + (-2.37) + \mathbf{2.37} = 14.63 + \mathbf{2.37} \qquad \text{• Add 2.37 to both sides.}$$
$$\mathbf{y = 17}$$

Check:

$$14.63 = y - 2.37$$
$$14.63 = \mathbf{17} - 2.37 \qquad \text{• Substitute 17 for } y, \text{ and simplify.}$$
$$14.63 = 14.63 \; ; \quad \text{True}$$

The solution $y = 17$ is correct.

(b)

$$16.5 + x = 30 - 15.2$$
$$16.5 + x = 14.8 \qquad \text{• Simplify.}$$
$$x = 14.8 - \mathbf{16.5} \qquad \text{• Add } -16.5 \text{ to both sides.}$$
$$x = -(16.5 - 14.8) \qquad \text{• Simplify the right side.}$$
$$x = \mathbf{-1.7}$$

The check is left as an exercise.

Example 2 Solve and check: $\dfrac{y}{3.4} + 1.02 = 5.9$

Solution

$$\dfrac{y}{3.4} + \mathbf{1.02} = \mathbf{5.9}$$

$$\dfrac{y}{3.4} + 1.02 - \mathbf{1.02} = 5.9 - \mathbf{1.02} \qquad \text{• Subtract 1.02 from both sides of the equation.}$$

$$\dfrac{y}{3.4} = 4.88$$

$$\dfrac{y}{3.4} \cdot \mathbf{3.4} = 4.88 \cdot \mathbf{3.4} \qquad \text{• Multiply both sides by 3.4. This will isolate } y \text{ with a coefficient of 1. Simplify the right side.}$$

$$\mathbf{y = 16.592}$$

Check: (Use a calculator).

$$\dfrac{y}{3.4} + 1.02 = 5.9 \qquad \text{• Given equation.}$$

$$\dfrac{16.592}{3.4} + 1.02 = 5.9 \qquad \text{• Substitute 16.592 for } y.$$

$$5.9 = 5.9 \; ; \quad \text{True} \qquad \text{• Use calculator to compute.}$$

The solution $y = 16.592$ is correct.

Example 3 Solve $\dfrac{1}{3}x + 0.5 = -17.8$.

Solution

$$\dfrac{1}{3}x + 0.5 = -17.8$$

$$\dfrac{1}{3}x + 0.5 + (\mathbf{-0.5}) = -17.8 + (\mathbf{-0.5}) \qquad \text{• Add } -0.5 \text{ to both sides.}$$

$$\frac{1}{3}x = -18.3$$

$$3 \cdot \frac{1}{3}x = 3 \cdot (-18.3)$$ • Multiply both sides by 3,

$$x = -54.9$$ since $3 \cdot \frac{1}{3} = 1$.

Check, using a calculator.

Note

Often we confront decimals and fractions in the same problem. We change the fractions to decimals, or vice verse. Sometimes, as above, that is not necessary.

Answers:

1. (a) $x = 4$ (b) $x = 24.62$

2. $w = 0.1746$ 3. $x = -\frac{1}{60}$ or $-0.01\overline{6}$

7.1 B. Solving Equations with variables on both sides.

We will continue to develop the skills related to solving equations with variables on **both sides** of the equation. There are no new concepts involved, just more steps.

• We can solve any first-degree equation using the following four step approach.

Procedure to solve linear equations:

Step 1   Simplify *each side separately*. This includes applying the distributive property and combining like terms.

Step 2   Use the addition principle to eliminate the variable term on the right side.

Step 3   Use the addition principle to eliminate any constant from the left side.

Step 4   Use the division or multiplication principle to make the coefficient of the variable one.

Step 5   Check the solution.

Remember that the main objective in solving an equation is to isolate the variable on the left side of the equation.

Solving equations is a double process of (1) finding the value of the unknown, and (2) checking this value in the original equation.

Example 4   Solve the equation $3x - 2 = x + 8$

Solution

$$3x - 2 = x + 8$$

$$3x - 2 + (-x) = x + 8 + (-x)$$ Add $(-x)$ to both sides.

$$2x - 2 = 8$$ Add 2 to both sides.

$$2x - 2 + 2 = 8 + 2$$

$$2x = 10$$

$$\frac{2x}{2} = \frac{10}{2}$$ Division principle.

$$x = 5$$

The solution is **5**.

Warm Up

4. Solve the equation:

$$5x - 3 = 2x + 7$$

Check: Substitute $x = 5$ on both sides of the given equation.

The left side $= 3(5) - 2 = \mathbf{13}$

The right side $= 5 + 8 = \mathbf{13}$ $\Big\rangle$ The same

The solution $x = 5$ is correct.

5. Solve the equation:

$3(x - 1) = 4x + 11$

Example 5 Solve the equation $2(4x + 3) = 3x + 5$.

Solution

$$2(4x + 3) = 3x + 5$$

$$8x + 6 = 3x + 5 \qquad \text{Distributive property.}$$

$$8x + 6 + (\mathbf{-3x}) = 3x + 5 + (\mathbf{-3x}) \qquad \text{Add } -3x \text{ to both sides.}$$

$$5x + 6 = 5 \qquad \text{Simplify both sides.}$$

$$5x + 6 + (\mathbf{-6}) = 5 + (\mathbf{-6}) \qquad \text{Add } -6 \text{ to both sides.}$$

$$5x = -1$$

$$\frac{5x}{5} = \frac{-1}{5} \qquad \text{Division principle.}$$

$$x = -\frac{1}{5} \text{ or } -0.2$$

The solution is $x = -0.2$.

Check: Left as an exercise.

6. Solve the equation

$.6(2x - 3) + .2 = x + .5$

Example 6 Solve the equation:

$$0.2(0.3x + 1) - 0.3(1.2x - 0.6) = x$$

Solution

$$0.2(0.3x + 1) - 0.3(1.2x - 0.6) = x$$

$$0.06x + 0.2 - 0.36x + 0.18 = x \qquad \text{Distributive property.}$$

$$0.38 - 0.3x = x \qquad \text{Combine like terms.}$$

$$0.38 - 0.3x + (-0.38) = x + (-0.38) \qquad \text{Add } -0.38 \text{ on both sides.}$$

$$-0.3x + (-x) = -0.38 \qquad \text{Add } -x \text{ on both sides.}$$

$$-1.3x = -0.38 \qquad \text{Divide both sides by } -1.3.$$

$$x = 0.29$$

The solution is $x = 0.29$.

Check: Left as an exercise.

7. Solve the equation:

$\frac{1}{2}x + \frac{1}{3}x = x - \frac{2}{3}$

Example 7 Solve the equation $\frac{3x}{5} - \frac{1}{10}x = x - \frac{5}{2}$.

Solution We can start by rewriting the equation using decimal equivalents.

$$0.6x - 0.1x = x - 2.5 \qquad \text{Simplify the left side by combining like terms.}$$

$$0.5x = 1.0x - 2.5 \qquad \text{Rewrite } x \text{ as } 1.0x.$$

$$0.5x + (\mathbf{-1.0x}) = 1.0x - 2.5 + (\mathbf{-1.0x}) \qquad \text{Add } -1.0x \text{ to both sides.}$$

$$-0.5x = -2.5$$

$$\frac{-0.5x}{-0.5} = \frac{-2.5}{-0.5} \qquad \text{Divide both sides by } -0.5.$$

$$x = 5$$

Check the solution by substituting $x = 5$ in the given equation.

In the equation below, we will work with fractions that do not have exact decimal equivalents.

Example 8 Solve the equation: $\dfrac{2y}{3} = \dfrac{1}{2}\left(-\dfrac{3}{2} + \dfrac{y}{3}\right).$

Solution

$$\dfrac{2y}{3} = \dfrac{1}{2}\left(-\dfrac{3}{2} + \dfrac{y}{3}\right) \qquad \text{The given equation.}$$

$$\dfrac{2}{3}y = -\dfrac{3}{4} + \dfrac{1}{6}y \qquad \begin{array}{l}\text{Use distributive property}\\\text{to simplify the right side.}\end{array}$$

$$\dfrac{2}{3}y + \left(-\dfrac{1}{6}y\right) = -\dfrac{3}{4} + \dfrac{1}{6}y + \left(-\dfrac{1}{6}y\right) \qquad \text{Add } \left(-\dfrac{1}{6}y\right) \text{ to both sides.}$$

$$\left(\dfrac{2}{3} + \dfrac{-1}{6}\right)y = -\dfrac{3}{4} \qquad \dfrac{2}{3} + \dfrac{-1}{6} = \dfrac{4}{6} + \dfrac{-1}{6} = \dfrac{3}{6} = \dfrac{1}{2}.$$

$$\dfrac{1}{2}y = -\dfrac{3}{4}$$

$$\dfrac{2}{1} \cdot \dfrac{1}{2}y = \dfrac{2}{1} \cdot \dfrac{-3}{4} \qquad \begin{array}{l}\text{Multiply both sides by the}\\\text{reciprocal, } \dfrac{2}{1}.\end{array}$$

$$y = -\dfrac{3}{2}$$

The solution is $y = -\dfrac{3}{2}.$

Check: Left as an exercise.

8. Solve the equation:

$$\dfrac{1}{2}\left(\dfrac{3x}{7} + \dfrac{1}{2}\right) = \dfrac{x}{7} - \dfrac{1}{4}$$

Answers:

4. $x = \dfrac{10}{3}$

5. $x = -14$

6. 10.5

7. $x = 4$ **8.** $x = -7$

7.1 C.   Solving equations containing several unknowns where the values of all except one are known

Consider the following equations (formulas):

1. $P = 2l + 2w$ is the relation between the Perimeter (P), the length (l), and the width (w) of a rectangle. It contains three quantities. We may be given the values of any two to find the value of the third.

2. $h = ut - 16t^2$ is the relationship between the height (h) of a stone above the ground after (t) seconds, when it is thrown up with a speed of (u). It contains three quantities. We may be given the values of any two and find the value of the third.

3. $A = P + Prt$ is the relationship between the value of the initial investment (P) after (t) years when invested at an annual rate of simple interest (r), where (A) is the amount after t years.

Sometimes formulas are stated using words. This is true of several common formulas listed below:

> Profit = Income – Cost
>
> Original Price – Discount = Sale Price
>
> Average = $\dfrac{\text{Total of the numbers}}{\text{Count of the numbers}}$
>
> Change = Final value – Starting value

Such standard relationships exist in almost every sphere of human endeavour. Using such standard relationships we can find the values of some unknowns given the values of others. In this objective we shall discuss only those situations where all but one value of the unknowns are given and we are required to find the value that is not given.

Procedure

Substitute the given values of the unknowns and solve for the value that is not given.

Warm-Up

9. The volume of a right circular cylinder with base of radius r and height h is given by:
$$V = 3.14\, r^2 \cdot h.$$
For $V = 39.2\, cm^3$, and $r = 3.4\ cm$ find the height h to two decimal places.

Example 9 The volume of a right circular cylinder with base of radius r and height h is given by $V = 3.14\, r^2 \cdot h.$

For $V = 24.12\, cm^3$, and $r = 2.5\ cm$, find the height h to two decimal places.

Solution Substitute $V = 24.12$ and $r = 2.5$ in the equation $V = 3.14\, r^2 h.$

$$24.12 = 3.14\, (2.5)^2 h$$

$$24.12 = 3.14\, (6.25)\, h$$ • Divide both sides by the coefficient of h and switch sides.

$$h = \frac{24.12}{(3.14)(6.25)}$$ • Use calculator to compute the value.

$$\approx \mathbf{1.23\ cm}.$$

10. A ball is thrown vertically up with a speed of 70.4 ft/sec. Find the height of the ball after 3.2 seconds, if height (h), speed (s), and time(t) are related by $h = st - 16t^2$.

Example 10 A ball is thrown vertically up with a speed of 60.5 ft/sec. Find the height of the ball after 2.5 seconds, if height (h), speed(s), and time (t) are related by $h = st - 16t^2$.

Solution Substitute $s = 60.5$ and $t = 2.5$ in

$$h = st - 16t^2$$

$$h = (60.5)\,(2.5) - 16\,(2.5)^2$$

$$= 151.25 - 100$$

$$= \mathbf{51.25\ ft}$$

11. Use the formula in Example 11 to find Celsius temperature that corresponds to 93.58° F. (Round your answer to two decimal places).

Example 11 The formula relating temperatures measured in degrees Fahrenheit (F) and degrees Celsius (C) is

$$F = 1.8C + 32.$$

Find the Celsius temperature that correspond to 71.05° F.

Solution

$$F = 1.8C + 32$$ Substitute 71.05 for F.

$$71.05 = 1.8C + 32$$ Switch sides.

$$1.8C + 32 + (-32) = 71.05 + (-32)$$ Add (−32) to both sides.

$$1.8C = 39.05$$

$$\frac{1.8C}{1.8} = \frac{39.05}{1.8}$$ Divide both sides by 1.8.

$$C \approx \mathbf{21.694°}$$ Use a calculator.

Example 12 During a clearance sale, an electronic store sold a video cassette recorder for $225.75. If the recorder was sold at a discount of $22.50, what was the original price of the recorder?

Solution

Let x represent the original price of the video cassette recorder.

Translate the problem into symbols:

Original price – discount = sale price

$$x \ - \ 22.50 \ = \ 225.75$$

To solve this equation for x, add 22.50 on both sides.

$$x \ - \ 22.50 + \mathbf{22.50} \ = \ 225.75 + \mathbf{22.50}$$

$$x \ = \ \mathbf{\$248.25}$$

Check: Since $248.25 - 22.50 = 225.75$ is true, the original price of the recorder was $248.25.

12. The price of a radio decreased by $1.37 over the past four months. What was the price four months ago if the radio now sells for $14.89 ?

Answers:

9. $h = 1.08$ cm   **10.** $h = 61.44$ ft

11. $C \approx 34.21°$ **12.** $16.26

Exercise 7.1

A. **In exercises 1-26, solve the equation and check your answer.**

1. $x - 8.3 = -21.7$

2. $3.25 + y = 7.9$

3. $y - 1.89 = 7.11$

4. $7.68 = 5.45 - y$

5. $x + 8.3 = 6.44 - 9.74$

6. $x + 37.6 = 4.8 - 7.25$

7. $0.25x - 0.35 = 1.15$

8. $1.3y + 2.7 = 19.6$

9. $\dfrac{x}{3.05} - 1.06 = 2.3$

10. $1.7 = 0.5 + \dfrac{y}{1.03}$

11. $9x + 8.57 = -124.9$

12. $1.8w + 32 = 63.14$

13. $0.2(t + 6.3) = 17.5$

14. $21.21 + 0.5x = 27.15$

15. $14.4 = 0.44x + 5.6$

16. $1.25t - 0.1 = 9$

17. $\dfrac{y}{12.1} - 0.06 = 1.04$

18. $12.50 = 80p - 130$

19. $5x + 18.5 = 27.05$

20. $\dfrac{w}{2.1} + 0.03 = 4.09$

21. $0.3x + 3.8 + 0.1x = 5.72$

22. $-5.1x + 7.04 - 0.89x = -1.07$

23. $13x - 8x - 10x = -35.45$

24. $0.9x - 18.4 = -22.9$

25. $0.12x + 0.25x - 4.3x = 5.895$

26. $\dfrac{x}{3.2} - 0.05 + 1.2x = 4.37$

B. **In exercises 27-59, solve the equation and check your answer using a calculator.**

27. $\dfrac{2}{3}x + \dfrac{3}{5} = x$

28. $3x + \dfrac{1}{3} = 2 - \dfrac{x}{3}$

29. $\dfrac{x}{2} - 4 = \dfrac{x}{3} + \dfrac{3}{2}$

30. $\dfrac{x}{3} - \dfrac{11}{2} = 1 - \dfrac{x}{2} - \dfrac{x}{4}$

31. $\dfrac{1}{2}y - \dfrac{3}{10} = \dfrac{3}{4}y + \dfrac{1}{5}y$

32. $\dfrac{3}{10} - \dfrac{1}{2}t = \dfrac{2}{5}t - \dfrac{1}{5}$

33. $\dfrac{3}{4}p - 3 = \dfrac{1}{2}p + 2$

34. $\dfrac{1}{3}x - \dfrac{5}{12} = \dfrac{5}{8}x - \dfrac{3}{4}x$

35. $\dfrac{5}{6}x - 1 = \dfrac{2}{3}x + 2$

36. $\dfrac{1}{3}(3x+5) = \dfrac{1}{2}(4x - 2) + \dfrac{1}{6}$

37. $\dfrac{p}{10} + \dfrac{7}{20} = 3p + \dfrac{1}{2}p - \dfrac{2}{5}p$

38. $\dfrac{2}{5}y - \dfrac{7}{10} = \dfrac{1}{3}y + \dfrac{1}{6}$

39. $\dfrac{y}{6} + \dfrac{3}{2} = \dfrac{4y}{3} + \dfrac{3}{4}$

40. $\dfrac{2x}{3} + \dfrac{5}{6} = \dfrac{5x}{8} - \dfrac{3}{4}$

41. $\dfrac{2}{3}x - \left(x + \dfrac{1}{4}\right) = \dfrac{1}{6}(x + 3)$

42. $\dfrac{3}{4}x - 5 = \dfrac{2}{3}x + 1$

43. $15 + x = \dfrac{3}{2}x$

44. $\dfrac{x}{2} + \dfrac{1}{3} = \dfrac{3}{4}$

45. $65 + 12x = 5 - 3x$

46. $\dfrac{1}{4} + 3x + \dfrac{13}{2} = \dfrac{3}{4}x$

47. $4\dfrac{1}{6}x + 4 = x - 2\dfrac{1}{3}$

48. $4x - 1\dfrac{1}{3} = 5(1 - 4x)$

49. $\dfrac{3}{5}\left(x - \dfrac{1}{2}\right) = \dfrac{1}{5}\left(x + \dfrac{1}{2}\right)$

50. $\dfrac{1}{2}(x + 1) = \dfrac{1}{3}(x - 1)$

51. $.3p = .5(p + 8 - .2p)$

52. $x + .2(x + 1) = .2(x + 9)$

53. $x - .2(x + 1) = 2(x + 3)$

54. $2(.2x + 1) - .3(x + 2) = .4(x - 1)$

55. $5x - .12 = 1.2 - .5x$

56. $1.6 - .3y = 7y - .20$

57. $.7(4x - 5) = x + .7$

58. $.4x = 5 - .2(x + 1)$

59. $.4y = -.5y$

C. In exercises 60-70, solve for the unknown.

60. $A = \dfrac{1}{2}h(b + c)$; find h, given $A = 30$, $b = 8.5$, and $c = 7.2$.

61. $A = P + Prt$; find P, given $A = 2440$, $r = 3.2$, and $t = 20.5$.

62. $C = \dfrac{5}{9}(F - 32)$; find F, given $C = 35.4$.

63. $V = \pi r^2 h$; find V, given $r = 4.3$, $h = 7.5$, and $\pi = 3.14$.

64. $V = \pi h^2 \left(r - \dfrac{h}{3}\right)$; find r, given $h = 7.8$, and $V = 308.2$.

65. $S = 2\pi r(r + h)$; find h, given $r = 6.5$, and $S = 620.5$.

66. $S = \pi r\left(r + \sqrt{r^2 h^2}\right)$; find S, given $r = 2.3$, and $h = 4.7$.

67. $V = \dfrac{1}{3}\pi r^2 h$; find r, given $V = 120.6$, $h = 9.6$, and $\pi = 3.14$.

68. $V = \pi r^2 \left(r - \dfrac{h}{3}\right)$; find h, given $V = 308.4$, $r = 7.5$, and $\pi = 3.14$.

69. $l = a + (n - 1)d$; find l, given $n = 30$, $a = 5.4$, and $d = 1.2$

70. $S = \dfrac{n}{2}(a + l)$; find S, given $n = 8$, $a = 2.7$, and $l = 13.9$.

7.2 APPLICATIONS USING DECIMALS

Introduction

We use decimal numbers in everything we deal with; money, measurements, interest rates, bank accounts, or payment of bills. In this section, we will discuss real world application problems that when translated to mathematical symbols, become an equation with decimals.

The main task in solving an application problem is to understand the problem itself and to be able to translate the problem into mathematical symbols. We have divided the problems in this section in two categories: problems related to change, including profit-cost; and problems related to rates, including unit rates and unit prices.

Objectives

Upon completing this section, you will be able to:

A. Solve application problems using formulas;

B. Solve applications involving "% of"; and

C. Solve applications involving ratios, rates, unit rates, or unit prices.

7.2 A.   Solving applications using Formulas

- *Change:*

> **Change = Final value – Starting value**

Raymond wants to calculate the distance between his home and the college. When he leaves home the odometer on his car reads 107,261.8 miles. When he arrives at the college the odometer reads 107,313 miles. What is the distance between his home and the college?

We evaluate the distance by finding the *change* in the odometer reading:

Distance = Change in Odometer reading = Final odometer reading – initial odometer reading

$$= 107,313 \text{ miles} - 107,261.8 \text{ miles}$$
$$= 51.2 \text{ miles}$$

Example 1   At the beginning of April an account balance was $12,098.52. At the beginning of May the balance was $7,212.65. What was the change in balance?

Solution   Change = **Final amount – Initial amount**
$$= 7,212.65 - 12,098.52$$
$$= -4,885.87 \qquad \text{Negative change}$$

The account balance decreased by **$4,885.87**.

> **Warm-Up**
>
> 1. At noon the barometric pressure was 29.83 inches. By 2 PM it was 30.01 inches. How much did it change?

- *Profit:*

> **Profit = Income – Cost**

The break even point occurs when either Profit = zero or when Income = Cost

Example 2   Ice cream cones are sold by a vendor for $1.65 each. The vendor pays $425 per month to rent his booth. What is his profit for a month in which he sells 4,017 ice cream cones and spends $2,209.35 on supplies?

Solution   Profit = Income – Cost
    = (Price × cones sold) – (Rent + Supplies)
    = ($1.65 × 4,017) – ($425 + $2,209.35)
    = $6,628.05 – $2,634.35
    = $3,993.70

His profit is **$3,993.70**

> **Warm-Up**
>
> 2. If shirts cost $3.15 each to make and are sold by a crafts person for $17.50 each, what is the craft person's profit on the sale of 42 shirts? The cost for renting a booth at the craft show was $110.

- *Average:*

  An average is a single number representative of two or more numbers.

  $$\text{Average} = \frac{\text{Sum of all the numbers}}{\text{Count of the numbers}}$$

Warm-Up
3. Find the average rain fall per week in August, if the rain fall recorded for the four weeks are: 1.55 in, 0.1 in, 0.25 in, and 0.94 in. (Round your answer to hundredths place.)
Answers:
1. 0.18 inches   **2.** $492.70 **3.** 0.71 in

Example 3   Find the average cost of a TI-83 calculator. They are sold at the bookstore for $103.95, at K-Mart for $89.95, and at Sam's Club for $85.75.

Solution

$$\text{Average} = \frac{\$103.95 + \$89.95 + \$85.75}{3}$$

$$= \frac{\$279.63}{3}$$

$$\approx \textbf{\$93.22, to the nearest cent}$$

7.2 B.   Solving application problems involving "% of".

Decimals are commonly used when translating percent statements. Recall that "of" means "multiply" when relating two quantities. Recall also that "%" means "per 100": 5% is translated as $\frac{5}{100}$.

Warm-Up
4. Find the amount withheld for Medicare from Samatha's $420 gross pay. The Medicare tax is 1.45% of gross pay.
Answer:
4. $6.09

Example 4   Find the amount of Samantha's paycheck withheld for social security tax. Social security tax equals 6.2% of gross pay. Samantha's gross pay for the week was $420.

Solution   Let x represent the social security tax.

Social security tax $= 6.2\%$ of gross pay.

$$x = \frac{6.2}{100} \cdot 420$$

$$= 0.062 \cdot 420$$

$$= \textbf{26.04} \qquad \text{\$26.04 was withheld.}$$

7.2 C.   Solving Applications Involving Ratios, Rates, Unit Rates or Unit Prices.

- *Ratio:*

  The ratio of two quantities a and b is just the quotient or the fraction $\frac{a}{b}$ simplified to lowest terms.

Warm-Up
5. What is the ratio of the side to the perimeter, for the square shown below.

1.2 m

Example 5   For the given figure, find the ratio of the height to the base, as a fraction in lowest terms.

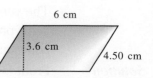

6 cm

3.6 cm

4.50 cm

Solution   The ratio of the height to the base is:

$$\frac{\text{Height}}{\text{Base}} = \frac{3.6 \text{ cm}}{6 \text{ cm}}$$

$$= \frac{3.6 \times \mathbf{10}}{6 \times \mathbf{10}}$$ Build as a fraction using 10 to move the decimal to the right.

$$= \frac{36}{60} = \frac{3 \times 12}{5 \times 12} = \frac{3}{5}$$

The ratio of the height to the base is 3 to 5.

- **Rates:**

The above example involved comparison with the same units (labels). Multiplication by a power of 10 played the role of converting the decimal to a whole number, so that the ratio could be expressed as a reduced fraction. The same strategy is used when we express **rates** as simplified fractions. Recall that rates involve relations or comparisons with different units (labels).

Example 6   During a rain storm 6.5 inches of rain was recorded in 2.5 hours. At what rate did it rain during this time?

Solution   Rate $= \dfrac{\text{Total rain}}{\text{Time duration}}$

$$= \frac{6.5 \text{ inches}}{2.5 \text{ hours}}$$

$$= \frac{65 \text{ inches}}{25 \text{ hours}} = \frac{13 \text{ inches}}{5 \text{ hours}}$$

During the storm the rain fell at the rate of **13 inches every 5 hours** .

Warm-Up

6. On a drawing, 0.5 cm represents 3.25 meters. Write this scale as a rate in lowest terms.

- **Unit Rates:**

The most common use of rates is **unit rates.** Recall that unit rates are rates in which a quantity of one type of item is compared to a single unit of some other item. They are often indicated by "per" which means "for 1", or each, in the question.

Example 7   A runner ran 7.8 miles in 1.2 hours. What was his speed? Speed = distance covered per hour.

Solution   Let x represent his speed.   Speed in miles per hour.

$$x = \text{Speed} = \frac{\text{Distance covered}}{\text{Time taken}}$$

$$= \frac{7.8 \text{ miles}}{1.2 \text{ hours}}$$ Divide 7.8 by 1.2 to find the unit rate.

$$= \frac{6.5 \text{ miles}}{1 \text{ hour}}$$

$$= \textbf{6.5 miles per hour}$$

His speed was 6.5 miles per hour (or 6.5 miles in 1 hour.)

Warm-Up

7. If 15 minutes are needed to solve 4 problems, what is the average time needed to solve each problem?

- **Unit Price:**

A common use of unit rates is in unit prices. In a unit price, the cost of 1 item or unit is evaluated. The cost is always in the numerator of the ratio (fraction).

$$\textbf{Unit price} = \frac{\text{Total Cost}}{\text{Quantity}}$$

Warm-Up

8. A dozen eggs costs $0.99. What is the cost per egg? Round the answer to the nearest cent.

Example 8 5.2 pounds of meat cost $14.69. What is the cost per pound?

Solution Let x represent the cost per pound.

$$x = \frac{\$14.69}{5.2\ \text{pounds}} = \frac{\$2.825}{1\ \text{pound}}$$

Divide 14.69 by 5.2 to find the unit rate.

$$= \$\,2.825\ \textbf{per pound}$$

 Note   Unit prices are usually given with three or four decimal places.

- **Using Unit Rates to Compare Prices**

Recall that common denominators are needed to compare fractions. To compare prices, we convert rates to unit prices, and then compare. All the unit rates have the same denominator, 1. In determining unit prices, the cost is always in the numerator and the quantity is in the denominator.

Warm-Up

9. Which is a better buy for cinnamon: 3.5 ounces for $2.39 or 4 ounces for $2.59.

Example 9 20 ounces of liquid dish soap cost $1.49, while 32 ounces cost $1.88, and 14 ounces cost $.72. Which is the best buy?

Solution Compare the unit prices

Rate 1: $\dfrac{\$1.49}{20\ \text{ounces}} = \dfrac{\$0.0745}{1\ \text{ounce}}$ = **$.0745 per ounce**

Rate 2: $\dfrac{\$1.88}{32\ \text{ounces}} = \dfrac{\$0.0588}{1\ \text{ounces}}$ = **$.0588 per ounce**

Rate 3: $\dfrac{\$.72}{14\ \text{ounces}} = \dfrac{\$0.0514}{1\ \text{ounces}}$ = **$.0514 per ounce**

$.72 for 14 ounces is the best buy.

- *Using Proportions to solve Rate Problems*

We get a proportion if we equate two ratios. Two ratios are equivalent if their cross products are equal. We use this fact to solve rate problems as explained in the following examples.

Warm-Up

10. If there are 9 calories in one gram of fat, how many calories are in a tomato with 0.2 gram of fat?

Example 10 On a map, 1 inch represents 2.5 miles. The distance on the map between two cities is 4.25 inches. How many miles apart are the cities?

Solution Let x represent the miles between the two cities.

	Case I	Case II
Distance on map	1 inch	4.25 inch
Actual distance	2.5 miles	x miles

Solve the proportion:

$$\frac{1\,\text{in}}{2.5\,\text{mi}} \bowtie \frac{4.25\,\text{in}}{x\,\text{mi}} \rightarrow \quad \begin{array}{c} 2.5\,(4.25) \\ \hline x \end{array}$$

Write the proportion making sure that the labels match on both sides.

$$x = 4.25 \ (2.5)$$ • Solve using cross products.

$$= 10.625 \text{ miles}$$

The cites are approximately 10.6 miles apart.

Check by estimating: We have about 4 times as many inches.
We expect about 4 times as many miles, about 10 miles.

Example 11   Hamburger costs $2.15 per pound. How much
hamburger can be purchased for $20.

11.   If potatoes cost $0.39 per pound,
how much can be purchased for $5?

Solutions   Let x represent the pounds of hamburger that can be
bought for $20.

	Case I	Case II
Cost	$2.15	$20
Pounds	1 lb	x lb

Solve the proportion:

$$\frac{\$2.15}{1 \text{ lb}} \quad \frac{\$20}{x \text{ lb}} \quad \begin{array}{l} \to \ 20 \\ \to \ 2.15 \cdot x \end{array}$$ • Write the proportion, checking that labels match.

$$2.15 \cdot x = 20$$ • Solve using cross products.

$$\frac{2.15}{2.15} x = \frac{20}{2.15}$$ Divide both sides by 2.15.

$$x \approx \mathbf{9.3 \ lb}$$

You can purchase 9.3 pounds of hamburger for $20.

Check by estimating: We have about 10 times as much money.
We expect about 10 lbs.

 Note   This problem could also be solved as a unit rate equation: $\frac{\$}{lb} \times lb = \$$

$$\frac{\$2.15}{1\,lb} \cdot x\,lb = \$20$$

$$2.15 \cdot x = 20$$

$$x = 9.3\,lb$$

Example 12   If 6.5 yards of satin cloth cost $34.50, what will be the
cost for 20 yards?

Warm-Up

12.   If a 50-pound dog requires 2.1 ml of
vaccine, how much vaccine is needed
for a 120-pound dog?

Solution   Let $x represent the cost of 20 yards.

	Case I	Case II
Cost	$34.50	x
Length	6.5 yds	20 yds

Solve the proportion:

$$\frac{\$34.50}{6.5 \text{ yds}} \quad \frac{\$x}{20 \text{ yds}} \quad \begin{array}{l} \to \ 6.5 \cdot x \\ \to \ 34.50 \cdot 20 \end{array}$$ • Write the proportion, checking that labels match.

$$6.5 \cdot x = (34.50)(20)$$ • Solve using cross products.

$$6.5x = 690$$

$$\frac{6.5x}{6.5} = \frac{690}{6.5}$$ • Divide by 6.5.

$$x \approx \$106.15$$

The cost is $106.15 for 20 yards.

Check by estimating: We have about 3 times the number of yards. We expect about 3×35 or $105.

Answers:

5. $\frac{1}{4}$ 6. $\frac{2 \text{ cm}}{13 \text{ m}}$

7. 3.75 minutes per problem

8. 8 cents   9. 4 ounces for $2.59

10. 1.8 calories of fat

11. 12.8 lb   12. 5.04 ml

Exercise 7.2

A. 1. Before deductions George has a gross income of $1,975 per month. The monthly deductions are: health insurance, $75.50; union dues $28; retirement contribution $65.37; and income tax $197.50. Find his actual take-home (net) pay.

2. Ms. Monica had $1,795.39 in her checking account. How much does Monica have in her checking account after depositing two checks for the amount of $4,533.48 and $1,365.32?

3. Donald makes a gross salary (before deductions) of $2,458 per month. His monthly deductions are: federal income tax, $237; state income tax, $146; social security, $152.40; medicare, $35.61; retirement contribution, $73.74; union dues, $31; and health insurance, $121.45. Find his actual take-home (net) pay.

4. Boris goes shopping with $50 in cash. He pays $8.79 for a cassette tape and $21.88 for a sweater. On the way home he buys $14.75 worth of gas. How much cash does he have after shopping?

5. At the end of November, the balance in Phillips checking account was $7,316.82. At the end of January, the balance was $2,738.97. What was the change in his balance from November to January?

6. At the beginning of January, Jeanni's checking account balance was $13,598.54. At the beginning of February, the balance was $19,342.79. What was the increase in her balance?

7. At the beginning of a trip the odometer read 78,934.7 miles. At the end of the trip the odometer read 79,456.3 miles. How many miles were traveled?

8. Determine the temperature change for a February day with an early morning temperature of $-12.7°C$ and a late afternoon temperature of $12.5°C$.

9. Addy had $6,732.75 in his checking account. He wrote checks for $345.13, $189.26, and $354.79. Then he deposited $437.99 back in his account. What is the balance in his account?

10. Pizza slices are sold by a vendor for $3.99 each. The vendor pays $556 per month to rent his booth. What is his profit for a month if he sells 5,234 pizza slices and spends $7,695.47 on supplies?

11. Berg sold jeans in a craft show for $15.99 each. What is Berg's profit on the sale of 589 pairs of jeans, if each pair of jeans costs him $6.59 each and he paid $435 to rent his booth at the craft show?

12. Robin buys 500 shirts for $6,678.75 and sells them for $19.99 each. What is his profit?

13. Ruby buys an old car for $8,796.99 and she spends $1,356.78 on repairs and sells the car for $13,546.99. What is her profit?

14. A dry-cleaning company spent $1,400 for rent, $2,567.83 for supplies and $4,356.35 for employee payroll during the month of February. During that month, $11,289.44 was paid by customers. Find the company's profit for February.

15. A student starts a home business making designer belts. He spent $480.35 for tools. During the first three months the student spent $380.60 on materials. After three months, 450 belts had been sold to local merchants for $13.50 each. What was the student's profit at the end of three months?

16. A campus club held a dance to raise money for a local charity. They spent $550 for the DJ, $273.45 for the refreshments, and $57.26 for decorations and supplies. They sold 243 tickets for $10.50 each. What was their profit from the event?

17. The temperature of Atlanta, Georgia during four months was: 70.8° F, 72.5° F, 73.9° F, and 75.6° F. What was the average monthly temperature of Atlanta during these months?

18. The rain gauge at the water reservoir in Washington, D.C. recorded the following rainfall during a five months period: 5.6 cm, 6.7 cm, 6.5 cm, 7.3 cm, and 5.9 cm. What was the average monthly rainfall in Washington D.C. during these months?

19. John is advised to go for a long morning walk by his doctor. He walks 1.8 mi on the first day, 1.7 mi on the second day, 2.3 mi on the third day, and 2.5 mi on the fourth day. How many miles, on an average, does he walk each day?

20. The weight of five new born babies in a hospital is: 7.6 lb, 6.9 lb, 7.9 lb, 6.8 lb, and 7.5 lb. What is the average weight of a new born baby to the nearest tenth of a pound?

21. The following prices per pound of Vermont Cheddar cheese were found at six supermarkets:

    $8.70, $7.60, $7.90, $8.30, $7.80, and $8.50. What is the average price per pound rounded to the nearest tenth?

B. 22. Find 3.25% of $400.　　　　　　　　　　**23.** Find 12.5% of $15.65.

24. The discount is 25% of the regular price. Find the discount for a dress regularly priced at $94.50.

25. During a spring sale, the discount on suits is 33% of the regular price. Find the discount on a suit that regularly sells for $204.90. Then find the sale price.

26. Asian Americans count 17.5% of the population in a town. Find the number of Asian Americans if the population of the entire town is 1,468 persons.

27. The finance charge is 2.5% of the amount purchased. What finance charge will be charged for a $2,012 cruise.

C. 28. For the given figure, find the ratio of the height to the base, as a fraction in lowest terms.

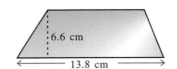

29. For the given figure, find the ratio of the height to the base, as a fraction in lowest terms.

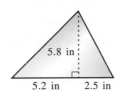

30. For the given figure, find the ratio of the base to the diagonal. Write as a fraction in lowest terms and as a decimal rounded to the tenths.

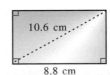

31. Two students do the same type of job at different office supply stores. Samantha earns $7.80 per hour while Latrice earns $6.90 per hour. Simplify the ratio of Samantha's hourly wage to Latrice's hourly wage.

32. Peter walks $4\frac{3}{5}$ miles in the same time that Domingo walks 6.9 miles. Simplify the ratio of Peter's distance to Domingo's distance.

33. A Mallard duck flies at speeds around 39 mph. A sparrow flies at 24 mph. Write the simplified ratio of the sparrow's speed to the duck's speed.

34. At the local drugstore, Claritin sells for $20.55 for 20 tablets. The generic store brand of the same medicine sells for $13.95 for 20 tablets. Write the simplified ratio of the price of Claritin to the price of the generic brand.

35. If 3.75 inches of snow falls in 4.5 hours, how much snow is falling per hour? Write this also as a rate in lowest terms.

36. If a car travels 105 miles in 1.5 hours, what is its rate (speed) in lowest terms?

37. If 4.5 ounces of gold cost $1,530.45, what is the cost per ounce? (Round to the nearest cent).

38. A car is driven 375.5 miles in 4.25 hours. What is the average speed of the car, in miles per hour?

39. A long-distance telephone call between Washington D.C. and London, U.K. costs $8.75 for 30.5 minutes. What is the rate in cents per minute?

40. William travels 789.6 miles in 16.37 hours. Approximately how many miles does he travel per hour? Round to the nearest tenth of a mile.

41. Mrs. Berg buys 5 cans of orange juice at $1.05 per can, 12 candy bars for $0.75 each , and 4 kg of apples at $2.25 per kg. How much did she spend?

42. Dr. Brown has three options to get his new car financed by the New Citi Bank:

    First: 48 monthly installments at $408.15 per month

    Second: 42 installments at $486.33 per month

    Third: 60 installments at $316.62 per month

    Which option yields the least expensive total cost?

43. Robin earns $4.35 an hour. He works for 33.25 hours. Find Robin's actual earnings rounded to the nearest cent.

44. What is the cost per ounce of a 12-ounce package of potato chips that costs $2.16 ?

45. Robin travels 75.34 miles on a bicycle in 8.6 hours. What is his average speed to the nearest tenth of a mile per hour?

$$\left(\text{Use formula} : \text{Speed} = \frac{\text{distance}}{\text{time}} \right).$$

46. A piece of fabric, 613.5 yards, is to be divided into pieces, measuring 2.15 yards in length. How many pieces can be obtained measuring the exact length? How much fabric is wasted?

47. What is the approximate weight of one box of apples if 68 such boxes weigh 1,479.68 pounds?

48. Ohm's law is given by the formula $E = I R$, where E is the voltage (number of volts); I is the current (number of amperes); and R is the resistance (number of ohms). What is the resistance, to the nearest thousandth, if the voltage is 220 volts, and the current is 7.85 amperes?

49. William travels 789.6 miles in 16.37 hours. Approximately how many miles does he travel per hour? Exactly how many miles (to the nearest tenth of a mile) does he travel per hour?

50. Wilson's Readymade Garment Store buys 1,000 shirts for $15,650.75. What is the cost of each shirt to the nearest cent?

51. An athlete's weight decreases from 185.5 lb to 169.75 lb in a year. What is the average decrease in weight per month rounded to the nearest tenth of a pound?

52. Kim bought a Honda Accord car for $18,799.99 and it has depreciated to $ 7,650.78 in 5.5 years. What is the average depreciation per year rounded to the nearest cent?

53. During a rain storm 14.6 cm rain was recorded in 2.3 hours. At what rate (cm per hour) did it rain during that time?

54. The distance between Atlanta and Chicago is 694.8 miles. What is the scale of a map on which the distance between Atlanta and Chicago is 6.4 in?   (*Hint*: 1 inch = ? miles)

55. On a survey map of a rectangular lot, the length is shown as 8.2 cm. If the length of the lot is 60.8 yd, determine the scale of the map. (*Hint*: 1 cm = ? yd)

56. If 6.3 pounds of caramels cost $23.99, determine the cost per pound.

57. If 42.5 kg of cashews cost $199.99, determine the cost per kg to the nearest cent.

58. A 0.75 lb package of cheese costs $3.99. Find the cost per pound to the nearest cent.

59. The gas cost for traveling in a Toyota Corolla from Atlanta to Washington is $ 75.50. If Washington is 750 miles away from Atlanta, what is the cost per mile for gas?

60. What is the cost of one box of apples, if 524 such boxes cost $2,548.79? Round the answer to the nearest cent.

61. Which is a better buy for tomato ketchup: 15 ounces for $0.99 or 35 ounces for $2.19?

62. Which is the best buy for spaghetti sauce: 33 ounces for $1.30, or 39 ounces for $1.59, or 45 ounces for $1.99?

63. Which is a better buy for taco shells: 18 in a box for $3.99 or 12 in a box for $2.49?

64. Which is a better buy for fancy tuna: $2.59 for 6.25 oz or $1.89 for 5.75 oz?

65. Which is a better buy for grapefruit juice: $4.99 for 33.5 oz or $6.99 for 45.75 oz?

66. On a map, 1 inch represents 125 miles. The distance between two cities on the map is 3.25 inches. How many miles apart are the cities?

67. On a map, 1 cm represents 85 miles. The distance between Washington D.C. and New York is 2.95 cm. How many miles apart are the cities?

68. One pound of oranges can yield 8.43 oz of orange juice. How much juice can be obtained from a box of oranges having a net weight of 49.9 pounds? Round the answer to the nearest tenth of an ounce.

69. One serving of fish steak is 0.45 lb of fish. How much fish steak is required for 35 servings?

70. If there are 8.9 calories in one gram of fat, how many calories are in 0.45 gram of fat?

71. The tickets for a fashion show are sold for $75 each. If the lights, music, and stage arrangements cost $5,750.50, and the hall rental costs $4,696.99, how many tickets must be sold to have a profit of $6,000?

72. The tickets for a dinner/dance are sold for $65 each. If the dinner costs $12.75 per head, music costs $450, and the hall rental costs $650, how many tickets must be sold to break even?

73. The tickets for a dinner/dance are sold for $55 each. If the dinner costs $13.75 per person, the music costs $540, and the hall rental costs $559, how many tickets must be sold to have a minimum profit of $5,425?

74. If bananas cost $0.45 per pound. How many pounds can be purchased for $6.50?

75. Apples cost $0.99 per pound. How many pounds can be purchased for $8?

76. Chicken costs $1.99 per pound. How much chicken can be purchased for $7.50?

77. Under typical conditions 1 ft of snow melts to 1.3 inches of water. To how many inches of water will 7.5 ft of snow melt?

78. To control fever, a doctor suggests that a child should be given 1 mg of Tylenol for every 0.07 kg body weight. If the dosage is proportional to the child's weight, how much Tylenol is recommended for a child whose weight is 25.5 kg?

79. An 8.5-lb turkey breast provides 35 servings of meat. How many pounds of turkey breast would be needed for 55 servings?

80. Tires are often priced according to the number of miles they are expected to be driven. A tire priced at $69.99 is expected to be driven 35,000 mi. How much would you pay for a tire that is expected to be driven 45,000 miles?

81. Use the formula $F = 1.8\,C + 32$ to find:
    (a) the Celsius temperature that corresponds to 35.6° F.
    (b) the Fahrenheit temperature that corresponds to 17.3° C.

82. If the sum of a number and 6.2 is multiplied by 3, the result is the same as 9 times the number decreased by 2.4. Find the number.

83. If 6.1 is added to a number, the result exceeds 2.3 times the number by 3.4. What is the number?

84. Find the number, which when divided by 3.2 is 1.2 less than the number.

85. Laura travels 1.24 hours in the morning to drive to her office from home and she travels 0.25 hour extra to return home in the evening from her office. How long does Laura drive every day for her office?

86. The total cost of a shirt and a calculator was $48.65. If the cost of the shirt was $10.75 less than the cost of the calculator, what was the cost of each item?

87. The sum of the complementary and supplementary angles of an angle is 210.7°. Find the angle.

88. The price of two laptops is $3,562.83. The less expensive laptop is $356.99 less than the other. What is the price of each laptop rounded to the nearest cent?

89. The total cost of a 40 GB hard disc and an 80 GB hard disc is $152.84. The cost of the 40 GB disc is $42.53 less than the cost of the 80 GB disc. What is the cost of each disc to the nearest cent?

90. The length of a cold rolled steel shaft is 24.5 ft. It is to be divided into two parts such that one piece is 2.5 times the other piece. What is the length of each piece rounded to the tenth of a feet?

91. A classic car is selling for $450.99 more than three times its original price. If the selling price now is $9,855.99, what was the original price of the car?

7.3 SQUARE ROOTS AND THE PYTHAGOREAN THEOREM

Objectives

After completing this section, you will be able to:

A. Evaluate expressions involving square roots; and

B. Use the Pythagorean Theorem to solve problems involving right triangles.

IMPORTANT VOCABULARY

1. A **perfect square** is a number which is a square of some integer. For example, 1, 16, and 64 are perfect squares because

$$1 = 1^2 ; \quad 16 = 4^2 ; \quad 64 = 8^2.$$

2. A number a is called **square root** of another number b if $a^2 = b$. 4 is the square root of 16 since $4^2 = 16$.

Similarly, 3 is the square root of 9 since $3^2 = 9$.

3. The symbol $\sqrt{}$, called the **radical sign**, is used for square roots:

$$\sqrt{16} = 4 \quad (\text{Read: "The square root of 16 is 4."}) ; \quad \sqrt{9} = 3.$$

4. The complete expression such as $\sqrt{16}$ or $\sqrt{45}$ is called a **radical**, and the number under the radical sign is called the **radicand**. In the radical $\sqrt{16}$, 16 is the radicand.

5. A **right triangle** is a triangle in which one angle is a right angle (90°). **The Hypotenuse** of a right triangle is the side opposite the right angle; the remaining two sides are called the **legs**.

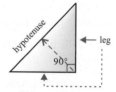

Figure 7.1

6. The **Pythagorean Theorem** states that "In a right triangle, the square of the hypotenuse is equal to the sum of the squares of the two legs." (The theorem was discovered by **Pythagoras**, a famous Greek mathematician).

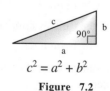

$$c^2 = a^2 + b^2$$

Figure 7.2

7.3 A. Evaluating Expressions Involving Square Roots

1. Introducing Square Roots:

We already know how to find the 'square' of a number: we multiply the number by itself. For example,

$$3^2 = 3 \cdot 3 \qquad = 9 \qquad \longleftarrow \quad \text{Square of 3}$$

$$(-5)^2 = (-5) \cdot (-5) \quad = 25 \qquad \longleftarrow \quad \text{Square of } -5$$

and $\quad (6)^2 = (6) \cdot (6) \qquad = 36 \qquad \longleftarrow \quad \text{Square of 6}$

If an *integer* is **squared** (that is, it is multiplied by itself), the result is called a **perfect square**; thus, in the above examples, 9, 25 and 36 are perfect squares. In general terms,

A number n is a **perfect square** if $n = m^2$ for some **integer** m.

The squares of the first 20 positive integers are shown in Table 7.1.

SQUARES OF POSITIVE INTEGERS FROM 1 TO 20				
$1^2 = 1$	$5^2 = 25$	$9^2 = 81$	$13^2 = 169$	$17^2 = 289$
$2^2 = 4$	$6^2 = 36$	$10^2 = 100$	$14^2 = 196$	$18^2 = 324$
$3^2 = 9$	$7^2 = 49$	$11^2 = 121$	$15^2 = 225$	$19^2 = 361$
$4^2 = 16$	$8^2 = 64$	$12^2 = 144$	$16^2 = 256$	$20^2 = 400$

Table 7.1

This table shows that there are only 20 perfect squares (the highlighted numbers in the table) from 1 to 400.

Since $4^2 = 16$, we say that 4 is the **square root** of 16.

Since $15^2 = 225$, we say that 15 is the **square root** of 225.

In general terms, we say that **a number a is the square root of a number b if $a^2 = b$.**

- We identify the square root of a number by the symbol $\sqrt{}$ (called a **radical sign**).

$$\sqrt{16} = 4 \qquad \text{(Read: "The square root of 16 is 4.")}$$

$$\sqrt{225} = 15 \qquad \text{(Read: "The square root of 225 is 15.")}$$

- It should be noted that each perfect square has two square roots, one positive and the other negative. For example, since $5^2 = 25$ and $(-5)^2 = 25$, both 5 (or $+5$) and -5 are square roots of 25. The *positive* square root of a number is called its **Principal Square Root**. Unless mentioned otherwise, the term **square root** and the symbol $\sqrt{}$ are used to represent only this principal (or positive) square root; thus,

$$\sqrt{25} = 5 \quad (\text{not} -5).$$

For the negative square root of 25, we write $-\sqrt{25} = -5$.

As a special case, for 0, $\sqrt{0} = -\sqrt{0}$
$$= 0.$$

2. Finding Square Roots:

From the above discussion we know that a is the square root of b if $a^2 = b$. Interpreting this in symbols, (when a is positive) we can say

$$\sqrt{b} = a \text{ if } b = a^2, \text{ or equivalently, we may say that } \sqrt{a^2} = a \ (a \geq 0);$$

 Important Observation

Since the square of every real number is non-negative, the number b in the above definition is always non-negative. That is, *we do not define* square roots of negative numbers. The square roots of negative numbers are called imaginary numbers. Discussion of such numbers is beyond the scope of this book.

The square roots of perfect square numbers from 1 to 400 can be easily obtained from Table 7.1.

$$\sqrt{64} = \sqrt{8^2}\,; \qquad \sqrt{100} = \sqrt{10^2}\,; \qquad \sqrt{196} = \sqrt{14^2}\,; \text{ and so on.}$$
$$= 8\,; \qquad\qquad\qquad = 10\,; \qquad\qquad\qquad = 14$$

Also, $-\sqrt{64} = -8\,; \; -\sqrt{100} = -10\,; \; -\sqrt{196} = -14$, and so on.

For convenience, the square roots of the perfect square numbers from 1 to 400 are listed below in Table 7.2.

SQUARE ROOTS OF PERFECT SQUARES FROM 1 TO 400				
$\sqrt{1} = 1$	$\sqrt{25} = 5$	$\sqrt{81} = 9$	$\sqrt{169} = 13$	$\sqrt{289} = 17$
$\sqrt{4} = 2$	$\sqrt{36} = 6$	$\sqrt{100} = 10$	$\sqrt{196} = 14$	$\sqrt{324} = 18$
$\sqrt{9} = 3$	$\sqrt{49} = 7$	$\sqrt{121} = 11$	$\sqrt{225} = 15$	$\sqrt{361} = 19$
$\sqrt{16} = 4$	$\sqrt{64} = 8$	$\sqrt{144} = 12$	$\sqrt{256} = 16$	$\sqrt{400} = 20$

Table 7.2

To be able to quickly recognize the perfect square numbers from 1 to 400 and their square roots, you should work the exercises in the Rapid Drill given below.

RAPID DRILL

Rapid Drill: Find the following square roots mentally as fast as you can. Check your answer from table 7.2

1. $\sqrt{4}$ 2. $\sqrt{9}$ 3. $\sqrt{16}$ 4. $\sqrt{1}$ 5. $\sqrt{100}$ 6. $\sqrt{196}$ 7. $\sqrt{25}$ 8. $\sqrt{36}$

9. $\sqrt{64}$ 10. $\sqrt{81}$ 11. $\sqrt{0}$ 12. $\sqrt{49}$ 13. $\sqrt{400}$ 14. $\sqrt{225}$ 15. $\sqrt{144}$ 16. $\sqrt{289}$

17. $\sqrt{324}$ 18. $\sqrt{169}$ 19. $-\sqrt{9}$ 20. $-\sqrt{100}$ 21. $\sqrt{361}$ 22. $-\sqrt{25}$ 23. $-\sqrt{225}$ 24. $-\sqrt{144}$

25. $-\sqrt{169}$ 26. $-\sqrt{81}$ 27. $-\sqrt{1}$ 28. $-\sqrt{36}$ 29. $-\sqrt{400}$ 30. $-\sqrt{289}$ 31. $\sqrt{256}$ 32. $-\sqrt{256}$

33. $-\sqrt{196}$ 34. $-\sqrt{361}$ 35. $\sqrt{121}$ 36. $-\sqrt{121}$

Answers:

1. 2   2. 3   3. 4   4. 1   5. 10   6. 14   7. 5   8. 6   9. 8   10. 9   11. 0   12. 7

13. 20   14. 15   15. 12   16. 17   17. 18   18. 13   19. −3   20. −10   21. 19   22. −5   23. −15   24. −12

25. −13   26. −9   27. −1   28. −6   29. −20   30. −17   31. 16   32. −16   33. −14   34. −19   35. 11   36. −11

The table 7.2 can be used to find the square roots of many more numbers. For example, we know that $\sqrt{49} = 7$. We can use this result to find the square roots of 4,900, 0.49, 0.0049, 490,000, and so on.

$\sqrt{4900}$	$\sqrt{0.49}$	$\sqrt{0.0049}$	$\sqrt{490,000}$
$= \sqrt{49 \times 100}$	$= \sqrt{\dfrac{49}{100}}$	$= \sqrt{\dfrac{49}{10,000}}$	$= \sqrt{49 \times 10,000}$
$= \sqrt{7^2 \times 10^2}$	$= \sqrt{\left(\dfrac{7}{10}\right)^2}$	$= \sqrt{\left(\dfrac{7}{100}\right)^2}$	$= \sqrt{7^2 \times 100^2}$
$= \sqrt{70^2}$	$= \sqrt{(0.7)^2}$	$= \sqrt{(0.07)^2}$	$= \sqrt{(700)^2}$
$= 70$	$= 0.7$	$= 0.07$	$= 700$

Example 1   Find the value of each of the following expressions:

(a) $\left(\sqrt{121}\right)^2$ (b) $\left(-\sqrt{49}\right)^2$ (c) $\left(\sqrt{7}\right)^2$

Solutions

(a) $\left(\sqrt{121}\right)^2 \;=\; (11)^2 \;=\; 121$

(b) $\left(-\sqrt{49}\right)^2 \;=\; (-7)^2 \;=\; 49$ Alternatively, the square of a negative number is positive:

$$\left(-\sqrt{49}\right)^2 = \left(\sqrt{49}\right)^2 = (7)^2 = 49$$

(c)   Even though we do not know the exact value of $\sqrt{7}$, its square must be 7;

thus, $\left(\sqrt{7}\right)^2 = 7$.   Recall the definition: $\left(\sqrt{b}\right)^2 = b$

- The square roots of numbers other than perfect squares, such as $\sqrt{2}$, $\sqrt{3}$, and $\sqrt{18}$, are non-terminating, non-repeating decimals. The values of such square roots can be approximated as decimal numbers with the help of a calculator.

Recall that the ratio of two integers or fractions are also called **rational** numbers. But the square roots of numbers that are not perfect squares, like $\sqrt{2}$ or $\sqrt{3}$, cannot be expressed as rational numbers. Such numbers are called **irrational** numbers.

Example of **Rational numbers**: $5,\ 1,\ -4,\ \dfrac{2}{5},\ \dfrac{-5}{3},\ \dots$

such numbers can be expressed as terminating decimals, or non-terminating repeating decimals.

$$5 = 5.0,\quad 1 = 1.0,\quad -4 = -4.0,\quad \frac{2}{5} = 0.4,\quad \frac{-5}{3} = -1.\overline{6}$$

Examples of **Irrational** numbers: $\sqrt{2}, \sqrt{5} \dots$

Such numbers can be expressed as non-terminating and non repeating decimals using a calculator.

> **Remark:**   There is a process of finding the square roots of numbers other than perfect squares. This process is very long and laborious. Since square roots of such numbers can be easily computed with calculators, we are not discussing that method here.

To compute the value of the square root of a number we use the key labelled $\sqrt{x}$ or $\sqrt{}$. For example, let us find $\sqrt{5}$ accurate to five decimal places:

 ENTER: $\boxed{\sqrt{}}$ $\boxed{5}$ $\boxed{=}$ 2.236067977;   In some calculators, the key for square root is $\boxed{\sqrt{}}$. Often it is

above another key, requiring that the student enter the $\boxed{\text{shift}}$ key first.

thus, $\sqrt{5} \approx 2.236067977$ Accurate to nine decimal places.

≈ 2.23607.   Accurate to five decimal places.

- All numbers that can be located on the number line, rational or irrational, are called **Real** numbers. Any number that can be expressed in decimal form is a real number. The number line is often referred to as the real number line.

Warm-Up

2. Estimate the value of each square root, Then use a calculator to evaluate the square root accurate to four decimal places:

(a) $\sqrt{45}$

(b) $-\sqrt{11}$

(c) $-\sqrt{213}$

3. Estimate $\sqrt{89}$ to one decimal place.

Answers:

1. (a) 256   (b) 144   (c) 12

2. (a) 6.7082   (b) −3.3166   (c) −14.5945

3. ≈ 9.4

 Example 2   Use a calculator to evaluate the square root accurate to three decimal places.

(a) $\sqrt{15}$ (b) $-\sqrt{39}$ (c) $3 + 2\sqrt{3}$

Solutions

(a)   ENTER: $\boxed{\sqrt{x}}$ $\boxed{15}$ $\boxed{=}$

   DISPLAY: 15;   3.8729833 ≈ 3.873 up to three decimal places.

   thus, $\sqrt{15} \approx 3.873$ accurate to three decimal places.

(b)   The value of $-\sqrt{39}$ is the negative of the value of $\sqrt{39}$.

   ENTER: $\boxed{-}$ $\boxed{\sqrt{x}}$ $\boxed{39}$ $\boxed{=}$

   DISPLAY: −39;   6.2449979 ≈ 6.245 up to three decimal places.

   thus, $-\sqrt{39} \approx -6.245$ accurate to three decimal places.

(c)   To compute $3 + 2\sqrt{3}$,

   ENTER: $\boxed{3}$ $\boxed{+}$ $\boxed{2}$ $\boxed{\sqrt{x}}$ $\boxed{3}$ $\boxed{=}$ 6.4610161 ≈ 6.461

Example 3   Estimate $\sqrt{5}$ to one decimal place.

Solution   5 is between 4 and 9,

   So $\sqrt{5}$ is between $\sqrt{4}$ and $\sqrt{9}$.

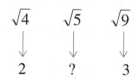

   Since $\sqrt{5}$, is closer to $\sqrt{4}$ than to $\sqrt{9}$, it is probably around 2.2 or 2.3.

   $\sqrt{5} \approx 2.2$ or 2.3

   (The actual value to three decimal place is $\sqrt{5} \approx 2.236$.)

7.3 B.   Using the Pythagorean Theorem to Solve Problems Involving Right Triangles

- A triangle in which one angle is a right angle (90°) is called a **right triangle** (Figure 7.3). The side opposite to the right angle is called the **hypotenuse**. The hypotenuse is always the *longest* side of a right triangle. Each of the other two sides is called a **leg**.

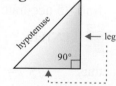

A right triangle and its parts.

Figure 7.3

⟨**Note**⟩   It is known that the sum of the angles of every triangle is always 180°. Thus, in any right triangle, there can be only one right angle.

- The **Pythagorean Theorem** states that "**In a right triangle, the square of the hypotenuse is equal to the sum of the squares of the two legs**". Thus, if the two legs of a right triangle are represented by a and b, and the hypotenuse is represented by c (Figure 7.4), then

$$c^2 = a^2 + b^2$$

> The theorem is credited to Pythagoras, a Greek philosopher who lived in the 5th and 6th centuries B.C.

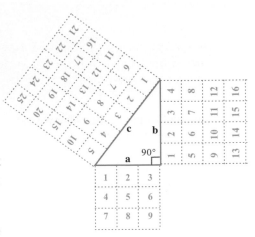

- Certain ordered triplets, such as 3, 4, and 5, can be the sides of a right triangle, satisfying the Pythagorean theorem (see Figure 7.4): $5^2 = 3^2 + 4^2$.

Such triplets are known as Pythagorean Triplets. $(7, 24, 25)$; $(10, 24, 26)$; $(16, 30, 34)$ are some more examples of **Pythagorean Triplets**:

Figure 7.4

$$25^2 = 7^2 + 24^2 \qquad 625 = 49 + 576 \quad \text{(True)}$$
$$26^2 = 10^2 + 24^2 \qquad 676 = 100 + 576 \quad \text{(True)}$$
$$34^2 = 16^2 + 30^2 \qquad 1156 = 256 + 900 \quad \text{(True)}$$

In the following examples, we will use this theorem to:

(i) determine whether or not a triangle with all the three sides given is a right triangle; and

(ii) find the length of the third side of a right triangle when the other two sides are known.

The examples discussed below include some problems involving the use of square roots discussed earlier in this section.

Example 5 Use the Pythagorean theorem to show that a triangle with sides 5 cm, 12 cm, and 13 cm must be a right triangle [or, that (5, 12, 13) is a Pythagorean triplet].

Solution

If the triangle is a right triangle, then the **longest** side (13 cm) must be the hypotenuse, and the square of the hypotenuse must be equal to the sum of the squares of the legs. That is, the relationship

$$13^2 = 5^2 + 12^2 \qquad \text{must be true.}$$

Since $\qquad 169 = 25 + 144 \qquad$ is true, the triangle is a right triangle.

Example 6 Use a calculator and the Pythagorean theorem to find the length of the hypotenuse of a right triangle with two legs 9 cm and 15 cm long. Round your answer to two decimal places.

Solution

Let x = the length of the hypotenuse. Draw a right triangle (not necessarily to scale) and label the given parts.

By the Pythagorean theorem,

$$x^2 = 9^2 + 15^2$$
$$x^2 = 81 + 225$$
$$x^2 = 306$$

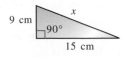

Find $\sqrt{306}$ using a calculator.

Warm-Up

5. Determine which of the following triangles is a right triangle.

   (a) A triangle with sides 3 in, 4 in, and 6 in.

   (b) A triangle with sides 6 in, 8 in, and 10 in.

6. Find the length of the hypotenuse of a right triangle with legs of length 6 cm and 10 cm. Approximate the length of the hypotenuse accurately to two decimal places.

$$\longrightarrow \quad x = \sqrt{306}$$ $\sqrt{306} \approx 17.49285568 \approx 17.49$

$$\longrightarrow \quad x = 17.49.$$

The length of the hypotenuse is approximately 17.49 cm.

7. Find the length of the unknown side of the right triangle.

? 90° 10 in.

26 in.

Example 7 Given a right triangle ABC, with right angle at B, find AB if AC = 20 in and BC = 5 in. Approximate the length of AB to two decimal places.

Solution

• Draw a right triangle and label its parts as indicated in the problem.

Let x represent the length of AB. The square of the hypotenuse must be equal to the sum of the squares of the legs.

A

x 20 in

B   5 in   C

$$AC^2 = AB^2 + BC^2$$ • Use the Pythagorean theorem and solve the resulting equation.

$$20^2 = x^2 + 5^2$$

$$400 = x^2 + 25$$ • Add −25 to both the sides.

$$400 + (-25) = x^2 + 25 + (-25)$$

$$375 = x^2 \ \text{ or } \ x^2 = 375$$

$$x = \sqrt{375}$$

$$\approx 19.36491673$$

AB ≈ 19.36 in.   Accurate to two decimal places

8. A man starts from a point and walks 10 km and then north 10 km. Find the distance from the starting point rounded up to two decimal places.

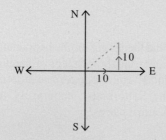

Example 8 A 10 m ladder is placed against a wall. If the foot of the ladder on the ground is 3 m from the wall, find the height of the ladder on the wall, accurate to two decimal places.

Solution Let x = the height reached on the wall. By the Pythagorean theorem,

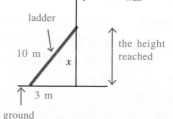

$$10^2 = x^2 + 3^2$$

$$100 = x^2 + 9$$

$$100 - 9 = x^2 + 9 - 9$$

$$x^2 = 91$$

$$x = \sqrt{91} \approx 9.5393920$$ Using a calculator.

$$x \approx 9.54$$ Accurate to two decimal places.

The height of the ladder is approximately 9.54 m.

Answers:

5. (a) not a right triangle.

(b) a right triangle.

6. $2\sqrt{34}$ cm ; 11.66 cm

7. 24 in   **8.** 14.14 km

Exercise 7.3

A. **In exercises 1-14, state whether or not the number is a perfect square.**

1. 1,024 2. 45 3. 81 4. 54 5. 484 6. 900 7. 800

8. 400 9. 225 10. 729 11. 580 12. 2,916 13. 625 14. 700

In exercises 15-28, use your understanding of squares and square roots to find the value of the expression.

15. $\left(\sqrt{81}\right)^2$ 16. $\left(\sqrt{3}\right)^2$ 17. $\left(\sqrt{45}\right)^2$ 18. $\left(\sqrt{76}\right)^2$ 19. $\left(-\sqrt{36}\right)^2$ 20. $\left(-\sqrt{121}\right)^2$ 21. $-\sqrt{121^2}$

22. $-\sqrt{484}$ 23. $\left(\sqrt{19}\right)^2$ 24. $\sqrt{121}$ 25. $-\sqrt{23^2}$ 26. $\left(\sqrt{398}\right)^2$ 27. $\sqrt{400}$ 28. $-\sqrt{72^2}$

29. Do you think that $\sqrt{14}$ is more or less than 4? Justify your answer.

30. Do you think that $\sqrt{75}$ is more or less than 9? Justify your answer.

31. $\sqrt{18}$ is between which two integers?

32. $\sqrt{62}$ is between which two integers?

In exercises 33-52, estimate the value of each square root to one decimal place. Then use your calculator to check the answers.

33. $\sqrt{27}$ 34. $\sqrt{56}$ 35. $\sqrt{15}$ 36. $\sqrt{110}$ 37. $\sqrt{360}$

38. $\sqrt{429}$ 39. $\sqrt{34}$ 40. $\sqrt{47}$ 41. $\sqrt{115}$ 42. $\sqrt{95}$

43. $\sqrt{203}$ 44. $\sqrt{21}$ 45. $\sqrt{52}$ 46. $\sqrt{14}$ 47. $\sqrt{415}$

48. $\sqrt{426}$ 49. $\sqrt{29}$ 50. $\sqrt{54}$ 51. $\sqrt{75}$ 52. $\sqrt{8}$

In exercises 53-62, use a calculator to evaluate the given radical expression accurate to 4 decimal places.

53. $3+\sqrt{2}$ 54. $-\sqrt{175}$ 55. $\sqrt{432}$ 56. $-\sqrt{56}$ 57. $\sqrt{38}-\sqrt{15}$

58. $1+2\sqrt{6}$ 59. $\sqrt{6}+\sqrt{13}$ 60. $-\sqrt{110}$ 61. $2-\sqrt{5}$ 62. $\sqrt{26}-5$

B. **In exercises 63-71, use the Pythagorean theorem to determine whether or not the triplet of numbers represent the sides of a right triangle.**

63. $(4, 5, 6)$ 64. $(5, 12, 13)$ 65. $(3, 4, 5)$ 66. $(8, 12, 15)$ 67. $(5, 6, 8)$

68. $(6, 8, 10)$ 69. $(6, 9, 12)$ 70. $(8, 12, 13)$ 71. $(30, 40, 50)$

In exercises 72-75, check whether the triangle is a right triangle or not.

72.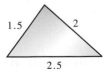

73.

74.

75.

76. Verify that the following triplets are all Pythagorean triplets.

   (a) (3, 4, 5)   **(b)** (5, 12, 13)   **(c)** (8, 15, 17)   **(d)** (7, 24, 25)

   (e) (6, 8, 10)   **(f)** (10, 24, 26)   **(g)** (16, 30, 34)   **(h)** (14, 48, 50)

   (i) (9, 12, 15)   **(j)** (15, 36, 39)   **(k)** (24, 45, 51)   **(l)** (21, 72, 75)

Observe carefully the pattern in the above triplets, written one below the other, and then find some more Pythagorean triplets.

In exercises 77-87, use the Pythagorean theorem to find the unknown side of the right triangle (accurate to two decimal places). Use a calculator, if needed.

77.

78.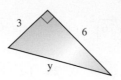

79.

80.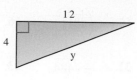

81.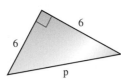

82.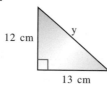

83.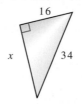

84.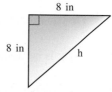

85.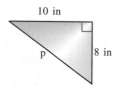

86.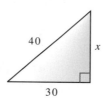

87.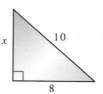

88. A 36 ft ladder is used to reach the top of a 28 ft wall. Find the distance of the base of the ladder on the ground from the wall, accurate to two decimal places. (Sketch a diagram first)

89. A group of students decided to collect as many dollars from each member of the group as is the number of members. If the total collection amounts to $2,209, find the number of members in the group. (Work with small numbers first, to observe the pattern for money collected.)

90. A gardener plants 17,956 trees in such a way that there are as many rows as there are trees in a row. Find the number of trees in a row. (Start with small numbers first and observe the results.)

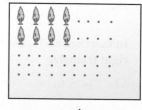

91. From a church steeple, which is 150 ft high, a rope is to be attached from the top to the ground 85 ft from its base, what must be the length of the rope, accurate to one decimal place?

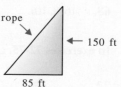

92. Find the length of a rectangle whose width is 18 yd. and whose diagonal is 30 yd. (Sketch the figure.)

93. A ladder 20 ft long is set with its foot 8 ft from the base of a vertical wall and with its top against the wall. How high up the wall does it reach? (Sketch a diagram)

7.4 APPLICATIONS TO GEOMETRY

IMPORTANT VOCABULARY 💾

1. A **formula** is a general statement, usually an equation, that expresses a relationship between two or more variables. For example, $A = lw$ expresses the relationship between the area (A), length (l), and width (w) of a rectangle.

2. A **circle** is the set of all points in a plane having the same distance from a fixed point.

The fixed point is called the **center** of the circle. **Figure 7.5**

The fixed distance between the center of the circle and any point on the circle is called the **radius** (plural: radii) of the circle. The letter **r** is used to represent the radius of a circle.

3. A *diameter* is a line segment which passes through the center and whose end points lie on the circle. The term **diameter** is commonly used to mean the length of any diameter, and is represented by the letter **d**. Note that $d = 2r$.

Figure 7.6

4. The **circumference** of a circle is a special name for the perimeter of the circle (that is, the distance around the circle), and is expressed in linear unit of measurement (*e.g.*, inches, centimeters, feet).

5. The Greek letter π (read: pi) is used as the symbol for the ratio of the circumference of a circle to its diameter:

$$\left(\pi = \frac{\text{circumference}}{\text{diameter}} \right).$$ π is an **irrational number** (a non-terminating, non-repeating decimal), and its value,

up to 10 decimal places is 3.1415926535 ... $\pi \approx 3.14$ and $\pi \approx \frac{22}{7}$.

7.4 A.   Solve Applications with Decimals Involving the Perimeter and Area of Polygons

- The term '**perimeter**' of a geometric figure as defined earlier, is used for the length of the boundary or the *distance* along the boundary (Figure 7.7).

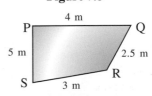

Figure 7.7

- The perimeter of a polygon is the sum of the lengths of all its sides, and is generally denoted by P. For example, the perimeter of a triangle whose sides measure 4 cm, 5.2 cm, and 3.5 cm (Figure 7.8) is given by

$$P = 4 \text{ cm} + 5.2 \text{ cm} + 3.5 \text{ cm}$$
$$= 12.7 \text{ cm}.$$

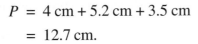

Figure 7.8

- The perimeter of the quadrilateral in Figure 7.9 is given by

$$P = PQ + QR + RS + SP$$
$$= 4 \text{ m} + 2.5 \text{ m} + 3 \text{ m} + 5 \text{ m}$$
$$= 14.5 \text{ m}$$

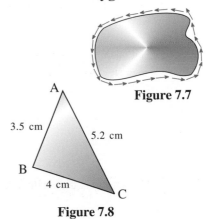

Figure 7.9

- The perimeter of a parallelogram ABCD (Figure 7.10) is given by

$$P = AB + BC + CD + DA$$

But CD = AB, and DA = BC

Therefore, $\quad P = AB + BC + AB + BC$

$$= 2\,AB + 2\,BC$$

$$= 2(AB + BC), \text{ which is twice the sum of AB and BC.}$$

Figure 7.10

> **Perimeter of a parallelogram = 2(sum of two non-parallel sides)**

Any two non-parallel sides of a parallelogram through a *common* vertex are called **adjacent sides**.

- The lengths of any two adjacent sides of a rectangle are generally called the **length** (longer side) and the **width** of the rectangle. Thus, the perimeter of a rectangle is:

> **Perimeter of a rectangle = 2($l + w$) or 2l + 2w or $l + w + l + w$**

- In the case of a square, all the four sides are equal. If the length of each side of square is s, then by the definition of perimeter:

> **Perimeter of a square** $= s + s + s + s$
> $$= 4s$$

Warm-Up

1. Find the perimeter of the following trapezoid:

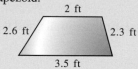

2 ft
2.6 ft   2.3 ft
3.5 ft

2. Find the perimeter of a rectangle with 9.1 in. and 6.2 in. as two adjacent sides.

3. Find the perimeter of square with side equal to 12.3 cm.

Example 1   Find the perimeter of the polygon in Figure 7.11.

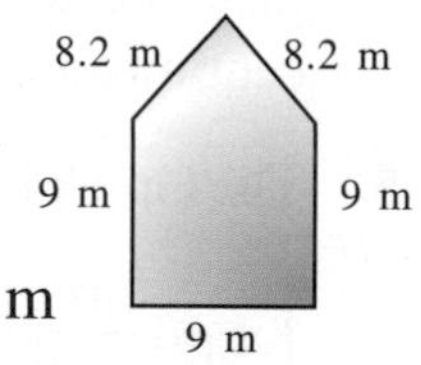

Solution

$$P = 9\,m + 9\,m + 9\,m + 8.2\,m + 8.2\,m$$
$$= (9 + 9 + 9 + 8.2 + 8.2)\,m$$
$$= 43.4\,m$$

8.2 m   8.2 m
9 m   9 m
9 m

Figure 7.11

Example 2   Find the perimeter of the rectangle with 4.4 in. and 3.5 in. as two adjacent sides.

Solution

$$\text{Perimeter} = 4.4\,in + 3.5\,in + 4.4\,in + 3.5\,in$$
$$= 15.8\,in$$

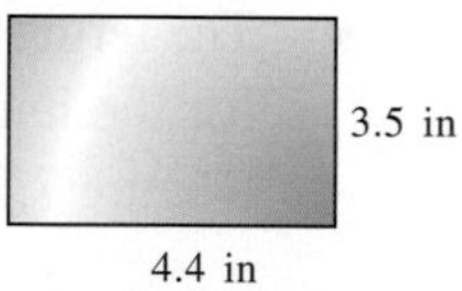

or $\text{Perimeter} = 2\,(l + w)$
$$= 2\,(4.4\,in + 3.5\,in)$$
$$= 2 \cdot (7.9)\,in$$
$$= 15.8\,in$$

3.5 in
4.4 in

Figure 7.12

Example 3   Find the perimeter of a square whose side is 5.7 cm.

Solution

Note that the perimeter of a square
$$= 4\,(\text{length of its side})$$
$$= 4 \cdot 5.7\,cm$$
$$= 22.8\,cm.$$

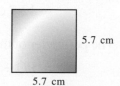

5.7 cm
5.7 cm

Figure 7.13

Example 4 Given the perimeter $P = 319.6$ m, find the lengths of the sides of the triangle in Figure 7.14.

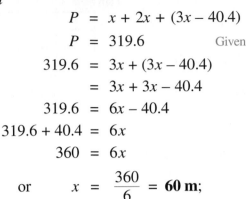

Figure 7.14

Solution

$$P = x + 2x + (3x - 40.4)$$
$$P = 319.6 \qquad \text{Given}$$
$$319.6 = 3x + (3x - 40.4)$$
$$= 3x + 3x - 40.4$$
$$319.6 = 6x - 40.4$$
$$319.6 + 40.4 = 6x$$
$$360 = 6x$$

or $\quad x = \dfrac{360}{6} = \mathbf{60 \ m};$

hence, the lengths of the sides are:

AB $= x = \mathbf{60 \ m}$,

AC $= 2x = 2 \ (60 \ \text{m}) = \mathbf{120 \ m}$,

BC $= 3x - 40.4 = 3(60 \ \text{m}) - 40.4 \ \text{m} = \mathbf{139.6 m}$.

Example 5 A rectangular field is 130 m long and 80 m wide. Find the length of wire needed to fence all around the field. Find also the cost of fencing at the rate of $3.05 per meter.

Solution

Length of wire needed to fence all around the field

= the perimeter of the field

= 2(130 m + 80 m)

= 420 m.

For the second part of the problem:

Cost of 1 m of wire = $3.05;

The cost of 420 m of wire = $(420 \ \text{m})\left(\dfrac{\$3.05}{1 \ \text{m}}\right) = \mathbf{\$1{,}281.00}$.

Figure 7.15

4. Find the sides of the parallelogram if its perimeter is 249.8 yd.

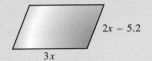

5. A rectangular field is 45 m long and 30 m wide. Find the length of wire needed to fence all around the field. Find also the cost of fencing at the rate of $3.05 per meter.

- **Finding the Area of a Rectangle or a Square**

The term 'area' of a geometric figure, as discussed earlier, is used for the measure of the plane region enclosed by the boundary of the figure. The measure of the boundary, the perimeter, cannot be used to find the area. For example, the rectangles in Figure 7.16 have the *same* perimeter (check), but it will be seen later in this discussion, that they do not enclose the same areas. The rectangles in Figure 7.17 have *unequal* perimeters (check) but we shall see that they enclose the same area.

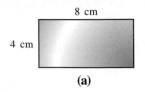

(a)

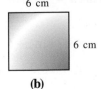

(b)

Figure 7.16

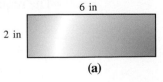

(a)

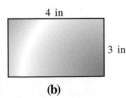

(b)

Figure 7.17

Unit of area: To measure the area of a plane region, we use unit squares, a square whose sides measure one unit length. *The area of a region is the number of unit squares in the region.*

Consider a rectangular region that is 6 cm by 4 cm. We complete the region with unit squares as in Figure 7.18. Observe that there are 24 unit squares.

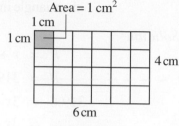

Figure 7.18

The number of unit squares $= 6 \times 4 = 24$

$$\text{Area} = 6 \text{ cm} \times 4 \text{ cm} = 24 \text{ cm}^2$$
$$= 24 \times (1 \text{ cm}^2) = 24 \text{ cm}^2$$

$$\boxed{\text{Area of a rectangle} = \text{length} \times \text{width}}$$

⚠ **Caution:** To find the area of a plane surface by using a formula, all of its dimensions must be expressed in the same unit of measurement.

Warm-Up

6. Find the area of a rectangle whose length is 4 m and width is 95 cm. (1 m = 100 cm)

7. Find the area of square with a side equal to 3.5 cm.

8. Find the area of the region enclosed in the following figure:

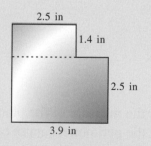

Example 6 Find the area of a rectangle whose length is 5.7 ft and width is 3.5 ft.

Solution

$$\begin{aligned}
\text{Area} &= \text{length} \times \text{width} \\
&= 5.7 \text{ ft} \times 3.5 \text{ ft} \\
&= 19.95 \text{ ft} \times \text{ft} \\
&= \mathbf{19.95 \ ft^2}
\end{aligned}$$

Example 7 Find the area of a square whose side is 2.5 cm.

Solution

$$\begin{aligned}
\text{Area} &= 2.5 \text{ cm} \times 2.5 \text{ cm} \\
&= 6.25 \text{ cm} \times \text{cm} \\
&= \mathbf{6.25 \ cm^2}
\end{aligned}$$

Example 8 Find the area of the region enclosed in Figure 7.19.

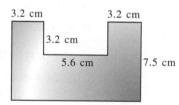

Figure 7.19

Solution

The given area is composed of rectangular or square regions as shown in Figure 7.20.

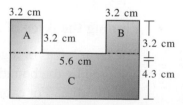

Figure 7.20

The required area = area of a square A + area of rectangle B + area of square C

$$= (3.2 \text{ cm})(3.2 \text{ cm}) + (3.2 \text{ cm})(3.2 \text{ cm}) + (12 \text{ cm})(4.3 \text{ cm})$$
$$= 10.24 \text{ cm}^2 + 10.24 \text{ cm}^2 + 51.6 \text{ cm}^2$$
$$= 72.08 \text{ cm}^2.$$

Example 9   Find the width of a rectangular parking lot whose area is 885 m^2 and length is 36 m. Round the answer to the nearest hundredths of a meter.

Solution

Let the width $= x$.

Since the area $=$ (length) $\cdot$ (width), we get

$$885 \text{ m}^2 = (36 \text{ m} \cdot x)$$

$\downarrow$ Given area $\quad$ $\downarrow$ $=$ length

Set area $= 885$ m^2, and $l = 36$ m. Solve the equation for x.

$$x = \frac{885 \text{ m}^2}{36 \text{ m}} = \left(\frac{885}{36}\right) \text{m}$$

$$= 24.58\overline{3} \text{ m}$$

$$\approx 24.58 \text{ m to the nearest hundredths of a meter.}$$

The width of the parking lot is approximately 24.58 m.

Example 10   Find the cost of leveling a 1,560 yd^2 rectangular playground at the rate of 50 cents per square yard. Find also the cost of fencing around it at $2.50 per yd, given that the width of the playground is 32 yd.

Solution   Cost of leveling 1 yd^2 = $0.50

$$\text{The cost of leveling } 1,560 \text{ yd}^2 = (1,560)\text{yd}^2 \cdot \frac{\$0.50}{1 \text{ yd}^2}$$

$$= \$780.00$$

For the second part of the problem:

We must know the perimeter of the playground. First we find the length of the playground. If l denotes the length (in yd) then using the formula for the area of a rectangle:

$$A = l \cdot w$$

$$1,560 \text{ } sq. \text{ } yd = l\,(32 \text{ yd})$$

$$l = \frac{1,560 \text{ sq. yd}}{32 \text{ yd}} = \left(\frac{1,560}{32}\right)\text{yd}$$

$$= 48.75 \text{ yd}$$

The length of the fence = The perimeter of the playground

Perimeter $= 2(48.75 \text{ yd} + 32 \text{ yd}) = 161.5 \text{ yd}$

Cost of fencing $= \$2.50$ per yard

$$\text{Cost of fencing } 161.5 \text{ yd} = (161.5) \text{ yd} \cdot \frac{\$2.50}{1 \text{ yd}}$$

$$= \$403.75;$$

The cost of fencing the playground $= \$403.75$.

Warm-Up

9. Find the length of a rectangular field whose area is 1365 sq. yd and width is 54 yd. Round off the answer to the nearest tenth of a yard.

10. Find the cost of plowing a field whose area is 1170 m^2 at 70 cents per square meter. Find also the cost of fencing it at $2.70 per meter, given that the length of the field is 45 m.

- ## Areas of Some Frequently Used Polygons

The formulas for the perimeter and the area of some special polygons are listed in Table 7.3.

Table 7.3

Formulas for the Perimeter and Area of Some Polygons

Polygon	Perimeter (P)	Area (A)
1. Triangle	$P = a + b + c$ = sum of the three sides	$A = \frac{1}{2} bh$ = $\frac{1}{2}$ (base)(height)
Right Triangle	$P = a + b + c$ = sum of the three sides	$A = \frac{1}{2} ab$ = $\frac{1}{2}$ (product of two legs)
2. Square	$P = 4a$	$A = a^2$ = (side)^2
3. Rectangle	$P = l + w + l + w$ = $2(l + w)$, (l is length, and w is width)	$A = l \times w$ = (length) (width)
4. Parallelogram	$P = 2(a + b)$ = (twice the sum of two adjacent sides)	$A = b \times h$ = (base) (height)
5. Trapezoid	$P = a + b + c + d$ = (sum of the four sides)	$A = \frac{1}{2} (b + d) h$ = half the sum of parallel sides multiplied by the distance between them

Warm-Up

11. Find the area of each of the following triangles:

(a)   **(b)**

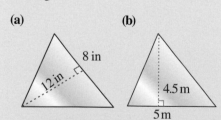

Example 11   Find the area enclosed by each of the following triangles:

(a)   **(b)**

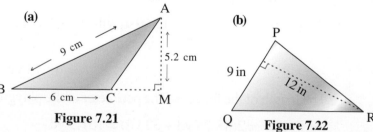

Figure 7.21   **Figure 7.22**

Solutions

(a)   Using the side BC for the base and AM for the height, the area is given by

$$A = \frac{1}{2} \text{ (base) (height)}$$

$$= \frac{1}{2} (6 \text{ cm}) (5.2 \text{ cm}) = 15.6 \text{ cm} \times \text{cm} = \textbf{15.6 cm}^2.$$

(b) We take 9 in as the base and 12 in as the height.

$$A = \frac{1}{2} (9 \text{ in}) (12 \text{ in}) = \mathbf{54 \text{ in}^2}$$

Example 12   Find the area of the following parallelogram:

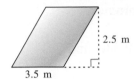

Figure 7.23

Solution

We are given a side and the corresponding height.

$$\begin{aligned} \text{The area} &= \text{base} \times \text{height} \\ &= (3.5 \text{ m}) (2.5 \text{ m}) = (3.5)(2.5) \text{ m}^2 \\ &= \mathbf{8.75 \text{ m}^2}. \end{aligned}$$

Example 13   Find the area enclosed by the polygon ABCDE.

Solution

The required area is composed of four right triangles and one trapezoid.

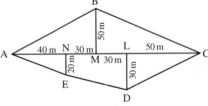

Figure 7.24

Area of $\triangle$ AEN $= \dfrac{1}{2} (20)(40) = \mathbf{400 \text{ m}^2}$

Area of $\triangle$ ABM $= \dfrac{1}{2}(40 + 30) (50) = \mathbf{1{,}750 \text{ m}^2}$

Area of $\triangle$ BCM $= \dfrac{1}{2} (50)(50 + 30) = \mathbf{2{,}000 \text{ m}^2}$

Area of $\triangle$ CDL $= \dfrac{1}{2}(50)(30) = \mathbf{750 \text{ m}^2}$

Area of trapezoid DLNE $= \dfrac{1}{2}(30 + 20) (30 + 30)$

$$= \dfrac{1}{2} (50)(60) = \mathbf{1{,}500 \text{ m}^2} \, ;$$

The area of the polygon ABCDE

$= 400 \text{ m}^2 + 1{,}750 \text{ m}^2 + 2{,}000 \text{ m}^2 + 750 \text{ m}^2 + 1{,}500 \text{ m}^2$

$= \mathbf{6{,}400 m^2}.$

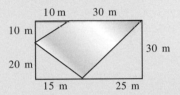

7.4 B. Solve Applications Involving the Circumference and Area of Circles

- **Finding the diameter and radius of a circle**

Figure 7.25 is a circle with center O. The segment AB passing through the center O and having end points on the circle is the **diameter**.

The segment OB or OA or OC with one end point at the center and other end point on the circle is called the **radius**.

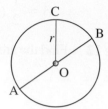

Figure 7.25

> If the length of the diameter is d and that of the radius is r, then
>
> $$d = 2\,r \quad \text{or} \quad r = \frac{d}{2}.$$

Warm-Up

14. Find the length of the radius.

24.8 cm

Example 14 Find the length of the radius of the circle in Figure 7.26.

Solution

$$r = \frac{d}{2}$$
$$= \frac{14.6 \text{ cm}}{2}$$
$$= \textbf{7.3 cm}$$

14.6 cm

Figure 7.26

15. Find the length of the diameter.

8.7 cm

Example 15 Find the length of the diameter of the circle in Figure 7.27.

Solution

$$\begin{aligned} d &= 2\,r \\ &= 2 \cdot 5.8 \text{ cm} \\ &= 11.6 \text{ cm} \end{aligned}$$

5.8 cm

Figure 7.27

- **Finding the Circumference of a Circle, Given the Diameter or the Radius**

The circumference of a circle is the length around its boundary.

Recall that the perimeter of any geometric figure is the distance along its boundary. The perimeter of a polygon can be found simply by adding the lengths of the line segments forming its boundary. We cannot use that method to find the perimeter of a circle, since there are no line segments to measure. However, we can use a thread (or a thin rope or a tape) to measure the perimeter of a circle (Figure 7.28). We call the perimeter of a circle the circumference.

(a)

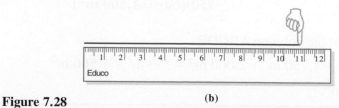

Figure 7.28

(b)

- Consider the three circles shown in Figure 7.29.

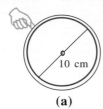

(a)

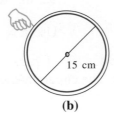

(b)

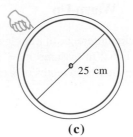

25 cm

(c)

Figure 7.29

If we measure the length around each circle and also measure the diameter, then the ratio of these two measures will be the same for all three circles.

For Figure 7.29(a) the ratio $\dfrac{C}{d} \approx \dfrac{31.4 \text{ cm}}{10 \text{ cm}} = \mathbf{3.14}$ *C* is the circumference;   *d* is the diameter.

For Figure 7.29(b) the ratio $\dfrac{C}{d} \approx \dfrac{47.10 \text{ cm}}{15 \text{ cm}} = \mathbf{3.14}$

For Figure 7.29(c) the ratio $\dfrac{C}{d} \approx \dfrac{78.5 \text{ cm}}{25 \text{ cm}} = \mathbf{3.14}$

> The ratio between the circumference and the diameter is always constant. This constant is named **π (pi)**. Its approximate value is 3.14 or $\dfrac{22}{7}$.
>
> $$\frac{C}{d} = \pi \ \text{ or } \ C = d\pi \ \text{ or } \ C = 2\,r\cdot\pi$$
> $$= 2\,\pi\,r.$$

◁Note   The exact value of π is a non-terminating and non-repeating decimal number. π is an irrational number.

Example 16   Find the circumference of a circle whose radius is 1.8 cm. Use π ≈ 3.14.

Solution   If *C* denotes the circumference, then

$$C = 2\,\pi\,r$$ Formula

$$= 2\,\pi\,(1.8 \text{ cm})$$ *r* = 1.8 cm

$$\approx 2\,(3.14)\,(1.8 \text{ cm})$$ π = 3.14.

$$= 11.304 \text{ cm}.$$

$C \approx 11.3$ cm to the nearest tenth of a centimeter.

Warm-Up

16. Find the circumference of a circle whose diameter is 21.5 in. Use π ≈ 3.14.

Warm-Up

17. Find the circumference of a circle whose diameter is 6.2 m (assume $\pi = 22/7$). Round the answer to tenths of a meter.

Example 17 Find the circumference of a circle whose diameter is 2.5 m. Round the answer to tenths of a meter.

Use $\pi = \dfrac{22}{7}$.

Solution

The circumference $C = \pi \cdot d$

$$= \frac{22}{7}\,(2.5\,\text{m})$$

$$= \frac{22}{7} \cdot \frac{25}{10}\,\text{m} = \frac{55}{7}\,\text{m} \approx 7.86\,\text{m} \approx \mathbf{7.9\ m}\ ;$$

The circumference ≈ 7.9 m.

18. A cow is tied by a rope of length 7 ft. Find the length of the boundary that include the portion where she will be able to graze.

Example 18 The diameter (d) of a wheel is 63 cm. Find the distance travelled by the wheel in 100 revolutions.

Solution

Distance travelled in one revolution = circumference

First, we find the distance travelled in one revolution which is the same as the circumference (C) of the wheel.

$$C = \pi d$$

$$\longrightarrow \quad C = 3.14 \times 63 = \mathbf{197.82\ cm;}$$

(This is the distance travelled by the wheel in 1 revolution.)

The distance travelled by the wheel in 100 revolutions

$$= 100 \times 197.82\ \text{cm}$$

$$= 19{,}782\ \text{cm}.$$

• **Area of a Circle, Given the Length of its Radius**

Consider a circle of radius r.

Divide this into two semi-circles as shown in Figure 7.30 a. Cut the shaded part into small wedges as shown in Figure 7.30 c.

(a)

(b)

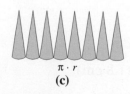

$\pi \cdot r$

(c)

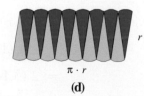

$\pi \cdot r$

(d)

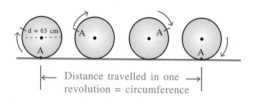

Figure 7.30

Stretch these pieces along a line as shown in Figure 7.30 c. The length of the line is $\pi \cdot r$, half the circumference. The height of each piece is r, the radius of the circle.

Do the same with the other half of the circle and place it on top of Figure 7.30c, upside down. We get Figure 7.30 d.

We observe that the area of the circle is approximately the same as the area of the rectangle with dimensions πr and r.

$$\text{Area of the circle} = \pi r \cdot r$$
$$= \pi r^2$$
$$= \pi (\text{radius})^2.$$

Warm-Up

Example 19   Find the area of a circle whose radius is 5 cm. Use $\pi = 3.14$.

19. Find the area of circle whose radius is 3 in.

Solution

The area, $A = \pi \cdot r^2$

$$= \pi \cdot (5 \text{ cm})^2$$
$$\approx 3.14 \, (25 \text{ cm}^2)$$
$$= 78.5 \text{ cm}^2 \, ;$$

The area is 78.5 cm^2.

Example 20   Find the area of a circle whose diameter is 12.4 cm. Use $\pi = 3.14$.

20. Find the area of a circle whose diameter is 4.2 cm. Round to the nearest tenths.

Solution

The area $= \pi \cdot r^2 = \pi \cdot r \cdot r$

$$= \pi \cdot \frac{d}{2} \cdot \frac{d}{2} \qquad \frac{d}{2} = \frac{12.4 \text{ cm}}{2} = 6.2 \text{ cm}$$
$$\approx 3.14 \times 6.2 \text{ cm} \times 6.2 \text{ cm}$$
$$\approx 120.7 \text{ cm}^2.$$

Example 21   A region is bounded by a semi-circle and three sides of a rectangle. Find the perimeter and the area of the region. Use $\pi = 3.14$.

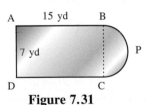

Figure 7.31

21. A paper is in the form of a rectangle ABCD, where AB = 22 cm and AD = 14 cm. A semi-circular portion with BC as diameter is cut-out. Find the perimeter and area of the remaining paper.

(Use $\pi = \frac{22}{7}$).

Solution

Since $\overset{\frown}{BPC}$ is a semi-circle, BC = 7 yd is a diameter. Therefore, the radius of the semi-circle = 3.5 yd.

The perimeter of the region:

$$= CD + DA + AB + \overset{\frown}{BPC}$$

$$= 15 \text{ yd} + 7 \text{ yd} + 15 \text{ yd} + \frac{1}{2}(2 \pi r) \qquad \overset{\frown}{BPC} = \frac{1}{2} \text{ (circumference of a circle)}$$

$$= 37 \text{ yd} + \frac{1}{2} \cdot 2 \cdot (3.14) \cdot (3.5) \text{ yd}$$

$$\approx \textbf{48 yd.}$$

The area of the region

= Area of rectangle ABCD + area of semi-circle BPC.

$= l \cdot w + \dfrac{1}{2}$ (Area of a circle of radius = 3.5 yd)

$= (15 \text{ yd})(7 \text{ yd}) + \dfrac{1}{2} \pi (3.5 \text{ yd})^2$

$= 105 \text{ yd}^2 + \dfrac{1}{2} \cdot (3.14) \cdot 12.25 \text{ yd}^2$

$= (105 + 19.23) \text{ yd}^2$

$= \mathbf{124.23 \text{ yd}^2}.$

22. Find the area of the rim (shaded portion) with labelled dimensions.

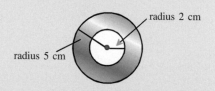
radius 2 cm
radius 5 cm

Example 22 Find the area of the shaded portion in the figure with dimensions as shown.

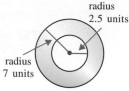
radius 2.5 units
radius 7 units

Figure 7.32

Solution   To find the area of the shaded portion, we subtract the area of the inner circle from the area of the outer circle.

Area of the outer circle

$A = \pi r^2$

$A = 3.14 \times (7)^2$

$A = 3.14 \times 49$

$A = \mathbf{153.86 \text{ sq. units}}$

Area of the inner circle

$A = \pi r^2$

$A = 3.14 \times (2.5)^2$

$A = 3.14 \times 6.25$

$A = \mathbf{19.625 \text{ sq. units.}}$

Subtract: 153 . 86   *Area of the outer circle*
           − 19 . 625   *Area of the inner circle*
           ─────────
            134 . 235

The area of the shaded portion is 134.235 sq. units.

Answers:

14. 12.4 cm	**15.** 17.4 cm
16. 67.5 in.	**17.** 19.5 m
18. 43.96 ft.	**19.** 28.26 in.^{2}
20. 13.8 cm^2	
21. $P = 80$ cm, $A = 231$ cm^2	
22. 65.94 cm^2	

7.4 C.   Solve Applications Involving Volumes and Surface Areas of Solids

A **rectangular solid** (Figure 7.33) is a solid bounded by six rectangular faces. The angle between any two adjacent edges is a right angle. Two of the parallel faces are called **bases**, and the other four faces are called **sides**. The length (l), width (w), and the height (h) of a rectangular solid are shown in Figure 7.34.

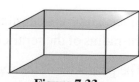
Figure 7.33

- **The volume V of a rectangular solid** is given by the formula:

$V = $ (Area of the base) $\cdot$ (height)

$= (l \cdot w) \cdot h$

$= l \cdot w \cdot h$

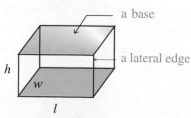
a base
a lateral edge
h
w
l
Figure 7.34

Example 23   Find the volume (V) of a rectangular solid whose length is 4.5 inches, width is 3.2 inches, and height is 2.8 inches.

Solution

Volume: $V = l \cdot w \cdot h$

$\qquad = (4.5 \text{ in}) \, (3.2 \text{ in}) \, (2.8 \text{ in})$

$\qquad = 40.32 \text{ in.}^3$

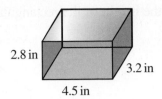

2.8 in

3.2 in

4.5 in

Figure 7.35

- **Volume of a Cube:**

A **cube** is a special rectangular solid whose length, width, and height are all equal. All the six faces of a cube are squares of the same size (Figure 7.36). All the edges of a cube are equal. The volume (V) of a cube is given by the formula:

$$V = a \cdot a \cdot a$$
$$= a^3,$$

where a is the length of one of its edges.

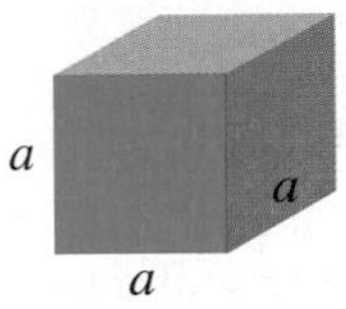

a

a

a

Figure 7.36

Example 24   Find the volume of a cube whose side measure is 1.7 meters.

Solution

$$V \;=\; S^3 \;=\; (1.7 \text{ m}) \, (1.7 \text{ m}) \, (1.7 \text{ m})$$

$$= 4.913 \text{ m}^3.$$

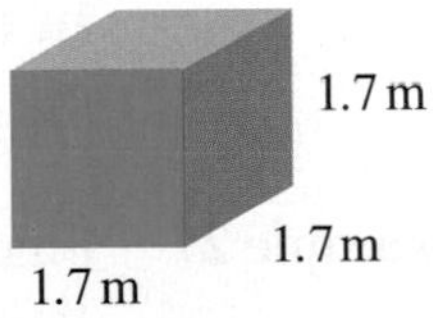

1.7 m

1.7 m

1.7 m

Figure 7.37

Example 25   A firm is shipping rectangular crates 4.2 ft by 6.5 ft by 10 ft in a truck 40 ft by 24 ft by 10 ft. How many of these crates can be loaded in this truck?

Solution

- First we find the volume of each crate.

$$V \;=\; (4.2 \text{ ft}) \cdot (6.5 \text{ ft}) \cdot (10 \text{ ft})$$

$$= \textbf{273 ft}^3.$$

- Find the volume or capacity of the truck.

$$V \;=\; (40 \text{ ft}) \cdot (10 \text{ ft}) \cdot (24 \text{ ft})$$

$$= \textbf{9600 ft}^3$$

- The number of crates in the truck

$$= \frac{\text{capacity of the truck}}{\text{volume of each crate}} \;=\; \frac{9{,}600 \text{ ft}^3}{273 \text{ ft}^3}$$

$$\approx \textbf{35.164}$$

Number of crates = 35.

- ## Surface Area of a Rectangular Solid

A **rectangular solid** has six sides or three pairs of parallel sides. All of these sides are rectangles. If l is the length, w the width, and h the height of the rectangular solid, then:

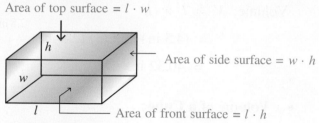

Area of top surface = $l \cdot w$

Area of side surface = $w \cdot h$

Area of front surface = $l \cdot h$

Surface Area = $2 (l \cdot w + w \cdot h + l \cdot h)$

Figure 7.38

Warm-Up

26. Find the surface area of a rectangular solid whose length is 24.5 cm, width is 16.8 cm, and height is 14.4 cm.

27. Find the surface area of a cube whose side is 2.4 cm.

Answers:

23. 945 cm³   24. 74.088 in³

25. 69,377   26. 2,012.64 cm³

27. 34.56 cm²

Example 26   Find the surface area of a rectangular solid whose height is 3.5 ft, width is 6.2 ft, and length is 7.5 ft.

Solution   Surface Area $= 2 (lw + lh + wh)$;

where $l = 7.5$ ft, $w = 6.2$ ft, $h = 3.5$ ft

$= 2(7.5 \cdot 6.2 + 7.5 \cdot 3.5 + 6.2 \cdot 3.5)$ ft²

$= 2(46.5 + 26.25 + 21.7)$ ft²

$= \mathbf{188.9\ ft^2}$

In the case of a cube, since $l = w = h =$ side, the surface area of a cube $=$ **6 (side)²**.

Example 27   Find the surface area of a cube whose side measure is 10 meters.

Solution

Surface Area $= 6$ (side)², where side $= 10$ m

$= 6(10\ m)^2 = 6(100)m^2 = \mathbf{600\ m^2}$

Exercise 7.4

A. In exercises 1–5, find the perimeter.

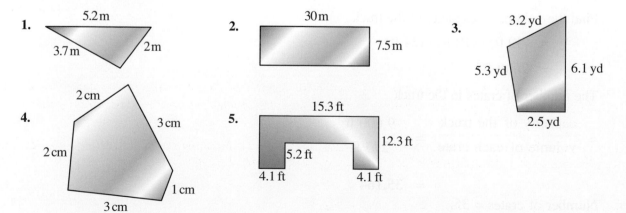

1. 5.2 m, 3.7 m, 2 m

2. 30 m, 7.5 m

3. 3.2 yd, 5.3 yd, 6.1 yd, 2.5 yd

4. 2 cm, 3 cm, 2 cm, 1 cm, 3 cm

5. 15.3 ft, 12.3 ft, 5.2 ft, 4.1 ft, 4.1 ft

In exercises 6-14, find the area.

6.

1.8 cm

Square

7.

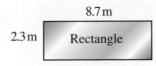

8.7 m

Rectangle

2.3 m

8.

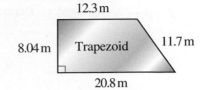

12.3 m

Trapezoid

8.04 m   11.7 m

20.8 m

9.

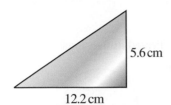

5.6 cm

12.2 cm

10.

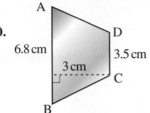

A

D

6.8 cm   3.5 cm

3 cm

C

B

11.

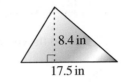

8.4 in

17.5 in

12.

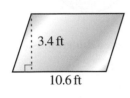

3.4 ft

10.6 ft

13.

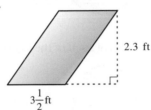

2.3 ft

$3\frac{1}{2}$ ft

14.

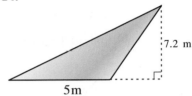

7.2 m

5 m

In exercises 15-20, find the area of the shaded region.

15.

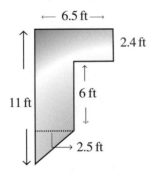

← 6.5 ft →

2.4 ft

6 ft

11 ft

2.5 ft

16.

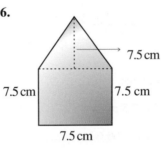

7.5 cm

7.5 cm   7.5 cm

7.5 cm

17.

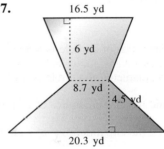

16.5 yd

6 yd

8.7 yd

4.5 yd

20.3 yd

18.

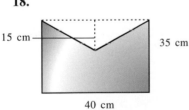

15 cm

35 cm

40 cm

19.

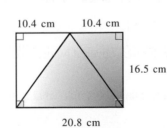

10.4 cm   10.4 cm

16.5 cm

20.8 cm

20.

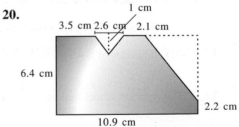

1 cm

3.5 cm 2.6 cm 2.1 cm

6.4 cm

2.2 cm

10.9 cm

Applications

21. The length and width of a rectangular field are 75 yd and 45 yd, respectively. Find the cost of fencing twice all around the field at the rate of $2.75 per yd. Also find the cost of ploughing the field at the rate of 65 cents per square yard.

22. In exchange for a square plot of land, whose side is 84.5 m, a man wants to buy a 144 m long rectangular plot of the same area as the square plot. Determine the width of the rectangular plot correct to two decimal places.

23. Which parking lot is bigger: 85 m by 54 m, or 80 m by 59 m?

B. 24. Fill in the following table using the given information about a circle (answers may be left in terms of π).

	Radius	Diameter	Circumference	Area
(a)	5	?	?	?
(b)	?	9	?	?
(c)	?	?	18π	?
(d)	12	?	?	?

In exercises 25-27, find (a) the circumference and (b) the area of the circle with the indicated dimensions.

25.

15.8 m

26.

3.5 in

27.

20.4 ft

In exercises 28 -30, find (a) the perimeter and (b) the area of each of the figure with the indicated dimensions.

28.

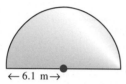

←6.1 m→

29.

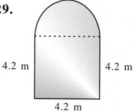

4.2 m   4.2 m

4.2 m

30.

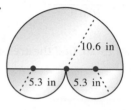

10.6 in

5.3 in   5.3 in

31. The radius of a circle is 4.5 cm. Find its diameter.

32. The diameter of a circle is 48.6 cm. Find its radius.

33. Find the circumference of a circle with a radius 7.5 m.

34. Find the circumference of a circle with a diameter 200.6 in.

35. Find the radius of a circle with circumference 38.5 m.

36. The distance around the top of a circular table is 80 cm. Find its radius.

37. Find the area of a circle whose diameter is 2.25 ft.

38. The diameter of a wheel is 8 ft. Find the distance covered by the wheel in 45 revolutions.

39. If a carriage wheel makes $71\frac{2}{3}$ turns while going 300 yards, what is its diameter?

40. A horse is tied by a rope of length 56 m. Find the area that the horse will be able to graze. Use $\pi = 3.14$.

41. The radius of the wheel of a vehicle is 70 cm. Find the distance covered by the wheel in making 10 revolutions. Express the answer in meters.

42. The diameters of two concentric circles are 8 cm and 12 cm. Find the area of the ring-shaped region (called an *annulus*) bounded by the two circles.

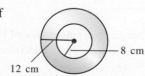

8 cm

12 cm

43. Find the radius of a circular garden if its circumference is 109.9 meters.

44. A triangle of sides 27.5 cm, 31.4 cm, and 35.3 cm is made of a thin wire. The wire is then bent to form a circular ring. Find the radius of the ring.

45. Find the area of the quarter of a circle shown in the figure.

3 m

46. Find the area of the hallway as shown in the following figure. It consists of a quarter circle and two rectangles.

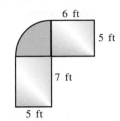

6 ft

5 ft

7 ft

5 ft

In exercises 47-50, find the volume of the solid without the shaded portion, if any, using the information given in the figure.

47.

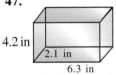

4.2 in

2.1 in

6.3 in

48.

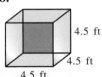

4.5 ft

4.5 ft

4.5 ft

49.

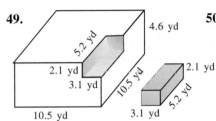

4.6 yd

5.2 yd

2.1 yd

3.1 yd

10.5 yd

10.5 yd

2.1 yd

3.1 yd

5.2 yd

50.

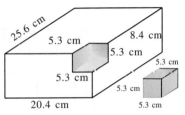

25.6 cm

5.3 cm

8.4 cm

5.3 cm

5.3 cm

5.3 cm

20.4 cm

5.3 cm

5.3 cm

51. Find the volume of a cube whose side measure is:

(a) 3.1 m   **(b)** 1.75 cm

52. A container is 2 ft by 1.5 ft by 5 ft. How many cubic feet of sand can be filled in this container?

In exercises 53-56, find the surface area of the solids using the information given in the figure.

53.

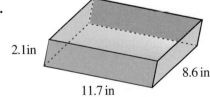

2.1 in

8.6 in

11.7 in

54.

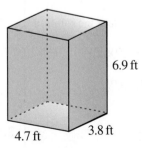

6.9 ft

4.7 ft

3.8 ft

55.

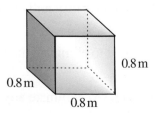

0.8 m

0.8 m

0.8 m

56.

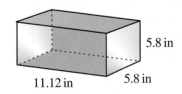

5.8 in

11.12 in

5.8 in

57. A park is in the form of a 120 yd × 100 yd rectangle. At the center of the park, there is a circular flower bed. The area of the park excluding the flower bed is 8,700 sq. yd. Find the radius of the circular flower bed to the nearest tenth of a yd. Use $\pi = 3.14$.

58. The diameter of the wheel of a railway engine is 1.5 meters. How many revolutions does it make in going through a distance of 1,884 meters. Use $\pi = 3.14$.

59. In the figure, first find the diameter of the circle (use the Pythagorean theorem), and then find the area of the shaded portion.

(*Hint:* Area of the shaded portion = area of the circle − area of the rectangle)

$$= \pi \left(\frac{d}{2}\right)^2 - (12)(5).$$

60. The diameter of a circular garden is 140 yd. A 7 yd wide road runs all around (outside) the garden. Find the cost of levelling the road at $3.50 per sq. yd. Use $\pi = 3.14$.

7.5 CHAPTER SUMMARY

Examples

1. Solve: $\dfrac{x}{1.75} - 4.5 = 2.06$:

$$\frac{x}{1.75} - 4.5 + \mathbf{4.5} = 2.06 + \mathbf{4.5}$$

$$\frac{x}{1.75} = 6.56$$

$$\frac{x}{1.75} \times \mathbf{1.75} = 6.56 \times \mathbf{1.75}$$

$$x = 11.48$$

Check: Use a calculator to check the solution.

$$\frac{11.48}{1.75} - 4.5 = 2.06.$$

$$2.06 = 2.06 \quad \text{True.}$$

2. Solve: $5x - 0.12 = 1.2 - 0.5x$

Step 1   Not required.

Step 2 $5x - 0.12 + \mathbf{0.5x} = 1.2 - 0.5x + \mathbf{0.5x}$

Step 3 $5.5x - 0.12 + \mathbf{0.12} = 1.2 + \mathbf{0.12}$

$$5.5x = 1.32$$

Step 4 $\dfrac{1}{\mathbf{5.5}} \times 5.5x = \dfrac{1}{\mathbf{5.5}} \times 1.32$

$$x = 0.24$$

1. Solving Equations with the Variable on One Side only

Step 1   If x is on the right side, rewrite the equation, switching the two sides.

Step 2   Simplify each side separately if possible, using the distributive property and combining like terms.

Step 3   Eliminate any constant on the side with x by adding its opposite to both sides.

Step 4   Eliminate any numerical coefficient of x by dividing both sides by that number (or multiplying both sides by its reciprocal).

Step 5   Check the resulting solution.

2. Solving Equations with the Variable on Both sides

Step 1   Simplify *each side separately*. This includes applying the distributive property and combining like terms.

Step 2   Use the addition principle to eliminate the variable term on the right side.

Step 3   Use the addition principle to eliminate any constant form on the left side.

Step **4** Use the division or multiplication principle to get the variable alone.

Step **5** Check the solution.

3. Solving equations containing several unknowns when values for all except one are known

Procedure

Substitute the given values of the unknowns and solve for the value not given.

4. Averages, Ratios, Rates and Proportions

I Finding the average of a group of numbers:

Step **1** Add all the numbers in the group and obtain the sum.

Step **2** Divide the sum obtained in step 1 by the count of numbers in the group.

II Finding Ratios, Rates, Unit Rates, and Proportions

a. **Ratios:** The ratio of two quantities a and b is the quotient or the fraction $\dfrac{a}{b}$ simplified to lowest terms.

b. **Rates:** Rates involve comparisons with different units (labels).

Examples

Step 5 Use a calculator to check the solution.

$$5 \times 0.24 - 0.12 = 1.2 - 0.5 \times 0.24$$
$$1.08 = 1.08 \quad \text{True}$$

3. Solve $A = P + Prt$ for P, given; $A = \$2,440$, $r = 0.032$, and $t = 8.5$.

Substitute for A, r, and t in

$$A = P + Prt = P(1 + rt)$$
$$2440 = P(1 + 0.032 \times 8.5)$$
$$2440 = P(1.272)$$
$$P = \frac{2440}{1.272}$$
$$= \$1918.2389$$
$$\approx \mathbf{\$1,918}$$

4. The average of 2.03, 0.05, 1.7 and 0.8 is

$$\frac{(2.03 + 0.05 + 1.7 + 0.8)}{4} = \frac{4.58}{4}$$
$$= 1.145$$
$$\approx \mathbf{1.15}$$

4a. In the given figure, find the ratio of the height to the base as a fraction in lowest terms.

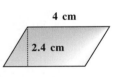
4 cm
2.4 cm

Solution:

The ratio of the height to the base is:

$$\frac{\text{Height}}{\text{Base}} = \frac{2.4 \text{ cm}}{4 \text{ cm}}$$
$$= \frac{2.4 \times 10}{4 \times 10} = \frac{24}{40} = \frac{3}{5}$$

The ratio of the height to the base is 3 to 5.

4b. During a rain storm 6.4 inches of rain was recorded in 3.2 hours. At what rate did it rain during the time?

Solution:

$$\text{Rate} = \frac{6.4 \text{ inches}}{3.2 \text{ hours}} = \frac{6.4 \times 10 \text{ inches}}{3.2 \times 10 \text{ hours}}$$
$$= \frac{64 \text{ inches}}{32 \text{ hours}}$$
$$= \frac{2 \text{ inches}}{1 \text{ hour}} \cdot$$

It rained 2 inches every hour.

Examples

4 c. Light travels 55,000 miles in 5 seconds. What is the speed of light in miles per second?

Solution:

$$\text{Speed} = \frac{55,000 \text{ miles}}{5 \text{ seconds}} = \frac{11,000 \text{ miles}}{1 \text{ second}}$$

The speed of light is 11,000 miles/sec.

c. **Unit Rates:** A unit rate is the rate in which a quantity of one type of item is compared to a single unit of some other item.

4d. A dozen eggs cost $1.36, what is the cost per egg?

Solution:

$$\text{Cost of one egg} = \frac{\$1.32}{12 \text{ eggs}} = \frac{\$0.11}{1 \text{ egg}}$$

The cost is $0.11 per egg.

d. **Unit Price :** In a unit price, the cost of 1 item or unit is calculated. The cost is always in the numerator of the fraction.

4e. A Georgia school has 100 teachers for every 3,000 students. How large is the faculty, if the school has 2,100 students.

Solution: Let the faculty strength be x.

	Case I	Case II
Student	3,000	2,100
Faculty	100	x

$$\frac{x}{2100} \diagdown \frac{100}{3000} \rightarrow \frac{210,000}{3,000x}$$

$$3,000x = 210,000$$

$$x = \frac{\overset{70}{\cancel{210,000}}}{\cancel{3,000}}$$

The school has 70 teachers.

e. **Using Proportions to solve Rate Applications:**

Procedure to solve rate application:

***Step* 1** Identify the unknown and define it by a variable.

***Step* 2** Set up an information table.

***Step* 3** Set up a proportion.

***Step* 4** Solve the proportion for the unknown.

5. Square roots and the Pythagorean theorem

IMPORTANT VOCABULARY

5a. The numbers 9, 16, and 64 are perfect squares because $9 = 3^2$; $16 = 4^2$; $64 = 8^2$.

a. **Perfect Square:**

A number n is a perfect square if $n = m^2$ for some integer m.

5b. The numeber 2 is the square root of 4 because

$2^2 = 4$.

b. **Square Root:**

A number a is called the square root of another number b if $a^2 = b$.

5c. $\sqrt{36} = 6$ (Read: the square root of 36 is 6); $\sqrt{25} = 5$.

c. **Radical Sign:**

The symbol $\sqrt{}$ (read: **radical sign**) is used for square roots.

Examples

d. Radical:

An expression such as $\sqrt{45}$ or $\sqrt{25}$ is called a radical and the number under the radical sign is called the radicand. In $\sqrt{45}$, 45 is the radicand.

5d. In the radical expression $2 + \sqrt{3}$, $\sqrt{}$ is the radical sign and 3 is the radicand.

e. Irrational Numbers:

Square roots of numbers which are not perfect squares are called **irrational numbers**. We can compute their values as non-repeating and non-terminating decimals using a calculator.

5e. The following are examples of numbers that cannot be expressed as rational numbers. They are irrational numbers.

$\sqrt{2} = 1.414213...$ Using a calculator.

$\sqrt{3} = 1.73205...$ Using a calculator.

6. Right Triangles and the Pythagorean Theorem

a. Right Triangle:

A triangle in which one angle is a right angle (90°) is called a **right triangle**. The side opposite to the right angle is called the **hypotenuse** of the right triangle and the arms of the right triangle are called the **legs** of the right triangle.

6a.

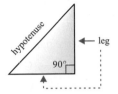

b. Pythagorean Theorem

"In a right triangle, the square of the hypotenuse is equal to the sum of the squares of the two legs". Thus, if the two legs of a right triangle are represented by a and b, and the hypotenuse is represented by c, then

$$c^2 = a^2 + b^2$$

6b.

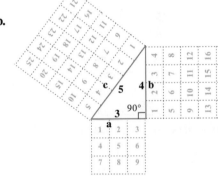

c.

Using the Pythagorean Theorem, we can find the length of a side if the lengths of the other two sides are known.

Example Find the hypotenuse of the triangle.

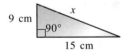

Solution:

$$x^2 = 9^2 + 15^2$$
$$= 306$$
$$\rightarrow \quad x = \sqrt{306}$$
$$= 17.49255568$$
$$\approx \mathbf{17.49\ cm}$$

7. Pythagorean Triplet

The ordered triplet, such as $(3, 4, 5)$ that represents the sides of a triangle, satisfying the Pythagorean Theorem is called a Pythagorean Triplet.

7. Show that $(7, 24, 25)$ is a Pythagorean triplet.

Solution:

$$25^2 = 7^2 + 24^2$$
$$625 = 19 + 576$$
$$625 = 625 \qquad \text{True}$$

Therefore, 7, 24, 25 is a Pythagorean triplets.

8. Finding The Perimeter of polygons

8a.

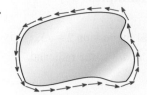

a. **Perimeter:** The **perimeter** of a geometric figure is the length of the boundary or the *distance* along the boundary.

8b.

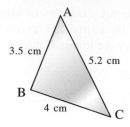

$P = 4\,cm + 5.2\,cm + 3.5\,cm$
$\quad = \textbf{12.7 cm}$

b. **Perimeter of A Polygon:**

The perimeter of a polygon is the sum of the lengths of all its sides, and is generally denoted by P.

8c. Find the perimeter of the parallelogram:

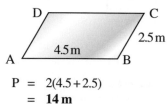

$P = 2(4.5 + 2.5)$
$\quad = \textbf{14 m}$

c. **Perimeter of a parallelogram:**

The perimeter of a parallelogram is two times the sum of the adjacent sides of the parallelogram.

8d. Find the perimeter of the rectangle:

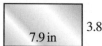

3.8 in
7.9 in

$P = 2(l + w) = 2(7.9 + 3.8)$
$\qquad\qquad = 2(11.7)$
$\qquad\qquad = \textbf{23.4 in}.$

d. **Perimeter of a rectangle:**

The perimeter of a rectangle is two times the sum of the length and width of the rectangle.

8e. Find the perimeter of the square:

8.6 in

$P = 4s$
$\quad = 4 \times 8.6$
$\quad = \textbf{34.4 cm}$

e. **Perimeter of a square:**

The perimeter of a square is four times the length of the side of the square.

9. Area of rectangles and squares

9a. Find the area of a rectangle whose length is 2.5 m and width is 1.4m.

$A = lw$
$\quad = 2.5 \times 1.4$
$\quad = \textbf{3.5 m}^2$

a. **Area of a rectangle:**

The area of a plane region is the number of unit squares in the region.

Area of a rectangle = length × width

9b. Find the area of a square whose side is 4.5m.

$A = s^2 = (4.5)^2$
$\qquad = 20.25\,m^2$
$\qquad \approx \textbf{20.3 m}^2$

b. **Area of a square:**

The area of a square is s^2 where s is the length of a side of the square.

10. Circle

A **circle** is the set of all points in a plane having the same distance from a fixed point.

The fixed point is called the **center** of the circle.

The fixed distance between the center (C) of the circle and any point (P) on the circle is called the **radius** (plural: radii) of the circle.

10.

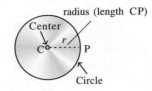

- **Diameter:**

  A *diameter* is a line segment passing through the center and whose end points lie on the circle.

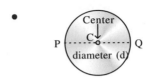

- **Circumference:**

  The **circumference** of a circle is a special name for the perimeter of the circle (that is, the distance around the circle), and is expressed in a linear unit of measurement (*e.g.*, inches, centimeters, feet).

11. Circumference of a circle

The perimeter of a circle is called the circumference of the circle and is 2π times the radius of the circle or π times the diameter of the circle.

$$\text{Circumference} = 2\pi r$$
$$= \pi d$$

11. Find the circumference of the circle

8.4 cm

Here, $d = 8.4$ cm. $r = \dfrac{d}{2} = 4.2$ cm

$$\begin{aligned} C = 2\pi r &= 2 \times 3.14 \times 4.2 \\ &= 26.376 \\ &\approx \textbf{26.4 cm} \end{aligned}$$

$$\begin{aligned} C = \pi d &= 3.14 \times 8.4 \\ &= 26.376 \\ &\approx \textbf{26.4 cm} \end{aligned}$$

12. Area of a circle

The area of a circle is π times the square of its radius.

$$\begin{aligned} \text{Area} &= \pi(\text{radius})^2 \\ &= \pi r^2 \end{aligned}$$

12. Find the area of the circle

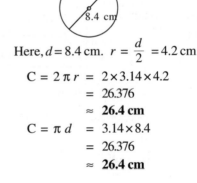

Here $r = \dfrac{d}{2} = \dfrac{12.8}{2} = 6.4$ in

$$\begin{aligned} A = \pi r^2 &= 3.14(6.4)^2 \\ &= 128.644 \\ &\approx \textbf{128.6 in}^2 \end{aligned}$$

13. Volume of a rectangular solid and cube

A **rectangular solid** is a solid bounded by six rectangular faces; the angle between any two adjacent edges is a right angle. Two of the parallel faces are called **bases**, and the other four faces are called **sides**. The length (*l*), width (*w*), and the height (*h*) of a rectangular solid are shown in the figure.

13.

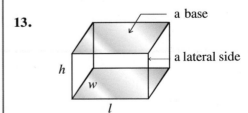

a base

a lateral side

a. Find the volume of the solid shown in the figure.

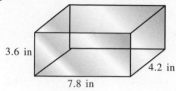

$V = l \cdot w \cdot h = 7.8 \times 4.2 \times 3.6$

$= 117.936$

$\approx$ **117.9 in^3**

b. Find the volume of the cube, 7.6 in. on each side.

$V = s^3 = (7.6)^3$

$= 438.97$

$\approx$ **439 in^3**

14 a.

Example

Find the surface area of the rectangular solid.

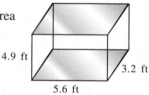

$S = (l \cdot w + w \cdot h + h \cdot l)$

$= (5.6 \times 3.2 + 3.2 \times 4.9 + 4.9 \times 5.6)$

$= 61.04$

$\approx$ **61 ft^2**

b. Find the surface area of the cube.

$S = 6s^2 = 6(7.9)^2$

$= 374.46$

$\approx$ **374 ft^2**

7.9 ft
7.9 ft
7.9 ft

---

a. **Volume of a rectangular solid** is given by the formula:

$V = $ (Area of the base) $\cdot$ (height)

$= (l \cdot w) \cdot h$

$= l \cdot w \cdot h$

b. **Volume of a Cube:**

A **cube** is a special rectangular solid whose length, width, and height are all equal. All the six faces of a cube are squares of the same size. All the edges of a cube are equal in length. The volume (V) of a cube is given by the formula:

$V = s \cdot s \cdot s$

$= s^3,$

where s is the length of one of its edges

14. **Surface area of a rectangular solid and cube**

a. **Surface Area of a Rectangular Solid**

A **rectangular solid** has six faces or three pairs of parallel faces. All of these faces are rectangles. If l is the length, w the width, and h the height of the rectangular solid, then:

Surface Area $= 2 (l \cdot w + w \cdot h + l \cdot h)$

Area of the top surface $= l \cdot w$

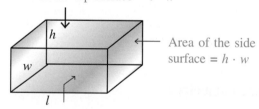

Area of the side surface $= l \cdot h$

b. **Surface Area of a Cube**

In the case of **a cube**, since, $l = w = h = s$, the surface area of a cube is

$= 2(s^2 + s^2 + s^2)$

$= 6s^2$

7.6 REVIEW EXERCISE

In exercises 1-17, solve the equation and check your answer using a calculator.

1. $x + 4.56 = 7.31$ **2.** $x - 13.36 = -4.97$ **3.** $5.4x = 3.19$ **4.** $-7.82x = -4.73$

5. $1.2x + 3.5 = 4.25$ **6.** $193.6 = 11.6y - 398$ **7.** $0.45 - 0.32x = 0.21$ **8.** $0.51x = 1.43 - 8.92$

9. $-5.895 + 0.25y = 4.3y - 0.12y$ **10.** $-7.345 - 0.43y = 3.7 + 0.17y$ **11.** $6.321 + 0.375y = -1.739 + 6.41y$

12. $\frac{1}{2}(x - 1) = 4x - 1$ **13.** $0.3x - 0.8 = 8 - 3x$ **14.** $0.3(x - 8) = 0.5(x - 2)$

15. $2(3x - 0.9) + 0.3(2x - 9) = 0.6x$ **16.** $\frac{2}{5} - (2x - 3) = 0.3(x + 2) + 4$ **17.** $\frac{4}{5}x - \frac{1}{2}(4x + 2) = 0.3(5 - 3x) - 1$

18. The formula for finding the area of a trapezoid is $A = \frac{1}{2}h(b + c)$, where b and c are the lengths of the parallel sides and h is the distance between them.

(a) Find the area of a trapezoid if $h = 4.5$ in, $b = 8.4$ in, and $c = 11.7$ in.

(b) Find h, if $A = 40.8$ ft^2, $b = 3.1$ ft, and $c = 7.5$ ft.

(c) Find b, if $A = 20.4$ yd^2, $h = 1.6$ yd, and $c = 3.9$ yd.

19. Samuel left 0.37 of his wealth for his son, 0.43 for his daughter, and the rest for his wife. If his wife's share was worth $29,545.99, what was the total worth of Samuel's property?

20. Mr. Laurant has $25,783.46 in his checking account. If he writes a check for $9,668.78, what is the balance in his account?

21. For the given trapezoid, find the ratio of the perimeter to its height. Write as a fraction in lowest terms, and as a decimal rounded to the nearest tenth.

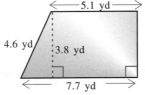

22. For the given parallelogram, find the ratio of the perimeter to the height. Write as a fraction in lowest term and a decimal rounded to the nearest tenth.

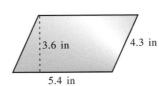

23. State whether or not the given number is a perfect square. If so, express it as a perfect square.

(a) 365   **(b)** 225   **(c)** 2025   **(d)** 576

24. If we know that $(2.645)^2 = 6.996025$ and $(2.646)^2 = 7.001316$, what can be said about $\sqrt{7}$?

25. Use your understanding of squares and square roots to evaluate the given expression.

(a) $\sqrt{79^2}$ **(b)** $-\sqrt{64}$ **(c)** $\left(-\sqrt{40}\right)^2$ **(d)** $-\left(\sqrt{116}\right)^2$

26. Use the Pythagorean theorem to determine whether or not the given triplet of numbers can represent the sides of a **right** triangle.

(a) $(20, 21, 29)$ **(b)** $(4, 4, 5)$ **(c)** $(15, 9, 12)$ **(d)** $(5, 12, 13)$

27. Use a calculator to find the value of the radical expression rounded to three decimal places.

(a) $\sqrt{79}$ **(b)** $\sqrt{478}$ **(c)** $-\sqrt{45}$ **(d)** $5\sqrt{8} + 10$ **(e)** $4 - 2\sqrt{6}$

28. Find the number of revolutions that a wheel of diameter $\frac{7}{11}$ m will make in going 4 km. (Use $\pi = \frac{22}{7}$; 1 km = 1,000 m).

29. The circumference of a circle is 36.11 m. Find

    (a) the diameter of the circle, and   **(b)** the area of the circle up to two decimal places.

    (Use a calculator for computations.)

30. If an airplane passes directly over the head of a man at an altitude of 2 miles, how far is the plane from his position after it has flown 3 miles farther at the same altitude?

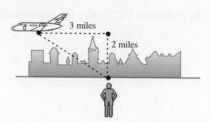

31. It is known that each of the following figures is a right triangle. Use the Pythagorean theorem to find the unknown side (accurate to two decimal places).

    (a)   **(b)**   **(c)**

In exercises 32-33, find the perimeter of the given figure.

32. 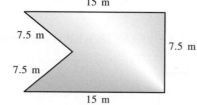   **33.**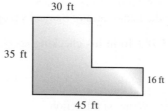

In exercises 34-35, find the area of the figure, using appropriate formulas.

34. 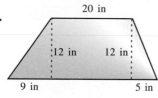   **35.**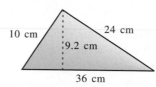

In exercises 36-37, find the perimeter and the shaded area. Use $\pi \approx 3.14$.

36. 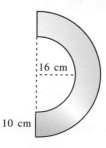   **37.**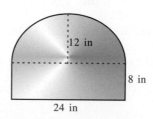

38. Name the figure and find its volume and surface area using the information given in the figure.

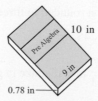

7.7 SELF TEST

In exercises 1-6, solve the equation and check your answer using a calculator.

1. $2x + 13.9 = 3x + 15.4$

2. $1.01x - 3.05 = 2.17 - 2.89x$

3. $\dfrac{2x}{3.5} + 0.4 = -1.1x + 3.78$

4. $\dfrac{x}{0.2} - 3.5 = 2\left(x - \dfrac{1}{2}\right)$

5. $\dfrac{0.3x}{4} - 2\left(x - \dfrac{3}{4}\right) = \dfrac{0.2}{4}(x - 4)$

6. $0.4(x - 0.3) = \dfrac{5}{4}(7 - 4x)$

7. The formula for finding the volume of a rectangular solid is $V = lwh$, where l is the length, w is the width, and h is the height of the solid.

(a) Find the volume of the rectangular solid, if $l = 6.2$ in, $w = 3.5$ in, and h is 4.6 in.

(b) Find the height h, if $V = 21.8$ cm^3, $w = 3.2$ cm, and $l = 4.9$ cm.

(c) Find the length l, if $V = 38.6$ ft^3, $w = 3.8$ ft, and $h = 2.7$ ft.

8. A photograph which is 9.8 in wide is mounted on a frame which is 12.6 in wide and 15.7 in long. What is the length of the photograph assuming the border around the photograph is uniform?

9. Use the Pythagorean Theorem to determine whether or not the triangle in the figure is a right triangle.

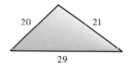

10. Find the length of the unknown side using the Pythagorean theorem.

(a)

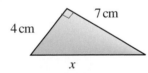

(b)

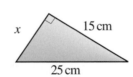

In exercises 11-15, find the perimeter of the figure.

11.

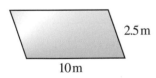

12.

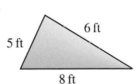

13.

14.

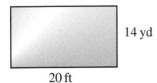

15.

16. The perimeter of an equilateral triangle is 48 cm. What is the length of each of its sides?

17. Find the area of a rectangle whose length is 16 m and width 12 m.

18. Find the area of the shaded region in the figure.
(The measurements are given in inches.)

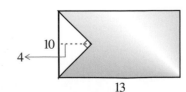

19. A metal sheet in the shape of an oval is to be made from a rectangular piece of metal as shown in the figure. How much metal will not be used? Use $\pi \approx 3.14$.

(*Hint:* Find the area of the shaded portion.)

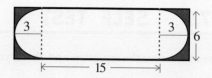

20. If the circumference of a circle is 52.752 in, find both the length of its diameter and the length of its radius.

21. About how many minutes does it take for light to reach Earth from the sun if the distance is about 93,000,000 miles and light travels 186,000 miles per second?

22. In the figure, first find the diameter of the circle (Use the Pythagorean theorem), and then find the area of the shaded portion.

8

Percent with Business Applications

```
┌─────────────────────────────────────────────────────────────┐
│ 🖉 00821Disc                                      _ □ ×        │
│ File  View  Control  Debug                                    │
│─────────────────────────────────────────────────────────────│
│ Objective:  Solve Problems using Percent Formula              │
│        Important Terms │ Verify Skill │ Discussion            │
│           Procedure                    Example                │
│ To solve percent problems using the   36% of what number is 198? │
│ formula :                                                     │
│                                        R    •    B    =    A  │
│ Step 1  In each problem, identify which ↓    ↓    ↓    ↓   ↓  │
│         numbers represent R, A, and B,                        │
│         and which is the unknown.      36% of what number is 198? │
│                                                               │
│ Step 2  Translate the statement into an  36/100 · B = 198  Translate. │
│         equation of the form  R · B = A                       │
│         or  R = A/B·  and solve the       B = 198/0.36        │
│         resulting equation for the unknown.  B = 550          │
│                                                               │
│                                        Check:                 │
│ Step 3  Check that the answer is       36% of 550 should be less than ½ │
│         reasonable.                    of 550 or 275.         │
│                                        198 is less than ½ of 550. │
│                                        The answer seems correct. │
│  🖨  🛠                    36% of 550 is 198.                  │
│                                        Copyright © 2005 Educo International, Inc. │
└─────────────────────────────────────────────────────────────┘
```

8.1   **Understanding Percents** ■

8.2   **Solving Percent Problems using Formula *A = R × B*** ■

8.3   **Business Applications (I): Markup, Discount, Sales Tax, Profit, Commission and Tipping** ■

8.4   **Business Applications (II): Simple Interest and Compound Interest** ■

8.5   **Business Applications (III): Buying a Home or a Car** ■

8.6   **Chapter Summary** ■

8.7   **Review Exercise** ■

8.8   **Self Test** ■

8

Percent with Business Applications

Contents

PERCENTS WITH APPLICATIONS

Introduction

In this chapter, we will discuss how to compute percentages, and apply this concept to real-life situations such as Profit, Discount, Sales Tax, Tipping, Simple Interest, and Compound Interest.

Our discussion will also focus on developing skills for estimating percent and using a calculator to solve percent related problems.

The discussion in this chapter is divided into five sections:

> **8.1**   *Understanding Percents;*
>
> **8.2**   *Solving Percent Problems using the Formula $A = R \cdot B$;*
>
> **8.3**   *Business Applications (I): Markup, Discount, Sales Tax, Profit, Commission, and Tipping;*
>
> **8.4**   *Business Applications (II): Simple Interest and Compound Interest; and*
>
> **8.5**   *Business Applications (III): Buying a Home or a Car.*

8.1   UNDERSTANDING PERCENTS

IMPORTANT VOCABULARY

1. **Percent** means "per hundred".

    Example: 16% means 16 per 100 or $\frac{16}{100}$.

    Percent is the ratio of a number to 100.

2. The symbol '%' is read as "percent" and indicates a ratio to 100.

> **Objectives**
>
> After completing this section, you will be able to:
>
> A. Change percents to numbers in fraction or decimal form;
>
> B. Change rational numbers to percents; and
>
> C. Determine the percentage and base for common percent expressions.

8.1 A.   Changing Percents to Numbers in Fraction or Decimal Form.

The term **percent** is an abbreviation of the Latin phrase "per centum" which means "per hundred". The word **per**, as mentioned earlier, means "for each" and indicates a ratio, or division.

Examples:

$$4\% = \frac{4}{100} = 0.04 \quad \text{and} \quad 25\% = \frac{25}{100} = 0.25$$

• If a fraction has a denominator of 100, it can be written and read as percent.

Examples: $\frac{27}{100} = 27 \cdot \frac{1}{100} = 27\%$ $\frac{8.5}{100} = 8.5\%$ $\frac{16\frac{2}{3}}{100} = 16\frac{2}{3}\%$

In each of the above examples the denominator 100 is dropped and the percent symbol is attached.

Procedure to change a percent to a number in fraction or decimal form:

Step 1   Write the meaning of the percent: a ratio with the denominator 100.

Step 2   Use the rules for operations on fractions or decimals to simplify the expression.

Warm-Up

1. Change the percents to decimals.

(a) 45.6%

(b) 0.15%

(c) 110%

Example 1   Change the given percents to decimals.

(a) 12.4%   (b) 0.21%   (c) 80%

Solutions

(a) $12.4\% = \dfrac{12.4}{100}$

Rewrite as a ratio. Simplify using the shortcut for decimal division by 100.

$= 0.124$

(b) $0.21\% = \dfrac{0.21}{100}$

Rewrite as a ratio. Simplify using the shortcut for decimal division by 100.

$= 0.0021$

(c) $80\% = \dfrac{80}{100} = 0.80$

$= \mathbf{0.8}$

Rewrite as a ratio. Simplify using the shortcut for decimal division by 100.

• When we change a percent to a fraction, sometimes we can reduce the fraction. Sometimes it is necessary to simplify by dividing using rules of fractions. Recall that dividing by 100 is the same as multiplying by $\dfrac{1}{100}$.

> Dividing by 100 is equivalent to multiplying by $\dfrac{1}{100}$.

Warm-Up

2. Write the following as fractions:

(a) 4%

(b) 156%

(c) $4\frac{2}{5}\%$

Example 2   Write the following percents as fractions (or mixed numbers):

(a) 16%   (b) 428%   (c) $5\frac{3}{4}\%$ (d) 0.5%

Solutions

(a) $16\% = \dfrac{\overset{4}{\cancel{16}}}{\underset{25}{\cancel{100}}} = \dfrac{4}{25}$

Rewrite as the ratio of 16 to 100 and simplify.

(b) $428\% = \dfrac{428}{100} = 4\dfrac{\overset{7}{\cancel{28}}}{\underset{25}{\cancel{100}}} = 4\dfrac{7}{25}$

Rewrite as the ratio of 428 to 100 and simplify.

(c) $5\frac{3}{4}\% = \dfrac{5\frac{3}{4}}{100}$

$= \dfrac{23}{4} \cdot \dfrac{1}{100}$

Change division by 100 to multiplication by $\frac{1}{100}$.

$= \dfrac{23}{400}$

(d) $\quad 0.5\% = \dfrac{0.5}{100}$ $\qquad$ Simplify using decimal division.

$\qquad\qquad = 0.005$

$\qquad\qquad = \dfrac{5}{1000}$ $\qquad$ Write the decimal as a fraction and simplify.

$\qquad\qquad = \dfrac{1}{200}$

Example 3 $\quad$ Convert the following percents to decimals. Round to the nearest thousandth, if the decimal has more than three decimal places.

$\qquad$ **(a)** $\ 35\dfrac{1}{2}\%$ $\qquad$ **(b)** $\ 27\dfrac{1}{6}\%$ $\qquad$ **(c)** $\ 3\dfrac{3}{5}\%$

Solutions

(a) $\ 35\dfrac{1}{2}\% = 35.5\%$ $\qquad$ Rewrite the fraction as a decimal.

$\qquad\qquad = \dfrac{35.5}{100}$ $\qquad$ Rewrite as a ratio.

$\qquad\qquad = 0.355$ $\qquad$ Simplify using decimal division.

(b) $\ 27\dfrac{1}{6}\% = 27.16\overline{6}\%$ $\qquad$ $\dfrac{1}{6} = 0.1\overline{6}$

$\qquad\qquad = \dfrac{27.1\overline{6}}{100}$ $\qquad$ Rewrite as a ratio.

$\qquad\qquad = 0.2716\overline{6}$ $\qquad$ Simplify using decimal division.

$\qquad\qquad \approx 0.272$ $\qquad$ Round to the nearest thousandth.

(c) $\ 3\dfrac{3}{5}\% = 3.6\%$ $\qquad$ $\dfrac{3}{5} = 0.6$

$\qquad\qquad = \dfrac{3.6}{100}$ $\qquad$ Rewrite as a ratio.

$\qquad\qquad = 0.036$ $\qquad$ Simplify using decimal division.

(d) $\ 2.06\%$

3. Change the percents to decimals.

$\qquad$ **(a)** $\ 6\dfrac{1}{2}\%$

$\qquad$ **(b)** $\ 14\dfrac{2}{3}\%$

$\qquad$ **(c)** $\ 54\dfrac{1}{2}\%$

Answers:

1. **(a)** 0.456 $\qquad$ **(b)** 0.0015 $\qquad$ **(c)** 1.10

2. **(a)** $\dfrac{1}{25}$ $\quad$ **(b)** $\dfrac{39}{25}$ $\quad$ **(c)** $\dfrac{11}{250}$ $\quad$ **(d)** $\dfrac{103}{5000}$

3. **(a)** 0.065 $\qquad$ **(b)** 0.1467 $\qquad$ **(c)** 0.545

• $\quad$ There are other ways to simplify some of the above problems, using the rules for fractions and decimals. For instance, $5\dfrac{3}{4}\%$ could be rewritten as 5.75% in the very beginning and a decimal division by 100 used instead of a fraction division, yielding $0.0575 = \dfrac{575}{10,000} = \dfrac{23}{400}$. Be sure that you involve the number 100 in your calculations. If you do not, you are not working with percent.

8.1 B.   Changing Rational Numbers to Percents

$$\frac{18}{100} = 18\%$$

18% expresses the ratio of 18 to 100.

- A ratio, whose denominator is not 100, can also be expressed as a percent. We need to find an equivalent ratio with the denominator of 100. Consider the ratio 3 to 5. Using skills for finding equivalent fractions, we can find the equivalent ratio with the denominator 100.

$$\frac{3}{5} = \frac{3}{5} \cdot \frac{20}{20} = \frac{60}{100} = \mathbf{60\%}$$

$\frac{3}{5}$ equals 60%

The fact that $1 = \frac{100}{100} = 100\%$, suggests the more general method below.

$$\frac{3}{5} = \frac{3}{5} \cdot 100\% = \left(\frac{3}{\cancel{5}} \cdot \frac{\cancel{5} \cdot 20}{1}\right)\% = \mathbf{60\%}$$

$$\frac{5}{16} = \frac{5}{\cancel{16}_4}(\overset{25}{\cancel{100}}\%) = \frac{125}{4}\% = \mathbf{31\frac{1}{4}\%}$$

Note that when we multiply by 100%, we do not change the amount, since we are really multiplying by 1. We simply get an equivalent expression for the original fraction.

Decimal numbers and mixed numbers can also be converted to percents using the method above.

For instance, to convert 0.13 to percent, we simply multiply by 100%.

$$\mathbf{0.13} = 0.13(100\%) = (0.13 \cdot 100)\% = \mathbf{1\,3\,.\,\%} \quad \text{Multiply by 100, using the decimal shortcut.}$$

$$0.13 = 13\%$$

Procedure to change a rational number (integer, fraction, or decimal) to a percent:
Multiply the number by 100%

Warm-Up

4. Write as percents.

(a) 0.34

(b) 0.03

(c) 4.8

Example 4   Change the given decimals to percents.

(a) 0.75   (b) 0.05   (c) 2.7

Solutions

(a) **0.75** $= (0.75)(100\%) = \mathbf{75\%}$ Multiply by 100, move the decimal, 2 places to the right.

(b) **0.05** $= (0.05)(100\%) = \mathbf{5\%}$ Multiply the number by 100%.

(c) **2.7** $= (2.7)(100\%) = \mathbf{270\%}$ Multiply by 100%.

Example 5 Change each of the following fractions or mixed numbers to a percent:

(a) $\dfrac{11}{20}$ (b) $2\dfrac{3}{4}$ (c) $7\dfrac{3}{25}$

Solutions

(a) $\dfrac{11}{20} = \dfrac{11}{\underset{1}{20}} \times \overset{5}{\cancel{100}}\% \quad = \mathbf{55\,\%}$

(b) $2\dfrac{3}{4} = 2.75 \cdot 100\% \quad = \mathbf{275\,\%}$

or $2\dfrac{3}{4} = \dfrac{11}{\underset{1}{\cancel{4}}} \cdot \overset{25}{\cancel{100}}\% = \mathbf{275\,\%}$

(c) $7\dfrac{3}{25} = 7\dfrac{12}{100}$

$= 7.12$ • Change the number to a decimal.

$= 7.12 \cdot 100\%$ • Change the decimal to percent.

$= \mathbf{712\,\%}$

Example 6 Albert saves 16% of his monthly income, while his friend Roger saves $\dfrac{3}{20}$ of his monthly income. Who is saving more, if their monthly income is the same?

Solution Convert $\dfrac{3}{20}$ into a percent:

$\dfrac{3}{20} = \dfrac{3}{\underset{1}{20}} \cdot \overset{5}{\cancel{100}}\% = \mathbf{15\%}$

therefore, Roger saves 15% of his monthly income. It is given that Albert saves 16% of the same amount. Thus, Albert's savings are more than Roger's.

The following table shows some percents and their decimal and fraction equivalents. They are frequently used in percent applications.

Common Percent - Decimal - Fraction Equivalents

1%	=	0.01	=	$\frac{1}{100}$	$6\frac{1}{4}\%$	=	0.0625	=	$\frac{1}{16}$
2%	=	0.02	=	$\frac{1}{50}$	$8\frac{1}{3}\%$	=	$0.08\overline{3}$	=	$\frac{1}{12}$
5%	=	0.05	=	$\frac{1}{20}$	$12\frac{1}{2}\%$	=	0.125	=	$\frac{1}{8}$
10%	=	0.1	=	$\frac{1}{10}$	$16\frac{2}{3}\%$	=	$0.16\overline{6}$	=	$\frac{1}{6}$
20%	=	0.2	=	$\frac{1}{5}$	$33\frac{1}{3}\%$	=	$0.33\overline{3}$	=	$\frac{1}{3}$
25%	=	0.25	=	$\frac{1}{4}$	$37\frac{1}{2}\%$	=	0.375	=	$\frac{3}{8}$
50%	=	0.5	=	$\frac{1}{2}$	$62\frac{1}{2}\%$	=	0.625	=	$\frac{5}{8}$
75%	=	0.75	=	$\frac{3}{4}$	$66\frac{2}{3}\%$	=	$0.66\overline{6}$	=	$\frac{2}{3}$
100%	=	1.0	=	1	$87\frac{1}{2}\%$	=	0.875	=	$\frac{7}{8}$

5. Express the given numbers as percents.

(a) $\dfrac{3}{5}$

(b) $4\dfrac{3}{10}$

(c) $\dfrac{4}{125}$

6. Robert saves 8% of his monthly income, while his friend Eric saves $\dfrac{1}{10}$ of his monthly income. Who is saving more, if their monthly income is the same?

Answers:

4. (a) 34%   (b) 3%   (c) 480%

5. (a) 60%   (b) 430%   (c) 3.2%

6. Eric is saving more.

8.1 C.   Determining the percentage and base for common percent expressions.

Whenever percent is mentioned in an application, it always represents a ratio of two amounts: a percentage, a, and base b $\dfrac{P}{100} = \dfrac{a}{b}$.

For instance, if we are told that "the tax rate is 6%", we know that $\dfrac{6}{100} = \dfrac{a}{b}$. What amount does a represent and what amount does b represent? It is helpful to attach dollar signs to the numbers and reword the percent.

$$\dfrac{\$6}{\$100} = \dfrac{a}{b} \qquad \text{\$6 of } \mathbf{a} \text{ for every \$100 of } \mathbf{b}.$$

$$\dfrac{\$6}{\$100} = \dfrac{\text{tax}}{\text{purchases}} \qquad \text{\$6 of a tax for every \$100 of purchases.}$$

Notice that while a, the tax, is mentioned in the statement, there is no mention of b in the statement. This is very common in everyday life. It is taken for granted that we understand what the base, b, is, in most percent applications. The base, b, represents the whole or original amount (100%). In the example above it is assumed that we know that the tax is based on the purchases. The percentage amount, a, is always mentioned. The base, b, is seldom mentioned.

The **base** is either the **total amount** (whole), **or** in problems that involve increases or decreases, it is the **original amount**.

Warm-Up	Example 7

Warm-Up

7. In each of the following, determine what a and b represent. Then restate the relationship between a and b in English.

(a) The bank is offering loans with an interest rate of 7.3% APR.

(b) a 17% tip

(c) a loss of 10%

Example 7   In each of the following, determine what a and b represent. Then restate the relationship between a and b in English.

(a) The bank is offering loans with an interest rate of 6.5% APR.   APR : **A**nnual **P**ercentage **R**ate

(b) a 15% tip

(c) a profit of 30%

(d) a population decrease of 45%

Solutions

(a)   The bank is offering loans with a 6.5% APR.

$$\dfrac{\$6.50}{\$100} = \dfrac{\text{annual interest}}{\text{loan amount}}$$

$a = \$6.50$; $b = \$100$

The annual charge is $6.50 for every $100 borrowed.

(b)   a 15% tip

$$\dfrac{15\,¢ \longrightarrow \$0.15}{100¢ \longrightarrow \$1.00} = \dfrac{\text{tip}}{\text{cost}}$$

$a = \$.15$; $b = \$1$

A tip of $0.15 left for every $1.00 that the service **costs**.

(c) a profit of 30%

$$\frac{\$30}{\$100} = \frac{\text{profit}}{\text{amount spent}}$$

$a = \$30$; $b = \$100$

A $30 profit was earned for every $100 spent.

(**Note:** This indicated an income of $130 for every $100 spent.)

(d) a population decrease of 45%

$$\frac{45}{100} = \frac{\text{decrease}}{100}$$

$a = 45$; $b = 100$

The population decreased by 45 for every 100 persons.

(d) a population increase of 12%

Answers:

7. (a) $a = \$7.30$, $b = \$100$

The annual charge is $7.30 for every $100 borrowed.

(b) $a = \$17$, $b = \$100$

A $17 tip for every $100 that the service costs.

(c) $a = \$10$, $b = \$100$

There is a loss of $10 for every $100 spent.

(d) $a = 12$, $b = 100$

The population increases by 12 for every 100 persons.

Exercise 8.1

A. **In exercises 1-14, write the percent as a decimal number.**

1. 6.6%   **2.** 271.5%   **3.** 400%   **4.** 40%   **5.** 4%   **6.** 13.5%   **7.** 0.95%

8. 313%   **9.** 4.5%   **10.** 0.4%   **11.** 32%   **12.** 500%   **13.** 125%   **14.** 0.04%

In exercises 15-30, change the percent to a fraction and reduce to lowest terms.

15. 11.15%   **16.** 35%   **17.** 6.5%   **18.** 22.5%   **19.** 36%   **20.** 1.25%

21. 70%   **22.** 2.5%   **23.** 100%   **24.** 12.8%   **25.** 2.5%   **26.** 32%

27. $16\frac{1}{4}\%$ **28.** $4\frac{4}{9}\%$ **29.** 0.375%   **30.** $5\frac{3}{4}\%$

In exercises 31-38, convert the percent to a decimal and round to the nearest thousandth, when necessary.

31. $25\frac{2}{3}\%$ **32.** $5\frac{7}{8}\%$ **33.** $65\frac{1}{3}\%$ **34.** $22\frac{2}{5}\%$

35. $1\frac{2}{3}\%$ **36.** $2\frac{5}{12}\%$ **37.** $7\frac{3}{8}\%$ **38.** $12\frac{2}{3}\%$

In exercises 39-52, write the decimal number as a percent.

39. 0.505   **40.** 0.25   **41.** 2.58   **42.** 0.444   **43.** 35   **44.** 3.14   **45.** 0.01

46. 5.02   **47.** 2.7   **48.** 0.08   **49.** 0.659   **50.** 0.0015   **51.** 0.02   **52.** 2.043

B. **In exercises 53-68, convert the rational number or mixed number to a percent.**

Note: You may use a calculator to convert fractions to decimals.

53. $\frac{2}{5}$ **54.** $\frac{3}{25}$ **55.** $\frac{5}{16}$ **56.** $1\frac{13}{25}$ **57.** $\frac{7}{16}$ **58.** $\frac{1}{8}$

59. $\frac{17}{20}$ **60.** $\frac{11}{50}$ **61.** $2\frac{9}{40}$ **62.** $\frac{3}{8}$ **63.** $1\frac{3}{4}$ **64.** $\frac{23}{400}$

65. $\dfrac{7}{25}$ **66.** $\dfrac{17}{20}$ **67.** $\dfrac{21}{50}$ **68.** $1\dfrac{3}{40}$

In exercises 69-88, write the number as a percent. Round to the nearest tenth of a percent in each case.

69. $\dfrac{13}{6}$ **70.** $\dfrac{4}{9}$ **71.** $\dfrac{23}{6000}$ **72.** $\dfrac{2}{3}$ **73.** $1\dfrac{9}{11}$ **74.** $\dfrac{4}{7}$ **75.** 0.7452

76. 0.0317 **77.** 0.9 **78.** 0.09 **79.** 0.009 **80.** 0.05 **81.** 1.85 **82.** 0.4

83. $\dfrac{15}{28}$ **84.** $\dfrac{3}{4}$ **85.** $2\dfrac{1}{2}$ **86.** $3\dfrac{7}{15}$ **87.** $1\dfrac{4}{9}$ **88.** $\dfrac{3}{2,500}$

In exercises 89-104, complete the table in each row with an equivalent fraction, decimal, or percent.

	Fraction	Decimal	Percent		Fraction	Decimal	Percent
89.	$\dfrac{9}{10}$			**90.**		0.08	
91.			$66\dfrac{2}{3}\%$	**92.**	$\dfrac{7}{20}$		
93.		1.75		**94.**			45%
95.			50%	**96.**		0.5	
97.	$\dfrac{3}{25}$			**98.**	$\dfrac{3}{5}$		
99.		$0.\overline{333}$		**100.**			80%
101.	$\dfrac{5}{12}$			**102.**		0.05	
103.			100%	**104.**	$2\dfrac{2}{3}$		

In exercises 105-112, find the percent of profit for the investment. Identify which investment is better, (a) or (b).

105. **(a)** $300 made as profit by investing $6,000
  (b) $200 made as profit by investing $5,000

106. **(a)** $250 made as profit by investing $1,500
  (b) $300 made as profit by investing $1,600

107. **(a)** $245 made as profit by investing $3,000
  (b) $236 made as profit by investing $2,500

108. **(a)** $270 made as profit by investing $1,800
  (b) $256 made as profit by investing $1,600

109. **(a)** $150 made as profit by investing $2,500
  (b) $105 made as profit by investing $2,100

110. **(a)** $35 made as profit by investing $300
  (b) $24 made as profit by investing $250

111. **(a)** $120 made as profit by investing $1,200
  (b) $150 made as profit by investing $1,500

112. **(a)** A profit of $102 made on a $600 investment
  (b) A profit of $76 made on a $400 investment

C. **In exercises 113-124, determine what *a* and *b* represent. Then restate the relationship between *a* and *b*.**

113. The bank is offering loans with an interest rate of 7.2% APR.   (APR : **A**nnual **P**ercentage **R**ate)

114. The investment firm declares average earnings at 4.25% APR.

115. A 20% tip   116. A 7.25% tax   117. A profit of 28%   118. A loss of 12%

119. A population increase of 6%   120. A population decrease of 25%

121. A discount of 30%   122. A discount of 50%

123. A commission of 6%   124. A commission rate of 11%

Miscellaneous

125. Fifteen percent of Smith's salary is spent on food. What fraction of his salary is spent on food?

126. Twenty percent of a class received grade of 'A'. What fraction of the class received 'A'?

127. Over a ten-year period, values of land in a certain city increased by 11.5%. What fraction represents the increase?

128. Brooks and Foster form a partnership. If Brook's investment is $\frac{9}{16}$ of the total, find the percentage of his investment.

129. An airline sold 435 tickets for a certain flight and only 412 passengers boarded the plane. What percentage of sold tickets were used for that flight? Round your answer to the tenths place.

130. Mrs. Brown earns $1,200 per month and saves $112. What percent of her monthly income does she save?

131. In a bulb manufacturing factory, out of every 275 bulbs, 11 are found defective. What percent of the bulbs produced are defective?

132. In a class, there are 13 girls and 37 boys. What percent of the class are girls? What percent are boys?

133. The Wachovia Bank charges 8.3% interest on auto loans, while the Citi bank charges at the rate 0.09. Which of the two rates is higher?

134. Which one of the following fractions would be easier to change to a percent mentally? Explain your reasoning.

(a) $\frac{2}{5}$ or $\frac{8}{3}$ (b) $\frac{5}{6}$ or $\frac{3}{10}$ (c) $\frac{7}{25}$ or $\frac{15}{14}$ (d) $\frac{9}{4}$ or $\frac{7}{8}$

8.2 SOLVING PERCENT PROBLEMS

Objectives 📚

After completing this section, you will be able to:

A. Solve percent problems using the basic percent formula $A = R \cdot B$; and

B. Solve application problems involving percents.

IMPORTANT VOCABULARY 💾

1. The **Basic Percent Formulas** are:

Rate · Base = Amount

(or $Amount = Rate \cdot Base$) and $Rate = \dfrac{Amount}{Base}$

Using the first letter of each word, the basic formulas are

$$R \cdot B = A \qquad \text{or} \qquad R = \frac{A}{B}$$

In this formula:

R is the **rate or percent**, in decimal or in fractional form.

A is the **amount or percentage**, being compared to the base.

B is the **base** representing the "**whole**" or "**original amount**"; the number we are finding the percent of.

2. To **solve** a percent problem means to find the value of R, or B, or A when the other two values are known.

8.2 A. Solving Percent Problems using the Basic Percent Formula $A = R \cdot B$

1. The Basic Percent Formula

Let us consider the statement "6 % of 500 is 30". This statement involves three numbers:

The percent 6%, is the **Rate.** This is represented by the variable R.

The number 500, is the **Base** and we represent it by the variable B. The base is the number that usually follows the word "**of**" in the statement, the whole or the original amount.

The number 30 is **the Amount** or the percentage that is being compared to the whole, and we represent it by the variable A.

The above statement can be translated into an equation as illustrated below.

	Rate	•	**Base**	=	**Amount**
Statement →	6%	of	500	is	30
Equation →	$\dfrac{6}{100}$ or 0.06	•	500	=	30
	percent changed to fraction or decimal	"of" means multiply	follows "of"	"is" changed to =	Amount being compared to Base

The same information can also be translated using the formula: $Rate = \dfrac{Amount}{Base}$.

$$\text{Rate} \rightarrow \frac{6}{100} = \frac{30}{500} \begin{array}{l} \leftarrow \text{Amount} \\ \leftarrow \text{Base} \end{array}$$

Procedure to solve percent problems using the formula:

Step 1   In each problem, identify which numbers represent R, A, and B, and which is the unknown.

Step 2   Translate the statement into an equation of the form $R \cdot B = A$

or $R = \dfrac{A}{B}$, and solve the resulting equation for the unknown.

Step 3   Check that the answer is reasonable.

 Do not forget to express its value as a percent, if the unknown is R.

Example 1   Find: **(a)** $33\frac{1}{3}\%$ of 255   **(b)** $62\frac{1}{2}\%$ of \$2,400.

Solutions:

(a) $R \quad \cdot \quad B \quad = \quad A$

$33\frac{1}{3}\%$ of 255 is **what number?**   Complete the statement.

Identify R, A, find B.

Translate.

$\dfrac{33\frac{1}{3}}{100} \cdot 255 = A$ $\dfrac{33\frac{1}{3}}{100} = \dfrac{100}{3} \cdot \dfrac{1}{100} = \dfrac{1}{3}$

$\dfrac{1}{3} \quad \cdot \quad 255 = A$

$85 = A$

$33\frac{1}{3}\%$ of 255 is **85**.

Check:

$50\% \left(\text{or } \dfrac{1}{2}\right)$ of 260 = 130

$33\frac{1}{3}\%$ is less than 50%.

Since $85 < 130$, the answer seems correct.

(b) $R \quad \cdot \quad B \quad = \quad A$

$62\frac{1}{2}\%$ of \$2,400 is **what amount?**

Complete the statement.
Identify R, A, find B.
Translate.

$\dfrac{62\frac{1}{2}}{100} \cdot 2400 = A$ $\dfrac{62\frac{1}{2}}{100} = \dfrac{\overset{5}{\cancel{125}}}{2} \cdot \dfrac{1}{\underset{4}{\cancel{100}}} = \dfrac{5}{8}$

$\dfrac{5}{\cancel{8}_{1}} \cdot \dfrac{\overset{300}{\cancel{2400}}}{1} = A$

$1500 = A.$

$62\frac{1}{2}\%$ of $2,400 is **$1,500**.

Check:

$62\frac{1}{2}\%$ is more than 50% or $\frac{1}{2}$. Half of 2400 = 1200.

Since 1500 is more than 1200, the answer seems correct.

2. 42 is 6% of what number?

Example 2   36% of what number is 198?

Solutions R · B $=$ A

↑ ↑ ↑   ↑ ↑

36% of what number is 198?

$\frac{36}{100} \cdot B = 198$ Translate.

$0.36\,B = 198$

$\dfrac{0.36B}{0.36} = \dfrac{198}{0.36}$

$B = 550$

36% of **550** is 198.

Check:

36% of 550 should be less than $\frac{1}{2}$ of 550 or 275.

198 is less than $\frac{1}{2}$ of 550. The answer seems correct.

3. $66\frac{2}{3}\%$ of a number is 24. Find the number.

Example 3 $16\frac{2}{3}\%$ of what number is 75.5?

Solutions R · B $=$ A

↑ ↑ ↑   ↑ ↑

$16\frac{2}{3}\%$ of what number is 75.5?

$\dfrac{16\frac{2}{3}}{100} \cdot B = 75.5$

Translate.

$\dfrac{16\frac{2}{3}}{100} = 16\frac{2}{3} \div \dfrac{100}{1}$

$= \dfrac{\overset{50}{\cancel{50}}}{3} \cdot \dfrac{1}{\underset{2}{\cancel{100}}} = \dfrac{1}{6}$

$\dfrac{1}{6} \cdot B = \dfrac{75.5}{1}$

$\dfrac{6}{1} \cdot \dfrac{1}{6} B = \dfrac{6}{1} \cdot \dfrac{75.5}{1}$

Multiply both sides by the reciprocal of $\frac{1}{6} : \frac{6}{1}$.

$B = 453$

$16\frac{2}{3}\%$ of **453** is 75.5.

The check is left as an exercise.

- When finding the Rate, it is easiest to use $R = \dfrac{A}{B}$.

Example 4   **(a)** What percent of 112 is 7?

          (b) What percent of 75 is 8? Round to the nearest tenth of a percent.

Solutions

(a)
$$R \quad \cdot \quad B \quad = \quad A$$

What percent of 112 is 7?   We are looking for R.

$$R = \dfrac{A}{B}$$ Use $R = \dfrac{A}{B}$.

$$R = \dfrac{7}{112} \cdot 100\%$$ Change to percent.
                       Use a calculator.

$$= 6.25\%$$ $7 \div 112 \cdot 100$
                       $= 6.25$

6.25% of 112 is 7.

Check:

10% of 112 is 11.2, and 7 is smaller than that.

6.25% seems correct.

(b)
$$R \quad \cdot \quad B = \quad A$$

What percent of 75 is 8?   We are looking for R

$$R = \dfrac{A}{B} = \dfrac{8}{75} \cdot 100\%$$ Use $R = \dfrac{A}{B}$.
                                 Use calculator.

$$R \approx 10.7\%$$ $8 \div 75 \cdot 100$
                       $= 10.67 \approx 10.7$ rounded to tenths.

10.7% of 75 is 8.

Check:

10% of 75 is 7.5 which is close to 8.

The answer seems correct.

4.   **(a)** What percent of 280 is 112?

     (b) What percent of 48 is 16?

Answers:

1. (a) 125   (b) $200

2. 700   **3.** 36

4. (a) 40%   (b) $33\frac{1}{3}\%$

8.2 B.   Solve application problems involving percents

- Word problems involving percent can often be translated to the simpler form, "**what percent of what is what?**" This can be solved using either of the basic percent formulas: $R \cdot B = A$ or $R = \dfrac{A}{B}$.

In day to day living, we are often required to compute certain percents of a number. For example, if we invest $5,000 at the rate of 11% per year, we may want to know the interest for a year. We can reword this problem as shown below.

$$R \cdot B = A$$

11% of $5,000 is what number?

$$\frac{11}{100} \cdot 5000 = A$$

$$550 = A$$

The interest for one year is $550.

Check:

11% is close to 10%.

10% of 5000 is 500. The answer $550 is reasonable.

Warm-Up

5. Harsha pays 12% of her income towards house rent. If her rent is $750 per month, find her monthly income.

6. A family spends $120 for food out of a budget of $500. What percent goes for food?

Example 5 Marilyn saves 34% of her income. If she saves $680 per month, find her monthly income.

Solution

$$R \cdot B = A$$

34% of her income is the amount saved.

$$\frac{34}{100} \cdot B = 680$$

$$0.34 B = 680 \qquad \text{Divide both sides by 0.34.}$$

$$\frac{0.34B}{0.34} = \frac{680}{0.34}$$

$$B = 2000$$

Marilyn's monthly income is $2,000.

Check: $\qquad 34\% \approx \frac{1}{3}$

$\frac{1}{3}$ of 2000(or ≈ 2100) $\approx$ 700.

Since 700 is close to 680, the answer seems correct.

Example 6 In a particular month, the total budget of a family was $1,200. Out of this, $168 were allocated for outings. What percent of the total budget was allocated for outings?

Solution $\qquad R \cdot B = A$

what percent of the total budget is the amount for outings?

$$R = \frac{A}{B} \qquad R \text{ is unknown}$$

Use $R = \frac{A}{B}$.

$$R = \frac{\$168}{\$1200} \cdot 100\%$$

$$= 14\%$$

14% of the total budget was allocated for outings.

Example 7   Mr. Smith earned $15,000 last year. His total deductions amounted to 24% of his earnings. What was his take-home salary?

Solution

$$A \quad = \quad R \quad \cdot \quad B$$

$\boxed{\text{His total deductions}}$ were   24%   of $\boxed{\text{his earnings}}$

$$A \quad = \quad \frac{24}{100} \cdot \$15000$$

$$= \quad \$3,600$$

Take-home salary = Total earnings – Deductions

$$T \quad = \quad \$15,000 - \$3,600$$

$$T \quad = \quad \mathbf{\$11,400.}$$

Mr. Smith's take-home salary was $11,400.

Example 8   A census determines that 20% of the residents of a city are age 50 or over, and that $34\frac{1}{2}$% are age 25 or under. What is the percentage of the residents between the ages 25 and 50?

Solution   Since the percentage of the residents of age 50 or over = 20%, and the percentage of the residents of age 25 or under = $34\frac{1}{2}$%,

the percentage of the residents not covered in the above categories can be expressed as:

$$= \left(100 - \mathbf{20} - \mathbf{34\frac{1}{2}} \right)\%$$

$$= \quad 45\frac{1}{2}\% ;$$

$45\frac{1}{2}$% residents are between the ages of 25 and 50.

Example 9   A new automobile depreciates 13% during the first year, and 14% during the second year. What is its depreciated value at the end of the second year, if its original cost was $11,500 ?

Solution

$$A \quad = \quad R \quad \cdot \quad B$$

$\boxed{1^{st} \text{ year deprication}}$ = 13% of $\boxed{\text{original price}}$

$$= \quad \frac{13}{100} \cdot \$11,500$$

$$= \quad \mathbf{\$1,495}$$

The *base* for the depreciation is the original cost.

Deprication is a decrease

The depreciated value is the original value minus the depreciation.

The depreciated value at the end of the first year

7.   The list price of a TV set is $275. If you are given a 5% discount for paying cash, how much will you pay ?

8.   If $17\frac{1}{2}$% of a region is shaded in blue, 52% in pink, and the remaining part in yellow, what percent of the region is shaded in yellow?

9. A refrigerator is selling at a discount of 12%. A further discount of 3% is offered if paying with cash. How much will you pay for the refrigerator if its market price is $380, and you make the payment in cash? Round to the nearest cent, if necessary.

(Hint: The second discount is computed on the price after the first discount.)

$$= \$11,500 - \$1,495$$
$$= \mathbf{\$10,005}.$$

$$A \quad = \quad R \quad \cdot \quad B$$

$$\boxed{\begin{array}{c}2^{nd} \text{ year} \\ \text{deprication}\end{array}} = 14\% \text{ of } \boxed{\begin{array}{c}\text{value after} \\ \text{one year}\end{array}}$$

The depreciated value at the end of the first year is considered the original cost at the beginning of the second year.

$$= \frac{14}{100} \cdot \$10,005$$

$$= \mathbf{\$1400.70}$$

Therefore, the depreciated value of the automobile at the end of the second year was

The value at the end of the second year = The value at the beginning of the second year – the depreciation during the second year.

$$\$10,005 - \$1,400.70 = \mathbf{\$8,604.30.}$$

- An increase or decrease is often expressed in percents.
  For example:

  - a 15 % increase in salary
  - a 65 % increase in sales
  - a 20 % increase in temperature
  - an 8 % decrease in popularity of a presidential candidate

In all situations when a percent represents an increase or decrease, the base is always the amount.

For example, to find the percent of increase from $360 to $450:

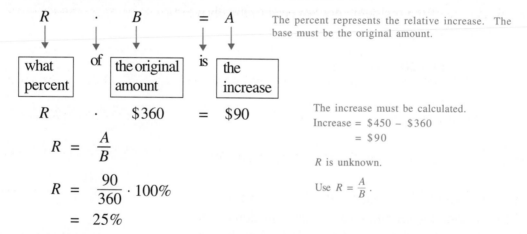

The percent represents the relative increase. The base must be the original amount.

$$R \quad \cdot \quad \$360 \quad = \quad \$90$$

$$R = \frac{A}{B}$$

$$R = \frac{90}{360} \cdot 100\%$$

$$= 25\%$$

The increase must be calculated.
Increase = $450 – $360
$\qquad = \$90$

R is unknown.

Use $R = \frac{A}{B}$.

There is a 25% increase in price from $360 to $450.

Consider another case. Suppose the price of an article decreases from $450 to $360. What is the percent of decrease?

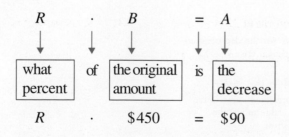

The percent represents the relative decrease. The base must be the original amount.

$$R \quad \cdot \quad \$450 \quad = \quad \$90$$

The decrease must be calculated.
Decrease= $450 – $360 = $90

$$R = \frac{A}{B}$$

R is unknown.

Use $R = \frac{A}{B}$.

$$R = \frac{\$90}{\$450} \cdot 100\%$$

Convert R to a percent.

$$= 20\%$$

There is a 20% decrease in price from $450 to $360.

Example 10 The daily wages of a carpenter are increased from $60 to $69. Find the percent increase.

Solution

$$R \quad \cdot \quad B \quad = \quad A$$

what percent	of	the original amount	is	the increase

$$R \quad \cdot \quad \$60 \quad = \quad \$9$$

Increase = $69 – $60
= $9

$$R = \frac{\$9}{\$60} \cdot 100\%$$

Convert to a percent.

Use $R = \frac{A}{B}$.

$$= 15\%$$

There is a 15% increase in the daily wages of the carpenter.

Warm-Up

10. The monthly salary of Kathy is increased from $1,875 to $2,100. What is the percent of increase in her monthly salary?

Answers:

5. $6,250	6. 24%
7. $261.25	8. 30.5%
9. $324.37	10. 12%

Exercise 8.2

A. In exercises 1-42, first write the related equation then solve for the unknown quantity. Use a calculator, if needed.

1. 3.75% of 1,000 is what number?

2. 6.25% of $1,200 is what number?

3. 125% of 200 is what number?

4. 5% of 85 is what number?

5. 27% of 900 is what number?

6. 40% of 1,365 is what number?

7. 16% of 350 is what number?

8. 3% of 2,180 is what number?

9. 43% of 400 is what number?

10. $16\frac{1}{2}\%$ of 550 is what number?

11. 18% of what number is 58.5?

12. $37\frac{1}{2}\%$ of what number is 60?

13. 16.2% of what number is 11.34?

14. 125% of what number is 100?

15. $33\frac{1}{3}\%$ of what number is 17?

16. 110% of what number is 105.6?

17. $12\frac{2}{3}\%$ of 135.42 is what number?

18. What percent of 320 is 80?

19. What percent of 224 is 168?

20. What percent of 32 is 40?

21. What percent of 114 is 38?

22. What percent of 975 is 175.5?

23. What percent of 73 is 36.5?

24. What percent of 180 is 120?

25. 12.5 is 8% of what number?

26. 150 is 150% of what number?

27. 56 is $1\frac{3}{4}\%$ of what number?

28. 24.5 is $33\frac{1}{3}\%$ of what number?

29. 10 is 1% of what number?

30. 27.5 is $2\frac{3}{4}\%$ of what number?

31. 11% of what number is 33? **32.** 30% of what number is 10.92? **33.** $875 is 35% of what amount?

34. 17.4 is 6% of what number? **35.** What percent of 285 is 114? **36.** What percent of 16,250 is 650?

37. What percent of $120 is $4.80? **38.** What percent of 22 is 7? Round to the nearest whole number percent.

39. What percent of $18.50 is $5.55? **40.** What percent of $65,000 is $4,875?

41. What percent of 1,850 is 9.25? **42.** What percent of 40 is 28?

In exercises 43-51, compute the percentage.

43. 7% of 480 **44.** 25% of 72 **45.** $33\frac{1}{3}$% of 135

46. $37\frac{1}{2}$% of 40 **47.** 40% of $40 **48.** 7.5% of $1,530

49. $31\frac{1}{4}$% of 120 **50.** $12\frac{1}{2}$% of 1,600 **51.** $16\frac{2}{3}$% of 375

52. Peter buys a motorcycle with a 14% one-year loan. If the interest payment is $112, how much is the loan?

53. In a statistical survey of 372 people, 93 people did not have a college degree. What percent of those surveyed did not have a college degree?

54. An ore contains 14% copper. How many kilograms (kg) of ore contains 77 kg of copper ?

55. A company buys a new car that costs $13,500. During the first year, it will depreciate $11\frac{1}{3}$% of its original value. What will be its value at the end of the year?

56. The value of a machine depreciates at the rate of 16% per year. If the price of a new machine is $6,250, what will be the value of the machine after **(a)** 1 year? **(b)** 2 years?

57. A firm buys a new car that costs $13,800. During the first year it will depreciate $12\frac{1}{2}$% of its original value. What will its value be at the end of the year? If it further depreciates 13% during the second year, assess its value at the end of the second year.

58. Cynthia earned $120.50 in one week. The following week she earned 50% more. How much did she earn the second week?

59. The cost of a certain article increases from $50 to $60. What is the percent increase?

60. The price of gasoline per gallon increased from $0.49 to $1.20 from 1971 to 1983. What was the percent of increase during this period?

61. Tax payments of $3,862 represented 4.3% of a company's gross income. What was the company's gross income? Round to the nearest dollar.

62. The number of students admitted to a school increased from 360 to 432 in the year 2004. Find the percent increase.

63. In 1924, the Internal Revenue Service (IRS) had $80 million in income and in 1935 the income was $627.2 million. What was the percent increase in income for the IRS during this period?

64. In an examination, 65% of the examinees passed. If the number of failures is 168, find the number of those who passed. (*Hint*: what % examinees failed?)

65. A man spends $3,500 and saves $12\frac{1}{2}\%$ of his income. Find his monthly income.

66. If 75% of the students in a school are boys and the number of girls is 420, what is the number of boys?

67. James buys a new van for $15,980. He pays 12% down. What is his loan amount?

68. The population of a city increased 15% since the last census. If the previous population was 124,000, what is the present population?

69. Beth Carrol donates 0.5% of her weekly salary to the CRY organization. Last week she donated $9.25. What was her salary last week?

70. In a school, 536 are boys and $33\frac{1}{3}\%$ are girls. Find the number of girls. (*Hint*: what % are boys?)

71. A student spends 36% of his monthly stipend on food. If the expenditure on food in a month is $225, find his monthly stipend.

72. In a basket containing 180 apples, 15% are rotten. How many apples are good enough to be sold?

73. What is the total number of workers in a factory if 15% of the workers in the factory are females and the number of male workers is 272?

74. In an election, there were two candidates, A and B. The total number of voters in their constituency was 60,000 and 80% of the total votes were polled. If 60% of polled votes were cast in favor of A, how many votes were cast in favor of B?

75. An alloy is made of 30% copper, 45% nickel and the rest of zinc. Find the mass of zinc in 640 g of the alloy.

76. In an orchard, $13\frac{1}{3}\%$ of the trees are apple trees. If the total number of trees in the orchard is 420, find the number of other types of trees in the orchard.

77. The cost of a particular brand of an automobile is now 140% of what it was five years ago. If the cost of the automobile five years ago was $7,850, what is the cost now?

78. Grade distribution in a certain class is given below.

15 *A*s, 5 *B*s, 7 *C*s, 23 *D*s' and 0 *F*s.

What percent of the students received a grade of *A*?

(*Hint*: Total number of students in class = 15 + 5 + 7 + 23 = 50.)

8.3 BUSINESS APPLICATIONS-I: MARKUP, DISCOUNT, SALES TAX, PROFIT, COMMISSION AND TIPPING

Objectives

After completing this section, you will be able to:

A. Solve application problems involving percent markup, discount, sales tax, and profit; and

B. Solve application problems involving percent commission and tipping.

Introduction

As discussed in earlier chapters, one of the most important parts of problem solving is understanding the problem itself. We must understand clearly what is known, what is unknown, and the relationship between the known and the unknown quantities. In this section and the next section, we will consider various kinds of business related problems that involve percents.

- As mentioned earlier, most of the word problems involving percent can be translated directly to percent equations.

- **The use of a calculator is recommended**, although you should keep in mind that a calculator is just a device to perform computations, and that it can not replace the necessary skills and abilities to solve problems. While using a calculator for computations, we should always keep the estimates in mind and make sure the final display on the calculator, as the answer, makes sense.

- **Rounding answers:** Calculations can result in answers with more decimal places than are necessary. Dollars are rounded to the nearest hundredths (cents). However, at times business people will round answers to the next higher cent regardless of the digit in the thousandths place: $56.842 \approx 56.85. **In our discussion, we will also round answers to the next higher cent regardless of the digit in the thousandths place.** Remember this is business and businesses operate from profits!

8.3 A. Mark up, Discount, Sales Tax, and Profit

1. **Markup:** In retail business, goods are purchased at one price, the **cost**, and are normally sold at a higher price, **the selling price.** This markup allows the business to cover the expenses and make a profit. For example, if a business purchased an article for $20, expecting expenses of $8 and a profit of $4, then the selling price should be $32. The **markup** is the amount added to the *cost* of an item to determine the **selling price.**

The markup can be expressed in dollars, or as a percent. In the above example, a $12 markup ($32 – $20), was added to the cost.

$$\text{Markup} = \text{Expenses} + \text{Net Profit}$$
$$\text{Selling Price} = \text{Cost} + \text{Markup}$$

The percent markup is based on the *original cost*.

Warm-Up

1. An electric iron is selling for $18.50. The markup is 30% of the selling price. Find the cost of the iron.

Example 1 The cost of a coffee maker is $28.50. The markup is 40% of the cost. What is the selling price of the coffee maker?

Solution Selling price = Cost + Markup.

Markup = 40% of the cost
= (0.40) ($28.50)
= **$11.40.**

We know the cost, and we must find the markup first.

The markup is $11.40;

Selling price = Cost + Markup
= $28.50 + $11.40
= **$39.90**.

The selling price of the coffee maker is $39.90.

Example 2   The cost of an article is $6.40 and the selling price is $10.24. What is the percent markup?

Solution   To find the percent markup, we first need cost, $6.40, and the markup.

Cost + Markup   =   Selling Price
$6.40 + Markup   = $10.24
Markup   = $10.24 − $6.24
=   3.84

We are trying to find the percent markup, R.

$$R \quad \cdot \quad B \quad = \quad A$$

The percent	of	the original amount	=	Markup
R	·	6.40	=	3.84

$$R = \frac{3.84}{6.40} \cdot 100\%$$

$$= \mathbf{60\%}$$

The markup is 60% of the cost.

Example 3   Calculate the selling price of a table costing $27.50, with anticipated expenses of 20% of the cost, and desired net profit of $10.50. Also find the markup.

Solution   Expenses = 20% of cost

$$= \frac{20}{100} \cdot \$27.50$$

$$= \$5.50$$

Markup = Expenses + net profit
= $5.50 + $10.50
= **$16.00**

Selling price = Cost + Markup
= $27.50 + $16.00
= **$43.50**

The selling price, $43.50, includes the markup of $16.

---

2. An article whose cost is $0.85 sells for $1.19. Find the percent of markup.

3. Calculate the selling price of a desk costing $43.75 with anticipated expenses of 16% of the cost, and a desired net profit of $15.25.

2. **Discount** (Markdown): You are probably familiar with almost daily "Special Sales" in stores. To attract customers or to sell goods that have been in stock for some time, manufacturers and retailers offer a **discount**, a *reduction* in the *original selling price*. That is, the original prices are lowered by a certain percentage, called the **percent of discount.** The discounted price is called the **sale price.** The **base** for the calculation of discount or the rate of discount is **always** the *original* selling price.

For example, if a Honda-Civic Car has a list price of $16,200 and is selling at a discounted price of $13,770, then:

The original selling price = $16,200; the sale price = $13,770;

and the amount of discount offered is $16,200 – $13,770 = $2,430.

The *percent* of discount, can be computed by using the percent equation, $R = \dfrac{A}{B}$

$$R = \frac{\$2,430}{\$16,200} \cdot 100\% = \mathbf{15\%}$$

Discounts are generally advertised as a percent "off" the selling price. For example,

"30% **off** on all items",

or "The White Sale is now 25% **off** the original price."

Warm-Up	**Example 4**

Warm-Up

4. A departmental store declares a $33\frac{1}{3}\%$ discount on the marked prices of selected items.

What do you pay for a toaster which is selling at the discounted price of $28.96?

Example 4 A general store in its annual inventory offered a 45% discount on the marked prices of all items.

What do we pay for an item marked $40?

Solution

We shall first find the amount of discount, then subtract this amount from the marked price.

Marked price = $40

Rate of discount = 45%

Discount = 45% of $40 $\frac{45}{100} = 0.45$

= 0.45 × 40

= **$18**

Sale price = Marked price – Discount

= $40 – $18

= $22

We pay $22 for a an item marked $40.

3. **Two or More Discounts:** After the original prices have been reduced by one discount, additional discounts may be offered to take into consideration the competing markets, as well as for promotional purposes.

When two successive discounts are offered on the same item, the first discount rate is based on the original price of the item, and the second discount rate is based on the price after the first discount. Similar procedures are used for more than two discounts. The discount rates are applied one by one to the successive sale prices.

Example 5   Find the final price of a color television listed at $375 and sold with successive discounts of 20% and 10%.

Solution

$$\text{The original price} = \$375$$

$$\text{First discount} = 20\% \text{ of } \$375$$

The rate of first discount is 20%, and it applies to the original selling price. Use 20% = 0.20.

$$= (0.20)\,(\$375)$$

$$= \mathbf{\$75}$$

$$\text{First sale price} = \$375 - \$75$$

$$= \mathbf{\$300}$$

$$\text{Second discount} = 10\% \text{ of } \mathbf{\$300}$$

Note this point. The second discount rate (10%) applies to the sale price after the first discount.

$$= (0.10)\,(300)$$

$$= \mathbf{\$30}$$

Final price = $300 – $30 = **$270**

The final price of the TV is $270.

Warm-Up

5. The marked price of a video camera is $440. It is sold at two successive discounts of 10% and 5%. Find the actual selling price of the camera.

⚠ **Caution:** | Wrong Solution

20% + 10% = 30%

Total Discount = 30% of $375 = $112.50

So, the net purchase price = $375 –$112.50 = **$262.50.**

This "wrong" solution is one of the most common mistakes in business mathematics. *Discounts of 20% and 10% are not the same as a discount of 30%.* Why ? Because the second discount rate is not based on the original list price. Adding the rates treats them as both being based on the list price. If we want to find the *actual* rate of discount in this problem, we divide the total discount ($75 + $30 = $105) by the original selling price, $375 ; 105 ÷ 375 = 0.28 = 28%. Thus, the single equivalent discount rate is 28%, not 30%. Therefore, two or more rates of discounts should be applied separately to successive net purchase prices.

Example 6   Find the cost of a motorcycle listed at $960 and sold with discounts of $33\frac{1}{3}\%$, 10%, and 5%.

Solution   The list price   = $960.

$$\text{First discount} = 33\frac{1}{3}\% \text{ of } \$960$$

Use $33\frac{1}{3}\% = \frac{1}{3}$;

$$= \$320$$

$\frac{1}{3}$ of $960 = \frac{1}{3} \cdot 960 = 320$.

$$\text{First } sale \text{ price} = \$960 - \$320 = \mathbf{\$640}$$

$$\text{Second discount} = 10\% \text{ of } \mathbf{\$640}$$

The second discount is based on the first *sale* price.

$$= (0.1)\,(\$640)$$

$$= \$64$$

$$\text{Second } sale \text{ price} = \$640 - \$64 = \mathbf{\$576}$$

Warm-Up

6. Find the net purchase price of a crystal dinner set listed at $920 and sold with a series of discounts of 15%, 10%, and 5%.

Third discount = 5% of **$576**

The third discount is based on the *sale* price after the second discount.

$$= 0.05 \times \$576$$

$$= \$28.80$$

Hence, the final selling price = $576 − $28.80

$$= \mathbf{\$547.20}$$

The final cost of the motor cycle is $547.20

4. **Sales Tax:** *Sales Tax* is a tax levied upon sales by states or cities to provide funds for various facilities or services. It is the responsibility of the seller to pay the tax to the government. In most instances, the seller collects sales tax from the buyer.

Sales tax is charged on the *actual selling price*. If an article is selling for $500 and the sales tax rate is 7%, then to find the final cost of the article, we first 'find the amount of the sales tax, and then add it to the sale price:

Sales tax = 7% of $500 = $\dfrac{7}{100} \cdot 500$ = **$35**.

The final cost of the article would be $500 + $35 = $535, which means, the buyer will pay $535 for the article.

The **rates of sales tax** vary from state to state and even within a state since counties and cities are allowed to levy taxes.

Warm-Up

7. If the sales tax is figured at 7.75%, how much tax will be added to the total purchase price of three text books, priced at $25.00, $35.00, and $52.00?

Example 7 If the sales tax rate is $7\dfrac{1}{4}\%$, what is the total amount to be billed to the buyer of the motorcycle in Example 6 above?

Solution To find the total amount of the bill, we first find the amount of the sales tax, and then add it to the selling price.

The sales tax is based on the selling price. In this case, the selling price is $547.20;

$$\text{Sales tax} = 7\tfrac{1}{4}\% \text{ of } \$547.20$$

$7\tfrac{1}{4}\% = 7.25\%$

$$= 0.0725 \times 547.20$$

$= 0.0725$

$$= \$39.672$$

$$= \mathbf{\$39.68}.$$

Rounded to the next higher cent regardless of the digit in the thousandths place.

Add the amount of sales tax to the selling price:

$ 547.20	The selling price.
+ 39.68	Sales tax.
$ 586.88	Total amount of the bill.

Including tax, the total amount of the bill is $586.88.

Example 8   A radio costing \$64.50 is marked up by $16\frac{2}{3}\%$ of the cost. It is then sold at a discount of 12%. If the sales tax rate is 7%, find the total amount to be billed to the buyer.

Solution

Cost = \$64.50.

Markup = $16\frac{2}{3}\%$ of \$64.50 $16\frac{2}{3}\% = 16\frac{2}{3} \cdot \frac{1}{100} = \frac{1}{6}$

$= \frac{1}{6} \cdot 64.50 = \mathbf{10.75}$

Marked price after markup = \$64.50 + \$10.75

Cost + markup = **\$75.25**

Discount = 12% of \$75.25   Discount is always on the marked price.
$= (0.12)(\$75.25)$
$= \$9.03$

Selling price = \$75.25 − \$9.03   Marked price minus discount
= **\$66.22**

Sales tax = 7% of \$66.22   Sales tax is charged on the actual selling price.
$= (0.07)(\$66.22)$
$= \$4.6354$
= **\$4.64**   Tax is rounded to the next higher cent.

Total cost = Selling price + Sales tax.
= \$66.22 + \$4.64
= **\$70.86**

8. What is the final sale price of a stereo costing \$42.70, marked up by $14\frac{2}{7}\%$ of the cost, and then sold at a discount of 10%? If the rate of sales tax is 7%, find the total sales tax to the nearest cent, and the amount paid by the buyer.

$\left(\text{Use } 14\frac{2}{7}\% = \frac{1}{7}.\right)$

5. **Profit:** Any person engaged in business −− a manufacturer, a wholesaler, or a retailer −− aims at making a profit. Suppose you bought a house for \$125,000 and after spending \$5,000 in improvements, sold it for \$140,000. You made a profit of \$10,000. The amount of profit is the difference between the selling price and all of the costs.

Profit = Income − Cost

- **Overhead Expenses:**   Often a business has to bear additional expenses such as expenses on transportation, rents, salaries, insurance, and so forth. These should all be included as *costs*.

Net Profit = Gross Profit − Overhead expenses

- **Percent of profit:**   The percent of profit, is a rate, R, that is based on the cost. For example, if an item that costs a store \$60 is sold for \$75, the store makes a profit of \$15.

$R = \frac{A}{B} = \frac{\text{profit}}{\text{cost}} = \frac{\$15}{\$60} = \frac{1}{4} = \mathbf{25\%}$.   That is, the profit of the store is 25% of the cost.

In this section the percent of profit will be based on **costs** and costs will include all expenses unless stated otherwise.

Warm-Up

9. An article costing $40 was marked up 20% and then sold at a discount of 10%. Find the percent of profit (or loss) based on the cost.

Example 9 Find the percent of profit earned on a camera costing $85.50, marked up $33\frac{1}{3}\%$, and then sold at a discount of 20%.

Solution We need to find the profit, after finding the sale price. Then we can determine the percent profit.

$$\text{Cost} = \$85.50$$

$$\textbf{Markup} = 33\frac{1}{3}\% \text{ of } \$85.50$$

$$= \textbf{\$28.50}$$

> $33\frac{1}{3}\%$ of 85.50
>
> $= \frac{1}{3} \cdot \$85.50$
>
> $= \$28.50$

$$\textbf{Marked price} = \text{Cost} + \text{Markup}$$
$$= \$85.50 + 28.50$$
$$= \textbf{\$114.00}$$

$$\text{Discount} = 20\% \text{ of } \$114.00$$
$$= (0.20)\,(\$114.00)$$
$$= \textbf{\$22.80}$$

> Discount is on the marked price.
> $20\% = 0.20$

$$\textbf{Selling price} = \text{Marked price} - \text{Discount}$$
$$= \$114.00 - \$22.80$$
$$= \textbf{\$91.20}$$

$$\textbf{Profit} = \text{Selling price} - \text{Costs}$$
$$= \$91.20 - \$85.50$$
$$= \textbf{\$5.70}$$

$$\text{Percent of profit, } R = \frac{\$5.70}{\$85.50}$$

> $R = \frac{\text{profit}}{\text{cost}}$

$$= \frac{5.70}{85.50} \cdot 100\%$$

$$= 6.\overline{6}\%$$

$$= 6\frac{2}{3}\%$$

> Remember: $0.\overline{6} = \frac{2}{3}$

The earned profit is $6\frac{2}{3}\%$ of the cost.

10. Jack buys an old typewriter for $245, and spends $20 on its repairs. He sells it for $254.40. Find the percent profit or loss.

Example 10 David buys an old car for $6,650. He spends $1,230 on its repairs and sells it for $8,276. Find his percent profit.

Solution

$$\text{Costs} = \$6,650 + \$1,230$$
$$= \textbf{\$7,880}$$

> Amount spent on repairs becomes a part of the costs.

$$\text{Selling price} = \$8,276$$

$$\text{Profit} = \text{Selling price} - \text{Costs}$$
$$= \$8{,}276 - \$7{,}880$$
$$= \$396$$

$$\text{Percent of profit, } R = \frac{\$396}{\$7{,}880} \cdot 100\% \qquad R = \frac{\text{profit}}{\text{cost}}$$
$$\approx 0.05$$
$$= 5\%$$

Remember, unless mentioned otherwise, profit is based on costs.

David's profit is 5%.

Answers:

1. $14.23   2. 40% of the cost price
3. $66   4. $19.31
5. $376.20   6. $668.61
7. $8.68
8. (a) $43.92   (b) $3.07   (c) $46.99
9. 8% profit.   10. 4% loss

8.3 B. Commission and Tipping

1. **Commission:** A *commission* is the money paid to a person for selling a company's products. Commissions are usually a percentage of the sales. The gross wages of a person paid on a *straight commission* depend strictly on the amount of sales and the rate of commission. For example, if a sales representative is paid a straight commission of $33\frac{1}{3}\%$ on all sales, and if his sales for this month are $960, then his gross wages for this month are

$$= 33\frac{1}{3}\% \text{ of } \$960$$

$$= \frac{1}{3} \text{ of } \$960 = \$320$$

Remember that $33\frac{1}{3}\% = \frac{100}{3} \cdot \frac{1}{100} = \frac{1}{3}$.

$\frac{1}{3}$ of $960 = $\frac{1}{3} \times 960 = \$320$.

- A monthly gross income of $320 is not very high. Because of the uncertain nature of the sales profession, many firms pay a fixed salary plus a commission on sales above a certain level of sales.

Example 11 Alice Clark earns a 25% commission on all sales over $600 a month plus a $1,000 monthly salary. If her sales this month are $2,170, find her gross earnings.

Solution Gross earnings are the sum of the monthly salary and the amount of commission earned.

Step 1 We first find the base for her commission

$2,170   Total sales for the month
− 600   Amount on which she does not earn a commission
$1,570   Base for commission

Step 2 We now find the amount of commission by finding 25% of the base.

Amount of Commission = 25% of $1,570

$$= 0.25 \times \$1{,}570$$

$$= \mathbf{\$392.50}$$

Warm-Up

11. A salesperson receives a monthly salary of $500 plus a commission of 6% on all sales over $3,500. If his sales for a particular month were $8,000, what were his gross earnings for that month?

Step 3   Finally, we add the amount of commission to her monthly salary.

$1,000.00   Salary
+ 392.50   Commission
$1,392.50   Gross earnings

Alice Clark's gross earnings are $1,392.50.

- Another commission plan is called a ***Graduated Commission Scale***. To encourage higher sales, a higher rate of commission is offered as sales increase. For instance, the scale might read as follows:

    10% on the first $1,000 of sales;

    15% on sales more than $1,000 through $2,000; and

    20% on all sales over $2,000.

The higher rates do not apply to all sales, but just to sales over the stated limits.

Warm-Up	**Example 12**

Warm-Up

12. Jane Arden works with a firm on a straight commission basis. The commission rates of the firm read as follows:

10% on the *first* $1,000 of sales
15% on the *next* $2,000
20% on all sales over $3,000

If Jane's sales are $4,200, find her gross wages.

Example 12   A real estate commission is to be computed using the following rates:

5% on the first $20,000 of sales;

10% on sales above $20,000 through $100,000,

and   15% on all sales over $100,000.

Find the gross commission on a $161,250 sale.

Solution   Note that the higher rates do not apply to all sales, but just to sales within the stated limits. We have three levels of commission rates to consider.

- Commission on the *first* $20,000 at the rate of 5%

    5% of 20,000 = $0.05 \times 20,000 = $ **$1,000** ;

- Commission on the *next* $80,000 at the rate of 10% $100,000 - $20,000 = $80,000

    10% of 80,000 = $0.10 \times 80,000 = $ **$8,000** ;

- Commission on the remaining $61,250 at the rate of 15%

    $161,250
    − $100,000
    ‾‾‾‾‾‾‾‾
    $61,250

    15% of $61,250 $= 0.15 \times 61,250$

    = **$9,187.50;**

Total commission   = $1,000 + $8,000 + $9,187.50

    = **$ 18,187.50.**

2. **Tipping:** It is customary to leave a percent of the bill amount, usually at a restaurant, as a payment to the server for providing good service. This is known as tipping. The amount of 'tip' may be any convenient percentage of the total amount of the bill (including tax) such as 5%, 10%, 15% or 20%, depending on the quality of service. Although 'tipping' is a voluntary act on the part of a customer (he may not even want to leave any tip in case of bad service), the usual tip is 15%.

The tip, is not usually an exact percent of the amount of the bill. When we say "a 15% tip", we mean that the amount of the tip is approximately 15% of the bill. It may be slightly less or slightly more than the exact 15% of the bill. Practically speaking, the amount of tip might depend on the change you have in your pocket, or you might leave a tip that makes the total of your expenses a whole dollar amount, or other considerations. As such, to calculate the amount of a tip, we need not use a calculator. The following is an interesting and convenient method to make an estimate of 15% of a bill. The method is based on two basic facts:

    1.   10% of a decimal number can be found by moving the decimal point 1 place to the left.

    2.   5% is half of 10%.

For example, to find 15% of a bill for, $45.60, we proceed as follows:

Round $45.60 to a whole number, $45.6 \approx 46$

$$10\% \text{ of } \$46 \ = \ \$4.60$$

$$5\% \text{ of } \$46 \ = \ \frac{1}{2}(4.6) = \$2.30$$

$$15\% \text{ of } 46 \ = \ 4.60 + 2.30 = \$6.90$$

A 15% tip for a bill of $45.60 is approximately $6.90 or $7.

We summarize this discussion in the following Special Rule of Thumb for calculating a 15% tip.

SPECIAL RULE OF THUMB FOR CALCULATING A 15% TIP	
Step **1**	Round off the amount of the bill to the nearest whole dollar.
Step **2**	Find 10% of the rounded amount by moving the decimal point 1 place to the left.
Step **3**	Divide the answer in step 2 by 2. This will represent 5% of the rounded amount.
Step **4**	Add the two amounts found in steps 2 and 3. This sum is the amount of tip.

Example 13   Harriet Marshall takes her friends out for lunch in a restaurant. The bill is $124.30 including tax. If she plans to leave a 15% tip, what should be the approximate amount of tip (use the rule of thumb)?

Warm-Up

13. Use the thumb-rule to calculate a tip of 15% if the bill amount is $87.75.

Solution

Step 1 $124.30 \approx$ **$124.00**   For ease of computation, round off the bill amount to the nearest whole dollar.

Step 2   Find 10% of $124.00

       10% of $124.00 = **$12.40**   Move the decimal point 1 place to the left.

Step 3 Now, 5% of $124.00 is half of $12.40.   Divide the amount
                                                obtained in step 2 by 2:
       $\frac{1}{2}$ of $12.40 = **$6.20**   12.40 ÷ 2 = 6.20.

Step 4 Add the amounts obtained in Steps 2 and 3: $12.40
                                                    + $6.20
                                    (Amount of Tip)   18.60

       The approximate amount of tip is $18.60.

Answers:

11. $770 **12.** $640

13. $13.20

       (In practice, any amount between $18 and $19 would serve
       the purpose of a 15% tip).

Exercise 8.3

A. **The following problems may involve several calculations. The use of a calculator is recommended. However, at times, using fraction equivalents of some percents (such as $33\frac{1}{3}\% = \frac{1}{3}, 14\frac{2}{7}\% = \frac{1}{7}, 16\frac{2}{3}\% = \frac{1}{6},...$) and doing calculations manually may be easier and more interesting. Follow the pattern of the solution as illustrated in the solved examples and take special care to label each amount of money as to what it represents. For sales tax calculations with dollars and cents with three or more decimal places, round the answers to the next higher cent regardless of the digit in the thousandths place.**

1. An article that costs a store owner $8.43 is to be marked up by $2.81. What is the percent markup based on the cost?

2. An article costing $26.00 is given a markup of 32%. What is the selling price?

3. A camera is priced to sell for $189.95. If the markup is 40% of the selling price, what is the cost of the camera?

4. The retail price of a tea set costing $21.00 is $27.30. What is the percent markup based on **(a)** cost? **(b)** selling price? Round the answer to the nearest whole number percent.

5. Calculate the selling price of a watch costing $64.50, with anticipated expenses of 15% of cost and a desired net profit of $12.50.

6. Find the selling price of an article costing $8.40, if a 35% markup is applied to the cost.

7. A stereo costing $99.40 is marked up by $28\frac{4}{7}\%$ and later sold at a discount of 20%. Find (a) the original selling price, and (b) the actual sale price of the stereo after the discount.

$\left(\text{Hint}: 28\frac{4}{7}\% = \frac{2}{7}\right)$

8. Find the purchase price of a dishwasher listed at $575, sold at a discount of 20%.

9. The Baxter Garment Store declares a discount of 30% on all items in the store. Find the marked price of a shirt if it is sold for $8.40.

10. Find the actual selling price of a computer desk listed at $450 and sold with successive discounts of 15% and 10%.

11. Find the selling price of a woolen blanket marked up by $62\frac{1}{2}\%$ of its original cost of $72.80.

12. An auto dealer paid $8,730 for a large order of special parts. This was **not** the original price. He was given a 3% discount off the original price because he paid cash. What was the original price of the parts?

13. A color television set was bought for $300 at a 20% off sale. What was the marked price of the television set?

14. The retail price of a lamp **after** a 15% markup is $12.65. Find the price before mark up, and the markup.

15. Mr. Hill earns a commission of $14\frac{2}{7}\%$ on all his sales plus a $150 monthly salary. If his sales this month are $1,499.40, find his income this month.

16. A car salesperson earns a straight commission of $7\frac{1}{4}\%$ on each car he sells. Determine his commission on the sale of a car for $9,650. Round the answer to the nearest dollar.

17. At a department store's $33\frac{1}{3}\%$ off white sale, shirts were originally marked for $7.50 and trousers for $12.60. What is the sale price of **(a)** shirts?   **(b)** trousers?

18. John Allen has a weekly salary of $80 and a 15% commission on total sales over $400. Find his weekly earnings if his sales figures are:

(a) $740   **(b)** $400   **(c)** $850   **(d)** $375

19. Mr. Smith works with Fleet Jeweller. He receives a salary of $175 per week plus 1% commission on his total sales. He gets an additional commission of 0.5% on all sales above $25,000. What are his total earnings for a week if he sells $54,000 worth of jewellery in that week?

20. A toaster costing $39.50 is sold for $45.25. Find the net profit or loss if operating expenses are
(a) $6.25   **(b)** $2.50

21. Mr. Johnson buys an old TV for $215 and spends $40 on its repairs. He sells it at a loss of 15%. At what price was the TV sold?

22. Mrs. Johnson visits a department store and buys the following articles:

one toaster for $75, one shirt for $15, one pair of shoes for $65, and one pair of jeans for $55.
Calculate the total amount of the bill including a 5% sales tax on the goods purchased.

23. A shopkeeper raises the prices of all the articles in his shop by 20% and then declares "15% off" on each article. What will a customer pay for an article whose original price was $1,350?

24. Income tax rates for the financial year 2002-2003 were as follows:

Income	Tax
Up to 12,000	No tax
12,001 to 28,000	15 %
28,001 to 38,000	18 %
Above 38,000	21 %

Calculate the income tax payable by Mr. Brown if his annual income was $75,000.

25. A real estate commission is to be computed using the following rates:
5% on the first $15,000 of sales;
10% on sales above $15,000, through $20,000 ; and
15% on all sales over $20,000.
Find the gross commission if the total sales are:

(a) $12,800   **(b)** $18,000   **(c)** $24,725

26. A new refrigerator that regularly sells for $1,500 is on sale at a 25% discount.

(a) What is the amount of discount?   **(b)** What is the sale price?
(c) If sales tax rate is 7%, what is the total cost of the refrigerator?

27. For a single person, there is no tax on income below $15,000. But all income in excess of $15,000, through $25,000, is taxed at 19%, and all income above $25,000 is taxed at 23%. What is the total tax to be paid by a single person whose income is $42,000?

28. A wall clock costing $37.50 is marked up $16\frac{2}{3}\%$ of the cost and then sold at a discount of 20%. Find the gross profit or loss.

29.   A house is bought for $45,000 and sold for $75,000. What is the percent profit?

30.   A stationary store sells calculators for $60 each. However, the cost to the store was only $48 each.
   (a)   What is the profit on each calculator?
   (b)   What is the percent profit based on cost?
   (c)   What is the percent profit based on selling price?

31.   A man makes a profit of $378 by selling a carpet for $2,750. Find his percent profit. Round it to the nearest whole number.

32.   A firm sells a trailer costing $775 for $1,025 and overhead expenses are $310. Find the profit or loss.

33.   Find the profit on a telescope costing $60.00, marked up by 20%, and then reduced for sale by 12%. What is the percent profit?

B.   **In exercises 34-37, use the Rule of Thumb to calculate a 15% tip. (Base the tip on the total bill, including tax.)**

34.   Jim Brown took his family out for dinner at Hamburger Haven. The bill was $24 plus a 6% sales tax
   (a) What amount did he leave as a 15% tip?   **(b)** How much did Jim pay including tip?

35.   Henry hosted a party at a restaurant to celebrate his twenty-fifth birthday and invited 15 of his friends. The bill was $235.00 plus a 7% sales tax. **(a)** What was the amount of the bill? **(b)** How much did Henry pay including a 15% tip?

36.   Suppose you go out for dinner and the bill is $33.60 including tax. If you plan to leave 15% tip, what should the tip be?

37.   A car rental agency charges $14.50 per day plus $0.15 per mile. Benjamin rents a car for one day and hires a driver to take a trip to his farm house. If the car is driven 225 miles, find the amount that Benjamin has to pay the agency for that day. If he decides to tip the driver about 15% of the bill, find the amount of the tip in whole dollars.

8.4   SIMPLE INTEREST AND COMPOUND INTEREST

Introduction

Objectives

After completing this section, you will be able to:

A. Solve applications of simple interest, using the formula I = Prt; and

B. Solve applications of compound interest using the formula $A = P\left(1+\dfrac{r}{n}\right)^{nt}$.

Just as rent is paid for the use of property and a salary is paid for the use of a person's services, **interest** is paid for the use of someone's money. When we borrow money, we pay *interest* and when we lend money, we earn *interest* on it. When we deposit our money in a bank, we receive interest on the money we keep there.

We say that **interest** is the money paid by the borrowers to the lenders for use of their money. The amount of money borrowed, deposited, or invested is called the **principal.** The ratio of interest to the principal is called the **interest rate**. The *rate* is always expressed as a percent or a decimal. The period for which the money is kept is called the **time.** The *time* is generally expressed in years or as a fraction of a year. The total sum of money that must be repaid by the user at the end of the time period is called the **amount**. The amount (A) is the principal (P) plus the interest (I). We can express it as:

Amount = Principal + Interest or $\boxed{A = P + I}$

There are two types of interests, simple and compound. Regardless of whether you are a borrower, lender, or investor, the calculations for finding interest are the same.

8.4 A.   Simple Interest

- When interest is calculated only on the principal for any length of time, it is called **simple interest**. Simple interest is calculated by the formula:

$$\text{Interest} = \text{Principal} \times \text{rate} \times \text{time} \quad \text{or} \quad \boxed{\mathbf{I = Prt}}$$

For example, let us find the interest on $500 borrowed at 8% for two years:

$$I = Prt$$
$$= 500 \times 0.08 \times 2$$
$$= \$80.00$$

P = \$500,   r = 8% = 0.08 ,   t = 2 yrs.

Using the formula: I = P · r · t

Multiply the principal by the rate, then multiply by the number of years.

Alternatively,

$$I = Prt$$
$$= \$500 \times 8\% \times 2$$
$$= \overset{5}{\cancel{500}} \times \frac{8}{\underset{1}{\cancel{100}}} \times 2$$
$$= \$80$$

Each factor is expressed in fraction form, and then reduced.

- To find the simple interest for time periods of less than one year, the time is expressed as a fraction of a year. For example, a time of nine months would be:

$$\frac{9 \text{ months}}{12 \text{ months}} = \frac{3}{4} \text{ of a year} \quad \text{or} \quad \frac{3}{4} \text{ year;}$$

and a time of 90 days would be:

$$\frac{90 \text{ days}}{365 \text{ days}} = \frac{18}{73} \text{ of a year} \quad \text{or} \quad \frac{18}{73} \text{ year.}$$

Find the simple interest on $500 borrowed at 8% for nine months.

$$I = Prt$$
$$= (500)(0.08)\left(\frac{9}{12}\right) = \mathbf{\$30} .$$

The simple interest on $500 at 8% for 90 days would be:

$$I = \overset{5}{\cancel{500}} \times \frac{8}{\underset{1}{\cancel{100}}} \times \frac{\overset{18}{\cancel{90}}}{\underset{73}{\cancel{365}}}$$
$$= \frac{720}{73} \approx \mathbf{\$9.86} .$$

- **Bankers Interest :**   Although the interest based on a 365 day year is the *exact interest*, in banking and business, it is a common practice to use 360 days in one year (30 days in each month). The figure of 360 generally makes calculations simpler, because 360 has many more factors than 365.

The bankers' interest on $500 at 8% for 90 days would be:

$$I = \overset{5}{\cancel{500}} \times \frac{\overset{2}{\cancel{8}}}{\underset{1}{\cancel{100}}} \times \frac{\overset{1}{\cancel{90}}}{\underset{1}{\underset{4}{\cancel{360}}}}$$
$$= \mathbf{\$10}$$

Note that this interest is more than the interest calculated above, namely, $9.86.

It should be noted that for the same principal, rate, and time, bankers' interest will always be more than the interest. (The denominator of 360 is smaller than the denominator of 365.)

In what follows, unless mentioned otherwise, we will use 360 days as one year.

Procedure to find any one of the four unknown quantities I (interest), P (principal), r (rate), or t (time) when the other three are known.

Step **1** Read the problem carefully to find out which of the four quantities; P (principal), r (rate percent), t (time expressed in years), and I (interest) are known.

Step **2** Substitute the known quantities in the formula $I = Prt$, and then solve the resulting equation for the unknown.

Warm-Up

1. Mrs. Johnson deposited $850 in a bank that pays a simple interest at the rate of 6.2% per year.

(a) Find the interest on this amount after three years.

(b) Find the total value of her deposit after three years.

2. William deposits $7,580 with a bank. The bank pays simple interest at the rate of 7.5% annually. Find the interest and the amount to be received by William after two and a half years.

Example 1 Ms. Johnson invested $8,250 with a finance company which pays 14.5% simple interest per year. Find the interest and the amount she is expected to receive after three years.

Solution

Step 1 We are given

$$P = \$8,250$$

$$r = 14.5\% = 0.145 \text{ (in decimal form)}$$

$$= \frac{145}{1,000} \text{ (in fraction form)}$$

$$t = 3 \text{ years.} \quad \text{We have to find the Interest (I).}$$

Step 2 Using the formula,

$$I = Prt$$

$$I = 8,250 \times 0.145 \times 3$$

$$= 3,588.75; \quad \text{(Use a calculator.).}$$

The interest for three years = **$3,588.75.**

The amount she is expected to receive after three years is

$8,250 + $3,588.75 = **$11,838.75.**

Example 2 Mr. Smith deposited $ 1,250 in a bank that pays a simple interest at the rate of 5.5% per year.

(a) Find the interest on this amount after $2\frac{1}{2}$ years rounded to the nearest cents.

(b) Find the total amount of his deposit after $2\frac{1}{2}$ years.

Solutions

(a) The interest $I = P \cdot r \cdot t$

$P = \$1,250$, $r = 5.5\% = 0.055$, and $t = 2\frac{1}{2} = 2.5$ years;

$I = 1,250 \times 0.055 \times 2.5$

$= \mathbf{68.75} \times 2.5$ 68.75 is the interest for one year.

$= 171.875$

$\approx \mathbf{\$171.88}$ rounded to the nearest cent.

(b) The total amount of the deposit after $2\frac{1}{2}$ years:

Amount $=$ Principal $+$ Interest

$=\ \$1,250 + \$171.88$

$=\ \mathbf{\$1,421.88}.$

Example 3   Henry loaned his uncle $975 at 10% for 146 days. How much simple interest did he earn?

Solution

Step 1 $P = \$975$, $r = 10\%$, $t = 146$ days $= \dfrac{146}{360}$ years , $I = ?$

Step 2 $I = P\,r\,t$

$= \$975 \times 10\% \times \dfrac{146}{360}$ Time must be expressed in years. (Recall that, we have agreed to use 360 days in a year, unless mentioned otherwise.)

$= \dfrac{975}{1} \times \dfrac{10}{100} \times \dfrac{146}{360}$

$\approx \mathbf{\$39.54}$

Example 4   What principal amount would you need to earn $672 in interest in two years if the rate of interest was 6%?

Solution

Step 1   In this problem, we know the interest, rate, time, and we want to find the principal.

$I = \$672$

$r = 6\% = 0.06$

$t = 2$ years

Step 2   Substitute these values into the formula $\mathbf{I = P\,r\,t}$ and solve for P.

$I = P \times r \times t$

$\longrightarrow\ 672 = P \times 0.06 \times 2$

3. What interest would Henry earn in Example 3 if his uncle insists on 365 days in a year?

4. What sum of money will yield $450 interest in six months at the rate of 9%?

$$672 = P \times 0.12 \quad \text{Simplify the right side.}$$

$$\frac{672}{0.12} = \frac{P \times 0.12}{0.12} \quad \begin{array}{l}\text{Divide both sides by 0.12 to}\\ \text{isolate P, the unknown.}\end{array}$$

$$5{,}600 = P$$

You would need a principal amount of **$5,600** invested at 6% to earn $672 in two years.

5. What interest rate would you be paying if you borrowed $7,000 for four years and paid $2,520 in interest?

Example 5 A sum of $550 was loaned out for two years at simple interest. The lender got back the total amount of $638. Find the rate of interest in percent per year.

Solution

Step 1   The quantities we know are:

$$P = \$550$$
$$t = 2 \text{ years}$$
$$A = \$638; \quad \text{(Amount = P + I)}$$

so, $I = \$638 - \$550 = \$88$

We have to find **r.**

Step 2
$$I = Prt$$
$$88 = 550 \times r \times 2 \quad \begin{array}{l}\text{Substitute the values of}\\ \text{the known quantities.}\end{array}$$
$$88 = 1{,}100 \times r$$
$$\frac{88}{1{,}100} = r \quad \text{Reduce and change to \%.}$$
$$r = \frac{{}^{8}88}{1100_{100}} = 0.08 = \mathbf{8\%.}$$

6. Find the time in which $2,000 will earn $150 simple interest at the rate of 10%. Express the time in a whole number period.

Example 6 In what time period will the principal $8,500 become $15,767.50 at 9% per year simple interest?

Solution

Step 1   We are given: $P = \$8,500$ $\quad\begin{array}{l}\text{Use A = P + I, or equivalently,}\\ \text{I = A - P.}\end{array}$

$$A = \$15{,}767.50;$$

so, $I = \$15,767.50 - \$8,500 = \mathbf{\$7{,}267.50}$

$$r = 9\% = 0.09 \quad \text{or} \quad \frac{9}{100}.$$

We have to find t = ?

Step 2 $\qquad$ I = Prt $\qquad$ Formula for simple interest

$$\$7{,}267.50 = \$8{,}500 \times 0.09 \times t$$ Substitute for the known quantities.

$$\frac{7{,}267.50}{8{,}500 \times 0.09} = t$$ (Use calculator for computations.)

t = 9.5 years or $9\frac{1}{2}$ years.

Answers:

1. (a) $158.10 $\qquad$ (b) $1,008.10
2. $1,421.25 ; $9,001.25
3. $39 $\qquad\qquad$ 4. $10,000
5. 9% $\qquad\qquad$ 6. $\frac{3}{4}$ yrs or 9 months

8.4 B. Compound Interest

- **Compound Interest:** Most people, both individuals and businesses, invest or deposit money with banks to make more money -- and this more money is the interest earned. The best kind of interest is *compound interest*. Compound interest is not the same as simple interest. To understand compound interest, let us look at an investment of $100 for two years at 6% simple interest. The simple interest earned for two years can be calculated by using the formula I = Prt:

$$I = \$100 \times .06 \times 2 = \$12 \qquad \text{6\% = 0.06}$$

The amount after two years will be

$$A = \$100 + \$12 = \mathbf{\$112.}$$

In other words, $100 invested for two years at 6% simple interest will amount to $112.

If the interest for the second year is computed on the *amount due* at the end of the first year rather than on the original principal, we get what is known as *compound interest*. Following is the step-by-step tabulation of the compound interest of the investment considered above.

Original investment (Principal) = $100

First year interest ($100 × 0.06) = $6

Amount due at the end of first year = $106 $\qquad$ This becomes the Principal for the second year.

Second year interest ($106 × 0.06) = $6.36 $\qquad$ $106 × .06 = $6.36

Amount due at the end of second year = **$112.36**

Thus, $100 invested for two years at 6% *compounded annually* will amount to $112.36, and the Compound Interest would be A − P = $112.36 − $100 = **$12.36.**

With compound interest, we earn interest not only on the principal, but also on the interest earned in the previous time period.

- **Other time periods for compounding interest:** Sometimes interest is compounded for periods other than annually. Interests can be compounded *semi-annually* (every six months), or *quarterly* (every three months), or even *monthly*. Let us examine the difference between annual and semi-annual compounding of $100 invested at 6% for **one** year. Annual compounding earned interest of $6.00. Semi-annual compounding will work as follows:

Original Principal = $100

First semi-annual interest

$$\$100 \times 0.06 \times \frac{6}{12} = \$100 \times 0.03 = \underline{\quad \$3 \quad}$$

Amount due after first time period = $103

Remember, in the formula I = Prt, t is expressed in years. The time period "semi-annual' means six months = $\frac{6}{12}$ year.

Second semi-annual interest

$$\$103 \times 0.06 \times \frac{6}{12} = \$103 \times 0.03 = \underline{\quad \$3.09 \quad}$$

Amount due after one year = $106.09

So, the compound interest = $106.09 – $100 = **$6.09.**

Note that semi-annual compounding has earned more interest ($6.09) than the interest of $6 earned by annual compounding. The amount of interest would have been even more if the interest were compounded quarterly. In fact, the *greater* the number of interest periods in a year, the higher the annual interest.

• **Compound Interest Formula:** The process of computing compound interest step-by-step as explained above is lengthy and time consuming, especially when there are more compoundings per year. Therefore, a formula will be of great help.

The following compound interest formula will help us find the total amount accumulated.

> **Compound Interest Formula:**
>
> When interest is compounded, the total amount A (principal plus the total interest) is given by the formula:
>
> $$A = P\left(1 + \frac{r}{n}\right)^{nt}$$
>
> where
>
> P = the principal
>
> r = the *annual* interest rate (in decimal form)
>
> t = time in *years*
>
> n = number of compounding periods in 1 year
>
> (For example, n = 2, if interest is compounded semi-annually; n = 12, if interest is compounded monthly.)
>
> If the interest is *compounded annually*, we have n = 1, and the formula reduces to
>
> $$A = P(1 + r)^t.$$

To find the total interest earned, we subtract the principal from the accumulated amount:

$$I = A – P$$

Warm-Up

7. Find the total amount and the compound interest on $6,000 for two years at 5% compounded annually.

Example 7 Find the total amount and the compound interest on $3,000 for four years at 5% compounded annually. (Use the formulas: $A = P(1 + r)^t$ and $I = A – P$.)

Solution In a compound interest problem, we first find the amount.

Formula for the amount is: $A = P(1 + r)^t.$

Here, P = $3,000 ; r = 5% = 0.05; and t = 4 years.

Substituting these values in the formula gives:

$$A = 3{,}000 \, (1 + 0.05)^4$$

$$A = 3{,}000 \, (1.05)^4.$$

We shall now use a calculator to compute the last expression.

Recall that we use the key $\boxed{x^y}$ to evaluate exponents.

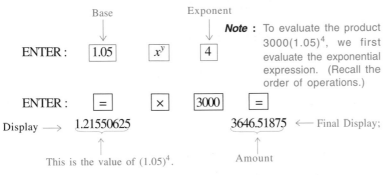

Base   Exponent

ENTER : $\boxed{1.05}$ $\boxed{x^y}$ $\boxed{4}$

Note : To evaluate the product $3000(1.05)^4$, we first evaluate the exponential expression. (Recall the order of operations.)

ENTER : $\boxed{=}$ $\boxed{\times}$ $\boxed{3000}$ $\boxed{=}$

Display ⟶ 1.21550625   3646.51875 ← Final Display;

This is the value of $(1.05)^4$.   Amount

Amount = \$3,646.52.

The compound interest is given by:

I = A − P = \$3,646.52 − \$3,000 = **\$646.52.**

The total amount is \$3,646.52 and the interest is \$646.52**.**

Example 8   Find the difference between compound interest compounded annually and simple interest on \$8,000 for three years at 4% annually.

Solution   P = \$8,000 ; r = 4% = 0.04, and t = 3 years.

To find compound interest, we first compute the total amount.

$$\mathbf{A} = \mathbf{P}(1 + r)^t$$

$$= 8{,}000 \, (1 + .04)^3$$

$$= 8{,}000 \, (1.04)^3$$

$$= \mathbf{\$8{,}998.92.}$$

ENTER : $\boxed{1.04}$ $\boxed{x^y}$ $\boxed{3}$

$\boxed{=}$ $\boxed{\times}$ $\boxed{8000}$$\boxed{=}$

1.124864   8,998.912

Value of $(1.04)^3$ Final Display

Compound Interest = A − P

$$= \$8{,}998.92 − \$8{,}000$$

$$= \mathbf{\$998.92.}$$

Simple Interest = Prt

Formula for simple interest is: I = Prt.

$$= \$8{,}000 \times 0.04 \times 3$$

$$= \mathbf{\$960}$$

ENTER : $\boxed{8000}$$\boxed{\times}$$\boxed{0.04}$$\boxed{\times}$

$\boxed{3}$ $\boxed{=}$ 960

Final Display

8. Find the difference between compound interest compounded annually and simple interest on \$1,250 for two years at 4% compound annually.

445

Difference = Compound Interest − Simple Interest

= $998.92 − $960

= **$38.92.**

9. If an account is compounded monthly, at 12% how much interest will be earned in 3 month on a deposit of $4,500 ?

Example 9 Jerry deposited $7,500 in a savings account and the interest is compounded quarterly at 8%. What will be the balance in his account in one year? Find the total interest earned in one year.

Solution We shall use the formula: $A = P\left(1 + \dfrac{r}{n}\right)^{nt}$

P = $7,500 ; r = 8% = .08;
n = 4 times per year; and t = 1 year.

Quarterly means *four* times per year.

Substituting the values in the formula gives:

$A = 7,500\left(1 + \dfrac{0.08}{4}\right)^{4\,(1)}$

ENTER : [1.02] [x^y] [4]
[=] [×] [7500] [=]
1.08243216   8118.2412
↑   ↑
Value of $(1.02)^4$ Final Display

= $7,500\,(1.02)^4$

= **$8,118.24**

The balance in the account after one year will be $8,118.24.

The **total interest** earned in one year will be

$8,118.24
−$7,500.00
―――――――
$618.24

$I = A - P$

10. Arnold deposits $4,000 in a fund with an interest rate of 10% for one and a half years. Find the amount he will get back and the compound interest earned if the interest is compounded semi-annually.

(*Hint:* Use n = 2 times per year.)

Example 10 Julie deposits $4,600 in a fund for three years with an interest rate of 15%. Find the amount she will get back and the compound interest earned if the interest is compounded monthly.

Solution We shall use the formula: $A = P\left(1 + \dfrac{r}{n}\right)^{nt}$.

P = $4,600 , r = 15% = 0.15

n = 12 times per year, t = 3 years

Substituting the values in the formula gives:

$A = 4,600\left(1 + \dfrac{0.15}{12}\right)^{12(3)}$

= $4,600\,(1 + 0.0125)^{36}$

= $4,600\,(1.0125)^{36}.$

We now use a calculator to compute the last expression .

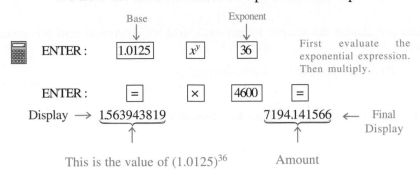

Base

Exponent

ENTER : 1.0125 x^y 36   First evaluate the exponential expression. Then multiply.

ENTER : = × 4600 =

Display → 1.563943819   7194.141566 ← Final Display

This is the value of $(1.0125)^{36}$ Amount

Julie will receive **$7,194.14.** And, the interest (I) earned is given by:

$$I = A - P = \$7,194.14 - \$4,600 = \mathbf{\$2,594.14.}$$

Exercise 8.4

A. In exercises 1-10, find the simple interest using the formula: **I = Prt.** Use 360 days in one year (30 days in a month), unless mentioned otherwise.   Use a calculator for calculations.

1.   Principal − $1,800, rate − 5%, time − 2 years

2.   P = $900, rate = 8% , time 3 years

3.   P = $2,500 , rate = 12% , time = 90 days

4.   P = $450 , rate = 9%, time = 6 months

5.   P = $5,000 , rate = $5\frac{1}{2}\%$, time = $3\frac{1}{4}$ years

6.   P = $600 , rate = 8%, time = 9 months.

7.   Principal = $600 , rate = $7\frac{1}{4}\%$, time = $5\frac{1}{2}$ years

8.   Principal = $4,500 , rate = 8% , time = 73 days.   (Use 365 days in one year.)

9.   Principal = $1,460, rate = $12\frac{1}{2}\%$, time = 219 days. (Use 365 days in one year.)

10.   Principal = $550, rate = 10%, time = 146 days.   (Use 365 days in one year.)

In problems 11-14, find the simple interest (I) and the amount (A). Use 360 days in a year. Use a calculator for calculations.

11.   Principal = $800, rate = $4\frac{1}{2}\%$, time = 75 days

12.   Principal = $8,500 , rate = 12% , time = 3 years

13.   Principal = $6,000 , rate = $5\frac{1}{2}\%$, time = 6 months

14.   Principal = $2,000 , rate = 15% , time = 2 years

15.   At what rate percent will $4,500 earn a simple interest $1,620 in four years?

16.   What rate of simple interest was applied if $50 interest was earned on $2,000 for three months.

17.   What is the rate of interest charged if a $2\frac{1}{2}$ - year loan of $2,500 is paid off with $2,812.50?

        (***Hint:*** The pay-off is principal plus interest so first find the interest earned.)

18.   What is the rate of simple interest charged if one has to repay $7,234.50 to pay off a 5-year loan of $5,460?

19.   Carmen borrowed $1,500 at 5% simple interest. After some time, she returned $1,800 and cleared the account. For how long did she keep the money?

20.   A savings account of $12,000 is drawing interest at 8%. **(a)** How much interest will be earned in six months? **(b)** How long will it take for the account to earn $1,440 in interest?

21. Find bankers' simple interest on a loan of $700 to a Cook company for 85 days at 8%. Round to the nearest cents. (360 days per year)

22. Arnold borrowed $3,475 from Alicia and cleared the account by paying $3,822.50. If Arnold paid 5% annually in interest, when did he return the money?

23. What sum of money will amount to $900 in four years at 5% simple interest?
    (*Hint:* Use A = P + Prt.)

B. In exercises 24-30, use one of the following formulas. Use a calculator for calculations.

$$A = P(1 + r)^t \; ; \; A = P\left(1 + \frac{r}{n}\right)^{nt} \; ; \; I = A - P$$

24. Find the compound interest on $25,000 for three years at 4% compounded annually.

25. Find the compound interest on $8,000 for three years at 10% compounded annually.

26. Find the amount that earned $1,600 at compound interest in one and a half years at 10% compounded semi-annually. (Semi-annually means twice a year.)

27. Rita Anderson deposits $4,000 in a fund for three years that pays 12% interest. Find the amount and the compound interest earned if the interest is compounded semi-annually.

28. Find the compound interest on $18,750 in two years if the rate is 4% for the first year and 8% for the second year.
    (*Hint:* First find the amount for the first year at 4%. Then, taking this amount as the principal, find the amount for the second year at 8%.)

29. Joseph borrowed $8,000 from a company which charges interest at 16%, compounded quarterly. He returned the money after nine months. How much did he pay to clear the debt?
    (Compounded quarterly is four times per year.)

30. Find the interest earned in three months on $5,000 compounded monthly at 8%.

In exercises 31-38, use the compound interest formula, $A = P\left(1 + \dfrac{r}{n}\right)^{nt}$, to find the amount and the interest earned as per the given information.

31.	$P = \$2,560,$	$r = 12\frac{1}{2}\%$,	$t = 1$ year,	interest compounded half-yearly.
32.	$P = \$320,$	$r = 10\%,$	$t = 1\frac{1}{2}$ year,	interest compounded six-monthly.
33.	$P = \$4,500,$	$r = 9\%,$	$t = 5$ years,	interest compounded monthly.
34.	$P = \$700,$	$r = 10\%,$	$t = 4$ years,	interest compounded annually.
35.	$P = \$10,000,$	$r = 8\%,$	$t = 2$ years,	interest compounded quarterly.
36.	$P = \$5,000,$	$r = 12\%,$	$t = 2$ years,	interest compounded quarterly.
37.	$P = \$7,000,$	$r = 9\%$,	$t = 3$ years,	interest compounded monthly.
38.	$P = \$1,500,$	$r = 10\%$,	$t = 2$ years,	interest compounded daily.

39. Find the difference between the compound interest compounded annually and the simple interest on $8,000 for three years at 5% per year.

40. Find the difference between the compound interest compounded annually and the simple interest on $500 for two years at $7\frac{1}{2}\%$.

41. Richard invested $2,000 in a finance company which pays compound interest at the rate of 10% compounded annually. George deposited an equal amount in another company which pays simple interest at 10%. What was the difference in the amounts received by both of them at the end of two years?

8.5 BUSINESS APPLICATIONS (III): BUYING A CAR; BUYING A HOME

Introduction

Installment buying is an important feature of our economy. A person who cannot afford the price of an item can usually follow the policy "buy now and pay later". In this type of purchase, the buyer gets the use of the item such as a car or a home and agrees to pay a specific amount over a specific number of weeks, months, or years. Most of the time he gets it financed by a bank or savings and loan company. Our aim in this section is to make you aware of the expenses involved in

Objectives
After completing this section, you will be able to:
A. Calculate the expenses involved in buying a car; and
B. Calculate expenses involved in buying a home.

the purchase of a car or a home. Often times, a certain amount is required as a **down payment**. With the knowledge gained in previous sections of this chapter, you will be able to calculate the total amount that you will have to pay for these purchases. It is important to mention that, as with finances in general, paying cash is cheaper than getting the purchase financed. Discussion in this section will focus on methods for computing the total cost of financing a home or a car.

8.5 A. Expenses Involved in Buying a Car

Your decision to buy a car can be a very expensive investment. Whether you buy a new or a used car, the following are the expenses involved in this purchase.

EXPENSES IN BUYING A CAR:	
Purchase Price:	The selling price agreed on by the seller and the buyer.
Sales Tax:	A fixed percent of the purchase price that varies from state to state.
License Fee:	Fixed by the state, often based on the type of car and its value.

Example 1   John Ferreira buys a used car for $6,500 (including the sale tax and the license fee), with a $2,000 down payment. The rest is paid in 36 equal monthly installment, at an annual charge of 8%. Find (a) the finance charge; and (b) the monthly payment.

Solution

$$\text{Total cost} = \$6,500$$
$$\underline{\text{Down payment} = -\$2,000} \quad \text{\small Subtract from the total cost.}$$
$$\text{Balance} = \$4,500$$
$$\text{(to be financed)}$$

(a)   Amount to be financed (P) = $4,500

$r = 8\% = 0.08$ *Express rate as a decimal.*

$t = 36$ months or 3 years   *Remember to express time in years.*

The finance charges (I) $= P \cdot r \cdot t$
$$= \$\,4,500 \times 0.08 \times 3$$
$$= \mathbf{\$1,080}$$

$1,080 is the amount of interest or finance charges.

Warm-Up

1. A car with a cash price (including sales tax and the license fee) of $8,500 is to be fully financed at an annual charge of 8% to be paid over a 24-months period. Find

    (a) the finance charge; and

    (b) the monthly payment. (Round to the nearest dollar.)

449

(b) Total amount to be paid in 36 monthly installments

= Balance + Finance charges

= $4,500 + $1,080 = $5,580;

The monthly payment = $5,580 ÷ 36

= **$155.**

The finance charges are $1,080 and the monthly installments are $155.

2. You are going to buy a car for $9,500. The bank will loan you 75% of the purchase price but you must pay a 7% sales tax and $175 license fee. How much cash do you need to buy the car?

Example 2   Sophia is planning to buy a car for $12,750. The bank will loan her 80% of the purchase price. She will be required to pay sales tax at 8% and a $250 license fee. How much ready cash will she need to make this purchase?

Solution

Step 1   First calculate the downpayment:

Loan from Bank = 80% of $12,750

= **$10,200**

Down payment = $12,750 − $10,200 = $2,550.

Step 2   Now, calculate the sales tax: Sales tax is calculated on the purchase price.

Sales tax = 8% of $12,750

= ($12,750) (0.08)

= **$1,020**

Step 3   Add all the cash expenses:

$2,550.00	Down payment
$1,020.00	Sales tax
+ 250.00	License fee
$3,820.00	

Answers:

1. (a) $1,360   **(b)** $411

2. $3,215

She will need **$3,820** to purchase the car.

8.5 B.   Expenses Involved in Buying a Home

Buying a home is perhaps one of the major decisions in one's life and probably the most expensive investment. The process of buying a home can be an anxiety laden experience. A lot of paper work, legal formalities, seemingly endless fees, and terminology used by realtors and lenders can be overwhelming. The purpose of this discussion is to make you familiar with the expenses that can be expected when a home is purchased, and related terminology.

EXPENSES INVOLVED IN BUYING A HOME:

Purchase Price: The selling price that you agree to pay.

Downpayment: The cash you pay to the seller.

Mortgage loan (first trust deed): Money Loaned to you by the bank (difference between purchase price and down payment)

Mortgage fee (or points): Loan fee charged by the lender (usually 1% to 3% of the mortgage loan).

Fire insurance: Insurance against loss of your home by fire (required by almost all lenders).

Recording fees: Local and state fees for recording you as the legal owner.

Property Taxes: Taxes that must be prepaid before the lender will give you a loan (usually six months in advance)

Legal Fees: Fees charged by a lawyer or escrow company or a title search company for completing all forms in a legal manner.

Example 3   Bill Carson wants to buy a home that is for sale for $225,000. The bank will loan him 75% of the selling price and charge 2% for a mortgage fee. He also would need to pay $300 for legal fees, $550 for property taxes, $275 for recording fees, and $500 for fire insurance.

(a) How much would he need for a downpayment?

(b) What would be the amount of the mortgage loan?

(c) What mortgage fee would he be paying?

(d) What amount of cash would Bill need to buy that home and what will be the amount of loan?

Solutions   The selling price is $225,000.

(a)   First find the down payment which will be 25% of $225,000 since the bank will loan 75%.

Down payment = 25% of $225,000

= 0.25 × $225,000

= **$56,250**

> The down payment
> = (100 − 75)%
> = 25%

He would need $56,250 for a down payment.

(b)   **The amount of the mortgage loan (trust deed)**

= selling price − down payment

= $225,000 − $56,250

= **$168,750**

> The same could be found by computing 75% of $225,000
> = 0.75 × 225000
> = $168,750

(c)   **Mortgage fee** = 2% of the mortgage loan

= 2% of $168,750

= 0.02 × 168,750

= **$3,375**

Warm-Up

3. A home is sold for $150,000. The buyer has to make a down payment of 20% of the selling price and pay a loan fee of 1% of the mortgage, $450 for fire insurance, $135 for recording fees, $375 for property taxes, and $325 for legal fees.

(a) What is the amount of the down payment?

(b) What is the amount of the mortgage?

(c) What is the mortgage fee?

(d) How much cash does the buyer need to make this purchase?

Answers:

3. **(a)** $30,000   **(b)** $120,000

    (c) $1,200   **(d)** $32,485

(d)   Add all cash expenses:

$56,250	Down payment
$3,375	Mortgage fee
$300	Legal fee
$550	Property Taxes
$275	Recording fees
$500	Fire insurance
$61,250	← Cash to complete purchase

Bill would need $61,250 in cash, and the bank will loan him $168,750.

Exercise 8.5

1. Kathy Hess decides to buy a $13,000 car. Her credit union agrees to lend her 80% of the cost. But she has to pay a 6% sales tax and a $125 license fee. How much cash does she need to buy the car?

2. To buy a used car for $8,500, you must pay 7% sales tax and a license fee of $95. If your bank agrees to finance 75% of your total expenses, how much ready cash will you need to buy the car?

3. You want to buy a car for $12,500. Your friend has told you that he will buy your old car for $6,000. If sales tax is figured at 6% of the selling price and the license fee is $175, how much additional cash will you need to purchase the car ? (You don't want to get a loan.)

4. Alex buys a car for $4,500 to be paid over a 36-month period with an 8% finance charge. Find **(a)** the finance charge; and **(b)** the monthly payment.

5. A car with a cash price of $7,800 is sold with down payment of $1,500. The remainder will be paid over 30 months at an annual charge of 9%. Find **(a)** the finance charge; and   **(b)** the monthly installment.

6. A new red convertible is for sale for $28,000. The license fee will be $350 and the sales tax will be 6.5% of the selling price. Your friend agrees to lend you 70% of the selling price for two years at 5% interest.

   (a) How much cash will you need to buy the convertible?   **(b)** How much will it actually cost you?

7. A 3-bedroom home is sold for $150,000. The buyer has to make a down payment of 30% of the selling price and pay a loan fee of 1.5% of the mortgage, $350 for the fire insurance, $170 for recording fees, $425 for taxes, and $480 for legal fees.

   (a) What is the amount of the down payment?   **(b)** What is the amount of the mortgage?

   (c) How much cash does the buyer need to complete the purchase?

8. Eric decides to buy a 4-bedroom home for $250,000. He has to make a down payment of 25% of the selling price, a loan fee of 1.5% of the mortgage, $550 for the fire insurance, $220 for recording fees, $580 for taxes, and $575 for legal fees.

   (a) What is the amount of the down payment?

   (b) What is the amount of the mortgage?

   (c) How much cash does Eric need to complete the purchase?

9. Five years ago John purchased a home for $50,000. When he sold it this year, he realized a 60% appreciation in the value of his purchase. What was his profit on the sale of his home?

10. Morris is planning to buy a home for $95,000. He has $6,000 in his savings for a down payment. The lender has told him that he need only put down 5% of the purchase price. There will be no mortgage fee; the fire insurance will be $300; legal fees will be $175; and taxes, $450. How much cash will Morris have left in his savings account if he decides to buy the home?

8.6 CHAPTER SUMMARY

Examples

Part I Important Terms and Symbols

1. **Percent** means 'per hundred' or hundredths: Percent is the ratio of a number to 100.

2. The symbol %, read "percent" is used for the factor $\frac{1}{100}$ or 0.01.

3. The word "**of**" in the expression "percent of" means to multiply.

4. The basic percent formula is $R \cdot B = A$ or $R = \frac{A}{B}$. In this formula:

   R is the **rate or percent** (converted to a decimal or fraction).

   A is the **amount or percentage** being compared to the base.

   B is the **base:** the 'whole' or original amount (that is, the number we are finding the percent of).

5. To **solve** a percent problem means to find one of the variables R, B, or A when the other two are known.

1. $5\% = 5$ hundredths
   $$= \frac{5}{100}$$

2. $8\% = 8 \cdot \frac{1}{100}$
   $$= 8 \cdot (0.01)$$
   $$= 0.08$$

3. 16% of $75 = \frac{16}{100}$ of 75
   $$= \frac{16}{100} \cdot 75 = 12$$

4. 16% of $75 = 12$,
   $R = 16\% = 0.16$
   $B = 75$
   $A = 12$

5. (a) What is 9% of 150?
   9% of $150 = A$
   $0.09 \times 150 = A$
   $A = 13.5$
   9% of 150 is 13.5

   (b) 9% of **what** is 13.5?
   $0.09\,B = 13.5$
   $$B = \frac{13.5}{0.09} = 150$$

   (c) What percent of 150 is 13.5?
   $$R = \frac{A}{B}$$
   $$R = \frac{13.5}{150} = 0.09 = 9\%$$

Part II Procedure and Rules

1. **Equivalence of percents, decimals and fractions:** Any of these forms of a number can be converted to the other two forms using the following procedures:

   Percent to Rational Numbers:

   (a) Percents can be converted to rational numbers (integers, decimals, or fractions) by

   i) rewriting the percent as a ratio to 100;

   ii) simplifying the ratio using the rules for reducing or dividing fractions.

1. (a) (i) $15.2\% = \frac{15.2}{100}$
   $$= 0.152$$

   (ii) $2.4\% = \frac{2.4}{100} = 2.4 \times \frac{1}{100}$
   $$= \frac{24}{10} \times \frac{1}{100} = \frac{3}{125}$$

Examples

(b) **(i)** $3.45 = 3.45 \cdot 100\% = 345\%.$

(ii) $\dfrac{13}{5} = \dfrac{13}{5} \cdot 100\% = 260\%.$

(c) $2.45 = \dfrac{245}{10^2} = \dfrac{245}{100} = \dfrac{49}{20} = 2\dfrac{9}{20}.$

(d) $\dfrac{13}{5} = \begin{array}{r} 2.6 \\ 5\overline{)13.0} \\ \underline{10} \\ 30 \\ \underline{30} \\ 0 \end{array}$

$= 2.6$

2. Ratio of 9 to 15 $= \dfrac{9}{15}$

$= \dfrac{\overset{3}{\cancel{9}}}{\underset{5}{\cancel{15}}} \cdot \overset{20}{\cancel{100}}\%_{1}$

$= 60\%.$

3. If you gain \$38 by investing \$200, then the **percent of profit**

$= \dfrac{\$38}{\$200} = \dfrac{19}{100} = 19\%.$

4. If the cost = \$28.50,

(a) Markup = 40% of the cost

$= (0.40)(28.50) = \$11.40.$

The selling price = S

$S = C + M = \$28.50 + \$11.40$

$= \$39.90$

(b) $R = \dfrac{\$11.40}{\$28.50} = 0.4 = 40\%$

5. If a store offers a 45% discount on an item that is listed for \$150, then

The **rate of discount** = 45% = 0.45

List price = \$150

Amount of discount = 45% of \$150

$= (0.45)(150)$

$= \$67.50$

Sale price = \$150 − \$67.50 = \$82.50.

(b) A rational number (integer, fraction, or decimal) can be converted to a percent by multiplying by 100%.

(c) **Decimal to Fraction** — Remove the decimal point and divide the resulting number by 10^n, where n is the number of decimal places. Reduce the fraction.

(d) **Fraction to Decimal** — Divide the numerator by the denominator.

2. **Percent Comparison of Two Numbers:** To find the percent comparison of two numbers:

Step **1** Write the ratio or comparison as a fraction.

Step **2** Multiply the fraction by 100%.

Step **3** Simplify.

3. **Percent of Profit:** The ratio of the money gained to the money invested when expressed as a percent is called the **percent of profit.**

Business Related Terms and Concepts

4. **(a)** **Markup:** *Markup* (M) is the amount that is added to the **cost** (C) of an item to arrive at the **selling price** (S). If M denotes the amount of markup, then

$M = S - C$ or $S = C + M$ or $C = S - M.$

(b) **Rate of markup:** Ratio of markup to cost.

$R = \dfrac{A}{B} = \dfrac{\text{markup}}{\text{cost}}$

5. **(a)** **Discount:** Reduction in original selling price.

(b) **Sale price** = (Original price) − (the discount)

(c) **Rate of Discount:** Percent of original price to be discounted.

Examples

6. **Sales Tax:** Tax on *actual* selling price.

6. If an item is sold for $500 and the rate of sales tax is 7%, then the amount of sales tax = 7% of $500 = $35.

Thus, the buyer will pay
$500 + $35 = $535.

7. (a) **Profit:** Income – Costs

   (b) **Percent of profit:**

   Percent of profit **based on cost** $= \dfrac{\text{profit}}{\text{cost}}$

   (Expressed as percent)

7. If an item that costs a store $60 is sold for $75, then the store makes a profit of $(75 – $60) = $15.

$$\left.\begin{array}{l}\text{Percent of Profit}\\\text{(based on cost)}\end{array}\right\} = \frac{\text{Profit}}{\text{Cost}} = \frac{\$15}{\$60} = \frac{1}{4}$$
$$= 25\%$$

8. **Commission:** Commission is the money paid to an agent or a person engaged in selling a firm's products.

8. If a person earns a commission of 25% on all sales over $600 a month and if his sales for a month are $2,170, then:
   The commission he earns
   $= 25\%$ of ($2,170 – $600)
   $= 25\%$ of $1,570
   $= (0.25)(\$1,570)$
   $= \$392.50$.

9. **Tip:** A tip is an amount that is paid to a waiter or waitress, or any other person for providing good service. The usual tip in a restaurant is approximately 15% of the bill amount.

RULE OF THUMB FOR CALCULATING A 15% TIP	
Step **1**	Round the amount of the bill to the nearest whole dollar.
Step **2**	Find 10% of the rounded amount by moving the decimal point one place to the left.
Step **3**	Divide the answer in Step 2 by 2. This will represent 5% of the rounded amount.
Step **4**	Add the two amounts found in Steps 2 and 3. This sum is the amount of tip.

9. To calculate a 15% tip (approximately) if the bill amount is $45.60:

   Step 1 $45.60 \approx \$46.00$

   Step 2 10% tip = $4.60

   Step 3 5% of tip = $\dfrac{\$4.60}{2}$
   $= \$2.30$

   Step 4 15% tip = $4.60 + $2.30
   $= \$6.90$.

Simple Interest and Compound Interest

10. **Simple Interest:** Interest calculated only on the *principal* for any length of time is called **simple interest**. The formula for simple interest is:

    Simple **I**nterest = **P**rincipal × **r**ate × **t**ime   or $I = p \cdot r \cdot t$;

    where   P = Principal = money borrowed, deposited, or invested
    r = rate of interest
    t = time (expressed in years or a fraction of a year)
    I = Interest.

    The Total Amount A is the sum of P and I; that is,

    $$A = P + I$$

10. To find the simple interest on $4,600 for three years at the rate of 15%:

    $$P = \$4,600$$
    $$r = 15\% = 0.15$$
    $$t = 3 \text{ years.}$$

    $\begin{aligned} I &= Prt \\ &= (\$4,600)(0.15)(3) \\ &= \$2,070. \end{aligned}$

    Also, $\begin{aligned} A &= \$4,600 + \$2,070 \\ &= \$6,670. \end{aligned}$

Example

11. Find the compound interest on $4,600 for three years at the rate of 15% compounded **monthly**.

We have
P = $4,600
r = 15% = 0.15
n = 12 times per year
t = 3 years

Substituting into the formula gives:

$$A = 4{,}600\left(1+\frac{0.15}{12}\right)^{(12)\,(3)}$$

$$= 4{,}600\,(1+0.0125)^{36}$$

$$= 4{,}600\,(1.0125)^{36}$$

$$= \$7{,}194.15. \quad \text{(Use a calculator.)}$$

The compound interest is given by:

Compound Interest = $A - P$
$$= \$7{,}194.15 - \$4{,}600$$
$$= \$2{,}594.15.$$

11. **Compound Interest:** In compound interest, we earn interest not only on the principal, but also on the interest earned in the previous time period.

Compound Interest Formula:

When interest is compounded, the total **amount** A (principal plus the total interest) is given by the formula:

$$A = P\left(1+\frac{r}{n}\right)^{nt}$$

where

P = the principal
r = the *annual* interest rate (in decimal form)
t = time in *years*
n = number of compounding periods in one year

If the interest is *compounded annually*, we have $n = 1$, and the formula reduces to

$$A = P\,(1 + r)^{t}.$$

Remark: The compound interest for the **first time period** is the same as the simple interest for that period.

8.7 REVIEW EXERCISE

In exercises 1-4, what percent of the figure is shaded?

1.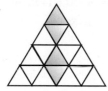

2.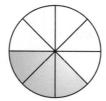

3.

4.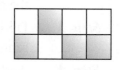

In exercises 5-8, write the percent equivalent to the given comparison.

5. 42 out of 200   **6.** 7 to 30   **7.** 15 out of 300   **8.** 5 to 100

In exercises 9-14, write the decimal number as a percent.

9. 0.08   **10.** $0.15\overline{6}$ **11.** 1.75   **12.** 1.07   **13.** 0.008   **14.** 0.8

In exercises 15-20, write the percent as a decimal number.

15. 2.55%   **16.** 37%   **17.** 125.4%   **18.** $16\frac{2}{5}\%$ **19.** 0.25%   **20.** 12.5%

In exercises 21-26, write the number as a percent.

21. $\dfrac{3}{8}$ **22.** $\dfrac{12}{40}$ **23.** $\dfrac{19}{4}$ **24.** $2\dfrac{1}{5}$ **25.** $\dfrac{13}{50}$ **26.** $\dfrac{5}{8}$

In exercises 27-32, write the number as a percent. Round to the nearest tenth of a percent.

27. $\dfrac{5}{3}$ 28. $\dfrac{5}{6}$ 29. $\dfrac{5}{8}$ 30. $\dfrac{7}{12}$ 31. $\dfrac{3}{80}$ 32. $\dfrac{7}{8}$

In exercises 33-38, change the percent to a fraction in lowest terms.

33. 35%   34. 2%   35. 3.2%   36. .4%   37. 360%   38. $37\dfrac{1}{2}\%$

In exercises 39-48, solve the percent problem by translating to an equation.

39. $2\dfrac{1}{4}\%$ of 41 = ?

40. 8.5% of $500 = ?

41. 3.5% of 75 inches

42. $66\dfrac{2}{3}\%$ of 96

43. 80% of *what* number is 28?

44. $16\dfrac{2}{3}\%$ of *what* number is 587?

45. 42% of *what* number is 15.75?

46. *What* percent of 86 is 172?

47. *What* percent of 150 is 78?

48. *What* percent of 90 is 21.87?

49. A man invests $\dfrac{2}{5}$ of $100 at 3% per year and the remainder at 5% per year. Find his annual income on the $100.

50. If the purchase price of a new car is $8,700, what is the total price of the car after adding 5% sales tax?

51. Calculate the percent of profit (rounded to the nearest tenth) for both (a) and (b), and identify which is the better investment.
    (a) $150 made as profit by investing $400   (b) $270 made as profit by investing $700

52. Find the gross profit or loss on a woolen suit costing $175.00 with 15% overhead costs and sold at a markup of 25% on cost.

53. A sales representative is paid a $37\dfrac{1}{2}\%$ commission on all sales in addition to a weekly salary of $45.00. If the sales in a week are $760.00, find his gross earnings for that week.

54. Use the Rule of Thumb to calculate a 15% tip on a restaurant bill of $27 plus a 5% tax.

55. The discount on a new coat was $175. This was a discount of 20%. (a) What was the original selling price of the coat? (b) What was the sale price? (c) What would a customer pay for the coat if a 7.25% sales tax is added to the sale price?

56. How much interest will be earned on a savings account of $3,000 in two years if   (a) the interest is compounded annually at 7.25%; and   (b) the interest is compounded semi-annually?

57. Kim deposits $5,215 in an account that pays 5.5% per year simple interest. How long must Kim keep the money in the bank so that the account is worth $6,000?

8.8 SELF TEST

1. Write as a percent: 0.0575

2. Write $2\frac{1}{3}\%$ as a decimal.

3. Write 145% as a fraction or a mixed number.

4. If 3 out of every 5 students are girls, what percent of the class is girls?

5. What number is 9% of 150?

6. Change $2\frac{5}{12}\%$ to a decimal rounded to the nearest tenths and the nearest thousandths.

7. What is $3\frac{1}{2}\%$ of 740?

8. 35 is what percent of 10?

9. 18 is 25% of what number?

10. Write $33\frac{1}{3}\%$ as a fraction.

11. 20% of what is $64?

12. Express 3.5% as a decimal.

13. A shirt is selling at a 15% discount on the marked price. If the marked price is $135.45, what is the selling price of the shirt? Round to the nearest ten cents.

14. The sale price of an article is $10.50. The list price is $15. Find the rate of discount offered.

15. What percent of $5\frac{1}{2}$ is $3\frac{1}{8}$? Round to the nearest tenths of a percent.

16. Find the amount of interest on $1,500 for two and a half years if the rate of simple interest is 4.5%.

17. Find the final retail price of an item with an original retail price of $75, reduced by 30%, and later raised by 15%. What is the net mark down?

18. A shirt costing $14.30 is sold for $21.10. Find the net profit if the operating expenses were

    (a) $5.35; and

    (b) $9.65.

19. A sales representative is paid a straight commission of $33\frac{1}{3}\%$ on all sales. If his sales for this month are $1,375.50, find his gross earnings.

20. John deposited $5,000 in his savings account that earns interest at 7% compounded quarterly. Find the amount John will receive after three years.

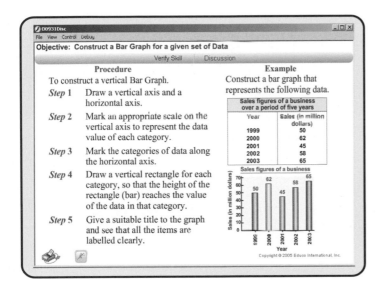

Basic Statistics, Plotting Points and Lines

9.1   **Mean, Median, Mode and Range** ■

9.2   **Reading Graphs: Bar, Line, Circle, Pictographs** ■

9.3   **Constructing Graphs** ■

9.4   **Plotting Points, Linear Equations in Two Variables and Graphing Lines** ■

9.5   **Chapter Summary** ■

9.6   **Review Exercise** ■

9.7   **Self Test** ■

BASIC STATISTICS, PLOTTING POINTS AND LINES

Introduction

The term *statistics* is used as a synonym for the word '**data**'-the numerical statement of facts. We talk of employment statistics, trade statistics, and population statistics.

Statistics is a mathematical *science* which deals with the collection, organization, presentation, analysis, and interpretation of data.

In this chapter we will introduce some *basic concepts* of statistics such as **mean**, **median**, **mode**, and **range** and learn how to compute these for a given set of data. We will learn to read and interpret data from different kinds of graphs (bar graphs, circle graphs, pictographs, line graphs, histograms, and frequency polygons). We will also learn to plot points and lines, and construct our own graphs from given data.

The chapter is divided into the following four sections:

    9.1   *Mean, Median, Mode, and Range;*

    9.2   *Reading Graphs: Bar Graphs, Line Graphs, Circle Graphs, Pictographs;*

    9.3   *Constructing Graphs from Given Data; and*

    9.4   *Plotting Points, Linear Equations in Two Variables, and Graphing Lines.*

9.1   MEAN, MEDIAN, MODE, AND RANGE

IMPORTANT VOCABULARY

1. By **data** we mean collected information in the form of a set of numerical values.

2. The **mean** is the common arithmetic average of the data.

3. The **median** is a value that represents the 'middle' of the data after the data has been arranged in order (increasing or decreasing).

4. The **mode** is the single data item that appears most frequently.

5. A **statistic** is a single number (mean, median, or mode) describing some characteristic of the data.

6. The **range** is the difference between the largest and the smallest data items.

> **Objectives**
>
> After completing this section, you will be able to:
>
> Find the mean, median, mode and range of a set of data items.

- **Numerical representation of data:** The process of analyzing and interpreting data basically involves finding some **special numerical values** called **statistics.** Each statistic describes or measures a particular characteristic of the data. In this section we will study only four numerical statistics that are easily calculated: Mean, Median, Mode, and Range. Out of these, the first three, the mean, median, and mode are measures that describe the '**average**' or the '**middle**' of a set of data and are called the **measures of central tendency.** The fourth one, the range, is called the **measure of spread.**

- ## The Mean

    The **mean** of a set of numbers (data) is the common arithmetic average or arithmetic mean. We calculate the mean of a set of observations by dividing the sum of the observations by the number of observations.

    $$\text{Mean} = \frac{\text{sum of all the observations in the data}}{\text{number of observations in the data}}$$

    For example, if the heights of six boys are:

    162 cm, 176 cm, 180 cm, 182 cm, 178 cm, and 175 cm

    then,

    the **mean** height $= \dfrac{162+176+180+182+178+175}{6}$ ← Add all the numbers in the data.

    ← Divide the sum by 6 as there are 6 data items.

    $= \dfrac{1,053}{6}$ (You may use a calculator for computations.)

    $= 175.5$ cm

Note   While giving the mean of a set of data, we must also mention the unit in which the observations have been measured/recorded. Thus, we say that the mean height is 175.5 cm. It is not proper to say that the mean height is 175.5.

- Following are two sets of data, Group I and Group II, that will be used in Examples 1-3.

Group I: Family incomes (weekly) in a survey of eleven workers are:

$350, $280, $450, $375, $470, $525, $450, $300, $500, $490, and $430.

Group II: The points scored by a basketball team in ten matches are:

28, 31, 27, 30, 55, 60, 65, 70, 100, and 84

Warm-Up

1. **(a)** Find the mean of the following data and identify whether or not it is a data-item:

    54, 57, 61, 57, 62, 58, and 57

Example 1   **(a)** Find the mean weekly income for the 11 workers in Group I.

(b) Find the mean score of the basketball team from the data in Group II.

Solutions   We know that $\text{mean} = \dfrac{\text{sum of the observations}}{\text{number of the observations}}$

(a)   Refer to the data in Group I

Step 1   Add the amounts of 11 salaries:

```
 350
 280
 450
 375
 470
 525
 450
 300
 500
 490
 430
4,620   ← Sum
```

You may use a calculator for calculations. The solution in compact form is written as:

Sum of the observations = 350 + 280 + 450 + 375 + 470 + 525 + 450 + 300 + 500 + 490 + 430 = $4,620.

The number of observations = 11.

Step 2　Divide the sum by 11.

$$\begin{array}{r} 420 \\ 11\overline{)4620} \\ 44 \\ \hline 22 \\ 22 \\ \hline 00 \\ 00 \\ \hline 0 \end{array}$$
← mean salary

The mean weekly salary is $420.

(b)　Refer to the data in Group II.

Step 1　The sum of the data values

$$= 28 + 31 + 27 + 30 + 55 + 60 + 65 + 70 + 100 + 84$$

$$= 550$$

Step 2　The mean $= \dfrac{550}{10}$ ← The sum of observations.

← The number of observations.

$= 55$ points　(Remember to mention the 'unit' of observations with the mean.)

The mean score of the basket ball team is 55 points.

(b)　Find the mean for the following data :

45, 77, 69, 95, 50, 81, 32, and 70

(Round the answer to two decimal places)

Answers:

1. (a) 58 ; yes　　**(b)** $64.875 \approx 64.88$

- **The Median**

In a set of data arranged in order, smallest to largest or largest to smallest, the **median** is the *middle* value.

For example, if the observed values are:

$$12, \ 14, \ 15, \ 17, \ \mathbf{21}, \ 24, \ 26, 27, 30$$

then the median is equal to **21**. Observe that there are four values in the data that are less than 21, and exactly the same number of values greater than 21.

If the number of observations is even as in the following data set,

$$12, 14, 15, \mathbf{17}, \mathbf{21}, 24, 26, 27,$$

then there are two middle terms; namely, **17** and **21**. In such cases, the **average of the two middle terms** is taken as the median; thus, the median of the data under consideration is $\dfrac{17+21}{2} = \mathbf{19}$.

The determination of **median** depends on whether there is an odd or an even number of observations. The procedure to find the median is as follows:

Procedure to find the median

Step **1**　Arrange the data in order, either from smallest to largest or largest to smallest.

Step **2**　**a.** If the number of items (n) is **odd**, the median is the middle term.

　　　　　　b. If n is **even**, the median is the average of the two middle terms.

Warm-Up

2. (a) Following are the ages (in years) of a group of seven friends. Find the median age.

54, 57, 61, 57, 62, 58, 57

(b) Find the median for the following data:

45, 77, 69, 95, 50, 81, 32, 70

Example 2 **(a)** Find the median weekly income for the 11 workers in Group I.

(b) Find the median score of the basketball team from the data in Group II.

Solutions To find the median we must express the data in descending or ascending order.

(a) Refer to the data in Group I.

Step 1 Rank the data in order from smallest to largest.

1.	2.	3.	4.	5.	6.	7.	8.	9.	10.	11.
280	300	350	375	430	**450**	450	470	490	500	525

↑

Step 2 Since there are 11 items (an **odd** number), of data, the median is the middle item (the sixth item);

Median weekly salary = $450.

(b) Refer to the data in Group II

Step 1 Rank the data in order:

1.	2.	3.	4.	5.	6.	7.	8.	9.	10.
27	28	30	31	**55**	**60**	65	70	84	100

↑   ↑

Step 2 Since there are 10 items (an **even** number) of data, there are two middle items, and the median is the average of these two.

$$\text{Median Score} = \frac{55+60}{2}$$

$$= 57.5 \text{ points}$$

The median score is 57.5 points.

Answers:

2. (a) 57 yrs   (b) 69.5

• The Mode and Range

The **mode** is also another measure of central tendency. It is that value of the data that occurs most frequently. For example, in the data

2 1 4 2 0 1 **3** 6 **3** 0 **3** 5 **3**

the value 3 occurs most frequently, so the mode of the data is 3.

> **Remark:** A set of data may have more than one mode; however, the data sets that we use in this text will have either one mode or no mode. If each number in the data occurs only once then the data has no mode.

Range is a rough measure of 'spread' and is given by the difference of the largest and the smallest data values. For example, the range of the data

20 10 5 35 15 19 20

is the difference $35 - 5 = \mathbf{30}$, as 35 is the largest and 5 is the smallest data value.

Remark: We have called the range "a *rough* measure of spread"; 'rough', because it simply tells us the span in which the data values lie but does not convey any thing about the way they are spread. There are other measures of spread such as **standard deviation** and **variance** that describe how compact the data values are spread around the central value. Discussion of such measures is beyond the scope of this text.

Example 3 Find **(a)** the **mode** and **(b)** the **range** for both sets of data in Groups I and II.

Solutions Once the data has been ranked, as was done in Example 2, the mode and the range are easily determined. For both groups, refer to their ranked data in Example 2.

(a) (i) For Group I, the mode = **$450.**

The value 450 appears the maximum number of times (twice in this case). Remember to use the unit in which the data items are measured.

(ii) Data in Group II have **no mode** since each value occurs only once.

(b) Range = (largest value) − (smallest value).

For Group I, range $= 525 - 280$

$= $245;$

In Group I, from ranked data in Example 2, the largest value = 525; the smallest value = 280.

For Group II, range $= 100 - 27$

$= 73$ points.

Remember to mention the unit.

Warm-Up

3. Find **(a)** the **mode** and **(b)** the **range** for the sets of data in Warm-Up 2 (a) and 2(b).

Answers:

3. (a) Mode of data in Warm-Up 2(a) = 57 yrs; No mode for data in 2(b).

 (b) Range of data in Warm-Up 2(a) = 8 yrs; Range of data in Warm-Up 2(b) = 63.

Exercise 9.1

In exercises 1-5, find the mean, median, mode (if any), and the range for the given set of numbers.

1. 60, 65, 55, 70, 90, 81, 76, 50, and 62 **2.** 5, 12, 2, 11, 8, 10, 7, 4, and 2 **3.** 85, 72, 70, 82, 72, 71, 84, and 75

4. 10, 5, 5, 2, 9, 8, 2, 3, 4, 6, 6, 5, and 9 **5.** 2.3, 3.5, 1.7, 1.9, 3.2, 2.3, and 2.4

In exercises 6-14, find the mean, median, mode (if there is one), and the range of the given data. Remember to use the unit of measurement in which the data items are measured.

6. The weekly salaries of six employees of Jack's establishment: $480, $210, $190, $185, $215, and $500

7. The ages (in years) of 16 boys selected at random from a class:

   14 16 13 14 15 12 14 15

   16 15 13 14 14 15 15 15

8. The weights (in kg) of 10 students surveyed in a chemistry class: 50 54 53 50 56 50 59 61 50 48

9. Earnings (in dollars) of a server/waiter in a restaurant from tips, for nine consecutive days:

   20 21 24 24 23 28 28 24 36

10. The body temperatures (in Fahrenheit degrees) of 8 people:

   99.2° 98.7° 96.4° 98.1° 100.2° 98.6° 99.8° 98.6°

11. The scores (out of 40) of 20 students surveyed in a Mathematics class:

24	17	26	35	36	23	19	21	20	19
20	18	20	21	18	22	23	23	23	18

12. The times, taken by 15 students to complete an experiment:

44	45	65	58	42	49	42	54
48	46	62	38	48	48	60	

(Round the answers to the nearest second.)

13. The heights (in cm) of 10 students selected at random from Dr. Anderson's course in Business Mathematics:

150   148   147   146   145   143   153   139   141   142

14. The time of 11 movies:

99 min	105 min	110 min	88 min	90 min	100 min
93 min	90 min	155 min	90 min	113 min	

In exercises 15-16, find the mean, median, and mode of the given series of observations.

15. 17, 8, 14, 12, 9, 3, 21, 5, 12, and 16

16. 26, 16, 14, 15, 17, 27, 26, 18, and 30

9.2   READING GRAPHS: BAR GRAPHS, LINE GRAPHS, CIRCLE GRAPHS, PICTOGRAPHS

Objectives 📗

After completing this section, you will be able to:

A. Read and interpret data from a bar graph and a line graph;

B. Read and interpret data from a circle graph (pie-chart); and

C. Read and interpret data from a pictograph.

IMPORTANT VOCABULARY 💾

1. A **graph** is a visual representation of numerical data.

2. A **bar graph** uses a number of bars, generally of equal width and different heights.

3. Bar graphs contain two **scales**, a **vertical scale** and a **horizontal scale**. The **vertical scale** represents one set of values, and the **horizontal scale** represents a second set of values.

4. In a **vertical bar graph**, bars are arranged vertically (Figure 9.1). In a **horizontal bar graph**, bars are arranged horizontally (Figure 9.2).

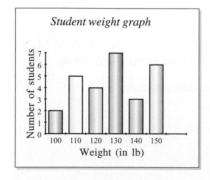

Figure 9.1

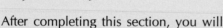

A : Black and White TV
B : Color TV with stereo
C : Color TV
D : Miniature TV

Figure 9.2

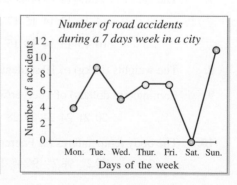

Figure 9.3

5. A **line graph** uses lines connecting points to show the variations in one set of values corresponding to the variations in another set of values. A line graph also has a horizontal and a vertical scale, like a bar graph. Figure 9.3 shows a line graph.

6. A **circle graph** or a **pie-chart** illustrates a whole unit divided into parts or percents. Each part is represented by a **sector** of a circle. The entire circle represents 100% (Figure 9.4).

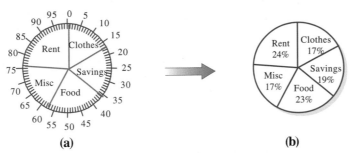

Monthly expenditure of a family

(a)   (b)

Figure 9.4

7. A **pictograph** uses symbol-pictures or drawings to represent numbers from a set. Each complete symbol represents a fixed number (Figure 9.5).

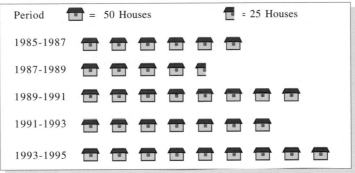

Number of houses built by Housing Corporation

Figure 9.5

9.2 A.   Reading and Interpreting Data from a Bar Graph and a Line Graph.

A bar graph contains two scales, a vertical scale and a horizontal scale, and a number of bars erected on one of the scales with equal spacing between them. Each bar represents only one value of the numerical data, so there are as many bars as the values in the numerical data. The height (or length) of each bar indicates the corresponding value of the numerical data.

Example 1   The total sale of goods in a general store between 10 AM to 2 PM is given in the following bar graph:

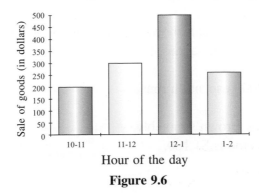

Figure 9.6

Warm-Up

1. Respond to the following questions using Figure 9.6:

   (a) Find the sales during the fourth (1-2) hour.

Warm-Up

(b) Express the sales during the third hour as a percent of the total sales between 10 AM and 2 PM.

Answer the following questions using the bar graph in Figure 9.6.

(a) Find the total sales during the first hour.

(b) Find the percent increase in sales from the second to the third hour.

Solutions

(a) $ 200   Read the vertical scale against the height of the bar on the top of 10-11 hour of the horizontal scale.

(b)   Sale during the second (11-12) hour   = $300

Sale during the third (12-1) hour   = $500

The percent increase in sales between the second and the third hour

$$= \frac{200}{300} \times 100\,\%$$ The actual increase = 500 − 300 = 200; divided by the base value = 300.

$$= 66.\overline{66}\,\%$$

$$\approx 67\% \text{ to the nearest whole number percent.}$$

2. Use the bar graph of Figure 9.7 to answer the following questions:

(a) How much is spent on clothes?

Example 2   Respond to questions in (a) to (d) using the bar graph in Figure 9.7.

Distribution of Mrs. Brown's monthly income

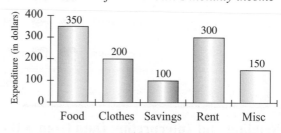

Figure 9.7

(b) What percent of the monthly income is saved by Mrs. Brown?

(a) What information is given by the bar graph?

(b) How much is spent on rent?

(c) What is the monthly income of Mrs. Brown?

(d) What percent of the income is spent on food?

(c) On which item does Mrs. Brown spend the maximum?

Solutions

(a) The bar graph shows the distribution of Mrs. Brown's monthly income on various items.   Suggested by the title of the bar graph.

(b) $300 is spent on rent.   The height of the bar representing the item Rent is 300.

(c) Mrs. Brown's monthly income is $1,100.   The total monthly income = the total expenditure = the sum of the heights of all the 5 bars = 350 + 200 + 100 + 300 + 150 = 1,100.

(d) The percentage of income spent on food:

$$= \frac{350}{1{,}100} \times 100\,\%$$

Percentage of income spent on

$$food = \frac{\text{Amount spent on food}}{\text{Total income}} \times 100\,\%$$

$$= \frac{350}{11}\,\% \approx \mathbf{31.82\,\%}$$

Example 3   Use the bar graph of the figure below to answer the questions in (a) to (c):

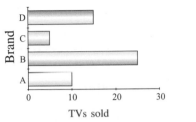

TV sales in a week of Whirlpool Electronics

A : Black and White TV
B : Color TV with stereo
C : Color TV
D : Miniature TV

(a) What information is given by the bar graph?

(b) How many color TV sets are sold during the week?

(c) Which type of TV set is the most popular?

Solutions

(a) The bar graph gives the details of the TV sales in a week at Whirlpool Electronics.

Suggested by the title of the bar graph.

(b) 5

The length of the bar for C, representing the color TV sets, is 5.

(c) The color TV set with stereo is the most popular.

The length of the bar for B, representing color TV with stereo, is longest. The maximum TV sets sold were of this brand.

Example 4   The number of computers sold by a company during the period 1999-2003 is shown in the following line graph:

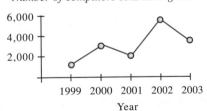

Number of computers sold during 1999-2003

Figure 9.8

Use this line graph to answer the following questions:

(a)   In which year did the company sell the maximum number of computers?

(b)   What is the increase in sales in 2003 over the sales in year 1999?

(c)   What is the percent increase in sales in 2003 over the sales in 1999?

3. Use the bar graph of Example 3 to answer the following questions:

(a)   What is the total number of TV sets sold in a week?

(b)   What is the ratio of the number of Black and White TV sets sold to Miniature TV sets sold?

(c)   Which is the least popular brand?

4. Use the graph of Figure 9.8 to answer the following questions:

(a)   How many computers were sold in the year 2000?

(b)   What is the decrease in sales in 2001 as compared to the sales in 2000?

(c) What is the percent decrease in sales in 2003 over the sales in 2002?

Answers:

1. (a) $250   **(b)** ≈ 40%

2. (a) $200   **(b)** 9.1%   **(c)** Food

3. (a) 55   **(b)** $\frac{2}{3}$ **(c)** Color TV

4. (a) 3,000   **(b)** 1,000   **(c)** $33\frac{1}{3}\%$

Solutions

(a) From the graph we find that the company sold the maximum number of computers in 2002. The highest point on the graph corresponds to 2002.

(b) The increase in sales in 2003 over those in 1999 is 3000.

Sales in 2003 = 4,000
Sales in 1999 = 1,000
Increase = 3,000

(c) The percent increase in sales in 2003 over the sales in 1999 is 300%.

Actual increase = 4,000 – 1,000
= 3,000.

Percent increase = $\frac{3,000}{1,000} \cdot 100\%$
(Sales in the ⟶
original base year)

= 300 %

9.2 B. Reading and Interpreting Data from a Pie-Chart (Circle Graph)

In a *pie chart* or *a circle graph* the whole unit is divided into parts. Each part or percent is represented by a sector of a circle whose size is proportional to the value of the data for that part.

To read data from a pie chart means to find a part of the whole as a *fraction* or as a *percent*. Generally, the circumference of the circle is shown divided in hundredths (see Figure 9.9). In that case, to know the percentage of a particular part, we count the number of hundredths on the arc of that sector, and that count is the required percentage. We explain the process in the following example.

Warm-Up

5. Use the circle graph of Figure 9.9 to answer the following questions:

(a) What percent of the funds are spent on library books?

(b) On which item is the expenditure greatest?

(c) If the total funds available are $2,750,000, how much is spent on sports?

Example 5   The following circle graph shows different budget items in a school budget:

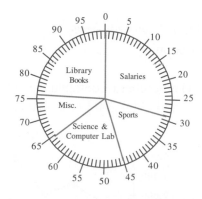

Figure 9.9

(a) What percent of the funds are spent on science and computer labs?

(b) On which item is the expenditure more, sports or library books?

(c) If the total funds available in the year 2004 are $3,570,000, how much will be spent on salaries, if the percentages for each expenditure item in 2004 remains the same?

Solutions

(a) 20%

Count the number of divisions between the markings 45 and 65 : 65 − 45 = 20.

(b) Library books

The area of the sector representing Library books is larger than the area of the sector representing 'Sports'.

(c) The amount spent on salaries

= 30 % of $3,570,000

$= \dfrac{30}{100} \times \$3,570,000$

= $1,071,000.

Salaries represents 30 % of the total funds. The total funds available are $3,570,00.

Example 6   A retired person has accumulated $650,000 in savings and wishes to invest this money. The types of investments and corresponding percentages recommended by a financial advisor are shown in the following circle graph. What amount of money should this person invest in each category?

Recommended Categories of Investment

Figure 9.10

Solution   The amount of money that should be invested in each category are as under:

(a) In Bonds = 40% of $650,000

= **$260,000**

(a) 40% of $650,000 = 0.40 × 650,000
= $260,000

(b) In Real Estate = 15% of $650,000

= **$97,500**

(b) 15% of $650,000 = 0.15 × 650,000
= $97,500

(c) In Stocks = 25% of $650,000

= **$162,500**

(c) 25% of $650,000 = 0.25 × 650,000
= $162,500

(d) In Cash = 20% of $650,000

= **$130,000**

(d) 20% of $650,000 = 0.20 × 650,000
= $130,000

Warm-Up

6. Another colleague of a person (Example 6) wants to follow the same recommendations (Figure 9.10). His accumulated savings are $500,000. Find the amount of money he should invest in each category.

Answers:

5. (a) 24%   **(b)** Salaries   **(c)** $440,000

6. Real estate: $75,000
Bonds: $200,000
Stocks: $125,000
Cash: $100,000

9.2 C.   Reading and Interpreting Data from a Pictograph

- A pictograph uses symbol-pictures to represent a number. Each complete symbol represents a fixed number and half the symbol represents half that number. Pictographs can be interpreted like bar graphs.

We discuss this in more detail in the following examples:

Warm-Up

7. Find the fraction of the total enrolment in the Algebra course, using the data in Figure 9.11.

Example 7 The following pictograph shows the number of students enrolled in four mathematics courses at a school.

Courses	Students enrolled
	☺ = 50 students
Pre-algebra	☺ ☺ ☺ ☺
Algebra	☺ ☺ ☺ ☺ ☺ ☺
Pre-calculus	☺ ☺ ☺
Calculus	☺ ☺

Figure 9.11

Answer the following questions using this pictograph:

(a) Find the number of students enrolled in the Algebra course?

(b) Which is the least popular course?

(c) What is the difference of enrollment in the Algebra course as compared to the Pre-calculus course?

Solutions

(a) The row for the Algebra course has six symbols of 50 students each; therefore, the number of students enrolled in the Algebra course

$$= 6 \times 50$$
$$= 300 \text{ students.}$$

(b) Compare the number of times the symbol appears in each row. The row for Calculus is the shortest indicating the least number of students enrolled in it. Calculus is the least popular course.

(c) Students enrolled in Algebra = 300
Students enrolled in Pre-calculus = 3 × 50 = **150**
The difference = 300 − 150 = **150**

The Algebra course has 150 more students enrolled than the Pre-calculus course.

8. Use the pictograph in Figure 9.12 to answer the following questions:

(a) How many cars were produced during the years 1999 - 2003?

Example 8 Figure 9.12 shows the number of cars produced by a company from 1999-2003.

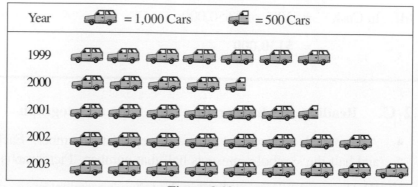

Number of cars produced by a company

Figure 9.12

Answer the following questions using the pictograph in Figure 9.12:

(a) How many cars were produced during the years 1999-2001?

(b) In which year was the production at a maximum?

(c) What percent of the total cars were produced in the year 1999?

(b) In which year was the production the least?

Solutions

(a) $\left(7 + 4\dfrac{1}{2} + 6\dfrac{1}{2}\right) \times 1000$

The numbers or symbols in the row of $1999 = 7; \ 2000 = 4\frac{1}{2}; \ 2001 = 6\frac{1}{2}$.

$= 18 \times 1000$

Total symbols = 18. Each symbol represents 1,000 cars.

$= 18,000$ cars.

(c) What percent of the total cars were produced in the year 2003?

(b) In the year 2003.

There are more number of symbols in the 2003 row than in any other row.

(c) Percent of the cars produced in 1999 compared to the total number of cars

Number of cars produced in $1999 = 7 \times 1,000 = 7,000$.

$= \dfrac{\text{Number of cars produced in 1999}}{\text{Total number of cars in five years}} \times 100\%$

Answers:

$= \dfrac{7,000}{35,000} \times 100\%$

7. $\dfrac{2}{5}$

$= 20\%$.

8. (a) 35,000 **(b)** 2000 **(c)** 25.7%

Exercise 9.2

A. **The following chart shows the total rainfall in a city recorded in the years 1998 to 2003. Answer the questions in exercises 1-4, using this graph.**

1. In which year did the city have the maximum rainfall?

2. In which year(s) did the city have the minimum rainfall?

3. How much rainfall was recorded in the year 2001?

4. What was the average rainfall during the six years? Round to the nearest tenth of an inch.

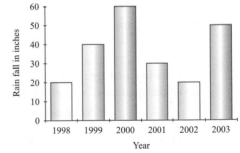

The following bar graph shows the number of cars produced by a company during the period 1997-2003. Answer the questions in exercises 5-10, using this graph.

5. In which year did the company produce the maximum number of cars?

6. How many cars were produced in the year 1999?

7. In which year(s) did the production exceed 25 thousand cars?

8. In which year(s) was the production less than 10 thousand cars?

9. What was the total number of cars produced in the years 2001 to 2003?

10. Find the average car production per year during the period 1997 to 2003. Round to the nearest thousand.

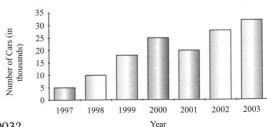

The following graph shows the number of vehicles passing through a crossroad during normal business hours on a particular day. Answer the questions in exercises 11-15, using this graph.

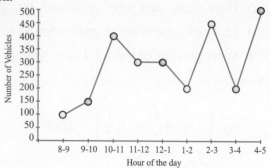

11. What type of graph is this?

12. How many vehicles passed through the crossroad between 10 and 11?

13. At what hour was the crossroad busiest?

14. How many cars crossed between 11 and 12?

15. At what hour of the day was the number of cars passing through the crossroad a minimum?

B. The following graph displays the way funds in a school are allocated to different expenditure line items in a particular year. Answer the questions in exercises 16-20, using this graph.

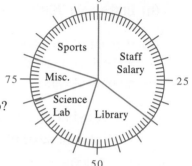

16. What kind of graph is this?

17. What percent of the funds are allocated to sports?

18. What percent of the funds are spent on library books and miscellaneous items?

19. If the total funds available are $4,520,000, what amount is spent on the science lab?

20. If the amount allocated to the library is $716,000, find the total amount of the funds available.

The following circle graph shows percents related to monthly sale of pizzas with various kinds of toppings by Pizza Hut. Answer the questions in exercises 21-24, using this graph.

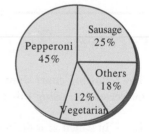

21. Which kind of pizza topping is the most popular?

22. About how many sausage pizzas were sold in the month in which the total number of pizzas sold was 1,800?

23. If about 2,000 pizzas were sold in a particular month, how many were sold with a vegetarian topping?

24. If in a particular month 720 pepperoni pizzas were sold, what is the total number of pizzas sold that month?

C. The following pictograph shows the number of farm owners in the country during the years 1995, 1999, and 2003. Answer the questions in exercises 25-30, using this graph.

Number of owners in the country

Year	♦ = 500 farm owners, ⊣ = 250 farm owner
1995	♦ ♦ ♦ ♦
1999	♦ ♦ ♦ ♦ ♦ ⊣
2003	♦ ♦ ♦ ♦ ♦ ♦ ♦

25. What was the number of farm owners in 1995?   **26.** What was the number of farm owners in 1999?

27. Find the increase in the number of farm owners in 1999 over that in 1995.

28. What was the number of farm owners in 2003?

29. What is the percentage increase in the number of farm owners in 2003 over their number in 1995?

30. Find the increase in the number of farm owners in 2003 over that in 1999.

The following pictograph shows the number of phone calls in a business office during the business hours before noon. Answer the questions in exercises 31-35, using this graph.

Hour	Number of phone calls
	= 50 Calls
8 - 9	☎ ☎ ☎
9 - 10	☎ ☎ ☎ ☎ ☎
10 - 11	☎ ☎ ☎ ☎ ☎ ☎ ☎ ☎
11 - 12	☎ ☎ ☎ ☎ ☎ ☎

31. What is the number of phone calls made between 8-9 a.m?

32. At what hour is the number of phone calls the greatest?

33. What is the total number of phone calls made between 8 and 12?

34. What is the average number of phone calls made per hour?

35. What percent of the total calls during the listed hours are made between 9-10 a.m?

9.3   CONSTRUCTING GRAPHS FROM GIVEN DATA

Introduction

After having learned to read and interpret data from various types of graphs, we discuss in this section the methods of constructing bar graphs and circle graphs. Whatever type of graph we may construct, it is very important that it is properly labelled and titled in order to convey its correct meaning.

> Objectives 📖
>
> After completing this section, you will be able to:
>
> A. Construct a bar graph for a given set of data; and
>
> B. Construct a circle graph for a given set of data.

9.3 A.   Constructing a Bar Graph

Except for a circle graph or a pictograph, all other graphs are constructed on a set of two perpendicular axes, one horizontal and the other, vertical. In *bar graphs*, bars are rectangles of uniform width with equal spaces in between them, constructed on one of the axes used as a base line. On the other axis, the scale of the heights of the rectangles is shown. The uniformity of width is maintained in this graph for easy comparison. The length of each bar represents the exact value of the data in the category represented by that bar.

Procedure to construct a vertical Bar Graph:

   Step 1   Draw a vertical axis and a horizontal axis.

   Step 2   Mark an appropriate scale on the vertical axis to represent the data value of each category (The scale must be uniform and must start with 0 at the origin, the point of intersection of the two axes.)

   Step 3   Mark the categories of data along the horizontal axis.

Step **4**   Draw a vertical rectangle for each category, so that the height of the rectangle (bar) reaches the value of the data in that category.

Step **5**   Give a suitable title to the graph and see that all the items are labelled clearly.

Warm-Up

1. Construct a bar graph showing the average rainfall recorded in the months of June to November in a city using the following information:

Month	Rainfall Recorded
June	23 cm
July	30 cm
August	38 cm
September	28 cm
October	21 cm
November	4 cm

Example 1   Construct a bar graph that represents the following data:

Sales figures of a business over a period of five years	
Year	**Sales (in million dollars)**
1999	50
2000	62
2001	45
2002	58
2003	65

Solution

Steps 1 and 2   Draw a vertical axis and a horizontal axis. Mark a scale on the vertical axis that will include the numbers from 0 to 65 million dollars.

(See Figure 9.13). On this graph we have chosen to mark the numbers from 0 to 70 using a scale of: 1 unit = 10 million dollars.

Step 3   On the horizontal axis, mark any *five* points (to represent the five categories of the data) and label them with the years 1999 to 2003.

(Note that we have not chosen any scale on the horizontal axis to mark the categories. Proper **care** has been taken to keep them equally apart.)

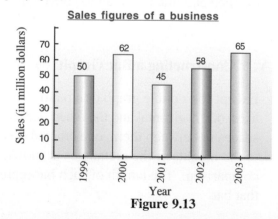

Figure 9.13

Step 4   Draw bars of equal width for each year, keeping the marked point in the center of the base for each rectangle. The height of each rectangle should correspond to the sales (in million dollars) in that particular year using the given information.

(For example, the height of the rectangle for the year 1999 reaches 50 mark on the vertical axis.)

Step 5 (a) Label the horizontal axis with "Year" to indicate that the points marked on it represent years.

(b) Label the vertical axis with "Sales in million dollars" or "Sales in dollars (in millions)" to indicate that any point on this axis represents that many million dollars.

(c) Give a suitable title to the graph to indicate what kind of information this graph exhibits. In this case, the title "Sales figures of a business" has been used.

Answer:

1.
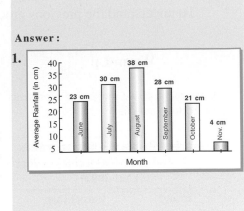

9.3 B. Constructing a Circle Graph or Pie Chart

- To draw a circle graph or pie chart, we need some information on angles and protractors. A protractor, shown in Figure 9.14, is an instrument used for measuring a given angle or for constructing an angle of given magnitude. It is semi-circular in shape, and is usually made of transparent plastic so that markings are visible when it is placed over straight lines. It has degree marks on the curved edge from 0 to 180 which enables us to read the measure of an angle, or construct an angle of a given measure.

It is clear from Figure 9.14 that the angle (AOB) at the center in a semi-circle measures 180°. The angle around the center in a circle is 360°.

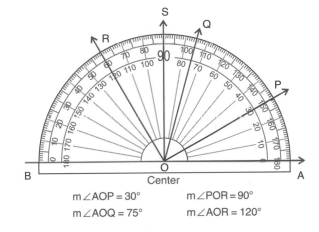

$m\angle AOP = 30°$ $m\angle POR = 90°$
$m\angle AOQ = 75°$ $m\angle AOR = 120°$

Figure 9.14

The portion of a circle between two radii is called a **sector** of the circle.

- To draw a **circle graph** or a **pie-chart**, we draw a circle and divide it into sectors that correspond to percentages of data in each category represented. This can be done by using the fact that the area of any sector is proportional to its central angle.

Since the complete circle is 360°, to find the central angle of the sector to represent a percent of the data, we multiply that percent in decimal form by 360°.

Procedure to construct a **circle graph** or **pie chart:**

Step 1 Find the central angle for each category by multiplying the corresponding percent (in decimal form) by 360°.

Step 2 Draw a circle.

Step 3 With the help of a protractor, draw each central angle and label each sector with the name and corresponding percent of each category.

Step 4 Give a suitable title to the graph.

To understand the previous procedure with more clarity, study the following example carefully.

Warm-Up

2. Construct a circle graph that represents the following data:

Market Shares of Various Brands of a Consumer Nondurable Product (Year 2002)	
Brand	**Percentage**
Brand "A"	38%
Brand "B"	24%
Brand "C"	12%
All others	26%

Example 2 Construct a circle graph that represents the following data:

Market Shares of Various Brands of a Consumer Product (Year 2002)		
	Category	**Percentage**
(a)	Brand A	35%
(b)	Brand B	29%
(c)	Brand C	15%
(d)	All others	21%

Solution

Step 1 Find each percent of 360°.

(a) 35% of 360° = 0.35 × 360°
= **126°**

(b) 29% of 360° = 0.29 × 360°
= **104.4°**

(c) 15% of 360° = 0.15 × 360°
= **54°**

(d) 21% of 360° = 0.21 × 360°
= **75.6°**

These are the measurements of the central angles of the sectors.

Step 2 Draw a circle of any radius, Figure 9.15

Step 3 Use a protractor to mark the central angles as close to the actual degree as possible and label each sector.

Step 4 We can use the same title for the graph that has been used for the table of data.

Answer:

2.

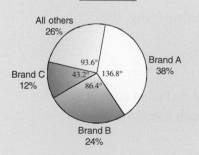

Market Shares of Various Brands of a Consumer Product (year 2002)

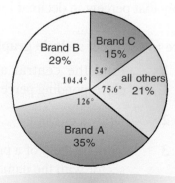

Figure 9.15

Exercise 9.3

A. 1. The expenditures in different categories of a certain school during the year 2002-2003 are given below. Construct a bar graph to represent the data.

Category	Expenditure (in Hundred Thousand Dollars)
Staff Salary	14
School Transportation	3
Maintenance	2
Boarding Expenses	6
Purchases	4
Miscellaneous	2

2. Construct a bar graph that represents the data.

State Expenditure on Education for the Fiscal Year 2003-04	
Item	**Expenditure (in Million Dollars)**
Primary Education	350
Secondary Education	300
University Education	290
Medical Education	120
Technical Education	180
Physical Education	60

3. The expenditure of a company under different budget line items (in thousand dollars) is as follows:

Head	Expenditure
Salary	350
Travelling Allowance	80
Machines	200
Rent	150
Interest	80
Others	180

Make a bar graph for this data.

4. Mr. Smith owns an electronics shop in Twin Shopping Mall. The following table shows appliances sold during a month. Represent the data on a bar graph.

Electronic Appliances	Frequency
Radios	16
Television Sets	10
Stereo Sets	8
Video Recorders	8
Grinders	12
Calculators	6

5. Construct a bar graph that represents the following data:

Population of the Five Largest Native American Tribes: 2000	
Names of Tribes	**Population (in Thousands)**
Cherokee	308
Navajo	219
Chippewa	104
Sioux	103
Choctaw	82

B. 6. The following table shows various reasons and percents related to train derailments. Construct a circle graph that represents this data.

Reasons for Train Derailments	
Bad Tracks	40%
Faulty Equipment	15%
Human Error	25%
Other Causes	20%

7. The following table shows the data Distribution of Employment by Occupational Groups in the year 2003. Construct a circle graph that represents this data.

Occupation	Percent Employed
Managerial	25%
Sales & Technician	35%
Production & Repair	20%
Operators & Laborers	15%
Farming & Forestry	5%

8. Construct a circle graph that represents the following data:

Budget Allocation for an Apartment Complex

Categories	Percent
Building Maintenance	25%
Gardening	15%
Pool	10%
Security	20%
Salaries for Other Jobs	30%

9. Construct a circle graph that represents the number of merit certificates awarded to students at the annual awards ceremony of a school for scoring above 85% on the final examination.

Subject	Number of Certificates
Mathematics	27
Physics	18
Chemistry	15
Biology	9
Electronics	16
Instrumentation	5

90 Total

Hint: First, determine the percent of awards given in each subject.

10. Construct a circle graph that represents the following data:

Monthly Expenses for a Family Budget	
Housing	25%
Food	30%
Clothing	10%
Entertainment	7.5%
Insurance	5%
Savings	10%
Miscellaneous	12.5%

9.4 PLOTTING POINTS, LINEAR EQUATIONS IN TWO VARIABLES, AND GRAPHING LINES

IMPORTANT VOCABULARY

1. A pair of real numbers *a* and *b*, when written in the form **(a, b)** is called an **ordered pair.** The numbers *a* and *b* are called the **coordinates** of the **ordered pair**. In the ordered pair (*a*, *b*), *a* is called the **first coordinate** and *b* is called the **second coordinate.**

   In an ordered pair, the order in which the numbers are written is important. Thus, (2, 3) is not the same as (3, 2).

2. Two **ordered pairs are equal** if and only if their corresponding coordinates are the same. Thus, (*x*, *y*) = (−1, 4) means *x* = −1 and *y* = 4.

> **Objectives**
>
> Upon completing this section, you will be able to:
>
> A. Plot a set of ordered pairs;
>
> B. Identify a linear equation in two variables *x* and *y*, which can always be written in the standard form *ax* + *by* + *c* = 0, and identify solutions of such equations as ordered pairs of real numbers; and
>
> C. Graph linear equations in two variables.

3. The **standard form** of a linear equation in two variables *x* and *y* is **ax + by = c** where *a*, *b*, and *c* are known real numbers and either *a* or *b* or both are not zero.

4. The solutions of a linear equation *ax* + *by* = *c* are ordered pairs of the form (*x*, *y*) which satisfy the equation. For example the ordered pair (2, −1) is a solution of 5*x* − 3*y* = 13 because the values *x* = 2 and *y* = −1 satisfy this equation:

$$5x - 3y = 13 \quad \longrightarrow \quad 5(2) - 3(-1) = 13$$
$$\longrightarrow \quad 10 + 3 = 13$$
$$13 = 13 \quad \text{(True)}$$

9.4 A. Graphing ordered pairs of Real Numbers

- **Introduction:**

  Just as each point on a line can be described by a number, each point in a plane can be described by a *pair of numbers*. The system most commonly used is the **Cartesian Coordinate System,** named in recognition of the French mathematician Rene Descartes (1596-1650) who discovered this method.

- **The Coordinate Plane:** Descartes developed a method for representing points and lines graphically by drawing a rectangular grid, called a *coordinate plane*. We can create a ***coordinate plane*** (Figure 9.16a) by drawing a horizontal number line called the ***x*-axis** (or the **horizontal axis**), and a vertical number line called the ***y*-axis** (or the **vertical axis**) on a plane, such as, the plane of your paper or the writing board in your class room.

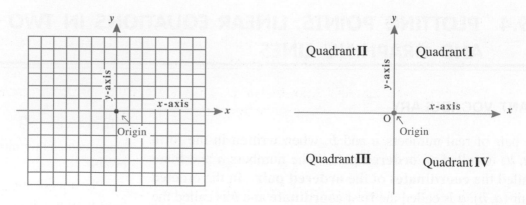

A rectangular Cartesian Coordinate Plane

Figure 9.16 (a)   Figure 9.16 (b)

The x-axis and the y-axis together are referred to as the **coordinate axes,** and their point of intersection (the zero point of both the number lines) is called the **origin**. The origin is designated by O. On the x-axis, the positive direction is to the right; and on the y-axis, the positive direction is upwards. Note that in this system (Figure 9.16 (b)), the coordinate axes divide the plane into four **quadrants**, numbered I, II, III, and IV counter-clockwise.

- **Graphing points in a coordinate plane:** Choose a scale for representing the real numbers on both the axes (Figure 9.17). The location of a point in the coordinate plane is determined by two numbers: the x-coordinate and the y-coordinate of the point as illustrated below:

Let P be a point in the plane. Draw perpendicular lines which connect the point P to the x-axis and y-axis respectively. The number x is called the **x-coordinate** and the number y is called the **y-coordinate** of the point P. The **coordinates** of a point are always written as an **ordered pair** in the form (x, y), the x-coordinate is written first. For each point in the plane, there corresponds one ordered pair of real numbers, called, the coordinates of the point.

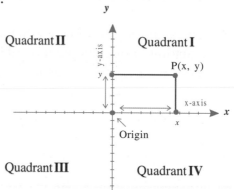

Figure 9.17

Conversely, each ordered pair of real numbers is represented by one point in the coordinate plane. For example, in Figure 9.18, the ordered pair (3, 2) is represented by the point whose x-coordinate is 3 and whose y-coordinate is 2. This point is named A in the figure, and is called the **graph of (3, 2).**

The x-coordinate of a point is sometimes called the **first coordinate** because it is written first in the ordered pair form (x, y) and the y-coordinate is called the **second coordinate** for a similar reason. Notice in Figure 9.18 that:

- The coordinates of the origin are (0, 0).

- A point is named by writing a single capital letter followed by the coordinates of the point.

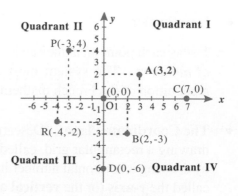

Figure 9.18

- Point A is located as follows.

  Start at the origin and move along the x-axis 3 units to the right (since 3 is *positive*), stop at $x = 3$, and then move 2 units vertically *up* (since 2 is *positive*).

- The sign of the x-coordinate (positive or negative) tells whether the point is located horizontally to the right of the origin ($x > 0$) or to the left of the origin ($x < 0$).

  Similarly, the sign of the y-coordinate (positive or negative) tells whether the point is located vertically above the origin ($y > 0$) or below the origin ($y < 0$).

- Points A, P, R, and B lie in different quadrants. The signs of the x-and y-coordinates of a point determine the quadrant in which the point is located (Figure 9.19). The point C (Figure 9.18) is on the x-axis and not in any quadrant. Similarly, the point D is on the y-axis, and not in any quadrant.

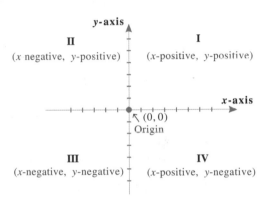

Figure 9.19

Example	signs of coordinates	location of point
A(3, 2)	(+, +)	Quadrant I
P(–3, 4)	(–, +)	Quadrant II
R(–4, –2)	(–, –)	Quadrant III
B(2, –3)	(+, –)	Quadrant IV
C(7, 0)	(+, 0)	x-axis
D(0, –6)	(0, –)	y-axis

- A point on the x-axis, such as C, will have its y-coordinate zero; a point on the y-axis, such as D, will have its x-coordinate zero.

Thus, just as any straight line can be converted to a number line by choosing a scale and marking numbers on it, in the same way, any plane can be converted to a *coordinate plane* by choosing a pair of coordinate axes, as explained in the above discussion. Also, to each point in the plane will correspond one ordered pair of real numbers, and conversely, each ordered pair of real numbers will correspond to one point in the plane.

To graph a point means to mark and label the point whose coordinates are given.

To locate a point means either to plot a point or to find the coordinates of a plotted point.

> **Remark:** In practice, to graph points or lines, we use *graph paper* with the grid already present (as in Figure 9.16(a)), but when we are working on plain paper, as is generally the case, we usually draw only the coordinate axis and mark the points as in Figure 9.18.

Example 1   Graph/plot the points:

(a) (2, –4)   (b) (–3, 5)   (c) (–5, –3)

(d) $\left(\dfrac{5}{2}, 4\right)$ (e) (3, 0)   (f) (0, –2)

(You should use graph paper if available).

Warm-Up

1. Plot the following points in a coordinate plane:

(a) A(3, −2)   (b) B(−4, 5)

(c) C(−3, −4)   (d) D$\left(\dfrac{7}{2}, \dfrac{9}{2}\right)$

(e) P (−4, 0)   (f) Q (0, 3)

Solutions

Step 1   Draw a pair of coordinate axis, and label the x-axis, the y-axis, and the origin (Figure 9.20).

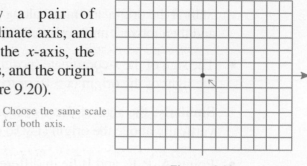

Choose the same scale for both axis.

Figure 9.20

Step 2   Now plot the given points one by one as explained below.

(a) To plot (2, −4):   *x-coordinate = 2; y-coordinate = −4*

Start from the origin and go to the **right** 2 units, then go **down** 4 units.

Positive x-coordinate indicates "going to the right".

Negative y-coordinate indicates "going down".

The point is labeled, A, in the figure. Point A is the graph of (2, − 4).

(b) To plot (−3, 5):   *x-coordinate = −3; y-coordinate = 5*

Start from the origin and goto the **left** 3 units, then go **up** 5 units.

The point is labeleld, B, in the figure. Point B is the graph of (−3, 5).

(c) To plot (−5, −3), start at the origin, first go **left** (Why?) 5 units, and then go **down** 3 units. The point is labeled, C, in the figure. Point C is the graph of (−5, −3).

(d) To plot $\left(\dfrac{5}{2}, 4\right)$, start at the origin, first go to the **right** 2.5 units $\left(\dfrac{5}{2} = 2.5\right)$, and then go **down** 4 units. The point is labeled, D, in the figure. Point D is the graph of $\left(\dfrac{5}{2}, 4\right)$.

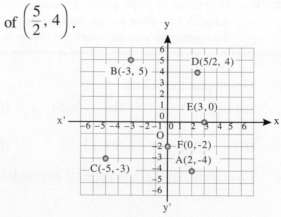

482

(e) To plot (3, 0), start at the origin, go **right** 3 units. Since the *y*-coordinate is 0, it means no vertical movement, down or up. The point labeled (E) is the graph of (3, 0).

(f) To plot (0, −2), start at the origin, go **down** 2 units. Since the *x*-coordinate is 0, there is no horizontal movement. The point labeled, F, is the graph of (0, −2).

Recall:

1. Any point whose *y*-coordinate is zero lies on the *x*-axis.

2. Any point whose *x*- coordinate is zero lies on the *y*-axis.

3. The coordinates of the origin are (0, 0).

Example 2 Find the coordinates of the points shown in Figure 9.21.

Solution

Note

Unless a scale is labeled on the *x*-axis or on the *y*-axis, the grid lines are assumed to be one unit apart in both the horizontal and vertical directions.

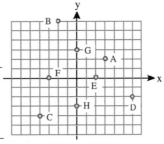

Figure 9.21

A: (3, 2)   B: (−2, 6)   C: (−4, −4)   D: (6, −2)

E: (2, 0)   F: (−3, 0)   G: (0, 3)   H: (0, −3)

Remark: You may have noticed that in the discussion and examples for this objective, we have primarily used ordered pairs of integers. This is because integers are relatively easy to locate on number lines.

Since fractions, decimal numbers or irrational numbers such as

$\frac{3}{8}$, −4.75, $-\sqrt{2}$, or π are located on number lines (the

x-axis and the *y*-axis) by **estimating** the corresponding positions of the points, an ordered pair with such components can be plotted. But even after graphing such points, you may not be able to read the precise coordinates because it is very difficult to distinguish between points such as 3.14 and

3.145 or $\frac{9}{28}$ and $\frac{9}{29}$ on a number line. Ordered pairs of this type are graphed in the accompanying Figure, Figure 9.22.

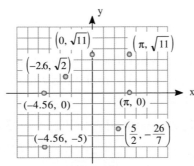

Figure 9.22

2. Find the coordinates of the points shown in the following figure.

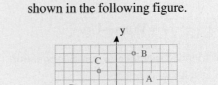

Answers:

1.

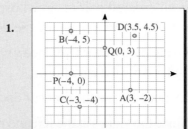

2. A (4, 1) B (2, 5) C (−2, 3) D (−5, 0)
    E (−3, −5) F (6, −3)

9.4 B.   Linear equations in two variables

- **First-degree or Linear Equations:** An equation in *one* variable is called a linear equation if the highest exponent of any variable is 1.

$$5x + 4 = 0 ; \quad 2x - 3 = 3x + 5 ; \quad 7t + 1 = 6$$

These are examples of linear equations in one variable.

$2x + 3y - 1 = 0$ is a linear equation in *two* variables, x and y;

$3p = 2q - 5$ is a linear equation in *two* variables, p and q;

$3x + 2y - z + 6 = 0$ is a linear equation in *three* variables, x, y, and z.

In this section, we shall discuss *linear equations in two variables*. Note that the equations $y = 2x^2 - x + 5$ and $3xy - 5x + y + 4 = 0$ are both equations in two variables, but neither of them are a linear equation. To be a linear equation, each **term** can contain at most only **one** variable, and its degree must be one.

Warm-Up

3. Identify whether or not the equation is a linear equation.

(a) $4x - 7 = 49y$

(b) $7x^2 - 4 = 9y$

(c) $4x - 9 = 7x - 2$

(d) $2xy - 4x = 9y - 7$

Example 3   Identify whether or not the equation is a linear equation.

(a) $2xy - 7 = x + 7y$ (b) $2x - 7 = 4$

(c) $3x - 2y = 7x + 4$ (d) $x^2 - 4xy + 7 = 0$

Solution

(a) $2xy - 7 = x + 7y$ is **not a linear** equation because the term $2xy$ contains two variables.

(b) $2x - 7 = 4$ **is a linear** equation, because each term contains atmost one variable and the term containing the variable is of degree one.

(c) $3x - 2y = 7x + 4$ **is a linear** equation, because each term contains atmost one variable and the term containing the variable is of degree one.

(d) $x^2 - 4xy + 7 = 0$ **is not a linear** equation, because the term x^2 is of degree two and the term $4xy$ contains two variables. On both counts it is not linear.

- **Solution of a linear equation in two variables:** A **solution** of an equation in *two* variables x and y is an ordered pair (x, y) whose values, x and y, make the equation a true statement. For example, let us set $x = 1$ and $y = -1$ in the equation $3x - 2y = 5$

Using parentheses, replace x with 1 and y with -1, and rewrite the equation

$$3x - 2y = 5$$
$$3(1) - 2(-1) = 5$$

Evaluate, using the order of operations. $5 = 5$ _{True}

Since the values at the left and right side are equal, the pair $(x = 1, y = -1)$ is a **solution** of the above equation.

Next, check to see if $(2, 1)$ is a solution to the equation.

Set $x = 2$ and $y = 1$, and evaluate the equation.

$$3x - 2y = 5$$
$$3(2) - 2(1) = 5$$
$$6 - 2 = 5 \quad \text{False}$$

The left side of the equation $\neq$ the right side.

Therefore, the ordered pair (2, 1) is **not a solution** of $3x - 2y = 5$.

It is important to note that besides $(1, -1)$ there are *many more* solutions of $3x - 2y = 5$. For example, you may verify that

$$(3, 2); \quad \left(0, -\frac{5}{2}\right); \text{ and } \left(\frac{5}{3}, 0\right) \text{ are also solutions of this equation. How many solutions are there?}$$

A linear equation in two variables has infinitely many solutions.

Example 4 Verify each of the following are solutions of the equation $2x + y = 7$. Write these solutions as ordered pairs of numbers.

(a) $x = 2, y = 3$ (b) $y = -1, x = 4$

Solutions

(a) Substitute 2 for x, $2x + y = 7$
and 3 for y
$$2(2) + 3 = 7$$
$$7 = 7 \quad \text{True}$$

The ordered pair (2, 3) is solution of $2x + y = 7$

(b) Substitute -1 for y, $2x + y = 7$
and 4 for x
$$2(4) + (-1) = 7$$
$$7 = 7 \quad \text{True}$$

The ordered pair $(4, -1)$ is solution of $2x + y = 7$

This solution is written as the ordered pair $(4, -1)$, and not as $(-1, 4)$, since the value of x is always the first coordinate in the ordered pair.

Example 5 Identify whether the given ordered pair is a solution of the indicated equation.

(a) $(-4, 5); \ 2x - y = 10$ (b) $(1, 1); \ x - y = 0$
(c) $(1, 3); \ 2y - x = 5$

Solutions

(a) $(\mathbf{-4, 5}); \ 2x - y = 10$

Substitute -4 for x and 5 for y.
$$2x - y = 10$$
$$2(\mathbf{-4}) - \mathbf{5} = 10$$
$$-8 - 5 = 10$$
$$-13 = 10 \quad \text{False}$$

Therefore, $(-4, 5)$ is not a solution of $2x - y = 10$.

Warm-Up

4. Verify that each of the following are solutions of the equation $3x + 2y = 10$

(a) $x = 2, \ y = 2$

(b) $x = 4, \ y = -1$

5. Identify whether the given ordered pair is a solution of the given equation

(a) $(3, 1) \ ; \ 2x - y = 4$

(b) $(1, 2)$; $x - y = -1$

(c) $(2, 5)$; $3x - y = 1$

(b) $(1, 1)$; $x - y = 0$

Substitute 1 for x and 1 for y.

$$x - y = 0$$
$$1 - 1 = 0$$
$$0 = 0 \qquad \text{True}$$

Therefore, $(1, 1)$ is a solution of $x - y = 0$.

(c) $(1, 3)$; $2y - x = 5$

Substitute 1 for x and 3 for y.

$$2y - x = 5$$
$$2(3) - 1 = 5$$
$$5 = 5 \qquad \text{True}$$

Therefore, $(1, 3)$ is a solution of $2y - x = 5$.

- In fact, for any specific value of x (or y), we can find a *specific* value of y (or x) which satisfies the given equation. Let us examine this fact. We will use the same equation, $3x - 2y = 5$.

Assign any value to x, say $x = 2$ **or** Assign any value to y, say $y = \dfrac{7}{2}$

Substitute 2 for x

$$3x - 2y = 5$$
$$\downarrow$$
$$3(2) - 2y = 5$$
$$6 - 2y = 5$$
$$-2y = -1$$
$$y = \frac{-1}{-2}$$
$$y = \frac{1}{2}$$

When $x = 2$, $y = \dfrac{1}{2}$

Therefore, the ordered pair $\left(2, \dfrac{1}{2}\right)$ is

another solution of $3x - 2y = 5$.

Substitute $\dfrac{7}{2}$ for y

$$3x \quad - \quad 2y = 5$$
$$\downarrow$$
$$3x - \quad 2\left(\frac{7}{2}\right) = 5$$
$$3x - 7 = 5$$
$$3x = 12$$
$$x = 4$$

When $y = \dfrac{7}{2}$, $x = 4$

Therefore, the ordered pair $\left(4, \dfrac{7}{2}\right)$ is

another solution of $3x - 2y = 5$.

Warm-Up

6. For the equation $3x + 4y + 6 = 0$, find the missing component of the ordered pairs in order for these pairs to be solutions

Example 6 For the equation $2x + 5y = 3$, find the missing coordinate of the ordered pairs in order for these pairs to be solutions.

(a) $(-3, ?)$ **(b)** $(?, 5)$

486

Solutions

(a) $(-3, ?);$ $2x + 5y = 3$ The first coordinate is -3.

$\longrightarrow$ $2(-3) + 5y = 3,$ Substitute -3 for x.

$\longrightarrow$ $-6 + 5y = 3$

$\longrightarrow$ $5y = 9$

$\longrightarrow$ $y = \dfrac{9}{5}$

The ordered pair is $\left(-3, \dfrac{9}{5}\right)$.

(b) $(?, 5);$ $2x + 5y = 3$ The second coordinate is 5.

$\longrightarrow$ $2x + 5 \cdot (5) = 3$ Substitute 5 for y.

$\longrightarrow$ $2x + 25 = 3$

$\longrightarrow$ $2x = -22$

$\longrightarrow$ $x = -11$

The ordered pair is $(-11, 5)$.

(a) $(-4, ?)$

(b) $(?, 3)$

Answers:

3. **(a)** Yes, linear   **(b)** No, not linear
   (c) Yes, linear   **(d)** No, not linear

4. **(a)** Yes   **(b)** Yes

5. **(a)** No   **(b)** Yes   **(c)** Yes

6. **(a)** $\dfrac{3}{2}$ **(b)** -6

• It is common to write the solution as an ordered pair (x, y).

The solutions of linear equations in two variables x and y are ordered pairs of the form (a, b) of real numbers such that the values $x = a$ and $y = b$ satisfy the given equation. Various solutions of the equation $3x - 2y = 5$ are

   $(1, -1)$; $(3, 2)$; $(0, -5/2)$; $(5/3, 0)$; $(2, 1/2)$; $(4, 7/2)$

They can also be arranged in a table as shown in Table 9.1

We will see in objective 9.4 C that these solutions of $3x - 2y = 5$ can be represented by points in a plane which lie on a straight line. This is probably the reason for calling such an equation a "linear equation".

Some Solutions of the equation
$3x - 2y = 5$

x	y
1	-1
3	2
0	$-5/2$
5/3	0
2	1/2
4	7/2

Table 9.1

Example 7   Complete the given table of values for the equation
$2x + y = 7$.

Solution

Let $x = -1$ $2x + y = 7$

$2(-1) + y = 7$

$-2 + y = 7$

$y = 9$

Let $x = 2$ $2x + y = 7$

$2 \cdot 2 + y = 7$

$4 + y = 7$

$y = 3$

x	y
-1	
2	
	3
	-2

Warm-Up

7. Complete the given table of values for the equation $4x + 3y = 11$.

x	y
	1
-3	
4	
2	
	0

Let $y = 3$

$$2x + y = 7$$
$$2x + 3 = 7$$
$$2x = 4$$
$$x = 2$$

Let $y = -2$

$$2x + y = 7$$
$$2x + (-2) = 7$$
$$2x = 9$$
$$x = 4.5$$

x	y
-1	9
2	3
2	3
4.5	-2

The completed table of values is shown.

8. Complete the following table of values for the equation $x = -2$

a)

x	y
	4
	-4
	0
	5

b)

x	y
	4
	4
	4

Example 8 Complete the following table of values for the equation $x = 3$.

(a)

x	y
	-3
	0
	5

(b)

x	y
	3
	3
	3

Solutions

(a) Since the given equation $x = 3$ does not contain y, the value of x is 3 for all values of y. The completed table of values is shown.

x	y
3	-3
3	0
3	5

(b) Since the equation $x = 3$ does not contain y, y can be given any value. For instance,

x	y
3	**0**
3	**1**
3	**2**

or

x	y
3	**-1**
3	**3**
3	**4**

Answers:

7.

x	y
2	1
-3	$\frac{23}{3}$
4	$-\frac{5}{3}$
2	1
$\frac{11}{4}$	0

8. (a)

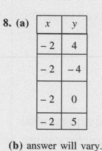

x	y
-2	4
-2	-4
-2	0
-2	5

(b) answer will vary.

9.4 C   The Graph of a Linear Equation

The **graph** of an equation in two variables x and y contains only those points whose coordinates satisfy the equation. In other words, the graph is the *set of points* whose coordinates (x, y) form solutions of the equation.

To obtain the graph of an equation in two variables x and y, we first prepare a table of values of x and y, and then we plot the corresponding points. The graph is then obtained by connecting these points.

Let us plot the graph of the equation whose solutions are given in the following table.

We plot the points (x, y) from this table. Observe that they all lie on a straight line "l" (see Figure 9.23).

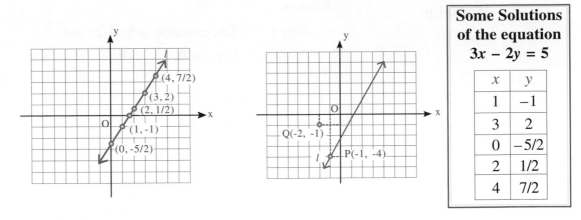

Figure 9.23   **Figure 9.24**

When we find more solutions of the equation $3x - 2y = 5$, we realize that every solution corresponds to some point on this line. The coordinates of any point on this line make the equation $3x - 2y = 5$ true, while the coordinates of any point *not* on the line make the equation $3x - 2y = 5$ false. For example, in Figure 9.24, we have taken a point P on l whose coordinates are $(-1, -4)$ and another point Q, not on l, whose coordinates are $(-2, -1)$. It can be verified easily that the pair $(-1, -4)$ is a solution of the equation $3x - 2y = 5$, while the pair $(-2, -1)$ is not.

$P(-1, -4):$ $3x - 2y = 5$ $Q(-2, -1):$ $3x - 2y = 5$

$3(-1) - 2(-4) = 5$ $3(-2) - 2(-1) = 5$

$-3 + 8 = 5$ True $-6 + 2 = 5$ False

Only two points are needed to draw a line, but, in order to check our work, it is always better to use three points. To graph a linear equation in x and y, we use the following procedure:

Procedure to graph a linear equation in x and y:

    Step **1**   Find any three solutions of the given equation by making a table of values. This can be done by assigning any three values to one of the variables and then finding the corresponding values of the other variable.

    Step **2**   Draw a set of coordinate axis and plot the solutions obtained.

    Step **3**   Draw the line connecting these points.

            (If you find that you are not able to draw a line which passes through all three points, this will indicate an error either in the calculation of the coordinates or in their plotting.)

 Note   Since plotting a point with fractional coordinates is not always convenient, it is advisable that the table of values should avoid fractions as much as possible.

Example 9   Graph the equation $5x + 2y = 4$, and show from the graph that $(4, -8)$ is a solution while $(-4, 8)$ is not.

Warm-Up

  9. Graph the equation $y = 2x + 2$, and show from the graph that $(-3, -4)$ is a solution while $(-4, -3)$ is not.

Warm-Up

Solution

Step 1   The equation is $5x + 2y = 4$

Let $x = \mathbf{0}$, $5(0) + 2y = 4$

$2y = 4$

$y = \mathbf{2}$

Let $x = \mathbf{2}$, $5(2) + 2y = 4$

$10 + 2y = 4$

$y = \mathbf{-3}$

Let $x = \mathbf{-2}$, $5(-2) + 2y = 4$

$-10 + 2y = 4$

$y = \mathbf{7}$

Table of values

x	y
0	2
2	-3
-2	7

Step 2   Draw the coordinate axis and plot the points $(0, 2)$, $(2, -3)$, and $(-2, 7)$. (Figure 9.25).

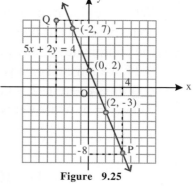

Step 3   Draw the line connecting the points. This line is the desired graph of the equation $5x + 2y = 4$.

Figure 9.25

For the second part of the question; If P is the point $(4, -8)$, we find from the graph that it lies on the line. Hence, $(4, -8)$ is a solution of $5x + 2y = 4$.

Again, if Q is the point $(-4, 8)$, we find from the graph that it *does not* lie on the line. Hence, the pair $(-4, 8)$ is not a solution of the equation $5x + 2y = 4$.

10. Graph the line $3x - 2y = 0$

Example 10   Graph the equation $2x - 3y = 0$.

Solution

Step 1   Construct a table of *three* solutions for the equation $2x - 3y = 0$.

x	y
0	0
3	2
-3	-2

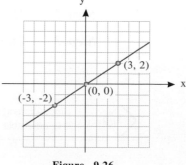

Figure 9.26

Step 2   Plot the points: $(0, 0)$, $(3, 2)$, $(-3, -2)$.

Step 3   Draw the straight line passing through the three points.

Note that the constant term in the equation $2x - 3y = 0$ is zero, and the line passes through the origin.

Example 11   Graph the equations (i) $x = 5$, (ii) $2y + 7 = 0$. Do you observe anything special about the graphs?

11. Graph the equations:

   (i) $x = -4$

   (ii) $y - 3 = 0$

Solutions

Graph of (i)

Step 1   Since y is not present in the equation $x = 5$, it can assume any value, but the value of x is always 5.

We use the table, shown, to graph the equation $x = 5$.

x	y
5	-2
5	0
5	3

Step 2   Plot the points $(5, -2)$, $(5, 0)$, and $(5, 3)$.

Step 3   Draw the line connecting the points. This line is the graph of the equation $x = 5$. (Figure 9.27)

Note that the graph of $x = 5$ is a **vertical line** through the point $(5, 0)$.

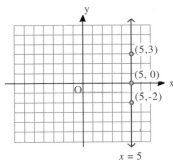

Figure 9.27

Figure 9.28

Graph of (ii)

Since the equation $2y + 7 = 0$, or equivalently $y = \dfrac{-7}{2}$, does not contain x, the value of y remains $\dfrac{-7}{2}$ for all values of x.

x	y
0	$-\dfrac{7}{2}$
3	$-\dfrac{7}{2}$
5	$-\dfrac{7}{2}$

We use the table, as shown, to graph the equation $2y + 7 = 0$. Plot the points $\left(0, -\dfrac{7}{2}\right)$, $\left(3, -\dfrac{7}{2}\right)$, and $\left(5, -\dfrac{7}{2}\right)$, . Draw a line through them. This line is the graph of the equation $2y + 7 = 0$ (Figure 9.28).

Note that the graph of $2y + 7 = 0$ or $y = -\dfrac{7}{2}$

is a **horizontal** line through the point $\left(0, -\dfrac{7}{2}\right)$.

Answers:

9.

10.

11. (i)

(ii)

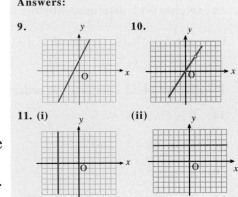

Remarks: 1. If the linear equation contains only the variable x, the graph is a **vertical** line.

2. If the linear equation contains only the variable y, the graph is a **horizontal** line.

Exercise 9.4

A. 1. Plot the ordered pairs on the same coordinate system.

(a) $(2, -3)$ (b) $(-4, 7)$ (c) $(3, 5)$ (d) $(6, 2)$ (e) $(-6, 2)$ (f) $(0, 0)$

2. Plot the ordered pairs on the same coordinate system.

(a) $(-4, 0)$ (b) $(0, 5)$ (c) $(-2, -2)$ (d) $(3, 0)$ (e) $(0, -5)$ (f) $(-3, -5)$

3. Without plotting the points, determine the quadrant in which the point lies.

(a) $(4, 5)$ (b) $(-3, -7)$ (c) $(4, -2)$ (d) $(-3, 2)$ (e) $(6, -7)$ (f) $(5, 13)$

4. Determine whether the following points lie on the x-axis or y-axis, or neither.

(a) $(-3, 0)$ (b) $(0, -1)$ (c) $(5, 0)$ (d) $(2, -3)$ (e) $(0, 4)$ (f) $(1, 4)$

5. Determine the coordinates of the points shown in the figure.

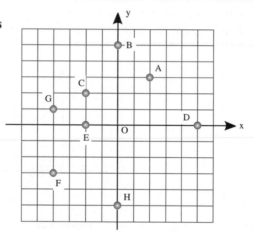

B. In exercises 6-13, determine whether the given ordered pair is a solution of the given equation.

6. $2x - 5y = 7$; $(6, 1)$ 7. $x + 3y = 5$; $(1, 2)$ 8. $3x - 2y = 12$; $(0, 6)$ 9. $2x + 5y + 10 = 0$; $(-5, 0)$

10. $x + 3 = 0$; $(-3, 2)$ 11. $x = 5$; $(7, 0)$ 12. $y = 1$; $(3, 1)$ 13. $2x = 3y$; $(6, 4)$

In exercises 14-22, complete the ordered pair so that it is a solution for the given equation.

14. $(-3, ?)$; $2x + y = 5$ 15. $(4, ?)$; $x - 3y = 2$ 16. $(?, -4)$; $2x + 3y = 8$

17. $(?, 2)$; $x = 8$ 18. $(?, 0)$; $2x + 7y + 10 = 0$ 19. $(0, ?)$; $3x + 5y = 10$

20. $(1, ?)$; $3x - 4y = 8$ 21. $(-2, ?)$; $2x + 7y = 10$ 22. $(?, 2)$; $5x - 3y + 1 = 0$

In exercises 23-31, complete the table of values for the given equation.

23. $x - 2y = 3$

x	y
-1	
3	
	2
	-1

24. $3x - 5y = 15$

x	y
0	
	0
4	
	3

25. $2x - y = -5$

x	y
-2	
	3
-3	
	5

26. $y + 3 = 4x$

x	y
-2	
0	
5	

27. $x = 5$

x	y
	-1
	0
	-2
	3

28. $7x + 3y = 2$

x	y
	-11
-1	
-4	-2
2	3

29. $2x + 10 = 0$

x	y
	10
	-8
	5
	-1

30. $y + 4 = 0$

x	y
-1	
3	
4	
5	

31. $3y - 6 = 0$

x	y
-1	
2	
0	
8	

C. In exercises 32-40, complete the table of values. Draw the graph of the equation by plotting these points.

32. $x = 3$

x	y
	0
	2
	5

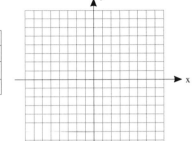

33. $y = 5$

x	y
-4	
0	
2	

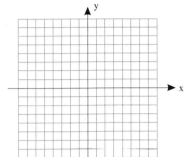

34. $x + 2 = 0$

x	y
	3
	-1
	4

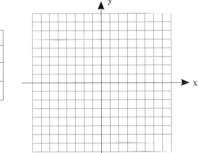

35. $2y + 11 = 5$

x	y
-3	
1	
3	

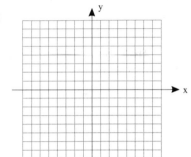

36. $2x + y = 0$

x	y
-3	
1	
3	

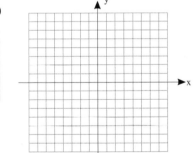

37. $3x = 5y$

x	y
	0
	3
	-3

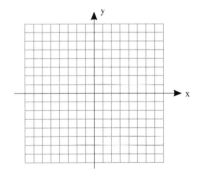

38. $2x + 3y = 2$

x	y
	2
4	
	0

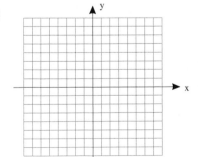

39. $3x = 1 + 4y$

x	y
	-1
3	
-5	

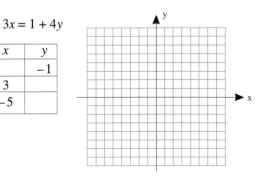

40. $x + 2y = 4$

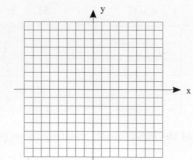

x	y
0	
2	
	2

In exercises 41-50, graph the linear equation.

41. $2x - 3y = 6$

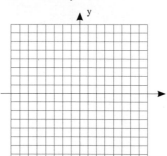

42. $x + 2y = 4$

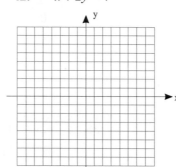

43. $x = 3y + 2$

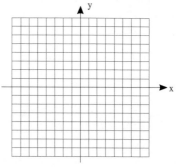

44. $2x + 3y = 5$

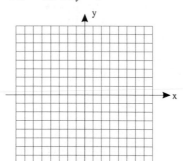

45. $y + 1 = 0$

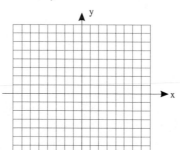

46. $x = -3$

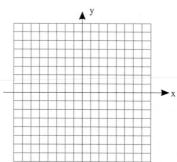

47. $3x - y = 4$

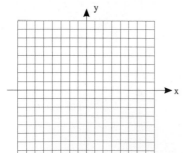

48. $x + y + 4 = 0$

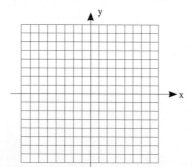

49. $y = 0$

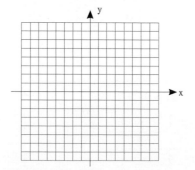

50. $x = 0$

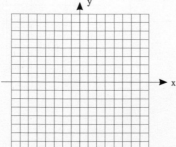

9.5 CHAPTER SUMMARY

Part I Definitions, Important Vocabulary, Symbols	Examples

Part I Definitions, Important Vocabulary, Symbols

1. By **data** we mean collected information in the set of numerical values measuring some information of interest.

2. A **statistic** is a single number describing some characteristic of the data.

3. The **mean** is the common arithmetic average of the data.

4. The **median** is a value that represents the "middle" of the data after the data has been arranged in order.

   (a) If there are an **odd** number of data items, then the median is the *middle* item.

   (b) If there are an **even** number of data items, then the median is the *average of the two middle* items.

5. The **mode** is the data item that occurs most frequently.

6. The **range** of a set of data is the difference between the largest and the smallest data items.

Examples

1. Ages, in years, of 10 students:
   18, 17, 19, 17, 20, 18, 18, 16, 21, 18

2. **The mean, median,** and **mode** are three *statistics* (These are called measures of central tendency.)

3. The **mean** of 5, 10, 12, and 19 is
   $$\frac{5+10+12+19}{4} = 11.5 .$$

4. (a) The **median** of
      19, 17, 15, **12**, 11, 10, and 8 is **12**

   (b) The median of
      2, 5, **6**, **8**, 10, and 15, is
      $$\frac{6+8}{2} = \frac{14}{2}$$
      $$= 7$$

   Note : The data have been arranged in ascending order.

5. The mode of the data
   2 1 1 0 3 2 1 5 1 is **1.**

6. The range of data
   20 25 31 40 45 is **45 − 20 = 25.**

7. A **graph** is a visual representation of numerical data.

8. The **scale** is the unit chosen to represent values.

9. A **bar graph** and a **line graph** contain two axis, **a vertical axis** and **a horizontal axis**.

Bar graph	Line graph	Circle graph

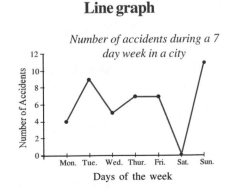

Student weight graph

Number of accidents during a 7 day week in a city

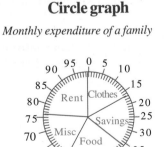

Monthly expenditure of a family

10. A **circle graph** or a **pie chart** uses a circle to show how a whole unit is divided into parts. The *percents* for each part are represented by the *sectors* of the circle.

11. A **pictograph** uses symbol-pictures. Each complete symbol represents a stated value.

A pictograph

Number of Houses Built by a Housing Corporation

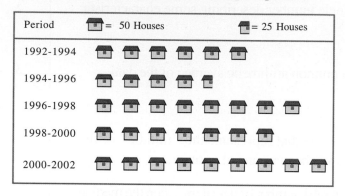

Examples

1.

A bar graph titled with vertical axis "Rainfall (in inches)" from 0 to 4 and horizontal axis "Month" showing Jan, Feb, Mar, Apr.

(a) A city recorded 2.5 inches rainfall in the month of February.

(b) The average rainfall in the four months

$$= \frac{2 + 2.5 + 4 + 1}{4}$$

$$= 2.375 \text{ in}$$

(c) The city had maximum rainfall in the month of March and minimum, in April.

2. The following line graph represents exactly the same information as the above bar graph. It can be interpreted the same way.

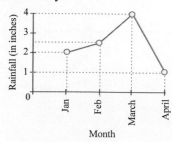

Month

Part II   Procedures and Rules

BAR GRAPHS AND LINE GRAPHS

1. To read and interpret data from a bar graph:

***Step* 1** Identify the bar representing the particular item.

***Step* 2** Read the height of the bar on the vertical scale.

***Step* 3** Use the data in the graph to draw certain conclusions.

2. To read and interpret data from a line graph:

***Step* 1** Identify the point on a horizontal scale representing the particular item.

***Step* 2** Read the height of the graph above the point from the vertical scale.

***Step* 3** Use the data to draw conclusions.

CIRCLE GRAPH OR PIE CHART

3. To read data from a circle graph:

Step **1** Identify the sector which represents a particular item.

Step **2** Count the segments on the arc of that sector to know the percent of the item as a part of the whole. If the segments are not shown, then read the percent shown for the sector.

Step **3** Interpret the data by drawing certain conclusions.

PICTOGRAPHS

4. To read and interpret data from a pictograph:

Step **1** To find the value of a particular item, count the number of symbols in the row of that item.

Step **2** Multiply that number by the number represented by the symbol. The product obtained is the value of the item.

Step **3** The data from a pictograph can be interpreted the same way as in other graphs.

5. To **construct** a vertical bar graph for a given set of data:

Step **1** Draw a vertical axis and a horizontal axis.

Step **2** Mark an appropriate scale on the vertical axis to represent the data value of each category (The scale must be uniform and must start with 0 at the origin, the point of intersection of the two axis.)

Step **3** Mark the categories of data along the horizontal axis.

Step **4** Draw vertical rectangles for each category (keeping the marked point in the center of the base of the rectangle) so that the height of the bar reaches the value of the data in that category.

Step **5** Give a suitable title to the graph and see that all the items are labelled clearly.

Examples

3. Annual expenditure of a school

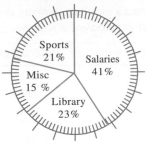

(a) Salaries represent 41% of the available funds.

(b) If the annual funds available are $1,750,000, then the amount spent on sports.

$= 21\%$ of $ 1,750,000

$= \dfrac{21}{100} \times 1,750,000$

$= \$367,500.$

4. Sale of TV sets at an appliances store

Day	Number of TV sets sold
	📺 = 10, ▯ = 5
Monday	📺 📺 📺 📺
Tuesday	📺 ▯

(a) The number of TV sets sold on

Monday $= 4 \times 10$
$\qquad\quad = 40$

(b) The number of TV sets sold on Monday is 25 more than are sold on Tuesday, since $40 - 15 = 25$.

5. Construct a bar graph showing the sales data of a business over a period of five years using the following information:

Year	Sales (in Million Dollars)
1998	50
1999	62
2000	55
2001	58
2002	65

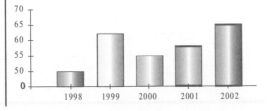

Examples

6. Given the following information, construct a pie chart showing the weekly pocket expenses of a student,

Expenses	Percentage
Movies	45%
Food	20%
Supplies	35%

Step 1 45% of 360° = 0.45 × 360° = **162°**
20% of 360° = 0.20 × 360° = **72°**
35% of 360° = 0.35 × 360° = **126°**

Steps 2, 3, 4

Weekly Pocket Expenses

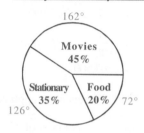

7. The equation $2x + 3y = 4$ is linear.
The equation $4xy + 2x = 7$ is not linear.

8. The ordered pair $(2, 1)$ is a solution of $x + 2y = 4$
since $2 + 2(1) = 4$ is true.
$(1, 3), (2, 5), (3, 7) \ldots$
are all solutions of $2x - y + 1 = 0$

9. Graph the equation $2x + y = 2$

x	y	(x, y)
0	2	$(0, 2)$
1	2	$(1, 2)$
2	-2	$(2, -2)$

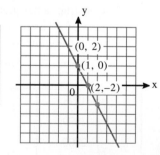

10.

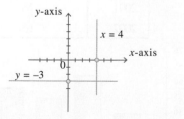

6. To construct a **circle graph** or **pie chart:**

Step **1** Find the central angle for each category by multiplying the corresponding percent in decimal form by 360°.

Step **2** Draw a circle.

Step **3** Draw each central angle and label each sector with the name and the corresponding percent of each category.

Step **4** Give a suitable title to the graph.

LINEAR EQUATIONS IN TWO VARIABLES

7. An equation is linear if each term contains only one variable and the variable is of degree one.

8. Solutions of a linear equations in x and y

1. An ordered pair is a **solution** of an equation in two variables if substitution of the values of the variables make the equation a true statement.

2. A linear equation has infinitely many solutions.

9. To graph a linear equation in two variables x and y;
- Find three ordered pairs satisfying the linear equation.
- Plot the corresponding points.
- Draw a straight line through the three points.

10. **(a)** The graph of $x = 4$ is a vertical line.

(b) The graph of $y = -3$ is a horizontal line.

9.6 REVIEW EXERCISE

In exercises 1-4, find (a) the mean, (b) the median, (c) the mode (if any), and (d) the range for the given data.

1.   25 50 60 40 25   2.   6 10 4 3 9 11 22 18

3.   5 8 16 12 11 15 10 12 6 12 20   4.   25 34 31 23 22 25 35 29 20 32

The following bar graph shows the average daily expenses for a travelling sales person in four cities. Answer the questions in exercises 5-8, using the given graph.

5.   What are the average daily expenses in Chicago?

6.   Which city is the most expensive out of the four?

7.   How much more expensive per day is Washington compared to Atlanta?

8.   How much more in percent does the sales person spend per day in Washington as compared to Chicago?

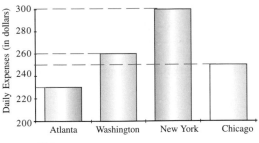

The following line graph indicates temperatures at five different times of a particular fall day. Answer the questions in exercises 9-12, using the given graph.

9.   At what time of the day was the temperature the lowest?

10.   At what time of the day was the temperature the highest?

11.   Between what two times did the temperature increase the most?

12.   How much cooler was it at 10 AM than at 2 PM?

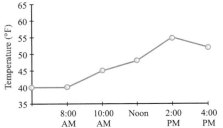

The following pie chart indicates the percentage of books in five different areas in a certain library. Answer the questions in exercises 13-17, using the given graph.

13.   What percent of books in the library are fiction books?

14.   Which category of books is smallest in number?

15.   If there are 25,000 books in the library, what is the number of science books in the library?

16.   Which of the two categories of books, science or history, has the larger number of books and by what percent?

17.   Reference books and other books together are what percent of the total number of books?

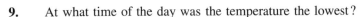

The following pictograph shows the number of computers sold in four years (2000-2003). Answer the questions in exercises 18-21, using the pictograph.

18.   How many computers were sold in 2000?

19.   Which year was the company's most successful year of sales?

20.   Find the percent increase in the sales from 2001 to 2003.

21.   In which year was the increase in the sale of computers the largest?

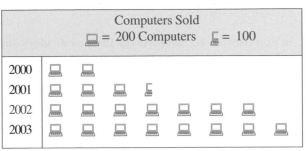

22. Construct a bar graph for the following data:

Number of Players on a Team

Sports (Game)	Number of Players
Cricket	11
Hockey	11
Foot Ball	11
Rugby	15
Water Polo	7
Net Ball	7

23. Construct a circle graph that represents the following data:

(*Hint:* Find the percents for each party by dividing the number of students affiliated with it by 1,000.)

Political Party Affiliation of 1,000 College Students

Party	Number of Students
Democrat	475
Republican	325
Others	200

24. Determine the coordinates of the points shown in the figure.

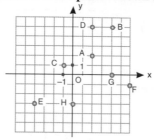

25. Plot the following ordered pairs on the same coordinate system.

a) $(-1, 3)$ b) $(2, 5)$ c) $(3, -7)$ d) $(-4, -1)$ e) $(3, 0)$

f) $(0, -2)$ g) $(0, 0)$ h) $(-8, 0)$

In exercises 26-28, determine whether the indicated ordered pair is a solution of the given equation.

26. $5x + 7y = 2$; $(1, -1)$ **27.** $-3x + 4y = 10$; $(-2, 1)$ **28.** $2x = 5y$; $(10, 4)$

In exercises 29-31, complete the ordered pair so that it is a solution of the equation.

29. $2x - 3y = 7$; $(-4, ?)$ **30.** $x + 3y = 5$; $(?, -2)$ **31.** $8x - 7y = 4$; $(?, 4)$

In exercises 32-36, complete the table of values for the equation.

32. $2x - y = 4$

x	y
1	
-3	
	3
	2

33. $y = 2$

x	y
-1	
2	
3	
-4	

34. $3y - 15 = 0$

x	y
6	
-5	
0	
4	

35. $x = -2$

x	y
	-1
	2
	0
	1

36. $6x - 5y = 11$

x	y
6	
	5
	-4
-4	

In exercises 37-41, complete the table of *x*-values and *y*-values for the given equation. Draw the graph by plotting these points.

37. $y = -5$

x	y
-2	
0	
3	

38. $x = 4$

x	y
	-3
	1
	2

39. $3x + 4y = 1$

x	y
-1	
3	
-5	

40. $2x = 3y$

x	y
-3	
	0
	2

41. $3y - 2x = 12$

x	y
	-2
6	
	6

9.7 SELF TEST

In exercises 1 and 2, find (a) the mean, (b) the median, (c) the mode (if any), and (d) the range for the given data.

1. The teaching experiences (in years) of math faculty members at a college:

5 8 3 18 12 15 21 23 25 30

2. The distances jumped (in centimeters) by 15 students at an athletic meet:

305   300   375   360   359   299   352   339

360   340   370   380   360   362   338

The following line graph shows the number of automobile accidents in a city over a period of five years. Answer the questions in exercises 3-5, using the given graph.

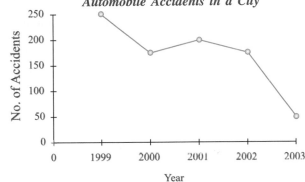

Automobile Accidents in a City

3. How many car accidents occurred in the year 2001?

4. What is the percent decrease or increase in the number of accidents in 2002 over that in 2001?

5. What was the total number of accidents in 1999 to 2001?

6. Determine whether the following statements are true or false. If a statement is false, revise it to make a true statement.

(a) If a symbol represents 25 ducks, then 5 symbols represent 125 ducks.

(b) There are three axis in a bar graph.

(c) In a pictograph, larger quantities are shown by larger symbols, and smaller quantities by smaller symbols.

(d) In a circle graph, a circle is divided into hundredths.

The following bar graph indicates the number of calories a person burns during a 1 hour activity. Answer the questions in exercises 7-9, using the given graph.

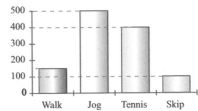

7. How many calories does a person burn in one hour playing tennis?

8. In which activity will you burn more calories, one hour of walking or one hour of jogging?

9. The person is advised by the doctor not to jog. How long should he walk to burn calories equivalent to one hour of jogging?

The following pie chart indicates expenses for a month as a percent of income in a family of four. Answer the questions in exercises 10-13, using the given chart.

10. Which item has the maximum expenditure?

11. If the total family income for a month is $3,000, how much is spent on clothing?

12. If the total family income for a month is $2,500, how much is spent on medical care and housing together?

13. What percent of the family income is spent on three items: Housing, Food, and Transportation?

14. Construct a bar graph that represents the following data:

Leading Tea Producers of the World in 1998

Country	Production (In Thousands of Tons)
India	490
China	300
Sri Lanka	201
Japan	96
USSR	80
Indonesia	62

15. Make a circle graph (pie chart) that represents the following data.

Annual Expenditure of a School

Category Expenditure	Percentage of total
Art & Craft	10%
Library	20%
Sports	10%
Salary	55%
Music	5%

16. Complete the ordered pairs for the given equation.

$3x - 2y = 11$; $(-1 , ?) , (2 , ?) , (? , 2) , (? , -1)$

17. Which of the following ordered pairs are solutions of the equation $2x + 3y = 7$?

$(2 , 1) , (-2 , 4) , \left(0, \dfrac{7}{3}\right) , (-1 , 3) , (7 , 0)$

Measurements

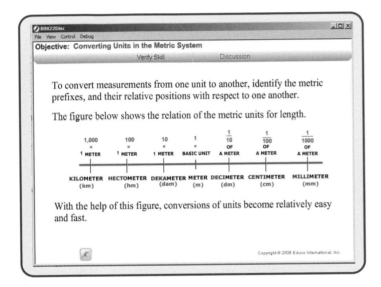

10.1 Basic Operations on Measurements in the Same System ■

10.2 Unit Conversions in the Same System ■

10.3 Unit Conversions Between English and Metric System ■

10.4 Estimating Measurements in the Metric System ■

10.5 Chapter Summary ■

10.6 Review Exercise ■

10.7 Self Test ■

MEASUREMENTS

Introduction

For measuring lengths, weights, time, distances, and volumes, we use units of measurement. These units are different, in measure and name, in the two most commonly used measurement systems:

1. the English System   (miles, pounds, gallons);
2. the Metric System   (kilometers, grams, liters).

This chapter is divided into four sections.

10.1 BASIC OPERATIONS ON MEASUREMENTS IN THE SAME SYSTEM

IMPORTANT VOCABULARY

1. A **measurement** is written with a number and a unit of measure. It shows "how many" or "how much".

    25 *lb*, 1.5 *m*, 10 *l* are examples of measurements.

2. The units of the **English System** of measurement are:

    i) length: **inch** (in.), **foot** (ft), **yard** (yd), **mile** (mi).

    ii) weight: **ounce** (oz), **pound** (lb), **ton**.

    iii) liquid volume: **teaspoon** (tsp), **tablespoon** (tbs), **fluid ounce** (fl oz), **cup** (c), **pint** (pt), **quart** (qt), **gallon** (gal).

> **Objectives**
>
> After completing this section, you will be able to:
>
> A. Multiply or divide any measurement by a number; and
>
> B. Add or subtract two measurements with common units.

3. The **basic** units of the **Metric System** are:

    i) meter :   denoted by **m,** is the basic unit of *length*.

    ii) gram :   denoted by **g**, is the basic unit of *weight* (or mass).

    iii) liter :   denoted by *l*, is the basic unit of *volume* (or capacity).

4. **Equivalent measures** are measures of the same thing using different units. For example,

    1 pound (1 *lb*) = 16 ounces (16 oz).

    4 quarts (4 qt) = 1 gallon (1 *gal*).

10.1 A.   Multiplying or Dividing any Measurement by a Number

- To determine size or quantity, a unit of measurement can be chosen arbitrarily. Then, multiples of this unit may be used to measure objects. For example, to measure length, we may choose a "hand-span", "pace", or "rod" as a basic unit of measurement.

Such units are non-standard units of length. If two people measure the length of an object using hand-span, pace, or a piece of rod, their answers may differ. However, if two persons measure the length of an object by using a fixed scale, such as rods of equal length, they will get the same answer. For consistency, we must have standard units of measurement.

- The **English System** of measurement uses 1 foot (1 ft) as the *standard* unit of *length*, while in the **Metric System** the standard unit of length is 1 meter (1 m). For most purposes, these standard units along with their multiples are sufficient. For measuring the lengths of shorter objects, in the English System, we use a smaller unit of length called an **inch**. If a length of 1 foot is divided into 12 equal parts, then the length of each part is 1 inch. That is, 1 inch = one-twelfth of a foot. The length measuring 1 inch is shown below:

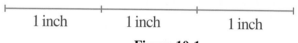

1 inch

To measure a larger object, we count how many of these inches are needed to measure the length. In Figure 10.1, we need three 1 inch units to measure the given line segment.

1 inch   1 inch   1 inch

Figure 10.1

We say that the length of the line is 3 times 1 inch, that is, 3 · (1 inch) or just 3 inches.

- In the **Metric System**, the standard unit of length is a '**meter**'. For measuring lengths of shorter objects, the system uses a smaller unit called "**centimeter**" denoted by **cm** (1 meter = 100 centimeters). In Figure 10.2 below, we need eight 1- centimeter measurements to measure the length of the line segment.

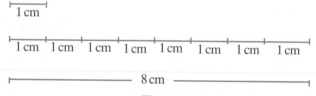

Figure 10.2

We say that the length of the line segment is 8 times 1 cm, that is, 8 · (1 cm) or just 8 cm.

- Similarly, we can multiply or divide any measurement by a number. Consider three jars, each containing 1 liter of water.

If we pour the water from these three jars into a bigger jar, what quantity of water is in the bigger jar? Surely, 3 liters; so,

$$3 \text{ liters} = 3 \cdot (1 \text{ liter}).$$

If there are 4 containers, each holding 3 liters of water, how many liters of water are in the 4 containers?

$$4 \cdot (3 \text{ liters}) = (4 \cdot 3) \text{ liters}$$
$$= 12 \text{ liters}.$$

- Similarly, if a rod of length 5 inches is divided into two equal parts, (Figure 10.3), what will be the length of each part?

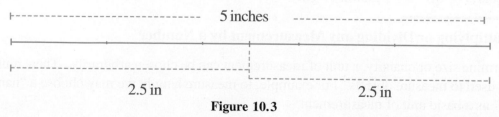

Figure 10.3

$$\begin{aligned}
\text{The length of each part} \ &= \ 5 \text{ inches} \div 2 \\
&= \ (5 \div 2) \text{ inches} \\
&= \ 2.5 \text{ inches.}
\end{aligned}$$

Thus, to multiply or divide a measurement by a number, we multiply or divide the two numbers and write the unit of measure.

$$4 \cdot (3 \text{ liters}) \ = \ (4 \cdot 3) \text{ liters} ; \qquad 5 \text{ in} \div 2 \ = \ (5 \div 2) \text{ in}$$

$$= \ 12 \text{ liters} \qquad\qquad\qquad\qquad = \ \frac{5}{2} \text{ in.}$$

Procedure to multiply or divide a measurement by a number:

    Step 1   Multiply or divide the two numbers.

    Step 2   Write the product or the quotient followed by the unit of measurement.

Example 1   Multiply or divide as indicated.

    (a)   Multiply 35 gallons by 6.

    (b)   Divide 43.7 yards into 19 equal lengths.

Solutions

    (a) $(35 \text{ gallons}) \cdot 6 \ = (35 \cdot 6) \text{ gallons}$
                             $= 210 \text{ gallons}$

- Multiply the numbers: $35 \cdot 6 = 210$.
- Write the product followed by the unit of measure.

    (b) $(43.7 \text{ yards}) \div 19 \ = \ (43.7 \div 19) \text{ yards}$
                                 $= \ 2.3 \text{ yards}$

- Divide the numbers: $43.7 \div 19 = 2.3$.
- Write the quotient, 2.3, followed by the unit of measure, yards.

Example 2   Perform the indicated operation.

    (a) $(8 \text{ hours}) \cdot (7)$ **(b)** $(45.6 \text{ dm}) \div 3$

Solutions

    (a) $(8 \text{ hours}) \cdot (7) \ = \ (8 \cdot 7) \text{ hours}$
                          $= \ 56 \text{ hours}$

- Group the numbers.
- Simplify.

    (b) $(45.6 \text{ dm}) \div 3 \ = \ (45.6 \div 3) \text{ dm}$
                         $= \ 15.2 \text{ dm.}$

- Divide the numbers.
- Simplify.

Example 3   If 1.5 lb of peanuts are distributed equally among 3 students, how much does each student get?

Solution

    To find the share of each student, we divide the total weight by the number of students.

$$\frac{1.5 \text{ lb}}{3 \text{ students}} \ = \ (1.5 \div 3) \text{ lb per student}$$

$$= \ 0.5 \text{ lb per student.}$$

- Divide the numbers.
- Write the quotient followed by the unit of measurement.

    Each student gets 0.5 lb of peanuts.

Warm-Up

1. **(a)** Multiply: 16.5 ounces by 7.

  (b) Divide 127 kg into 8 equal weights.

2. Perform the indicated operation.

  (a) $(4 \text{ miles}) (16)$

  (b) $(57 \text{ pounds}) \div 4$

3. If 1 qt of milk is poured equally into 4 tumblers, what is the quantity of milk in each tumbler?

4. There are 24 hours in a day. How many hours are there in 13 days?

Answers:

1. (a) 115.5 ounces   (b) 15.875 kg
2. (a) 64 miles   (b) 14.25 pounds
3. 0.25 qt
4. 312 hours

Example 4   If a can of soup contains 275 grams, how many grams are contained in seven cans?

Solution

To find the total quantity of soup in seven cans, we multiply the quantity in one can by seven.

$$\frac{(275 \text{ g})}{1 \text{ can}} \cdot 7 \text{ cans} = (275 \cdot 7) \text{ g}$$ • Multiply the numbers.

$$= 1925 \text{ g.}$$ • Write the product, followed by grams.

Seven cans contain 1,925 g of soup.

10.1 B.   Adding or Subtracting Two Measurements with Common Units

- Two or more measurements with **common units** can be added. For example,

$$3 \text{ g} + 7.5 \text{ g} = (3 + 7.5) \text{ g}$$ Group the numbers.

$$= 10.5 \text{ g} ;$$ Add the numbers.

$$14 \text{ cm} + 10 \text{ cm} + 3 \text{ cm} = (14 + 10 + 3) \text{ cm}$$ Group the numbers.

$$= 27 \text{ cm}$$ Simplify.

- Similarly, we can subtract two measurements with common **units**. For example,

$$25 \text{ gal} - 17 \text{ gal} = (25 - 17) \text{ gal}$$ Group the numbers.

$$= 8 \text{ gal.}$$ Subtract the numbers.

- English and metric measurement and their equivalents are listed in Tables 10.1 and 10.2 respectively.

TABLE 10.1 ENGLISH MEASUREMENTS AND EQUIVALENTS	
Length	**Time**
12 inches (in.) = 1 foot (ft)	60 seconds (sec) = 1 minute (min)
3 feet (ft) = 1 yard (yd)	60 minutes (min) = 1 hour (hr)
5,280 feet (ft) = 1 mile (mi)	24 hours (hr) = 1 day
	7 days = 1 week
Liquid Volume	**Weight**
3 teaspoons (tsp) = 1 tablespoon (tbs)	4 quarts (qt) = 1 gallon (gal)
2 table spoons = 1 fluid ounce (fl oz)	16 ounces (oz) = 1 pound (lb)
8 fluid ounces (fl oz) = 1 cup (c)	2,200 pounds (lb) = 1 ton
2 cups (c) = 1 pint (pt)	
2 pints (pt) = 1 quart (qt)	

TABLE 10.2   METRIC MEASUREMENTS AND EQUIVALENTS

Length (Basic Unit is 1 Meter)

1	millimeter	(mm)	=		= 0.001	m
1	centimeter	(cm)	=	10 millimeters	= 0.01	m
1	decimeter	(dm)	=	10 centimeter	= 0.1	m
1	METER	(m)	=	10 decimeters	= 1	m
1	dekameter	(dam)	=	10 meters	= 10	m
1	hectometer	(hm)	=	10 dekameters	= 100	m
1	kilometer	(km)	=	10 hectometers	= 1,000	m

Weight (Basic Unit is 1 Gram)

1	milligram	(mg)	=		= 0.001	g
1	centigram	(cg)	=	10 milligrams	= 0.01	g
1	decigram	(dg)	=	10 centigrams	= 0.1	g
1	GRAM	(g)	=	10 decigrams	= 1	g
1	dekagram	(dag)	=	10 grams	= 10	g
1	hectogram	(hg)	=	10 dekagrams	= 100	g
1	kilogram	(kg)	=	10 hectograms	= 1,000	g
1	metric ton		=	1,000 kilograms		

Liquid Measurements (Basic Unit is 1 Liter)

1	milliliter	(ml)	=		= 0.001	l
1	centiliter	(cl)	=	10 milliliters	= 0.01	l
1	deciliter	(dl)	=	10 centiliters	= 0.1	l
1	LITER	(l)	=	10 deciliters	= 1	l
1	dekaliter	(da$l$)	=	10 liters	= 10	l
1	hectoliter	(hl)	=	10 dekaliters	= 100	l
1	kiloliter	(kl)	=	10 hectoliters	= 1,000	l

TABLE 10.3   MONETARY SYSTEM

		1 cent	=	0.01	dollar
5 cents	=	1 nickel	=	0.05	dollar
10 cents	=	1 dime	=	0.1	dollar
10 dimes	=	1 dollar	=	1	dollar

Procedure to add or subtract two measurements with a common unit.

Step 1   Arrange the measurements in columns lining up the place values and units.

Step 2   Add or subtract as required and use the common unit.
Use equivalent measures, if necessary.

Example 5   Add or subtract as indicated.

(a) 45.6 l + 39.8 l (b) 26.5yd – 17.8 yd

Solutions

(a)
$$\begin{array}{r} \overset{1}{} \\ 45.6\ l \\ +\ 39.8\ l \\ \hline 85.4\ l \end{array}$$

- Arrange the measurements in columns. Line up the place values and common unit.

- Add the numbers and use the common unit with the sum.

Alternatively,

45.6 l + 39.8 l = (45.6 + 39.8) l • Group the numbers.

= 85.4 l • Simplify.

Warm-Up

5. Add or subtract as indicated.
(a) 19.2 lb + 23.9 lb

(b) 123 ft − 72.7 ft

(b)
$$\begin{array}{r} 26.5 \text{ yd} \\ -17.8 \text{ yd} \\ \hline 8.7 \text{ yd} \end{array}$$

- Arrange the measurements in columns. Line up the place values and the common unit.

- Subtract the numbers and use the common unit with the difference.

Alternatively,

26.5 yd − 17.8 yd = (26.5 − 17.8) yd

- Group the numbers.

= 8.7 yd.

- Simplify.

6. Perform the indicated operations.

   (a) 8 min 43 sec + 3 min 12 sec + 7 min 25 sec

Example 6   Perform the indicated operations.

   (a) 25 lb 5 oz + 7 lb 9 oz + 13 lb 6 oz.

   (b) 7 gal 2 qt − 4 gal 3 qt 1 pt.

Solutions

(a)
$$\begin{array}{rr} 25 \text{ lb} & 5 \text{ oz} \\ 7 \text{ lb} & 9 \text{ oz} \\ + \ 13 \text{ lb} & 6 \text{ oz} \\ \hline 45 \text{ lb} & 20 \text{ oz} \end{array}$$

- Write in columns. Line up the place values and units.

- Add.

= 45 lb + (1 lb + 4 oz) Since 20 oz is more than
= 46 lb 4 oz   1 *lb* (16 oz = 1 *lb* from Table 10.1), We change 20 oz to 1 *lb* 4 oz and add the pounds.

The sum is 46 lb 4 oz.

(b) 2 yd 1 ft 10 in
   + 4 yd 2 ft 11 in

(b)
$$\begin{array}{rrr} & {}^1 & {}^2 \\ 7 \text{ gal} & 2\!\!\!/ \text{ qt} & \cancel{0} \text{ pt} \\ -4 \text{ gal} & 3 \text{ qt} & 1 \text{ pt} \\ \hline & & 1 \text{ pt} \end{array}$$

- Write in columns. Line up the place values and units.

- Subtract pints (pt). Since 1 pt cannot be subtracted from 0 pt **borrow** 1 qt from the 2 qt and use 1 qt = 2 pt.

$$\begin{array}{rrr} {}^6 & {}^{\cancel{5}}\!\!\!\! & {}^2 \\ 7\!\!\!/ \text{ gal} & 2\!\!\!/ \text{ qt} & \cancel{0} \text{ pt} \\ -4 \text{ gal} & 3 \text{ qt} & 1 \text{ pt} \\ \hline 2 \text{ gal} & 2 \text{ qt} & 1 \text{ pt} \end{array}$$

- 3 qt can not be subtracted from the remaining 1 qt, so borrow 1 gal (4 qt) from the 7 gal and add it to the 1 qt.

- Subtract gallons.

The difference is 2 gal 2 qt 1 pt.

 Note

In practice, we do not write the solution in steps as shown above. The solution is written in only one step as follows:

$$\begin{array}{rrr} {}^6 & {}^{\cancel{5}} & {}^2 \\ 7\!\!\!/ \text{ gal} & 2\!\!\!/ \text{ qt} & \cancel{0} \text{ pt} \\ -\ 4 \text{ gal} & 3 \text{ qt} & 1 \text{ pt} \\ \hline 2 \text{ gal} & 2 \text{ qt} & 1 \text{ pt} \quad \textbf{Answer} \end{array}$$

Answers:

5. (a) 43.1 lb   **(b)** 50.3 ft

6. (a) 19 min 20 sec   **(b)** 7 yd 1 ft 9 in

Example 7   Application

Laura joins three pieces of jute-rope measuring 5 ft 4 in, 7 ft 9 in, and 10 ft 6 in. What is the total length of the three pieces ? If she needs a length measuring 8 ft 9 in, what is the measurement of the remaining length of rope?

Solution

To find the total length of all the pieces of rope joined, we add the lengths of the three pieces.

$$
\begin{array}{ll}
& 5\text{ ft} \quad 4\text{ in} \\
& 7\text{ ft} \quad 9\text{ in} \\
+ & 10\text{ ft} \quad 6\text{ in} \\
\hline
& 22\text{ ft} \quad 19\text{ in} = (22\text{ ft}) + (1\text{ ft} + 7\text{ in}) \\
& \qquad\qquad\quad = 23\text{ ft }7\text{ in}
\end{array}
$$

- Write the measurements of the three pieces in columns. Line up the place-values and the units.
- Add in columns.
- Since 19 inches is more than 1 ft (1 ft = 12 in), rewrite 19 inches as 1 ft 7 inches.

The total length of the rope is 23 ft 7 in.

Laura uses a length measuring 8 ft 9 in. To find the measurement of the remaining length of rope, we subtract 8 ft 9 in from the total length.

$$
\begin{array}{ll}
& \overset{22}{\cancel{23}}\text{ ft} \quad \overset{19}{\cancel{7}}\text{ in} \\
- & 8\text{ ft} \quad 9\text{ in} \\
\hline
& 14\text{ ft} \quad 10\text{ in}
\end{array}
$$

- Subtract inches. Since 9 inches cannot be subtracted from the 7 inches, we borrow 1 ft (=12 in) from the 23 ft, and add it to 7 inches to get 19 inches.
- Subtract 8 ft from the remaining 22 ft.

The length of the remaining rope is 14 ft 10 in.

Exercise 10.1

A. **In exercises 1-10, multiply or divide the measurement by the number as indicated.**

1. Multiply 27 oz by 8.
2. Multiply 32 m by 5.
3. Divide 486 lb by 54.
4. Divide 42 g by 7.

5. Multiply 35 cm by 6.
6. Divide 17 miles by 5.
7. Divide 15 gallon by 6.
8. Divide 18.9 oz by 14.

9. Multiply 4.25 kg by 16.
10. Divide 35 liters by 8.

In exercises 11-20, perform the indicated operation.

11. $2\dfrac{3}{4}(8\text{ g})$
12. $(8.95\text{ cm})(4)$
13. $(3.6\text{ ft}) \div 3\dfrac{1}{3}$
14. $(17.5\text{ oz}) \div 3\dfrac{1}{2}$
15. $(15.5\text{ m})(6)$

16. $(288\text{ qt}) \div 48$
17. $40\text{ kg} \div 1\dfrac{1}{2}$
18. $(16.5\text{ mg})(13)$
19. $3.44\ l \div 2.5$
20. $256\text{ gal} \div 8$

B. **In exercises 21-30, add or subtract as indicated.**

21. $54\text{ m} + 78\text{ m} + 12\text{ m}$
22. $3\text{ g} + 89\text{ g} + 32\text{ g}$
23. $38\ kl + 21\ kl + 43\ kl$
24. $96\text{ cm} - 48\text{ cm}$

25. $89\text{ min} - 48\text{ min}$
26. $56\text{ lb} - 29\text{ lb}$
27. $104\ ml - 52.6\ ml$
28. $2.56\text{ oz} + 9.3\text{ oz} - 3.8\text{ oz}$

29. $24.5\text{ yd} - 63.7\text{ yd} + 190\text{ yd} - 78\text{ yd}$
30. $9.82\text{ kg} - 7.728\text{ kg}$

In exercises 31-35, add the given measurements.

31.
$$
\begin{array}{ll}
& 3\text{ ft} \quad 8\text{ in} \\
& 7\text{ ft} \quad 4\text{ in} \\
& 20\text{ ft} \quad 8\text{ in} \\
+ & 12\text{ ft} \quad 10\text{ in} \\
\hline
\end{array}
$$

32.
$$
\begin{array}{ll}
& 6\text{ hr} \quad 20\text{ min} \\
& 3\text{ hr} \quad 10\text{ min} \\
+ & 5\text{ hr} \quad 15\text{ min} \\
\hline
\end{array}
$$

33.
$$
\begin{array}{ll}
& 5\text{ gal} \quad 3\text{ qt} \quad 1\text{ pt} \\
+ & 9\text{ gal} \quad 1\text{ qt} \quad 1\text{ pt} \\
\hline
\end{array}
$$

34.
$$\begin{array}{r} 6 \text{ yd} \quad 2 \text{ ft} \quad 8 \text{ in} \\ + \, 10 \text{ yd} \qquad\qquad 4 \text{ in} \\ \hline \end{array}$$

35.
$$\begin{array}{r} 23 \text{ lb} \quad 15 \text{ oz} \\ + \, 31 \text{ lb} \quad\; 8 \text{ oz} \\ \hline \end{array}$$

In exercises 36-40, subtract the given measurements.

36.
$$\begin{array}{r} 8 \text{ kg} \quad 235 \text{ g} \\ - \, 2 \text{ kg} \quad 839 \text{ g} \\ \hline \end{array}$$

37.
$$\begin{array}{r} 18 \text{ } kl \quad 500 \text{ } l \\ - \;\; 6 \text{ } kl \quad 900 \text{ } l \\ \hline \end{array}$$

38.
$$\begin{array}{r} 25 \text{ hr} \quad 37 \text{ min} \quad\; 9 \text{ sec} \\ - \, 12 \text{ hr} \quad 43 \text{ min} \quad 20 \text{ sec} \\ \hline \end{array}$$

39.
$$\begin{array}{r} 14 \text{ ft} \quad 5 \text{ in} \\ - \;\; 6 \text{ ft} \quad 9 \text{ in} \\ \hline \end{array}$$

40.
$$\begin{array}{r} 6 \text{ yd} \quad 1 \text{ ft} \quad 2 \text{ in} \\ - \, 2 \text{ yd} \quad 2 \text{ ft} \quad 6 \text{ in} \\ \hline \end{array}$$

Applications

41. A boy weighed 72.6 lb. He lost 2.78 lb due to illness. Find his weight after the weight loss.

42. From a 75 yd roll of ribbon, Linda used three pieces of ribbon measuring 19 yd 2 ft, 20 yd 1 ft, and 28 yd 1 ft 6 in. Find the length of ribbon remaining in the roll.

43. The sides of a rectangle are 7.62 ft, 5.10 ft, 7.62 ft, and 5.10 ft. Find the sum of the sides of this rectangle.

44. The weights of four laboratory samples were: 4.961 g, 5.006 g, 4.752 g, and 4.819 g. Find the average weight of these four samples.

10.2 UNIT CONVERSIONS IN THE SAME SYSTEM

Objectives

After completing this section, you will be able to:

A. Convert units in the English System; and

B. Convert units in the Metric System.

10.2 A. Converting Units in the English System

• We know that 12 inches and 1 foot are equivalent measurements:

$$12 \text{ inches} = 1 \text{ foot}$$

This equation shows that the ratio of 12 inches to 1 foot, or 1 foot to 12 inches is 1; thus:

$$\frac{12 \text{ inches}}{1 \text{ foot}} = \frac{1 \text{ foot}}{1 \text{ foot}} = 1 \quad \text{and} \quad \frac{1 \text{ foot}}{12 \text{ inches}} = \frac{12 \text{ inches}}{12 \text{ inches}} = 1$$

The ratio $\dfrac{12 \text{ inches}}{1 \text{ foot}}$ along with the identity property is used to convert a measurement in feet to a measurement in inches. Similarly, the ratio $\dfrac{1 \text{ foot}}{12 \text{ inches}}$ along with the identity property is used to convert a measurement in inches to a measurement in feet. These ratios $\dfrac{12 \text{ inches}}{1 \text{ foot}}$ or $\dfrac{1 \text{ foot}}{12 \text{ inches}}$ are also referred to as **conversion ratios.**

For example, to convert 5 feet to inches, we use the conversion ratio $\dfrac{12 \text{ inches}}{1 \text{ foot}}$.

$$5 \text{ feet} = (5 \text{ feet}) \cdot 1$$

Multiply by 1.

$$= \frac{5 \text{ feet}}{1} \cdot \frac{12 \text{ inches}}{1 \text{ foot}}$$

Substitute $\frac{12 \text{ inches}}{1 \text{ foot}}$ for 1. Divide out the common unit as a common factor.

$$= (5 \cdot 12) \text{ inches}$$

Simplify.

$$= 60 \text{ inches.}$$

- In some cases, it may be necessary to multiply by several different conversion ratios for one conversion. For example, let us convert 96 pints to gallons:

$$96 \text{ pints} = (96 \text{ pints}) \cdot 1 \cdot 1$$

$$= \frac{96 \text{ pints}}{1} \cdot \frac{1 \text{ quart}}{2 \text{ pints}} \cdot \frac{1 \text{ gallon}}{4 \text{ quarts}}$$

Use the equivalent measurement relations:

2 pints = 1 quart, 4 quarts = 1 gallon.

$$= \frac{96}{8} \text{ gallons}$$

Cancel the common units from the numerator and the denominator.

Simplify.

$$= 12 \text{ gallons.}$$

In converting units in the same system, the units of measurement are treated like factors and are cancelled before multiplying or dividing the numbers. Tables 10.1 and 10.2 will prove to be useful in making conversions of units.

Procedure to convert the units of a measurement in the same system:

Step **1**   List the needed conversions.

Step **2**   Multiply the given measurement by the appropriate conversion ratio(s).

Step **3**   Simplify, cancelling the common units.

Example 1   Convert the units of measurement.

(a) 7 pounds to ounces   (b) 27,456 feet to miles

(c) 3 days to minutes

Solutions

(a)   1 pounds = 16 ounce

Step 1   List the needed conversions.

$$7 \text{ pounds} = \frac{7 \text{ lb}}{1} \cdot \frac{16 \text{ oz}}{1 \text{ lb}}$$

Step 2   Multiply by the conversion ratio: $\frac{16 \text{ oz}}{1 \text{ lb}}$

$$= 7(16) \text{ oz}$$

$$= 112 \text{ oz.}$$

Step 3   Simplify, cancelling common units.

Therefore, 7 pounds is equivalent to 112 ounces.

(b)   1 mile = 5,280 ft

- List the needed conversions.

$$27,456 \text{ ft} = \frac{27,456 \text{ ft}}{1} \cdot \frac{1 \text{ mi}}{5,280 \text{ ft}}$$

- Multiply by the conversion ratio: $\frac{1 \text{ mi}}{5,280 \text{ ft}}$

Warm-Up

1. Convert the units of measurement.

(a) 15 yards to feet

(b) 800 pounds to tons

$$= \frac{27,456}{5,280} \text{ mi}$$ • Simplify, cancelling common units.

$$= 5.2 \text{ mi}$$ • Simplify.

Therefore, 27,456 ft is equal to 5.2 miles.

(c) 3 miles to yards

(c) 3 days to minutes   1 day = 24 hours
1 hour = 60 min

For days to hours

$$3 \text{ days} = (3 \text{ days}) \cdot 1 \cdot 1$$

For hours to minutes

$$= \frac{3 \text{ days}}{1} \cdot \frac{24 \text{ hr}}{1 \text{ day}} \cdot \frac{60 \text{ min}}{1 \text{ hr}}$$

$$= (3 \cdot 24 \cdot 60) \text{ min}$$

$$= 4,320 \text{ min}$$

Therefore, 3 days are equal to 4,320 minutes.

2. Convert as indicated.

(a) 432 in² to ft²

Example 2 Convert the units of measurements as indicated.

(a) 72 ft² to yd²   **(b)** $\dfrac{\$ 36}{\text{ft}^2} = \dfrac{? \text{ cents}}{\text{in}^2}$

Solutions

(a) 72 ft² to yd²

$$\text{ft}^2 = (\text{ft})(\text{ft}) \qquad\qquad \text{yd}^2 = (\text{yd})(\text{yd})$$

$$1 \text{ yard} = 3 \text{ ft}$$

$$72 \text{ ft}^2 = 72 \,(\text{ft})(\text{ft}) \cdot \frac{1 \text{ yd}}{3 \text{ ft}} \cdot \frac{1 \text{ yd}}{3 \text{ ft}}$$ Multiply twice by the conversion ratio: $\frac{1 \text{ yd}}{3 \text{ ft}}$.

$$= \frac{72}{3 \times 3} \,(\text{yd})(\text{yd})$$ Simplify, cancelling the common units.

$$= 8 \text{ yd}^2$$

(b) $\dfrac{81 \, lb}{\text{ft}^2} = \dfrac{? \text{ oz}}{\text{in}^2}$

(b) 1 dollar = 100 cents,   1 ft = 12 in

$$\frac{\$36}{1 \text{ ft}^2} = \frac{36 \text{ dollers}}{1 \text{ ft} \cdot 1 \text{ ft}} \cdot \frac{100 \text{ Cents}}{1 \text{ doller}} \cdot \frac{1 \text{ ft}}{12 \text{ in}} \cdot \frac{1 \text{ ft}}{12 \text{ in}}$$

$$= \frac{3600 \text{ cents}}{144 \text{ in}^2}$$ Simplify, cancelling out the common number factors.

$$= \frac{25 \text{ cents}}{\text{in}^2}.$$

Answers:

1. **(a)** 45 ft   **(b)** 0.364 tons **(c)** 5,280 yds

2. **(a)** 3 ft²   **(b)** $\dfrac{9 \text{ oz}}{\text{in}^2}$

10.2 B.   Converting Units in the Metric System

- The procedure explained in Objective 10.2A is general and can be used for converting units of measurement in any system of measurement. For equivalent measurements in the metric system, we can use Table 10.2.

  For example, let us convert 3 km to meters (m), use 1 km = 1000 m.

  — From km to meter

$$3 \text{ km} = (3 \text{ km}) \cdot 1$$

$$= \frac{3 \text{ km}}{1} \cdot \frac{1000 \text{ m}}{1 \text{ km}}$$

$$= 3{,}000 \text{ m}.$$

- As another example, let us convert 4,000 millimeter (mm) to dekameter (dam):

$$1 \text{ cm} = 10 \text{ mm}, \quad 1 \text{ dm} = 10 \text{ cm}, \quad 1 \text{ m} = 10 \text{ dm}, \text{ and } 1 \text{ dam} = 10 \text{m}$$

$$4000 \text{ mm} = \frac{4{,}000 \text{ mm}}{1} \cdot \frac{1 \text{ cm}}{10 \text{ mm}} \cdot \frac{1 \text{ dm}}{10 \text{ cm}} \cdot \frac{1 \text{ m}}{10 \text{ dm}} \cdot \frac{1 \text{ dam}}{10 \text{ m}}$$

$$= \frac{4{,}000}{10{,}000} \text{ dam}$$

$$= 0.4 \text{ dam}$$

  We observe that changing millimeter to dekameter is equivalent to dividing the number 4,000 by 10,000.

- Conversions from one unit of measurement to another in the Metric System involve multiplying or dividing by powers of 10 (or moving the decimal point).

  If we study Table 10.2 carefully, we will observe that the metric system of measurement is very similar to our base-ten place value system of numbers. Each unit of measurement is *named* by using a prefix (called a "metric prefix") to the basic unit, that can be obtained by multiplying or dividing the basic unit by powers of ten. Look at the following common metric prefixes. They tell how each unit of measurement relates to the basic unit.

Kilo means 1,000 or one thousand.	**Deci** means $\frac{1}{10}$ or one-tenth.
Hecto means 100 or one hundred.	**Centi** means $\frac{1}{100}$ or one-hundredth.
Deka means 10 or ten.	**Milli** means $\frac{1}{1{,}000}$ or one-thousandth.

- To convert measurements from one unit to another, we must identify the metric prefixes, their abbreviations, and their relative positions with respect to one another. Figure 10.4 shows the relation of the metric units for length.

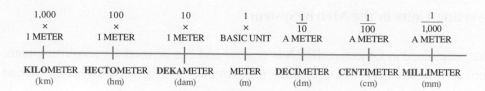

Figure 10.4

With the help of this figure, conversions of units become relatively easy and fast. To illustrate how to use this figure, let us reconsider the examples discussed above.

- Look at Figure 10.5 to convert 3 kilometers to meters.

Figure 10.5

Meter is 3 places to the *right* of kilometer. To change kilometers to meters we move the decimal point three places to the *right* (or multiply by 10^3).

    3 km = 3,000 m   3 = 3.0 km ⟶ 3 000 .

Again, to convert 4,000 millimeters to dekameters look at Figure 10.6:

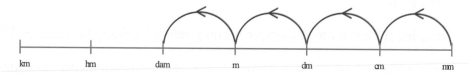

Figure 10.6

From the figure, we find that there are four places to the *left* from millimeter to dekameter.
To change millimeter to dekameter, we move the decimal point four places to the left (divide by 10^4).

4,000 mm = 4,000 ÷ 10^4 dam = 0.4 dam.

- While the above discussion was concerned only with length, it would apply to any other basic measurements in the Metric System.

- Figures 10.7 and 10.8 below are similar to Figure 10.4, they show the relationship between the metric units, weight and volume (or capacity).

Relationship of the Metric Units for Weight

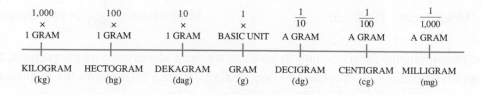

Figure 10.7

Relationship of the Metric Units for Liquid Volume (Capacity)

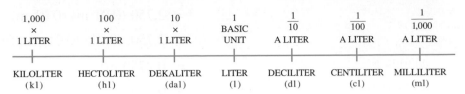

Figure 10.8

Procedure to convert from one metric unit of measurement to another metric unit:

Step 1   Write the number in the given measurement as a decimal number.

Step 2   Draw or visualize a line showing the positions of the metric prefixes.

Step 3   Move the decimal point the same number of places and in the same direction as you would from the original prefix to the new one in the prefix chart (Figures 10.4, 10.7, and 10.8).

Example 3   Convert the units of measurement.

(a) 7.3 liters to millimeters (*ml*).

(b) 6,500 centigrams (cg) to dekagrams (dag).

Solutions

(a)   7.3 liters   = 7.3 *l*   *Step 1* Not needed.

= 7,300 . *ml*   *Step 2*

= 7,300 *ml*   *Step 3* Move the decimal point to the right 3 places.

7.3 liters   = 7,300 *ml*

(b)   6,500 cg = 6,500. cg   *Step 1* Write 6,500 = 6,500.

= 6 . 500 dag   *Step 2*

= 6.5 dag   *Step 3* Move the decimal point to the left 3 places.

6,500 centigrams = 6.5 dekagrams.

Example 4   Convert:

(a) 18.7 meter per liter to kilometer per centiliter.

(b) 2,750 cm² to m²

Solutions

(a)   18.7 meter per liter = $\dfrac{18.7\ m}{1\ l}$

18.7 m = 0 . 018 7 km

and   1 *l* = 1 00 . *cl*

= $\dfrac{0.0187\ km}{100\ cl}$

$\dfrac{0.018}{100} = 0.00018$

= $\dfrac{0.000187\ km}{cl}$

= 0.000187 km per cl.

515

(b) 2.5 m² to cm²

(b)   2,750 cm² = 2,750 (1 cm) (1 cm)   1 cm = .01 m

= 2,750 (0.01 m) (0.01 m)

Answers:

= 2,750. (0.01) (0.01) (m)(m)

3.   **(a)** 87 g   **(b)** 0.032 da*l*

= 0.2750 m²

4.   **(a)** 480,000,000 mg/kl   **(b)** 25,000 cm²

= 0.275 m²

Example 5   Application

Maria, a pharmacist sees that the doctor has ordered doses of 0.9 g of Tetracyn per dose for his patient. If the available capsules contain 150 mg of Tetracyn, how many capsules will she write on the prescription?

Solution

We are given that there are 150 mg in 1 capsule. We are asked to find how many capsules are needed for 0.9 g. This is a rate problem invloving capsules and mg (or g).

0.9 g = 900 mg

Change 0.9 g to mg by shifting the decimal point to the right 3 places.

Case 1	Case 2
150 mg	900 mg
1 capsule	x capsule

Organize the information in a table.

$$\frac{150 \text{ mg}}{1 \text{ capsule}} = \frac{900 \text{ mg}}{x \text{ capsule}}$$

Write the proportion.

$$150x = 900$$

Solve using cross products.

$$x = 6$$

The pharamacist will write 6 capsules for each dose.

Exercise 10.2

A.   In exercises 1-20, convert the unit of measurement as indicated.

1.	84 inches	= _____	feet	**2.**	6 gallons	= _____	pints
3.	5 pounds	= _____	ounces	**4.**	27 feet	= _____	yards
5.	2.5 yards	= _____	inches	**6.**	112 ounces	= _____	pounds
7.	1 mile	= _____	inches	**8.**	7,920 yards	= _____	miles
9.	9.65 tons	= _____	pounds	**10.**	30 miles	= _____	feet
11.	264 yards	= _____	mile	**12.**	2.7 gallons	= _____	pints
13.	3,798 inches	= _____	feet	**14.**	540 hours	= _____	days
15.	75 teaspoons	= _____	tablespoons	**16.**	4.5 gallons	= _____	cups
17.	2 weeks	= _____	hours	**18.**	7 days	= _____	minutes
19.	18,828 seconds	= _____	hours	**20.**	82 feet	= _____	yards

In exercises 21-30, convert the units of measurement as indicated.

21. 88 feet per second to miles per hours.

22. 10 pounds per inch to pound per foot

23. $255 per hour to dollars per minute.

24. 8 ounces per inch to pounds per foot.

25. 3 quarts per minute to gallons per hour

26. 14 ft^2 to in^2

27. 45 dollars per ft^2 to cents per in^2

28. 12 cents per in^2 to dollars per yd^2

29. 25 pounds per ft^2 to tons per yd^2

30. 8.1 pound per yd^2 to pounds per ft^2

B. **In exercises 31-38, use the information given in Figure 10.9.**

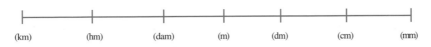

(km)   (hm)   (dam)   (m)   (dm)   (cm)   (mm)

Figure 10.9

31.   60 m   = _____ cm

32.   76.6 mm   = _____ m

33.   0.87 hm   = _____ dm

34.   27cm   = _____ dm

35.   3 mm   = _____ km

36.   1.50 m   = _____ km

37.   40 dm   = _____ mm

38.   5 mm   = _____ km

In exercise 39, fill in the blanks in Figure 10.10, with the units for metric weight. Then, use this information to complete exercises 40-47.

39.

kg   ____   ____   ____   ____   ____   ____

Figure 10.10

40.   12 dag   = _____ cg

41.   8 g   = _____ cg

42.   6,400 cg   = _____ hg

43.   232.4 dag   = _____ dg

44.   5 mg   = _____ kg

45.   0.4 g   = _____ mg

46.   42 dg   = _____ kg

47.   4.33 g   = _____ hg

In exercise 48, fill in the blanks in Figure 10.11, with the units for metric liquid measurement. Then, use this information to complete exercises 49-56.

48.

k l   ____   ____   ____   ____   ____   ____

Figure 10.11

49.   204 *l*   = _____ *hl*

50.   15 *ml* = _____ *l*

51.   0.06 *kl*   = _____ *cl*

52.   57 *dl* = _____ *ml*

53.   0.0768 *kl*   = _____ *l*

54.   200 *dal* = _____ *dl*

55.   7.6 *l*   = _____ *kl*

56.   496,533 *cl* = _____ *h l*

57. Convert 356 lb per in^3 to oz per cm^3.

58. Convert 40 meters per second to kilometers per hour.   **59.** Convert 17 kilometers per liter to meter per milliliter.

60. Convert 24,000 kg per km^2 to gram per m^2.

Applications

61. The weight (mass) of one pineapple is 1 kg 800 g and a second pineapple, 1,850 g. Which weighs more?

62. Maria walks at 3 km per hour while her brother's speed is 45 m per minute. Who walks faster, Maria or her brother?

63. A physician prescribes a dose of 1.6 g of steptomycin for his patient. If the drug is available in 100 mg tablets, how many tablets are needed for the prescribed dose?

10.3 UNIT CONVERSIONS BETWEEN ENGLISH AND METRIC SYSTEM

10.3 A. Converting Units of Measurements from English to Metric and Metric to English

Objective

After completing this section, you will be able to:

A. Convert units of measurement from English to Metric and from Metric to English.

B. Convert temperatures from Celcius to Fahrenheit, and from Fahrenheit to Celcius.

• Conversion of units from one system to another can be done in the same manner as it is done within the same system, provided we know the conversion relationship between the basic units in the two systems. We will perform some conversions between the English and Metric Systems. Table 10.4 facilitates conversion from English units to Metric units, while Table 10.5 can be used for conversion from Metric units to English units.

Table 10.4			Table 10.5		
English-Metric Conversions			Metric-English Conversions		
Length	1 inch	= 2.54 centimeters	1 centimeter	=	0.3937 inch
	1 foot	= 0.3048 meter	1 meter	=	3.281 feet
	1 yard	= 0.9144 meter	1 meter	=	1.094 yards
	1 mile	= 1.609 kilometers	1 kilometer	=	0.6214 mile
Weight	1 ounce =	28.35 grams	1 gram	=	0.0353 ounce
	1 pound =	453.59 grams	1 gram	=	0.0022 pound
Liquid	1 quart =	0.946 liter	1 liter	=	1.057 quarts
Volume	1 gallon =	3.785 liters	1 liter	=	0.2642 gallon

Since 1 in = 2.54 cm, we can use the conversion ratio $\dfrac{1\ in}{2.54\ cm}$ to convert 5 cm to inches.

$$5\ cm = \frac{5\ cm}{1} \cdot \frac{1\ in}{2.54\ cm}$$

• "Multiply by 1" in the form $\frac{in}{cm}$.

$$= \left(\frac{5}{2.54}\right) in$$

$$\approx 1.9685\ in$$

- Quite often, we may need to use conversion ratios, more than once. For example, to convert 2,450 inches to meters, we may proceed as below.

  We will need : 1 in = 2.54 cm, 1 m = 100 cm

  $$2,450 \text{ in} = \frac{2,450 \text{ in}}{1} \cdot \frac{2.54 \text{ cm}}{1 \text{ in}} \cdot \frac{1 \text{ m}}{100 \text{ cm}}$$

  $$= \frac{2,450 \, (2.54)}{100} \text{ m}$$

  $$= 62.23 \text{ m} ;$$

  $$2,450 \text{ in} \approx 62.23 \text{ m}.$$

- Conversions of measurements for weights and volumes can be done similarly.

- It should be noted that when units from one system are converted to the units of another system, we get approximate measurements. The reason is obvious. Since the systems were developed independently, there are no exact conversions. All conversion relations in Tables 10.4 and 10.5 are approximate.

> **Remark:** Results in the examples and exercises are rounded to two decimal places, unless specified otherwise.

Procedure to make conversions between the English and Metric Systems:

Step 1 List the needed conversions.

Step 2 Multiply the given unit(s) of measurement by appropriate conversion ratios using information in Tables 10.4 or 10.5.

Step 3 Simplify.

Example 1 Convert the units of measurement as indicated.

(a) 25 quarts to liters   (b) 3 kiloliters to gallons

Solutions

(a) 25 quarts to liters

We will need: $1l = 1.057$ qt

$$25 \text{ qt} = \frac{25 \text{ qt}}{l} \cdot \frac{1 \, l}{1.057 \text{ qt}}$$

- Multiply by conversion ratio.

$$= \frac{25}{1.057} l$$

- Simplify.

$$\approx 23.651844 \; l.$$

25 quarts ≈ 23.65 liters

(b) 3 kiloliters to gallons

We will need: $1 \; kl = 1000 \; l$, and $1l = 0.2642$ gal

Warm-Up

1. Convert the units of measurement as indicated.

   (a) 79 inches to centimeters

   (b) 3 kilograms to pounds

$$3 \text{ kiloliters } = 3 \ kl \cdot 1 \cdot 1$$

$$\approx \frac{3 \ kl}{1} \cdot \frac{1000 \ l}{1 \ kl} \cdot \frac{0.2642 \text{ gal}}{1 \ l}$$

$$= 3(1,000) \ (0.2642) \text{ gal}$$

$$= 792.6 \text{ gal}$$

$$3 \text{ kiloliters } = 792.6 \text{ gal}$$

2. Convert 55 pounds per foot to grams per meter

Example 2 Convert 35 centigrams per centimeter to ounces per inch.

Solution 35 centigrams per centimeter to ounces per inch.

We will need: 1 cg = 0.01 gm,

1 gm = 0.0353 oz , and 1 cm = 0.3937 in

$$35 \text{ cg per cm } = \frac{35 \text{ cg}}{1 \text{ cm}} \cdot 1 \cdot 1 \cdot 1$$

$$\approx \frac{35 \ cg}{1 \ cm} \cdot \frac{0.01 \ g}{1 \ cg} \cdot \frac{0.0353 \text{ oz}}{1 \ g} \cdot \frac{1 \ cm}{0.3937 \text{ in}} \quad \text{Multiply by conversion factors.}$$

$$= \frac{35 \, (0.01) \, (0.0353) \text{ oz}}{(0.3937) \text{ in}} \quad \text{Simplify.}$$

$$\approx \frac{0.0313817 \text{ oz}}{1 \text{ in}}$$

$$= 0.0307/\text{in}$$

35 centigrams per centimeter ≈ 0.03 ounces per inch.

Answers:

1. (a) 200.66 cm   **(b)** 6.6 lb

2. 81848.59 grams per meter

10.3 B Temperature Conversions

In the English System, temperatures are commonly read using Fahrenheit degrees. In countries using the Metric System, temperatures are commonly read using Celsius degrees. Most thermometers show the temperature in both units. Reading the values directly from a thermometer is one way to determine equivalent temperatures.

Warm-Up

3. Use the thermometer at the right to determine approximate values for the temperatures listed below.

(a)   5° C = ____° F

(b)   127° F = ____° C

(c)   18° F = ____° C

Example 3 Use the thermometer at the right to determine the values for the temperatures listed below.

(a)   0° C = ____° F

(b)   120° F = ____° C

(c)   14° F = ____° C

Solution Using the thermometer we are easily able to find these equivalents.

(a)   0° C = **32° F**

(b)   120° F ≈ **48.9° C**

(c)   14° F = **−10° C**

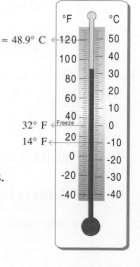

- The above method allows us to give approximate temperature equivalents. We are limited by the accuracy of the thermometer and our ability to read with precision.

- The second method, which give exact equivalents, is to use a formula. There are actually two formulas. One allows us to find Celsius temperature, when the Fahrenheit temperature is given, and the second allows us to find Fahrenheit temperature when the Celsius temperature is given.

$$C = \frac{5(F-32)}{9}$$ $$F = \frac{9}{5} \cdot C + 32$$

Example 4   Convert the following temperatures as indicated. Use the appropriate formula. If necessary, round to the nearest tenth of a degree.

(a) $72° \, F = \underline{\quad}° \, C$ (b) $37° \, C = \underline{\quad}°F$

Solution

(a)   Use the formula for finding temperatures in Celsius.

$$C = \frac{5(F-32)}{9}$$

$$= \frac{5(72-32)}{9}$$

$$= \frac{200}{9}$$

$$\approx 22.2$$

72° F ≈ 22.2° C

(b)   Use the formula for finding temperatures in Fahrenheit.

$$F = \frac{9}{5} \cdot C + 32$$

$$= \frac{9}{5} \cdot (37) + 32$$

$$= 98.6$$

37° C = 98.6° F

Example 5   **Application**

An Australian runner has recently run 1,500 m in 3 min 43 sec. Find his average rate in miles per hour. Round the answer to the nearest mile.

Solution   Since the runner has run 1,500 m in 3 min 43 sec.

His average rate $= \dfrac{1{,}500 \text{ m}}{3 \text{ min } 43 \text{ sec}}$

$= \dfrac{1{,}500 \text{ m}}{223 \text{ sec}}$

We need to change $\dfrac{1{,}500 \text{ m}}{223 \text{ sec}}$ to miles per hour.

Convert the denominator to a single unit, say seconds. Use : 1 min = 60 sec.

$3 \text{ min } = 3 \text{ min} \cdot \dfrac{60 \text{ sec}}{1 \text{ min}}$

$= 180 \text{ sec.}$

1 m = 3.281 ft, 1 mi = 5280 ft
1 min = 60 sec, 1 hr = 60 min

$$\frac{1,500 \text{ m}}{223 \text{ sec}} = \frac{1,500 \cancel{\text{ m}}}{223 \cancel{\text{ sec}}} \cdot \frac{3.281 \text{ ft}}{1 \cancel{\text{ m}}} \cdot \frac{1 \text{ mi}}{5280 \cancel{\text{ ft}}} \cdot \frac{60 \cancel{\text{ sec}}}{1 \cancel{\text{ min}}} \cdot \frac{60 \cancel{\text{ min}}}{1 \text{ hr}}$$ Multiply by the conversion factors.

$$\approx \left(\frac{1,771,740}{117,744} \right) \text{ mi per hr}$$ Simplify, using a calculator.

$$\approx 15.04739 \text{ mi per hr}$$

The average rate of the runner in miles per hour is approximately 15 miles per hour.

Exercise 10.3

In exercises 1-20, convert the measurements as indicated.

1. 3,450 inches to meters.
2. 625 gallons to liters.
3. 5.64 kilometers to miles.

4. 6.76 kilometers to miles.
5. 5.62 feet to meters.
6. 3,760 ounces to pound.

7. 378 inches to meters.
8. 0.064 kilometers to feet.
9. 3.15 miles to kilometers.

10. 628 inches to centimeters.
11. 21.6 feet per second to centimeters per second.

12. 10.3 feet per second to centimeters per second.
13. 30 miles per hour to kilometers per hour.

14. 66 miles per hour to feet per second.
15. 1,534 ounces to kilograms.

16. 3,720 grams to pounds.
17. 180 miles per hour to kilometers per hour.

18. 62 kilometers per second to miles per hour.

19. The shipping weight of a TV is 12 pounds. What is this in kilograms?

20. A box has dimensions 7 × 5 × 4.5 centimeters. Find its dimensions in inches.

Applications

21. A patient takes 15 *ml* of medication at a time. How many teaspoons should a nurse direct the patient to receive the proper dosage? (1 teaspoon = 5 ml).

22. A patient is to receive one pint of blood. What amount of blood should be administered if the container is marked in milliliters?

23. A quarter-inch wrench is to be used on a fitting. What size of wrench (in centimeters) does this fitting take?

24. The place with the most rain on earth is Mount Waialeale, Hawaii, with an average **annual** rainfall of 11,648 millimeters. What is the average rainfall in inches per month?

25. The **diameter** of No. 10 wire is 0.102 inches. What is its **radius** in centimeters?

26. If 1,000 cycles = 1 kilocycle, then 1,500 kilocycles per second equals how many cycles per minute?

In exercises 27-32, convert the temperatures as indicated.

27. $55° \text{ C} = \underline{\quad} ° \text{ F}$
28. $11° \text{ F} = \underline{\quad} ° \text{ C}$
29. $350 ° \text{ F} = \underline{\quad} ° \text{ C}$

30. $1000 ° \text{ F} = \underline{\quad} ° \text{ C}$
31. $-20 ° \text{ C} = \underline{\quad} ° \text{ F}$
32. $400° \text{ C} = \underline{\quad} ° \text{ F}$

10.4 ESTIMATING MEASUREMENTS IN THE METRIC SYSTEM

- **Estimating Measurements of Common Objects in the Metric System**

As observed in Section 10.2, the Metric System is very similar to our base-ten place value system of numbers. Since almost every country in the world uses the metric system, we will need to understand it to "think metric". The objective of this section is to help you think metric rather than make conversions between the English and the Metric Systems.

- **Estimating lengths, distances or heights**: We shall discuss estimation under three classifications.

    1. To measure **very small lengths**, we use millimeters (mm) or centimeters (cm). For example,

    Rainfall on a particular day in a city is 8 mm.

    The length of a pencil is 12 cm.

    The height of a doll is 25 cm.

    2. To measure **common life size objects**, such as, height of a building, depth of a well, length of cloth, height of a person, …, we use meters (m).

    The height of a horse is about 1.3 m.

    The height of a telephone pole is about 12 m.

    The height of a person is about 1.9 m.

    3. To measure **long distances**, we use *kilometers* (km). For example,

    The distance travelled by a motorist in one hour may be 56 km.

    The distance between two cities may be 75 km.

- **Estimating weight (or mass) of objects:** Normally, the weight of an object or quantity is measured in kilograms and grams. To express weights of various components in pharmaceutical products, we use milligrams (mg).

    A patient takes three 0.25 mg tablets of reserpine.

    The weight of a candy bar is 40 g.

    The average weight of a new-born baby is 3.8 kg.

    The weight of a medium sized bag of wheat is 298 kg.

- **Estimating the quantity of liquids and capacity of containers:** We measure the quantity of liquids and the capacity of containers in liters and milliliters. Generally, water, milk, oil, gasoline, and the like are measured in liters. Dosages of liquid medication are given in milliliters.

Example 1   Fill in the blanks with suitable units of Metric system:

(a)   A bucket can hold about 5 _____ of water.

(b)   The weight of one bag of rice is about 25 _____.

(c)   Your height is about 1 _____ 60 _____.

(d)   A family consumes about 22 _____ of wheat and 900 _____ of sugar every month.

(e)   A 7 month old child drinks about 450 _____ of milk at a time.

Solutions

(a)   Liter (*l*)

The commonly used units of volume are liter and milliliter. Milliliters are used for very small quantities.

(b)   Kilogram (kg)

Weight is normally measured in kg and g. The weight of a bag of rice cannot be 25 g since it is too small for a bag. It would be measured in kg.

(c)   1 m 60 cm.

The height of a person is usually measured in meters and centimeters.

(d)   22 kg of wheat and 900 g of sugar

A small measurement would be 22g of wheat; a family cannot consume 900 kg of sugar in a month.

(e)   milliliter (*ml*)

450 liters would be a very large quantity.

Example 2   Application

Which unit of measurement in the Metric System should be used with the number 1.72, so that the resulting measurement may represent the height of a person?

Solution

The commonly used units for length measurements are km, m, and cm.

1.72 km = 1,720 meters is too long for the height of a person.

1.72 cm is a very small measurement so it cannot represent the height of a person.

1.72 m may represent the height of a person.

Hence, the correct unit that should be used with the number 1.72 is m (meters)

Exercise 10.4

In exercises 1-25, choose the best estimate for the measurement of the object named.

1.   The length of a standard paper clip

(a)   3.2 mm   (b)   3.2 cm   (c)   3.2 m   (d)   3.2 km

2.   The length of a yardstick

(a)   5 m   (b)   1 m   (c)   10 cm   (d)   1 km

3.   The amount of liquid in a can of soda pop

(a)   355 *ml*   (b)   355 *l*   (c)   355 *kl*   (d)   5 ml

4. The amount of oil in a railroad tanker car
   (a) 43 *l*   (b) 43 *ml*   (c) 70 *kl*   (d) 75 *l*

5. The amount of liquid in a quart of milk
   (a) 4 *l*   (b) 100 *ml*   (c) .95 *l*   (d) 4 *ml*

6. The amount of liquid in a gallon of wine
   (a) 1 *l*   (b) 10 *l*   (c) 3.8 *l*   (d) 20.7 *l*

7. The height of a tree
   (a) 2.1 mm   (b) 10 cm   (c) 10 m   (d) 10 km

8. The height of a standard house door
   (a) 2.1 mm   (b) 2.1 cm   (c) 2.1 m   (d) 2.1 km

9. The height of an average man
   (a) 1.7 km   (b) 1.7 mm   (c) 1.7 cm   (d) 1.7 m

10. The height of a three-floor building
    (a) 12 m   (b) 5 m   (c) 500 m   (d) 50 cm

11. The distance from New York to California
    (a) 50 km   (b) 4,800 km   (c) 5,000 m   (d) 5,000 cm

12. The diameter of a dime
    (a) 1.7 cm   (b) 1.7 m   (c) 1.7 mm   (d) 1.7 km

13. The weight of a package of six hot dogs
    (a) 300 mg   (b) 300 g   (c) 300 kg   (d) 300 dag

14. The volume of a can of paint
    (a) 4 *ml*   (b) 4 *l*   (c) 4 *kl*   (d) 40 *kl*

15. The weight of a bird feather
    (a) 50 mg   (b) 50 g   (c) 50 kg   (d) 20 kg

16. The altitude of a plane
    (a) 2 mm   (b) 2 cm   (c) 2 m   (d) 2 km

17. The volume of a small bottle of perfume
    (a) 7 *ml*   (b) 7 *l*   (c) 7 *kl*   (d) 75 kl

18. The length of this page
    (a) 28 cm   (b) 28 mm   (c) 28 m   (d) 3 cm

19. The diameter of a large pizza
    (a) 0.5 m   (b) 20 cm   (c) 15 m   (d) 0.5 km

20. The amount of coffee in a 20-cup coffee pot

    (a)   200 *ml*   **(b)**   1 *l*   **(c)**   4.8 *l*   **(d)**   16 *l*

21. The weight of a dinner steak

    (a)   4 kg   **(b)**   14 kg   **(c)**   16 mg   **(d)**   280 g

22. The weight of a candy bar

    (a)   40 mg   **(b)**   40 g   **(c)**   4 g   **(d)**   4 kg

23. One drop from an eye dropper

    (a)   0.2 *ml*   **(b)**   200 *ml*   **(c)**   2 *l*   **(d)**   0.2 *kl*

24. The weight of a horse

    (a)   100 mg   **(b)**   500 g   **(c)**   100 kg   **(d)**   1,000 kg

25. The capacity of a car gas tank

    (a)   70 *ml*   **(b)**   200 *l*   **(c)**   70 *l*   **(d)**   1 *kl*

10.5 CHAPTER SUMMARY

Part I   Important Vocabulary and abbreviations

1. A **measurement** is written with a number and a unit of measurement.

         4.7 lb,   45 cm,   7 *l*

2. The units of the **English System** of measurements are:

Units of length (distance or height)	:	inch (in), foot (ft), yard (yd), mile (mi)
Units of weight (or mass)	:	ounce (oz), pound (lb), ton (ton)
Units of liquid volume	:	teaspoon (tsp), tablespoon (tbs), fluid ounces (fl. oz.), cup (c), pint (pt), quart (qt), gallon (gal) (or capacity)

3. The **basic** units of the **Metric System** are:

Basic unit of length : **meter (m)**
(distance or height)

Basic unit of weight : **gram (g)**
(or mass)

Basic unit of liquid : **liter (*l*)**
volume (or capacity)

4. Common **metric prefixes** and their relationship with the basic unit:

Kilo (k) means thousand (1,000) :

$$1 \text{ km} = 1{,}000 \text{ m}$$
$$1 \text{ kg} = 1{,}000 \text{ g}$$
$$1 \text{ } kl = 1000 \text{ } l$$

Hecto (h) means hundred (100) :

$$1 \text{ hm} = 100 \text{ m}$$
$$1 \text{ hg} = 100 \text{ g}$$
$$1 \text{ } hl = 100 \text{ } l$$

Deka (da) means ten (10) :

$$1 \text{ dam} = 10 \text{ } m$$
$$1 \text{ dag} = 10 \text{ g}$$
$$1 \text{ dal} = 10 \text{ } l$$

Deci (d) means one-tenth $\left(\dfrac{1}{10} \right)$:

$$1 \text{ dm} = \frac{1}{10} \text{ m}$$

$$1 \text{ dg} = \frac{1}{10} \text{ g}$$

$$1 \text{ } dl = \frac{1}{10} \text{ } l$$

Centi (c) means one-hundredth $\left(\dfrac{1}{100} \right)$:

$$1 \text{ cm} = \frac{1}{100} \text{ m}$$

$$1 \text{ cg} = \frac{1}{100} \text{ g}$$

$$1 \text{ } cl = \frac{1}{100} \text{ } l$$

Milli (m) means one-thousandth $\left(\dfrac{1}{1{,}000} \right)$:

$$1 \text{ mm} = \frac{1}{1{,}000} \text{ m}$$

$$1 \text{ mg} = \frac{1}{1{,}000} \text{ g}$$

$$1 \text{ } ml = \frac{1}{1{,}000} \text{ } l$$

5. **Equivalent measurements** use different units for the same thing.

$$2 \text{ ft} = 24 \text{ in} \qquad 1 \text{ oz} \approx 28.35 \text{ g}$$

Example

Part II   Procedures and Rules

BASIC OPERATIONS ON MEASUREMENTS

1. To multiply (divide) a measurement by a number:

   Step 1   Multiply (divide) the two numbers.

   Step 2   Write the product (quotient) followed by the unit of measurement.

1. (i) $14\,(6 \text{ cm}) = (14 \times 6) \text{ cm}$
      $= 84 \text{ cm}$

   (ii) $(37.5 \text{ lb}) \div 5 = 7.5 \text{ lb}$

Examples

2. (a)   15 ft 7 in
        8 ft 6 in
     + 10 ft 3 in
     _____
        33 ft 16 in = 33 ft + 12 in + 4 in
                      = 33 ft + 1 ft + 4 in
                      = 34 ft + 4 in
                      = 34 ft 4 in

(b)
   $\overset{11}{12}$ hr $\overset{60}{30}$ min
   − 7 hr 45 min
   _____
     4 hr 45 min

Borrow 1 hr:
1 hr = 60 min
and add to the 30 min

3. (a) Convert 7.3 yds to ft   1 yd = 3 ft

$$7.3 \text{ yd} = (7.3 \text{ yd}) \cdot \frac{3 \text{ ft}}{1 \text{ yd}}$$

$$= (7.3)(3) \text{ ft}$$

$$= \textbf{21.9 ft}$$

(b) Convert 43 ft to yd   1 yd = 3 ft.

$$43 \text{ ft} = (43 \text{ ft}) \cdot \frac{1 \text{ yd}}{3 \text{ ft}}$$

$$= \left(\frac{43}{3}\right) \text{ yd}$$

$$= 14\frac{1}{3} \text{ yd}$$

(c) Convert 2.5 days to minutes.   1 day = 24 hrs
                                             1 hr = 60 min

$$2.5 \text{ days} = (2.5 \text{ days}) \cdot \frac{24 \text{ hr}}{1 \text{ day}} \cdot \frac{60 \text{ min}}{1 \text{ hr}}$$

$$= (2.5)(24)(60) \text{ min}$$

$$= 3{,}600 \text{ min}$$

4. (a) Convert 537 centiliters (*cl*) to deka liters (*dal*):

$$537 \, cl = 537.0 \, cl$$

$$= 0.5370 \, dal$$

$$= 0.537 \, dal$$

(b) Convert $2\frac{7}{8}$ hectograms (hg) to grams (g):

$$2\frac{7}{8} = 2.875 \text{ hg}$$

$$= 287.5 \text{ g}$$

$$= 287.5 \text{ g}$$

---

2. To add or subtract measurements with common unit(s):

Step 1   Arrange the measurements in columns. Line up the place values and units.

Step 2   Add or subtract the numbers as required and use the common unit(s).

CONVERTING UNITS OF MEASUREMENTS

3. To convert units of measurement in the same system:

Step 1   List the needed conversions.

Step 2   Multiply the given measurement by appropriate conversion ratio(s).

Step 3   Simplify.

4. To convert from one metric unit of measurement to another metric unit:

Step 1   Write the number in the given measurement as a decimal number.

Step 2   Draw or visualize the following diagram showing the relative positions of the metric prefixes:

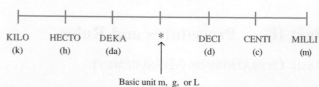

KILO   HECTO   DEKA   *   DECI   CENTI   MILLI
(k)   (h)   (da)   (d)   (c)   (m)

Basic unit m, g, or L

Step 3   Move the decimal point the same number of places and in the same direction from the original prefix to the new one using the diagram.

5. To make conversions between the English and Metric Systems:

Step **1** List the needed conversions.

Step **2** Multiply the given measurement by appropriate conversion ratio(s).

Step **2** Simplify.

Examples

5. (a) Convert 2.5 kiloliters (k*l*) to gallons (gal).

$$1 \text{ kl} = 1000 \; l$$
$$1l \approx 0.2642 \text{ gal}$$

$$2.5\,\text{kl} \approx \frac{2.5\,\cancel{kl}}{1} \cdot \frac{1000\,\cancel{l}}{1\,\cancel{kl}} \cdot \frac{0.2642\,\text{gal}}{1\,\cancel{l}}$$

$$= 660.5 \text{ gal} ;$$

$$2.5\,\text{kl} \approx 660.5 \text{ gal}$$

(b) Convert 525 in^2 to square meters.

$$\text{in}^2 = \text{in} \cdot \text{in}$$
$$525 \text{ in}^2$$

$$2.54 \text{ cm} \approx 1 \text{ in}$$
$$1\text{cm} = 0.01 \text{ m}$$

$$\approx \frac{525\,\cancel{in}^2}{1} \cdot \frac{(2.54)^2\,\cancel{cm}^2}{1\,\cancel{in}^2} \cdot \frac{(0.01)^2\,\text{m}^2}{1^2\,\cancel{cm}^2}$$

$$\approx 0.338709 \text{ m}^2$$

$$525 \text{ in}^2 \approx 0.339 \text{ m}^2$$

10.6 Review Exercise

In exercises 1-2, perform the indicated operations:

1. Multiply 3.14 lb by 2.5

2. Divide 873 gal by 9

In exercises 3-5, add or subtract as indicated:

3. 35 tons 1,768 lb – 14 tons 324 lb

4. 3 gal 1 qt 1 pt + 7 gal 2 qt 1 pt + 10 gal 3 qt

5. 7 hr 14 min 20 sec – 3 hr 53 min 50 sec

In exercises 6-8, write the equivalent measurement as indicated:

6. 7 gallons = ___ pints

7. 54 ft^2 = ___ yd^2

8. 164.8 ounces = ___ pounds

In exercises 9-11, convert the units of measurements as indicated:

9. 1.5 km / hr to meters per minute

10. 500 cents per hour to dollars per day

11. 25 lb/ft to ounces per inch

12. Fill in the blanks in the following figure with the common metric prefixes. Then use this information to complete the exercises 13-15.

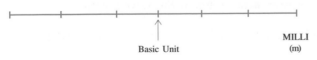

Basic Unit

MILLI
(m)

13. 1.682 *dam* = ___ *mm*

14. 572 *l* = ___ *hl*

15. 15,023 *m* = ___ *km*

In exercises 16-18, convert the given measurement as indicated:

16. 15 quarts to liters

17. 4 kiloliters to gallons

18. 0.055 km per minute to inches per second

10.7 Self Test

In exercises 1-5, estimate the conversion of units and choose the correct option to fill in the blank.

1. 25 in = _____ cm

    (a) 25   (b) 635   (c) 63.5   (d) $\dfrac{1}{25}$

2. 17 kg = _____ lb

    (a) 374   (b) 17   (c) 37.4   (d) 1/17

3. 21 gal = _____ l

    (a) 210   (b) 759.5   (c) $\dfrac{1}{21}$ (d) 79.49

4. 20 kilometers = _____ miles

    (a) 3   (b) 30   (c) 12   (d) 550

5. Mr. Smith built new book shelves and each shelf is $3\dfrac{1}{2}$ meters long.

    Length of each shelf ≈ _____ ft

    (a) 11.5   (b) 3.5   (c) 20.5   (d) 72

In exercises 6-10, give the approximate metric measurement.

6. The thickness of a dime

    (a) 1 mm   (b) 1 cm   (c) 0.0032 m   (d) 0.01 mm

7. The length of a new # 2 pencil

    (a) 20 mm   (b) 20 cm   (c) 0.5 m   (d) 2 cm

8. The length and width of a piece of standard-size $\left(8\dfrac{1}{2}"\times 11"\right)$ notebook paper

    (a) 80.5 cm × 110 cm   (b) 23.5 mm × 30.5 mm   (c) 2.35 m × 3.05 m   (d) 23.5 cm × 30.5 cm

9. The height of a 6-foot door

    (a) 18 m   (b) 1.8 m   (c) 180 m   (d) 0.018 m

10. The height of a 30-inch bike

    (a) 300 cm   (b) 750 cm   (c) 7.5 cm   (d) 75 cm

In exercises 11-13, convert the units of measurement. Round to the nearest tenth.

11. 6.4 mi = ___ km   12. 75 km = ___ mi   13. $\dfrac{1}{4}$ ton = ___ kg

14. Stella is driving on a road in Paris where the speed limit is posted as 110 km/hr. Can she drive 75 mi/hr and be within the speed limit?

15. A water pump delivers water at 40 gallons per minute. Express the rate to the nearest liter per minute.

ANSWERS

ANSWERS

CHAPTER 0

Section 0.1

1. Tens **3.** Tens **5.** Hundreds **7.** Thousands **9.** Trillions **11.** 7 **13.** 9 **15.** 2 **17.** 5 **19.** 3 **21.** 6 **23.** 4
25. 0 **27.** 3 **29.** 8 **31.** 5 **33.** Five hundred thirty-eight. **35.** Five thousand, six hundred twenty-two.
37. Ten thousand, eight hundred fifteen. **39.** Eight thousand, eight hundred eighty-eight. **41.** Forty-six thousand, two hundred eight.
43. Seven hundred three thousand, one hundred nine. **45.** One million, two hundred thirty-five thousand, nine hundred fifty-six. **47.** 70,599
49. 925 **51.** 34,910 **53.** 115,300,400,065 **55.** 8,056,290 **57.** Twelve thousand, seven hundred fifty dollars. **59.** $31,650,000

Section 0.2

1.

3.

5.

7.

9.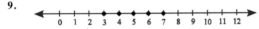

11. < **13.** = **15.** < **17.** = **19.** > **21.** > **23.** > **25.** 15 < 22 **27.** 28 > 24 **29.** 12 < 14 **31.** 0 < 1 **33.** 11 < 15
35. False ; 4 < 12 or 12 > 4 **37.** True **39.** True **41.** False ; 7 > 0 or 0 < 7 **43.** False; 14 < 19 or 19 > 14 **45.** True
47. True **49.** False ; 19 < 26 or 26 > 19 **51.** True **53.** True **55.** True **57.** 235 **59.** 527 **61.** 2,680 **63.** 5,730
65. 700 **67.** 10,429 **69.** 375 **71.** 15 < 22 **73.** 758 > 749 **75.** 25,140 > 24,952 **77.** 4,320,008 < 29,100,000
79. 99,990 > 99,909 **81.** 3,056,919 > 3,056,915 **83.** 700 **85.** 600 **87.** 5,480 **89.** 5,000 **91.** 1,751,000 **93.** 5,840
95. 52,430,000 **97.** 82,600,000 **99.** 1,620 **101.** 72,000 **103.** 1,000 **105.** 90,000 **107.** 40,000 **109.** 259,000 volumes
111. $4,690,000 **113.** Both are equal, (each is 50,000,000,000) **115.** y = 6, 7, 8 or 9 ; 6

Section 0.3

1. 7,613 ; 7,600 **3.** 4,840 ; 4,800 **5.** 39,977 ; 40,000 **7.** 704 ; 700 **9.** 24,747 ; 24,700 **11.** 159 ; 200 **13.** 13,802 ; 13,800
15. 3,047 ; 3,000 **17.** 42,516 ; 42,500 **19.** 2,731 ; 2,700 **21.** 56,036 ; 56,000 **23.** 32,798 ; 32,800 **25.** 155 ; 200
27. 41,417 ; 41,000 **29.** 6,080 ; 6,100 **31.** 1,053 **33.** 5,314 **35.** 2,145 **37.** 205 **39.** 0
41. 4,236 **43.** 342 **45.** 392 **47.** 670 **49.** 8,250 **51.** 95 **53.** 450
55. 251 **57.** 7,600 **59.** 24,000 **61.** 9,522 **63.** 8,036 **65.** 411,700 **67.** 23,358
69. 1,494,513 **71.** 925 **73.** 3,657 **75.** 38,808 **77.** 161,784 **79.** 156,416
81. 244,316 **83.** 2,313,367 **85.** 25,502,148 **87.** 358 R 6 **89.** 179 R 1 **91.** 456 R 0
93. 56 R 5 **95.** 34 R 15 **97.** 157 R 1 **99.** 48 R 0 **101.** 71 R 5 **103.** 39 R 0
105. 101 R 28 **107.** 715 R 149 **109.** 12 R 645 **111.** 23 R 56 **113.** 9 R 73 **115.** 1 R 0
117. 0 R 0 **119.** 959 R 13 **121.** 32 **123.** 209 R 5 **125.** 27 R 155 **127.** 115 R 189
129. 9 R 15 **131.** 29 R 282 **133.** 238 R 55 **135.** 182 R 132 **137.** 292 R 77 **139.** No
141. No **143.** Yes **145.** No **147.** No

Review Exercise 0.5

1. Thousands **3.** Tens **5.** Ones **7.** Hundred thousands **9.** 7 **11.** 2 **13.** 8

15. Eighty two thousand, one hundred forty-three. **17.** 253,060,047 **19.**

21. 500 **23.** 173,000 **25.** 30,000 **27.** 266,000 **29.** 500,000 **31.** 9,275 ; 9,300

33. 138,491 ; 138,500 **35.** 1,784 ; 1,800 **37.** 34,754 ; 34,800 **39.** 2,877,778 ; 2,877,800 **41.** 30,515

43. 2,550 **45.** 8,160 **47.** 1,351,944 **49.** 34,164 **51.** 86 R 6 **53.** 130 R 10

55. 75 R 296 **57.** 16 R 14

Self Test 0.6

1. Ten thousands **3.** Millions **5.** 6 **7.** 24,351 **9.** 7,250 **11.** 17,724 **13.** 7,400 **15.** 12 R 72

17. (a) 2,402 ; 2,400 (b) 8,323 ; 8,300 (c) 94,084 ; 94,100 (d) 731,667 ; 731,700

19. (a) 79 R 7 **(b)** 83 R 15

CHAPTER 1

Section 1.1

1.  **3.**  **5.**

7. 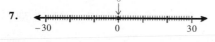 **9.**  **11.** 5 **13.** −21 **15.** 17 **17.** 0

19. −11 **21.** −35 **23.** 5 **25.** −14 **27.** −19 **29.** 0 **31.** −1,700 yd **33.** −$350 **35.** 17°C **37.** A loss of $125

39. 560 yd below sea level. **41.** 1504 B.C. (B.C. : Before Christ) **43.** 15°F above zero **45.** False ; 8 > −5 or −5 < 8

47. False ; $4 \geq -4$ or $-4 \leq 4$ **49.** True **51.** True **53.** False; $4 \geq -7$ or $-7 \leq 4$ **55.** False; 19 < 20 or 20 > 19

57. False ; 15 < 17 or 17 > 15 **59.** True **61.** True **63.** 8 **65.** 9 **67.** 0 **69.** 45 **71.** 10

73. 16 **75.** True **77.** False ; $\left|-9\right| > 5$ or $5 < \left|-9\right|$ **79.** True **81.** False ; $\left|-15\right| = 15$ **83.** False ; $8 = \left|-8\right|$

85. False ; $\left|0\right| < \left|-4\right|$ or $\left|-4\right| > \left|0\right|$ **87.** True **89.** No value **91.** 0 **93.** {−3, −2, −1, 0, 1, 2, 3}

95. {..., −10, −9, −8, 8, 9, 10, ...} **97.** {..., −1, −2, −3, 1, 2, 3, ...} **99.** {−6, −5, −4, −3, −2, −1, 0, 1, 2, 3, 4, 5, 6}

101. No value **103.** 26 **105.** 5 **107.** 5 **109.** 2 **111.** 26 **113.** −3° C **115.** 5,990 yd

Section 1.2

1. 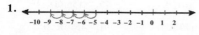 **3.**  **5.**

7.  **9.**  **11.**

13. 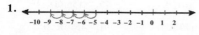 **15.**  **17.** 120 **19.** −129

21. −31 **23.** −22 **25.** −49 **27.** −14 **29.** −109 **31.** −99 **33.** −976 **35.** 400 **37.** −90 **39.** −3

41. 2 **43.** −1 **45.** 13 **47.** −136 **49.** −250 **51.** −246 **53.** −36 **55.** 9 **57.** 14 **59.** 144

61. 38 **63.** 333 **65.** 80 **67.** 113 **69.** Additive identity **71.** Additive inverse **73.** Additive inverse

75. Associative property **77.** -2 ; Commutative property **79.** -4 ; Associative property **81.** -13 ; Additive inverse

83. 6 **85.** -45 **87.** 14 **89.** 44 **91.** -140 **93.** 24 **95.** 13 **97.** -95 **99.** 110 **101.** 59

103. 48 **105.** -91 **107.** -11 **109.** -1 **111.** 41 **113.** 12 **115.** -23 **117.** $\approx -1,800$; 1,762

119. $\approx -9,000$; $-9,165$ **121.** $\approx 6,000$; 6,147 **123.** $\approx 9,000$; 8,245 **125.** $\approx -5,000$; $-5,743$ **127.** $\approx 11,000$; 10,690

129. $\approx 11,000$; 11,110 **131.** $\approx 13,100$; 13,135 **133.** $\approx 2,000$; 2,122 **135.** $\approx 4,000$; 4,000 **137.** $\approx 77,000$; 77,390

139. $\approx 220,000$; 217,765 **141.** -13 **143.** -20 **145. (a)** $-4°$ or a fall of $4°$ **(b)** $+11°$ or a rise of $11°$ **147. (a)** $20°$ E **(b)** $40°$ E

149. $400, $-1300 , $800 ; $-100 **151.** $112°$ F **153.** $28°$ F **155.** $75°$ C

Section 1.3

1. -27 **3.** -28 **5.** -64 **7.** -40 **9.** -27 **11.** 90 **13.** 128 **15.** 238 **17.** -90 **19.** 104 **21.** $-10,800$

23. 60 **25.** 24 **27.** 24 **29.** -1 **31.** 1,024 **33.** 88 **35.** 1,200 **37.** -144 **39.** 2,800 **41.** $\approx -200,000$; $-192,596$

43. $\approx -300,000$; $-293,618$ **45.** $\approx 300,000$; 281,671 **47.** $\approx -42,000$; $-36,575$ **49.** $\approx 800,000$; 747,530

51. $\approx -1,800,000$; $-1,473,371$ **53.** $\approx 1,950,000$; 1,952,349 **55.** $\approx 210,000$; 213,187 **57.** $\approx -2,400,000$; $-2,431,418$

59. $\approx -3,600,000$; $-3,492,612$ **61.** Commutative property of Multiplication **63.** Property of Multiplicative Identity

65. Distributive Property of Multiplication over addition **67.** -8 ; Multiplicative Identity **69.** 3 ; Associative Property

71. -25 ; Multiplicative Identity **73.** -9 **75.** -61 **77.** 5 **79.** undefined **81.** -42 **83.** 4 **85.** 0 **87.** -13

89. 49 **91.** -81 **93.** ≈ 10 ; 16 R 10 **95.** ≈ 10 ; 12 R 6 **97.** ≈ 10 ; 15 R 10 **99.** ≈ 10 ; 15 R 38 **101.** ≈ 10 ; 14 R 7

103. ≈ 40 ; 44 R 24 **105.** ≈ 50 ; 57 R 18 **107.** ≈ 70 ; 70 R 1 **109.** ≈ 90 ; 94 R 17 **111.** ≈ 60 ; 65 R 24 **113.** -360

115. $-1,067 \approx -1,000$ **117.** $2,528 \approx 2,500$ **119.** -63 **121.** -5 **123.** $-$4,140 ; $-$ 345 (or a deduction of $345)

Section 1.4

1. (a) 3 ; 5 **3. (a)** -2 ; 5 **5. (a)** 1 ; 48 **7. (a)** -5 ; 4 **9. (a)** 10 ; 3 **11. (a)** -7 ; 2 **13. (a)** 6 ; 4 **15. (a)** -6 ; 2

(b) 243 **(b)** -32 **(b)** 1 **(b)** 625 **(b)** -1000 **(b)** 49 **(b)** $-1,296$ **(b)** 36

17. (a) 20 ; 3 **19. (a)** 12 ; 2 **21.** 7^6 **23.** 10^3 **25.** 5^4 **27.** $2^3 \cdot 5^2$ **29.** $8^3 \cdot 9^2$ **31.** $6^4 \cdot (-11)^2$

(b) $-8,000$ **(b)** -144 **33.** 9,261 **35.** 42,875 **37.** 2,985,984 **39.** 32,768 **41.** 3 **43.** 39

45. 72 **47.** -512 **49.** 1 **51.** 0 **53.** 1,620 **55.** -3 **57.** 1 **59.** 13

61. 118 **63.** 7,000,000 **65.** 253 **67.** 253,000 **69.** 390,000 **71.** 708 **73.** 13,780 **75.** 3,020

77. 49,260 **79.** 12 R 450 **81.** 14 R 179 **83.** $40,000,000 **85.** $405,000,000 **87.** $12,000,000,000 **89.** $473,000,000,000

91. $199,000,000,000 **93.** 13 **95.** 21 **97.** 11 **99.** 25 **101.** 12 **103.** 8

105. 31 **107.** 9 **109.** 4 **111.** 1 **113.** 24 **115.** 11 **117.** -13 **119.** 10

121. 6 **123.** -32 **125.** -14 **127.** 157 **129.** -12 **131.** -31 **133.** 75 **135.** -19

137. -14 **139.** 19 **141.** 3 **143.** 49 **145.** -10 **147.** 1 **149.** -9 **151.** 3

153. 13 **155.** 0 **157.** -42 **159.** -1 **161.** -29 **163.** -2 **165.** 41 **167.** -22

169. 1 **171.** 3 **173.** -14 **175.** 14 **177.** 247 **179.** 126 **181.** -20 **183.** 0

Review Exercise 1.6

1. **3.** **5.**

7. 12 **9.** -16 **11.** -3 **13.** -5 **15.** 4 **17.** 0 **19.** 47 **21.** 27 **23.** 0

25. False ; $-18 < 7$ or $7 > -18$ **27.** True **29.** False ; $-(-9) = 9$ **31.** 16 and -16 **33.** $-2, -1, 0, 1, 2$

35. No value **37.** -9 **39.** -17 **41.** -5 **43.** -115 **45.** 11 **47.** $\approx 6,000$; 6,362 **49.** $\approx 10,000$; 10,278

51. -36 **53.** 30   **55.** 1   **57.** 6   **59.** -26 **61.** 4   **63.** 94   **65.** Reduced by 142 pages ; -142

67. 5,040   **69.** 0   **71.** -12 **73.** Undefined   **75.** $\approx -54,000,000$; $-52,716,993$ **77.** ≈ 50 ; 50 R 35

79. -23 **81.** -9 **83.** 0   **85.** -16 **87.** 54   **89.** 11   **91.** 5   **93.** 112   **95.** -18 **97.** 13

99. 19   **101.** -39 **103.** -12 **105.** -24 **107.** 24   **109.** 4   **111.** -24

Self Test 1.7

1.   **3.** $\{-4, -3, -2, -1\ 0, 1, 2, 3, 4\}$ **5. (a)** 14 **(b)** 35 **(c)** -7 **(d)** -12 **7.** -28

9. -60 **11.** $\approx 1,000$; 908   **13.** -600 **15.** -12 **17.** 0   **19.** ≈ -100 ; -104 R 36   **21.** 14

CHAPTER 2

Section 2.1

1. $8 + 2 = 10$ **3.** $30 \div 5 = 6$ **5.** $4 + 3 \cdot 5 = 19$ **7.** $17 - 2 \cdot 5 = 7$ **9.** $9^4 \neq 4^9$ **11.** $4x$ **13.** $11 \div x$

15. $2x + 5$ **17.** $x + 9$ **19.** $3(9 - x)$ **21.** $x - 6 = 19$ **23.** $3x + 10 = 25$ **25.** $x + 5 = 9$ **27.** $7x = 63$

29. $15 - 8 < 9$ **31.** $(12 - 10) < 15$ **33.** $6 \cdot 8 > 12$ **35.** $26 \div 13 = 2$ **37.** $48 \div 12 = 4$ **39.** $20 - 5 \cdot 3 \neq 6$ **41.** $3^4 = 9^2$

43. $12 + 18 = 35 - 5$ **45.** $7 \cdot 6 = 84 \div 2$ **47.** $6^2 - 3^2 = 27$ **49.** $3^4 + 7 > 50$ **51.** Expression **53.** Equation

55. Expression   **57.** Equation   **59.** -9 ; x^2 **61.** -5 ; x **63.** 15 ; x^2 **65.** No   **67.** No

69. -2 , 3   **71.** $-5x^3y$, $4yx^3$ **73.** $5y$ **75.** $3y - 7x + 4xy + 4y^2$ **77.** $67 + 7x$ **79.** $-20p - 34$

81. $-xy + 11x - y$ **83.** $4x^2 - 3b$ **85.** $8y - 8$; -32 **87.** $-26 - 29x$; 119 **89.** $4y^2 - 4y - 3$; 5

91. $5y^2 + 21y - 22$; -44 **93.** $-x^2 - 3x + 2$; -16 **95.** 1 ; 22   **97.** 21 ; 7   **99.** 39 ; 11

101. 27 ; 174   **103.** 14 ; 357   **105.** 84   **107.** 38   **109.** 52   **111.** 14   **113.** 25 **115.** -30

117. 39   **119.** 81   **121.** 7   **123.** 8   **125.** 12   **127.** 5   **129.** 729

131. 82   **133.** 418   **135.** 4,000

Section 2.2

1. 6   **3.** 11   **5.** 25   **7.** 5   **9.** 0   **11.** -7 **13.** -1 **15.** -6 **17.** -14

19. 0   **21.** $x = 8$ **23.** $x = 52$ **25.** $z = 16$ **27.** $z = 0$ **29.** $x = 4$ **31.** $x = 500$ **33.** $x = 3$ **35.** $x = 3$

37. $y = 9$ **39.** $x = -9$ **41.** $x = -3$ **43.** $y = -25$ **45.** $y = 5$ **47.** $t = 0$ **49.** $t = -12$ **51.** $x = -120$

53. $x = -8$ **55.** $x = -9$ **57.** $n = -125$ **59.** $x = -6$ **61.** $x = -12$ **63.** $x = -7$ **65.** $y = -5$ **67.** $x = -12$

69. $x = -9$ **71.** $x = 0$ **73.** $y = -6$ **75.** $x = 0$ **77.** $p = -7$ **79.** $x = -2$ **81.** $x = 1$ **83.** $y = 3$

85. -2 **87.** 4   **89.** -4

Section 2.3

1. $\$2,080$ **3.** $\$6,880$ **5.** $\$3,156$ **7.** $\$1,200$; $\$1,130$ **9.** $\$4,925$ **11.** $\$1,410$ **13.** $\$795$ **15.** $\$1,805$ **17.** $\$2,138$

19. $\$2,362$ **21.** 4,007 mile   **23.** $\$218.27$ **25.** $\$20,875$ **27.** $\$1,241$ **29.** $\$831,000$ **31.** $\$1,418$ **33.** $\$119.58$

35. $\$948$ **37.** $\$5,225$ **39.** 25 GB   **41.** 1,325 cans   **43.** 1,860 packages, 4 cans left over   **45.** 5 inches

Section 2.4

1. Ray   **3.** Ray   **5.** Angle   **7.** OA, OB, OC ; $\angle$AOB, $\angle$AOC, $\angle$BOC   **9.** Acute   **11.** Obtuse   **13.** Right

15. Right   **17.** Right ; 3 0' clock, answers vary   **19.** $74°$ **21.** $55°$ **23.** $48°$ **25.** $53°$ **27.** $90°$

29. $168°$ **31.** $40°$ **33.** $70°$ **35.** $108°$ **37.** $\angle$APB $= 58°$, $\angle$BPC $= 90°$, $\angle$CPD $= 32°$, $\angle$DPE $= 58°$

39. (a) Right   **(b)** Obtuse   **(c)** Acute   **(d)** Acute   **(e)** Obtuse   **(f)** Right   **(g)** Right

41. (a) Rectangle **(b)** Square   **(c)** Neither   **(d)** Rectangle   **(e)** Square   **(f)** Neither **(g)** Square   **(h)** Neither

43. 750 ft^2 ; 366 ft^2 ; $\$1,098$ **45.** 58 ft

Review Exercise 2.6

1. $2x$ **3.** $9 - x$ **5.** $9x + 7$ **7.** $2x + 9$ **9.** $\dfrac{7x}{x+8}$ **11.** $\dfrac{7}{x+8}$ **13.** $10x - x^2$ **15.** $x^2 - 3$ **17.** $\dfrac{x+7}{x-10}$

19. $4x - 7 = 1$; $x = 2$ **21.** $2x + 1 = 5$; $x = 2$ **23.** $2x + 3 = 12$, no solution in the set   **25.** $3 - 2x = x$; $x = 1$

27. $x^2 - x = 0$; $x = 0, 1$ **29.** $\dfrac{2}{x} = x + 1$; $x = 1$ **31.** $2x^2 - 1 = x$; $x = 1$ **33.** $13x$ **35.** $-11x$ **37.** $9x - 5$ **39.** $-20x + 6$

41. $3x^2 - 4x - 4$ **43.** $x^3 - 2x^2 - 2x$ **45.** 1 **47.** -3 **49.** 60 **51.** 52 **53.** 27 **55.** -72 **57.** -8 **59.** 22

61. -38 **63.** 7 **65.** 15 **67.** $x = -5$ **69.** $x = -62$ **71.** $x = 0$ **73.** $x = -30$ **75.** $x = 10$ **77.** 3 **79.** -11 **81.** 8

83. -11 **85.** 0 **87.** -15 **89.** \$16   **91.** 44 ft   **93.** $2°$ **95.** -18 **97.** 20 **99.** 7 cm   **101.** 315 miles   **103.** $38°$

105. **(a)** True   **(b)** True   **(c)** False ; If two lines intersect, then one pair of vertically opposite angles may consist of acute angles and the other pair obtuse angles.   **(d)** False ; two adjacent angles may be supplementary   **(e)** True

107. $45°$ **109.** $110°$; $70°$ **111. (a)** a right angle   **(b)** Acute angle   **(c)** Doesn't exist.   **113.** $138°$ **115.** $50°$, $90°$, $40°$

117. $\angle COA = 54°$, $\angle EOD = 90°$, $\angle FOB = 36°$, $\angle COF = 90°$, $\angle AOE = 36°$, $\angle BOD = 54°$ **119.** 74 m   **121.** 90 ft   **123.** 52 cm

125. AB = 32 yd , AC = 44 yd , BC = 74 yd   **127.** 24 **129.** 64 **131.** 150 in^2 **133.** 3,000 ft^2 **135.** 10,028 sq.ft.

Self Test 2.7

1. (a) $\dfrac{x}{11} + 5$ **(b)** $7(3 - x)$ **(c)** $12 - 2x = 5$ **(d)** $6x - 7 = 29$ **(e)** $2x + 7 \le 27$ **3.** -15 ; x^3 **5.** $4x^2 - 5x - 8$

7. $-3x + 4y + 5$ **9.** \$39,300   **11.** $x = 2$ **13.** $x = 3$ **15.** $x = 13$ **17.** $130°$

19. $\angle EOD = 130°$, $\angle BOF = 25°$, $\angle DOB = 25°$, $\angle AOC = 25°$ **21.** Area = 108 ft^2 ; Perimeter = 48 ft

23. Area = 8 in^2 ; Perimeter = 16 in

CHAPTER 3

Section 3.1

1. Odd ; $319 = 2 \cdot 159 + 1$ **3.** Even ; $9,210 = 2 \cdot 4,605$ **5.** Odd ; $5,799 = 2 \cdot 2,899 + 1$ **7.** Even ; $10,064 = 2 \cdot 5,032$

9. Even ; $876 = 2 \cdot 438$ **11.** Odd ; $44,683 = 2 \cdot 22,341 + 1$ **13.** Odd ; $1 = 2 \cdot 0 + 1$ **15.** Odd ; $24,863 = 2 \cdot 12,431 + 1$

17. Even ; $394 = 2 \cdot 197$ **19.** 2 , 3 , 4, and 9   **21.** 3, 5, and 9   **23.** None   **25.** 2 and 4   **27.** None   **29.** 2

31. 2 , 3 , 4, and 9   **33.** 3 and 9   **35.** 2, 3, 5, and 10   **37.** All of them   **39.** 2 , 4 , 5 , 10 , 25 , 50, and 100

41. 3   **43.** 2 , 3, and 4   **45.** 2 , 3, and 9   **47.** 3, 5, and 9   **49.** $72 \div 8 = 9$; $72 \div 9 = 8$ **51.** $(-40) \div (-10) = 4$; $4 \cdot (-10) = -40$

53. $(-210) \div (-30) = 7$; $7 \cdot (-30) = -210$ **55.** $(-99) \div 11 = -9$; $(-9) \cdot 11 = -99$ **57.** Yes   **59.** No

61. Yes   **63.** No   **65.** Yes   **67.** Yes   **69.** True   **71.** True ; 18 and 30   **73.** True

75. True   **77.** True ; 12 and 20 (both divisible by 4 and not by 8); 24 and 32 (both divisible by 4 and 8)

Section 3.2

1. Composite   **3.** Composite   **5.** Composite   **7.** Composite   **9.** Composite   **11.** $2 \cdot 3 \cdot 11$ **13.** $2^4 \cdot 3$ **15.** $2 \cdot 3^3$

17. $2 \cdot 3 \cdot 7^2$ **19.** $18 = 1 \cdot 18$ or $2 \cdot 9$ or $3 \cdot 6$; 1, 2, 3, 6, 9, 18   **21.** $28 = 1 \cdot 28$ or $2 \cdot 14$ or $4 \cdot 7$; 1, 2, 4, 7, 14, 28

23. $75 = 1 \cdot 75$ or $3 \cdot 25$ or $5 \cdot 15$; 1, 3, 5, 15, 25, 75   **25.** $325 = 1 \cdot 325$ or $5 \cdot 65$ or $13 \cdot 25$; 1, 5, 13, 25, 65, 325

27. $97 = 1 \cdot 97$; 1, 97   **29.** $140 = 1 \cdot 140$ or $2 \cdot 70$ or $4 \cdot 35$ or $5 \cdot 28$ or $7 \cdot 20$ or $10 \cdot 14$; 1, 2, 4, 5, 7, 10, 14, 20, 28, 35, 70, 140

31. $365 = 1 \cdot 365$ or $5 \cdot 73$; 1, 5, 73, 365   **33.** $65 = 1 \cdot 65$ or $5 \cdot 13$; 1, 5, 13, 65   **35.** 7 and 8   **37.** 4 and 18   **39.** 5 and 25

41. 9 and 11   **43.** 6 and 15   **45.** 6 and 18   **47.** 13 and 14   **49.** 6 and 8   **51.** 6 and 25   **53.** 5 and 26   **55.** 9 and 15

57. 8 and 12   **59.** 2, 3, 5, 7, 11, 13, 17, 19, 23, 29, 31, 37, 41, 43, 47, 53, 59, 61, 67, 71, 73, 79, 83, 89, and 97   **61.** 3, 5, and 7

63. 10 is deficient   **65. (a)** deficient   **(b)** deficient   **(c)** perfect   **(d)** abundant   **(e)** deficient   **(f)** abundant **(g)** abundant

Section 3.3

1. 60   **3.** 48   **5.** 36   **7.** 60   **9.** 2,520   **11.** 60   **13.** 300   **15.** 600   **17.** 600

19. 120   **21.** 60   **23.** 280   **25.** 360   **27.** 396   **29.** 4,410   **31.** 1890   **33.** $36x^2y^3$ **35.** $90x^2y^3$

37. ab^2x^2 **39.** $350xy^2$ **41.** $210x^2y$ **43.** $150a^2b^3$ **45.** 109,200 ; 1680, 1560, 1456, 1365   **47.** 996

49. 10:00 AM ; four bells ring 45, 30, 20, and 18 times, respectively   **51.** 1,000 g ; 10, 5, 4, and 2 packets respectively   **53.** 24

55. 12,240 cms   **57.** 12th block   **59. (a)** every 180 days   **(b)** 15, 12, and 10 trips respectively

Section 3.4

1. Rational number   **3.** Not a Rational number   **5.** Rational number   **7.** Not a Rational number   **9.** Rational number

11. Rational number   **13.** $\dfrac{-4}{5}, \dfrac{4}{-5}$ **15.** $\dfrac{-15}{7}, -\dfrac{15}{7}$ **17.** $\dfrac{3}{8}$ **19.** $\dfrac{3}{4}$ **21.** $\dfrac{2}{6}$ **23.** $\dfrac{7}{10}$ **25.** $\dfrac{11}{5}$

27.  **29.** **31.**

33. **35.** **37.**

39. **41.** **43.**

45. **47.**

49. **51.**

53.

55. $1\dfrac{3}{8}$ in ; $3\dfrac{2}{5}$ cm   **57.** $2\dfrac{1}{16}$ in ; $5\dfrac{1}{5}$ cm   **59.** $1\dfrac{3}{16}$ in ; 3 cm   **61.** $\dfrac{7}{3}$ **63.** 0   **65.** $\dfrac{7}{9}$ **67.** $\dfrac{9}{17}$ **69.** $\dfrac{19}{70}$

Section 3.5

1. $\dfrac{9}{15}, \dfrac{12}{20}, \dfrac{18}{30}$ **3.** $\dfrac{3}{24}, \dfrac{4}{32}, \dfrac{6}{48}$ **5.** $\dfrac{12}{15}, \dfrac{16}{20}, \dfrac{24}{30}$ **7.** $\dfrac{45}{48}, \dfrac{60}{64}, \dfrac{90}{96}$ **9.** $\dfrac{9}{21}, \dfrac{12}{28}, \dfrac{18}{42}$ **11.** $\dfrac{24}{33}, \dfrac{32}{44}, \dfrac{48}{66}$ **13.** $\dfrac{39}{54}, \dfrac{52}{72}, \dfrac{78}{108}$

15. $\dfrac{15}{20}$ **17.** $\dfrac{18}{30}$ **19.** $\dfrac{18}{21}$ **21.** $\dfrac{15}{35}$ **23.** $\dfrac{-16}{20x}$ **25.** $\dfrac{51x}{45x}$ **27.** $\dfrac{20y}{12}$

29. $\dfrac{39y}{-54y}$ **31.** $\dfrac{6x^2}{3xy}$ **33.** $\dfrac{7x}{3}$ **35.** $\dfrac{2}{3}$ **37.** $\dfrac{2}{5}$ **39.** $\dfrac{16}{25}$ **41.** $\dfrac{5}{6}$

43. $\dfrac{2}{9}$ **45.** $\dfrac{4}{13}$ **47.** $\dfrac{1}{2}$ **49.** $\dfrac{5}{9}$ **51.** $\dfrac{2}{5}$ **53.** $\dfrac{3}{4}$ **55.** $\dfrac{11}{14}$

57. $\dfrac{43}{59}$ **59.** $-\dfrac{1}{4}$ **61.** $\dfrac{4x}{5}$ **63.** $\dfrac{y}{5}$ **65.** $-\dfrac{1}{2y}$ **67.** $\dfrac{4v}{7}$ **69.** $-\dfrac{5}{8u}$

71. $-\dfrac{2a}{5}$ **73.** $-\dfrac{2}{3a}$ **75.** $-\dfrac{2y}{3x}$ **77.** $-\dfrac{y}{120x}$

Section 3.6

1. $\frac{16}{36}, \frac{21}{36}$ 3. $\frac{80}{90}, \frac{225}{90}, \frac{54}{90}$ 5. $\frac{8}{20}, \frac{5}{20}, \frac{14}{20}$ 7. $\frac{63}{72}; \frac{32a}{72}, \frac{33}{72}$ 9. $\frac{20a}{120}, \frac{15a}{120}, \frac{12a}{120}$

11. $\frac{12}{8x}, \frac{18x}{8x}, \frac{x^2}{8x}$ 13. $\frac{20}{24x}, \frac{3x^2}{24x}, \frac{30}{24x}$ 15. $\frac{8a^2}{18ab}, \frac{30b}{18ab}, \frac{27b}{18ab}$ 17. $\frac{2y}{10xy}, \frac{30y^2}{10xy}, \frac{35x^2}{10xy}$ 19. $\frac{8x^2}{6xy}, \frac{4x^2}{6xy}, \frac{3y^2}{6xy}$

21. >   23. >   25. <   27. <   29. =   31. >   33. >   35. <   37. Yes   39. No

41. Yes   43. Yes   45. No   47. Yes   49. No   51. $\frac{1}{3} < \frac{1}{2} < \frac{2}{3}$ 53. $\frac{11}{20} < \frac{2}{3} < \frac{13}{15}$ 55. $\frac{5}{8} < \frac{3}{4} < \frac{7}{5}$

57. $\frac{4}{5} < \frac{9}{10} < \frac{13}{10}$ 59. $\frac{2}{5} < \frac{4}{7} < \frac{3}{4}$ 61. $\frac{2}{3} < \frac{5}{6} < \frac{3}{2}$ 63. $\frac{9}{35} < \frac{2}{7} < \frac{3}{5}$ 65. $\frac{7}{12} < \frac{3}{4} < \frac{5}{6}$ 67. $\frac{3}{10} < \frac{1}{3} < \frac{2}{5} < \frac{3}{2}$

69. $\frac{2}{9} < \frac{7}{12} < \frac{3}{4} < \frac{5}{6}$ 71. 10   73. 6   75. 25   77. 7   79. 18   81. 30   83. 15   85. 2   87. $49x$ 89. $10v^2$

Section 3.7

1. Proper: $\frac{1}{3}, -\frac{2}{3}$; Improper: $5, \frac{6}{5}, -\frac{10}{3}$ 3. Proper: $\frac{5}{7}, -\frac{3}{19}$; Improper: $-15, \frac{19}{-5}$ 5. Proper: $-\frac{19}{36}, \frac{17}{241}$; Improper: $-214, \frac{75}{23}$

7. Proper: $\frac{5}{8}$; Improper: $\frac{9}{7}, -\frac{6}{5}, 2, \frac{4}{3}$ 9. Proper: $\frac{2}{5}, -\frac{7}{8}, \frac{3}{7}$; Improper: $-\frac{18}{5}, \frac{5}{2}$ 11. Proper: $\frac{3}{8}$; Improper: $-\frac{4}{3}, \frac{-5}{2}, \frac{23}{7}, -3$

13. $\frac{3}{2}$ 15. $\frac{-13}{4}$ 17. $\frac{26}{5}$ 19. $\frac{23}{5}$ 21. $\frac{47}{6}$ 23. $\frac{-17}{3}$ 25. $\frac{106}{9}$ 27. $\frac{73}{10}$ 29. $\frac{52}{45}$

31. $\frac{451}{6}$ 33. $\frac{901}{8}$ 35. $\frac{17}{2}$ 37. $\frac{11}{4}$ 39. $\frac{62}{3}$ 41. $\frac{-105}{8}$ 43. $\frac{-55}{7}$ 45. $\frac{-23}{4}$ 47. $\frac{-553}{10}$

49. $\frac{-242}{3}$ 51. $\frac{1301}{100}$ 53. $\frac{722}{5}$ 55. $4\frac{3}{4}$ 57. $2\frac{1}{3}$ 59. $-4\frac{1}{5}$ 61. $7\frac{5}{6}$ 63. $-6\frac{7}{8}$ 65. $13\frac{5}{10}$

67. $9\frac{11}{100}$ 69. $-83\frac{6}{9}$ 71. $-42\frac{9}{12}$ 73. $-19\frac{33}{80}$ 75. $-87\frac{7}{12}$ 77. $71\frac{2}{13}$ 79. $1\frac{17}{160}$ 81. $-90\frac{3}{10}$ 83. $35\frac{7}{15}$

85.    87.    89.

91.    93.   95.

97.   99.

Section 3.8

1. $\frac{1}{5}$ 3. $\frac{7}{24}$ 5. $\frac{11}{18}$ 7. $\frac{927}{1000}$ 9. $\frac{19}{30}$ 11. $\frac{23}{45}$ 13. $\frac{67}{295}$ 15. $\frac{4}{1}$ 17. $\frac{7}{3}$ 19. $\frac{5}{2}$

21. $\frac{13}{18}$ 23. $\frac{100}{7}$ 25. $\frac{50}{7}$ 27. $\frac{12}{5}$ 29. $\frac{5}{9}$ 31. $\frac{3}{10}$ 33. $\frac{5}{1}$ 35. $\frac{2}{1}$ 37. $7 per ticket

39. $39   41. $107   43. $37   45. 18 miles   47. 25 miles   49. (a) $\frac{1}{5}$ (b) $\frac{2}{15}$ (c) $\frac{1}{3}$ (d) $\frac{1}{3}$

51. (a) $\frac{31}{150}$ (b) $\frac{2}{25}$ (c) $\frac{26}{75}$ (d) $\frac{83}{150}$ (e) $\frac{23}{25}$ 53. $\frac{1}{4}$ 55. $\frac{3}{10}$ 57. $\frac{2}{5}$ 59. $\frac{7}{10}$

61. $\frac{7}{25}$ of the college students were receiving grants.   **63.** $\frac{1}{50}$ of the milk is fat. **65.** 25%   **67.** 40%

69. $\frac{3}{20}$ is the ratio of car expenses to his total income.   **71.** 11,000 miles/sec   **73. (a)** $\frac{30}{1}$ **(b)** 70 teachers

75. (a) 60° **(b)** $\frac{2}{1}$ **77.** $\frac{2}{3}$ **79.** $\frac{3}{4}$ **81.** $\frac{1}{4}$

Review Exercise 3.10

1. 5 and 25   **3.** 2, 3, and 9   **5.** 2 and 3   **7.** 6   **9.** 4   **11.** No   **13.** 3 and 5   **15.** 3 and 7   **17.** 3, 7, and 13

19. 7 and 13   **21.** Even ; 2 (3,947) **23.** Odd; 2(43) + 1   **25.** Even; 2(219)   **27.** Odd; 2(183) + 1   **29.** Odd ; 2(86) + 1

31. Odd ; 2(−401) + 1   **33.** No   **35.** No   **37.** Yes   **39.** Yes   **41.** Yes   **43.** Composite **45.** Composite **47.** Prime

49. Prime   **51.** $2 \cdot 3 \cdot 7^2$ **53.** $2^7 \cdot 3^2 \cdot 5 \cdot 7$ **55.** $2^3 \cdot 3^3 \cdot 5$ **57.** $1 \cdot 30, 2 \cdot 15, 3 \cdot 10, 5 \cdot 6$; 1, 2, 3, 5, 6, 10, 15, 30

59. $1 \cdot 120, 2 \cdot 60, 3 \cdot 40, 4 \cdot 30, 5 \cdot 24, 6 \cdot 20, 8 \cdot 15, 10 \cdot 12$; 1, 2, 3, 4, 5, 6, 8, 10, 12, 15, 20, 24, 30, 40, 60, 120

61. $1 \cdot 165, 3 \cdot 55, 5 \cdot 33, 11 \cdot 15$; 1, 3, 5, 11, 15, 33, 55, 165   **63.** $71 = 1 \cdot 71$; 1, 71

65. (a) 2340 **(b)** $2340 = 45 \cdot 52 = 36 \cdot 65$ **67. (a)** 140   **(b)** $140 = 4 \cdot 35 = 14 \cdot 10$ **69.** 180; $180 = 30 \cdot 6 = 60 \cdot 3 = 90 \cdot 2$ **71.** $60x^2$

73. $84xy^2z^2$ **75.** $484x^2y^2$ **77.** $\frac{9x}{0}$, and $\frac{14}{x-x}$ **79.**
81.

83.
85.
87.

89. $\frac{28}{36}$ **91.** $\frac{63}{81}$ **93.** $\frac{52x}{20x}$ **95.** $-\frac{5}{7}$ **97.** $\frac{75}{16}$ **99.** 15   **101.** 75   **103.** $28x^2y$ **105.** $\frac{7}{15}$

107. $\frac{14}{15}$ **109.** $\frac{3}{10} < \frac{2}{5} < \frac{5}{4}$ **111.** $\frac{5}{12} < \frac{7}{16} < \frac{11}{24} < \frac{3}{4}$ **113. (a)** $\frac{11}{5}$ **(b)** $\frac{38}{5}$ **(c)** $-\frac{38}{7}$ **(d)** $-\frac{89}{12}$

115. (a) $\frac{1}{4}$ **(b)** 25%   **117. (a)** 20%   **(b)** $\frac{4}{5}$ **(c)** $\frac{1}{4}$

Self Test 3.11

1. Yes   **3.** No   **5.** 1, 2, 4, 17, 34, 68 ; $1 \cdot 68, 2 \cdot 34, 4 \cdot 17$ **7.** 1, 3,7, 13, 21, 39, 91, 273   **9.** $\frac{2}{3}$

11. $\frac{28}{90}, \frac{-105}{90}, \frac{99}{90}$ **13.** $8\frac{3}{7}$

CHAPTER 4

Section 4.1

1. $\dfrac{3}{5}$ **3.** $\dfrac{7}{10}$ **5.** $\dfrac{9}{5}$ **7.** $2x$ **9.** $4x$ **11.** $\dfrac{13a}{8b}$ **13.** $\dfrac{49}{90}$ **15.** $\dfrac{17}{15}$ **17.** $\dfrac{8}{15}$ **19.** $\dfrac{25}{24}$ **21.** $\dfrac{17}{8}$

23. $\dfrac{17}{16}$ **25.** $15\dfrac{2}{15}$ **27.** $16\dfrac{1}{16}$ **29.** $\dfrac{37a}{21}$ **31.** $\dfrac{23b}{14}$ **33.** $\dfrac{23}{20a}$ **35.** $\dfrac{15+4b}{12a}$ **37.** $\dfrac{8a+21}{30b}$ **39.** Inverse

41. Identity **43.** Commutative **45.** Commutative **47.** $\dfrac{-3}{5}$, Commutative **49.** $\dfrac{11}{13}$, Identity **51.** $\dfrac{5}{9}$, Inverse

53. $\dfrac{2}{3}$, Associative **55.** $\dfrac{11}{30}$ **57.** $\dfrac{1}{48}$ **59.** $\dfrac{5}{28}$ **61.** $\dfrac{37}{150}$ **63.** $\dfrac{52}{165}$ **65.** 0 **67.** $-\dfrac{2}{25}$ **69.** $-\dfrac{1}{15}$

71. $-\dfrac{15}{14}$ **73.** $\dfrac{1}{63}$ **75.** $\dfrac{13}{16}$ **77.** $\dfrac{x}{4}$ **79.** $\dfrac{7-5x}{7}$ **81.** $\dfrac{x}{7}$ **83.** $\dfrac{x}{30}$ **85.** $\dfrac{5}{6x}$ **87.** $\dfrac{5}{12x}$ **89.** $\dfrac{23}{130y}$

91. $\dfrac{7}{12}$ **93.** $\dfrac{1}{20}$ **95.** $\dfrac{11}{20}$ **97.** $2\dfrac{11}{36}$ **99.** $\dfrac{17x-4}{45y}$ **101.** $\dfrac{18x^2-15x-4y^2}{24xy}$ **103.** $\dfrac{x-2y}{xy}$ **105.** $\dfrac{2}{3x}$

107. $\dfrac{12bx-7a}{9ab}$ **109.** $\dfrac{2a}{x}$ **111.** $\dfrac{3}{2x}$ **113.** $\dfrac{4x-19}{24}$ **115.** $\dfrac{16x-5}{16}$ **117.** $\dfrac{1}{3}$ **119.** $\dfrac{5}{8}$ **121.** $\dfrac{2}{11}$

123. $\dfrac{4}{13}$ **125.** $\dfrac{2}{15}$ **127.** $1\dfrac{1}{3}$ **129.** $2\dfrac{2}{7}$ **131.** $4\dfrac{7}{9}$ **133.** $7\dfrac{6}{11}$ **135.** $2\dfrac{10}{13}$

Section 4.2

1. $\dfrac{21}{40}$ **3.** $\dfrac{60}{11}$ **5.** $-\dfrac{16}{3}$ **7.** 0 **9.** $\dfrac{3}{4}$ **11.** $-\dfrac{1}{6}$ **13.** $\dfrac{21}{17}$ **15.** 1 **17.** $\dfrac{2}{5}$ **19.** $\dfrac{16}{35}$

21. $\dfrac{-5}{2}$ **23.** $\dfrac{-2}{3}$ **25.** $\dfrac{4}{45}$ **27.** $\dfrac{-1}{3}$ **29.** $\dfrac{16}{135}$ **31.** $-\dfrac{68}{35}$ **33.** -4 **35.** $-2\dfrac{5}{8}$ **37.** 16 **39.** $1\dfrac{1}{5}$

41. $\dfrac{6u}{7}$ **43.** $\dfrac{4}{x}$ **45.** $\dfrac{3n}{2}$ **47.** $\dfrac{x}{27}$ **49.** $\dfrac{a^2}{3b}$ **51.** 20 **53.** 1 **55.** $\dfrac{m}{5x}$ **57.** $\dfrac{37}{25}$ **59.** $-\dfrac{1}{13}$

61. undefined **63.** 27 **65.** $\dfrac{7x}{2}$ **67.** $\dfrac{1}{5x}$ **69.** $\dfrac{18x}{11y}$ **71.** $-\dfrac{14y}{3ax^2}$ **73.** $-8x$ **75.** undefined **77.** Associative Property

79. Multiplicative Inverse **81.** Commutative Property **83.** Multiplicative Identity **85.** $\dfrac{7}{10}$ **87.** $\dfrac{5}{4}$ **89.** -3

91. -1 **93.** $18x^2$ **95.** $\dfrac{1}{2}$ **97.** $-\dfrac{13}{2}$ **99.** 1 **101.** $\dfrac{6}{5}$ **103.** $\dfrac{16}{21}$ **105.** $-6\dfrac{5}{6}$ **107.** -3 **109.** $6\dfrac{2}{3}$

111. $\dfrac{3a^2b^2}{10}$ **113.** 1 **115.** **(a)** a product **(b)** $\dfrac{2}{3}$

Section 4.3

1. $4\dfrac{34}{45}$ **3.** $1\dfrac{1}{3}$ **5.** $\dfrac{1}{2}$ **7.** $\dfrac{1}{5}$ **9.** $\dfrac{-1}{8}$ **11.** $\dfrac{2}{3}$ **13.** $\dfrac{50}{81}$ **15.** $\dfrac{7}{8}$ **17.** $1\dfrac{23}{25}$

19. 2 **21.** $\dfrac{1}{2}$ **23.** $2\dfrac{13}{36}$ **25.** $4\dfrac{1}{60}$ **27.** $\dfrac{17}{32}$ **29.** $\dfrac{209}{270}$ **31.** 1 **33.** $\dfrac{2}{37}$ **35.** $2\dfrac{2}{65}$

37. -2 **39.** $2\dfrac{2}{25}$ **41.** $-5\dfrac{5}{28}$ **43.** $\dfrac{5}{24}$ **45.** $2\dfrac{1}{2}$ **47.** $-7\dfrac{3}{7}$ **49.** $1\dfrac{7}{20}$ **51.** $-29\dfrac{1}{3}$ **53.** $-2\dfrac{2}{5}$

55. **(a)** $\dfrac{-5\dfrac{1}{10}+6\dfrac{1}{2}}{-1\dfrac{3}{4}-4\dfrac{1}{2}}$ **(b)** $\left(-5\dfrac{1}{10}+6\dfrac{1}{2}\right)\div\left(-1\dfrac{3}{4}-4\dfrac{1}{2}\right)$ **57.** $\dfrac{1-\dfrac{1}{5}}{2\dfrac{1}{4}+\dfrac{-3}{8}}$; $\dfrac{32}{75}$ **59.** $\dfrac{-2\dfrac{1}{5}+4\dfrac{3}{10}}{6+\dfrac{3}{7}}$; $\dfrac{49}{150}$ **61.** $41\dfrac{38}{49}$ **63.** $10\dfrac{5}{8}$

Review Exercise 4.5

1. (a) $\frac{59}{35}$ (b) $\frac{5}{3}$ (c) $\frac{37}{24}$ (d) $\frac{1}{2}$ 3. (a) $\frac{1}{12}$ (b) $8\frac{5}{12}$ (c) $\frac{-6}{x}$ (d) $\frac{93}{7y}$

5. (a) $1\frac{9}{10}$ (b) $1\frac{11}{16}$ (c) $\frac{1}{5}$ (d) $\frac{2}{15}$ 7. (a) $\frac{-1}{3}$ (b) $8\frac{2}{5}$ (c) $\frac{8}{9}$ (d) $-11\frac{1}{4}$ (e) 84

9. Associative Property   11. Multiplicative Inverse   13. Associative Property   15. Multiplicative Identity

17. (a) $\frac{5}{8}$ (b) $\frac{1}{14}$ (c) undefined   (d) $\frac{-25}{37}$ 19. $\frac{3}{4}$ 21. $-\frac{1}{15}$ 23. $33y^2$

25. (a) $2\frac{13}{36}$ (b) $11\frac{11}{30}$ (c) $1\frac{3}{5}$ 27. (a) $1\frac{7}{8}$ (b) $-\frac{49}{102}$ (c) $\frac{29}{37}$

29. (a) $\dfrac{\frac{5}{7}-\frac{7}{3}}{-\frac{9}{4}+\frac{7}{8}}$ (b) $\left(\frac{5}{7}-\frac{7}{3}\right)\div\left(-\frac{9}{4}+\frac{7}{8}\right)$ (c) $1\frac{41}{231}$

Self Test 4.6

1. $1\frac{17}{24}$ 3. $-\frac{2x}{a}$ 5. $3\frac{3}{8}$ 7. $\frac{1}{2}$ 9. $3\frac{33}{80}$ 11. $\frac{x-2}{15}$

CHAPTER 5

Section 5.1

1. 1   3. $\frac{1}{3}$ 5. $\frac{7}{10}$ 7. $\frac{23}{12}$ 9. $\frac{23}{10}$ 11. $\frac{1}{2}$ 13. $\frac{18}{5}$ 15. $\frac{113}{36}$ 17. $\frac{12}{5}$ 19. $\frac{3}{8}$

21. $\frac{-7}{8}$ 23. $\frac{34}{9}$ 25. 6   27. $\frac{-14}{3}$ 29. $\frac{15}{2}$ 31. $\frac{7}{5}$ 33. $\frac{-117}{5}$ 35. $-\frac{7}{10}$ 37. $\frac{1}{14}$ 39. $\frac{-3}{16}$

41. $\frac{-2}{3}$ 43. -210 45. $\frac{-1}{5}$ 47. $\frac{-2}{15}$ 49. $\frac{-32}{15}$ 51. -6 53. 0   55. $\frac{161}{10}$ 57. $\frac{13}{5}$ 59. $\frac{38}{15}$

61. $\frac{20}{3}$ 63. -10 65. True   67. True   69. $\frac{45}{2}$ 71. $\frac{24}{7}$ 73. $\frac{45}{8}$ 75. $\frac{7}{5}$ 77. $\frac{34}{3}$

Section 5.2

1. $1\frac{2}{9}$ in   3. $21\frac{9}{16}$ lb   5. $9\frac{7}{15}$ ft^3 7. $20\frac{13}{24}$ in   9. $3\frac{11}{12}$ in   11. $5\frac{8}{15}$ m   13. $74\frac{7}{12}$ gallons   15. $\frac{37}{140}$

17. $\frac{83}{144}$ 19. $\frac{7}{225}$ 21. $3\frac{7}{30}$ 23. $\frac{3}{8}$ 25. $6\frac{2}{3}$ 27. $2\frac{5}{24}$ 29. $3\frac{7}{32}$ in   31. $14\frac{4}{9}$ yrs

33. 217   35. 100   37. 26   39. $\frac{8}{15}, \frac{7}{15}$ 41. $\frac{2}{5}$ 43. $\frac{1}{8}$ 45. 30 males, 10 females

47. $\frac{1}{9}$; $1350   49. $458\frac{1}{3}$ 51. $\frac{4}{21}$ 53. $\frac{1}{6}$; $405   55. $12   57. 79,200 citizens   59. 2320 students will transfer

61. $121\frac{19}{29}$ mi   63. $47\frac{7}{24}$ miles/gallon   65. $12\frac{1}{3}$ 67. $37,570\frac{5}{6}$ 69. $6\frac{1}{3}$ 71. $\frac{1}{8}$ min

73. $2\frac{1}{2}$ ml   75. $4\frac{2}{9}$ servings   77. $\frac{3}{4}$ gallons   79. 1105 ft/sec   81. 160 km/hr   83. 69 inches

85. $608\frac{2}{11}$ mi/hr   87. 252 mi   89. 1,064 mi   91. (i) 10 kg   (ii) 48 books   93. $294   95. $3\frac{3}{4}$ hrs

97. $5,250   99. (a) 8 hrs   (b) $357\frac{1}{2}$ mi   101. $14\frac{7}{10}$ grams   103. 60 mi   105. $2,250   107. $97\frac{3}{7}$ in

109. $11\frac{1}{2}$ min.   111. 39 lb/in^2 113. $35\frac{1}{5}$

Section 5.3

1. Sides: $1\frac{1}{8}"$, $\frac{7}{8}"$, $\frac{1}{2}"$; $P = 2\frac{1}{2}"$ **3.** Sides: $1\frac{1}{4}"$, $\frac{5}{8}"$, $\frac{1}{4}"$, $\frac{1}{4}"$, $\frac{3}{4}"$, $\frac{1}{4}"$, $\frac{1}{4}"$, $\frac{5}{8}"$; $P = 4\frac{1}{4}"$ **5.** $AB = \frac{5}{8}"$, $A = \frac{25}{64}$ in^2

7. $AB = 1\frac{1}{4}"$, $BC = \frac{3}{4}"$, $DC = \frac{7}{8}"$, $AD = \frac{5}{8}"$; $A = \frac{85}{128}$ in^2 **9.** $AB = 1"$, $BC = \frac{5}{8}"$, $CD = \frac{1}{2}"$, $AD = \frac{5}{8}"$; Distance between AB and

$CD = \frac{5}{8}"$; $A = \frac{15}{32}$ in^2 **11.** $AB = CD = 1"$, $BC = AD = \frac{5}{8}"$, Distance between AB and $CD = \frac{5}{8}"$; $A = \frac{5}{8}$ in^2

13. $AB = 1"$, $BC = \frac{7}{8}"$, $AC = 1\frac{3}{4}"$; $h = \frac{3}{4}"$; $A = \frac{3}{8}$ in^2 **15.** $35\frac{69}{80}$ cm^2 **17.** $419\frac{37}{56}$ cm^2 **19.** 44 ft **21.** $12\frac{4212}{5425}$ m

23. $15\frac{3}{4}$ ft^2 **25.** $3\frac{1}{2}$ in^2 **27.** $26\frac{2}{3}$ ft^2 **29.** (a) $22\frac{1}{3}$ yd (b) 30 yd^2 **31.** (a) $23\frac{1}{2}$ m (b) $34\frac{33}{64}$ m^2

33. (a) $29\frac{791}{1000}$ m^3 (b) $5\frac{23}{64}$ cm^3 **35.** 1,953 ft^3 **37.** $85\frac{23}{125}$ in^3 **39.** $847\frac{3}{20}$ in^2; $1410\frac{2}{5}$ in^3 **41.** $2\frac{29}{32}$ yd^3 **43.** 8 cm

45. $2\frac{3}{16}$ ft **47.** 20 cm **49.** $3\frac{15}{22}$ ft **51.** 22 in

Review Exercise 5.5

1. $x = 6$ **3.** $x = 8$ **5.** $x = 2$ **7.** $x = \frac{8}{5}$ **9.** $x = \frac{4}{3}$ **11.** (a) True (b) False **13.** (a) $x = 65$ (b) $x = 2\frac{1}{2}$ (c) $y = 8$

15. \$42 **17.** \$600 **19.** $17\frac{1}{2}$ in **21.** $2\frac{2}{3}$ vehicle per family **23.** (a) $12\frac{36}{47}$ gallons (b) \$ $15\frac{45}{47}$ **25.** $178\frac{14}{17}$ miles

27. $AB = \frac{3}{4}$ in, $BC = 1\frac{3}{4}$ in, $AC = 1\frac{1}{2}$ in, height $= \frac{5}{8}$ in; Area $= \frac{35}{64}$ in^2 **29.** $\frac{7}{72}$ ft^2 **31.** $\frac{2}{5}$ yd

33. (a) $37\frac{1}{27}$ ft^3 (b) $421\frac{7}{8}$ cm^3 **35.** $883\frac{11}{20}$ in^2; $1442\frac{1}{10}$ in^3

Self Test 5.6

1. $x = \frac{5}{12}$ **3.** $x = \frac{1}{4}$ **5.** 161 **7.** True **9.** 120 **11.** 200 passengers

13. $l = \frac{9}{8}$ in, $w = \frac{5}{8}$ in, $P = 3\frac{1}{2}$ in, $A = \frac{45}{64}$ in^2 **15.** $107\frac{89}{125}$ ft^3 **17.** $x = 8$ cm

CHAPTER 6

Section 6.1

1. 12.9 **3.** 9.024 **5.** 72.56 **7.** 4.8 **9.** 35.246 **11.** $2\frac{73}{100}$ **13.** $35\frac{432}{1000}$ **15.** $19\frac{5}{10}$ **17.** $27\frac{5}{1000}$ **19.** $3\frac{815}{1000}$

21. Four thousand five and eighty-three thousandths. **23.** Four hundred ninety-one and two hundred eighty-three throusandths.

25. Eight hundred forty-two and forty-nine ten thousandths. **27.** Twenty-nine and six hundred five thousandths.

29. Eight hundred five thousandths. **31.** 217.03 **33.** 0.349 **35.** 4,532.092 **37.** 1,000,092.12 **39.** 73.549

41. 275.6 **43.** 0.1 **45.** 45.0 **47.** 4.0 **49.** 5.28 **51.** 5.04 **53.** 23.548 **55.** 7.297 **57.** 257

59. 420 **61.** 275.6 **63.** 570 **65.** 1.0 **67.** 2,565.0 **69.** 754.93 **71.**

73.

75. 3.98 **77.** 1.457 **79.** $1.4 > 1.352$ **81.** $-6.2 < -6$

83. -4, 0.845, 2.75 **85.** -7.2, -4, 0.79, 2 **87.** 6.0 cm, 60 mm **89.** 1.7 cm, 17 mm

91. Dollars Ninety-five and thirty-five cents. **93.** Dollars Three hundred twenty-two and seventeen cents. **95.** \$2,073.50

97. 5,500.00 ; 5,500.0 ; 5,500 ; 5,500; The rounded value is same in all the cases. **99.** 2.08 pounds

Answers

Section 6.2

1. 49.7 **3.** 204.153 **5.** 42.1513 **7.** 510.23 lb **9.** 219.04 **11.** 49.215 **13.** 1.10 **15.** 5.544 **17.** 36.689

19. 24.102 **21.** 47.888 **23.** 0.1650 **25.** $554.15 **27.** 81.235 **29.** 6.04 **31.** −15.89 **33.** 114.892 **35.** 17.11

37. 5.427 **39.** −1.035 **41.** 1.55 **43.** 3.06 **45.** −154.49 **47.** 222.38 **49.** $-0.8x$ **51.** $54.76x$ **53.** $45.5x$

55. $-3.3x + 16.37$ **57.** 0.81 ; 0.8360 **59.** −1.0 ; −0.9530 **61.** −0.11 ; −0.1044 **63.** −0.99 ; −0.9870

65. 30 ; 23.4977 **67.** 43 ; 37.82 **69.** 2,200 ; 2,434.41 **71.** 640 lb ; 620.88 lb **73.** 301.644

75. 1.4093

Section 6.3

1. 0.08 **3.** 0.0015 **5.** 0.3705 **7.** −24.5 **9.** 41.5 **11.** 0.048 **13.** 6.1765 **15.** 209.76 **17.** 12.765 **19.** 1279.53

21. 5.4717 **23.** 0.00352 **25.** 10.591 **27.** 91.2 **31.** 175.8 **33.** 53,400 **35.** 752.35 **37.** 2,378.1 **39.** 5,200 **41.** 3,145

43. 1.6 **45.** 0.4 **47.** 3.007 **49.** .017 **51.** 30.7 **53.** −11.52 **55.** 0.58 **57.** 2.68 **59.** 0.08 **61.** 97.06

63. 12.50 **65.** 113.2 **67.** 5 **69.** 452 **71.** −2006 **73.** 384.375 **75.** 509 **77.** 1,584.8 **79.** 3,073.143

81. 0.07 **83.** 0.027 **85.** 19.8345 **87.** 0.074 **89.** 0.3535 **91.** 0.000832 **93. a.** 10.65 **b.** −0.04928 **c.** 0.000463

95. 56 ; 58.9536 **97.** 700 ; 1,022.25 **99.** 6 ; 6.2144 **101.** 200 ; 209.167 **103.** 0.02 ; 0.0205

105. 2 ; 2.05 **107.** 0.0175 ; 0.0178 **109.** 0.06 ; 0.0486 **111.** −6 ; −4.86

113. −18 ; −17.4018 **115.** 250 ; 229.325 **117.** 25 ; 21.266 **119.** −200 ; −180.829 **121.** −200 ; −346.6946

123. 15 ; 16.0101 **125.** 1.6 ; 1.3568 **127.** 3 ; 2.967

Section 6.4

1. $0.5\overline{3}$ **3.** 2.2 **5.** $2.\overline{142857}$ **7.** $0.\overline{45}$ **9.** $-4.5\overline{3}$ **11.** 0.675 **13.** −0.6875 **15.** $0.\overline{45}$ **17.** $0.\overline{84}$ **19.** 3.45

21. $0.\overline{63}$ **23.** 1.575 **25.** 0.8 **27.** 0.7 **29.** 0.8 **31.** 0.3 **33.** 2.8 **35.** 2.2 **37.** 3.42 **39.** 0.57

41. −3.143 **43.** 13.4 **45.** 2.286 **47.** 0.91 **49.** −4.85 **51.** 3.2143 **53.** 4.8 **55.** 8.467 **57.** $12\frac{3}{40}$ **59.** $-17\frac{7}{25}$

61. $\frac{27}{50}$ **63.** $\frac{1}{80}$ **65.** $\frac{842}{125}$ or $6\frac{92}{125}$ **67.** $\frac{7}{8}$ **69.** $\frac{7}{1000}$ **71.** $67\frac{17}{500}$ **73.** $5\frac{3}{40}$ **75.** $-\frac{19}{20}$ **77.** $\frac{1}{250}$

79. $-3\frac{1}{8}$ **81.** 3.04 **83.** 17.175 **85.** −1.25 **87.** 8.075 **89.** −5.067 **91.** 21.94 **93.** 58.793 **95.** −10.395 **97.** 199.92

99. −1.9 **101.** −7.068 **103.** −1.880 **105.** 0.54 **107.** −1.099 **109.** 37.96 **111.** 0.8 **113.** 1.2 **115.** −0.4 **117.** 11.02

119. −5.2 **121.** 19.78 **123.** −5.824 **125.** $\frac{71}{16}$ or $4\frac{7}{16}$ **127.** $-12\frac{1}{4}$ **129.** 7 **131.** $\frac{29}{4}$ or $7\frac{1}{4}$ **133.** $-1\frac{7}{10}$

135. 1.3 ; 1.238 **137.** 1.4 ; 1.404 **139.** 6.72 ; 6.937 **141.** −16.2 ; −16.162 **143.** 13.9 ; 13.967

145. 0.8 ; 0.820 **147.** 52.624 ; 53.475 **149.** −5.1 ; −5.205 **151.** 4.756 **153.** 4.365 **155.** 2.9625

157. 3.82429

Review Exercise 6.6

1. (a) 65.04
(b) 0.075
(c) 6.08
(d) 25.15
(e) 9.014

3. (a) Twenty-six and four hundred five thousandths.
(b) Six and Seventy-two hundredths.
(c) Two hundred and thirty-three thousandths.
(d) Eighty-two ten thousandths.
(e) Four hundred forty-four thousandths.

5. (a) 570
(b) 6.6
(c) 8.00
(d) 37.283

7. (a) $6.3x$
(b) $-12.9t$
(c) $3.06 y$

9. $6.11

11. (a) 0.735 (b) 641.4510 (c) 0.084 (d) 31.2708

13. (a) 70 ; 83.145   **(b)** 54 ; 53.067   **(c)** 3000 ; 2995.8741   **(d)** 450 ; 481.152

15. (a) 7,350   **(b)** 3,492   **(c)** 3.985   **(d)** 349.2

     (e) 0.002492   **(f)** −1470   **(g)** −0.23   **(h)** 0.59

17. (a) $-2\frac{3}{4}$ **(b)** $\frac{7}{20}$ **(c)** $\frac{3}{8}$ **(d)** $2\frac{39}{50}$ **(e)** $-24\frac{9}{10}$

19. (a) 4.56   **(b)** 0.75   **21.** ≈ 1.7 ; 1.689   **23.** ≈ − 0.4; −0.38095   **25.** 4.3   **27.** 393.7

Self Test 6.7

1. 434.245   **3.** 2,698,310.6   **5.** −10.2x **7.** 5042.49   **9.** −5.5875   **11.** −2.45   **13.** 1.994

15. $0.\overline{428571}$ **17.** −0.4375   **19.** ≈ 0.6   **21.** 15.70325

CHAPTER 7

Section 7.1

1. $x = -13.4$ **3.** $y = 9$ **5.** $x = -11.6$ **7.** $x - 6$ **9.** $r = 10.248$ **11.** $x = -14.83$ **13.** $t = 81.2$ **15.** $x = 20$

17. $y = 13.31$ **19.** $x = 1.71$ **21.** $x = 4.8$ **23.** $x = 7.09$ **25.** $x = -1.5$ **27.** $x = \frac{9}{5}$ **29.** $x = 33$ **31.** $y = -\frac{2}{3}$

33. $p = 20$ **35.** $x = 18$ **37.** $p = \frac{7}{60}$ **39.** $y = \frac{9}{14}$ **41.** $x = -\frac{3}{2}$ **43.** $x = 30$ **45.** $x = -4$ **47.** $x = -2$

49. $x = 1$ **51.** $p = -40$ **53.** $x = -\frac{31}{6}$ **55.** $x = \frac{6}{25}$ **57.** $x = \frac{7}{3}$ **59.** $y = 0$ **61.** $P \approx 1,473.43$ **63.** $V \approx 435.44$

65. $h \approx 8.69$ **67.** $r \approx 3.464$ **69.** $l = 40.2$

Section 7.2

1. $1608.63   **3.** $1660.80   **5.** $4,577.85   **7.** 521.6 miles   **9.** $6,281.56   **11.** $5,101.6   **13.** $3,393.22

15. $5,214.05   **17.** 73.2°F   **19.** 2.075 mi   **21.** $8.10   **23.** $1.96   **25.** $67.62; $137.28   **27.** $50.30

29. $\frac{58}{77}$ **31.** $\frac{26}{23}$ **33.** $\frac{8}{13}$ **35.** 0.83 in/hr, $\frac{5}{6}$ in/hr   **37.** $340.10   **39.** 28.69 cents/min

41. $23.25   **43.** $144.64   **45.** 8.8 mph   **47.** 21.76 lb   **49.** 40 mph; 48.2 mph   **51.** 1.3 lb

53. 6.348 cm/hr   **55.** 1 cm = 7.415 yd   **57.** $4 and cents 71   **59.** $0.1007   **61.** 35 oz for $2.19

63. 12 in a box for $2.49   **65.** $4.99 for 33.5 oz   **67.** 250.75 miles   **69.** 15.75 lb   **71.** 219

73. 158   **75.** 8.081 lb   **77.** 9.75 inches   **79.** 13.357 lb   **81. (a)** 2° C   **(b)** 63.14 F   **83.** 2.077

85. 2.73 hr   **87.** 29.65°   **89.** 40 GB disc ≈ $55.16;   80 GB disc ≈ $97.69   **91.** $3,135

Section 7.3

1. Yes   **3.** Yes   **5.** Yes   **7.** Not a perfect square   **9.** Yes   **11.** Not a perfect square   **13.** Yes   **15.** 81   **17.** 45   **19.** 36

21. −121   **23.** 19   **25.** −23   **27.** 20   **29.** $\sqrt{14} < 4$; $\sqrt{14} < \sqrt{16} = 4$ **31.** 4 and 5   **33.** $5 < \sqrt{27} < 6$; 5.196

35. $3 < \sqrt{15} < 4$; 3.873   **37.** $18 < \sqrt{360} < 19$; 18.974   **39.** $5 < \sqrt{34} < 6$; 5.831   **41.** $10 < \sqrt{115} < 11$; 10.724

43. $14 < \sqrt{203} < 15$; 14.248   **45.** $7 < \sqrt{52} < 8$; 7.211   **47.** $20 < \sqrt{415} < 21$; 20.372   **49.** $5 < \sqrt{29} < 6$; 5.385

51. $8 < \sqrt{75} < 9$; 8.660   **53.** 4.4142   **55.** 20.7846   **57.** 2.2914   **59.** 6.0550   **61.** -0.2361 **63.** No, $4^2 + 5^2 \neq 6^2$

65. Yes, $3^2 + 4^2 = 5^2$ **67.** No, $5^2 + 6^2 \neq 8^2$ **69.** No, $6^2 + 9^2 \neq 12^2$ **71.** Yes, $30^2 + 40^2 = 50^2$ **73.** No, $15^2 + 20^2 \neq 24^2$

75. Yes, $8^2 + 15^2 = 17^2$ **77.** $x = 9$ **79.** $x = 16$ **81.** $P = 8.49$ **83.** $x = 30$

85. $P = 12.81$ in   **87.** $x = 6$ **89.** 47   **91.** 172.4 ft   **93.** 18.33 ft

Section 7.4

1. 10.9 m   **3.** 17.1 yd   **5.** 65.6 ft   **7.** 20.01 m^2 **9.** 34.16 cm^2 **11.** 73.5 in^2 **13.** 8.05 ft^2

15. 33.85 ft^2 **17.** 140.85 yd^2 **19.** 257.4 cm^2 **21.** \$1320, \$2193.75   **23.** Second parking lot is bigger

25. (a) 49.612 m   **(b)** 195.9674 m^2 **27. (a)** 64.05 ft   **(b)** 326.85 ft^2 **29. (a)** 19.20 m   **(b)** 22.92 m^2 **31.** 9 cm

33. 47.12 m   **35.** 6.13 m   **37.** 3.98 ft^2 **39.** 1.33 yd   **41.** 44 m   **43.** 17.5 m

45. 7.07 m^2 **47.** 55.57 in^3 **49.** 473.299 yd^3 **51. (a)** 29.79 m^3 **(b)** 5.36 cm^3 **53.** 286.5 in^2 **55.** 3.84 m^2

57. 32.42 yd   **59.** 13 in ; 72.665 in^2

Review Exercise 7.6

1. $x = 2.75$ **3.** $x = 0.5907$ **5.** $x = 0.625$ **7.** $x = 0.75$ **9.** $y = -1.5$ **11.** $y = 1.336$ **13.** $\dfrac{8}{3}$

15. 0.75   **17.** -5 **19.** \$147,729.95   **21.** 5.6, $\dfrac{106}{19}$

23. (a) Not a perfect square   **(b)** Yes; $(15)^2$ **(c)** Yes; $(45)^2$ **(d)** Yes; $(24)^2$

25. (a) 79   **(b)** -8 **(c)** 40   **(d)** -116

27. (a) 8.888   **(b)** 21.863   **(c)** -6.708 **(d)** 24.142   **(e)** -0.899

29. (a) 11.5 m   **(b)** 103.82 sq. m   **31. (a)** 11.31 cm   **(b)** 10.2 in   **(c)** 17.49   **33.** 160 ft   **35.** 165.6 sq cm

37. 77.68 in ; 418.08 in^2

Self Test 7.7

1. $x = -1.5$ **3.** $x = 2.02$ **5.** $x = \dfrac{68}{79}$ **7. (a)** $V = 99.82$ in^3 **(b)** $h = 1.39$ cm   **(c)** $l = 3.76$ ft   **9.** Yes it is right triangle.

11. 25 m   **13.** $10\,\pi$ in or 31.4 in   **15.** 61.68 cm   **17.** 192 m^2 **19.** 7.74   **21.** 8.33 minutes

CHAPTER 8

Section 8.1

1. 0.066   **3.** 4   **5.** 0.04   **7.** .0095   **9.** 0.045   **11.** 0.32   **13.** 1.25   **15.** $\dfrac{223}{2000}$

17. $\dfrac{13}{200}$ **19.** $\dfrac{9}{25}$ **21.** $\dfrac{7}{10}$ **23.** 1   **25.** $\dfrac{1}{40}$ **27.** $\dfrac{13}{80}$ **29.** $\dfrac{3}{800}$ **31.** 0.257

33. 0.653   **35.** 0.017   **37.** 0.074   **39.** 50.5%   **41.** 258%   **43.** 3500%   **45.** 1%   **47.** 270%

49. 65.9%   **51.** 2%   **53.** 40%   **55.** 31.25%   **57.** 43.75%   **59.** 85%   **61.** 222.5%   **63.** 175%

65. 28%   **67.** 42%   **69.** 216.7%   **71.** 0.4%   **73.** 181.8%   **75.** 74.5%   **77.** 90%   **79.** 0.9%

81. 185%   **83.** 53.6%   **85.** 250%   **87.** 144.4%   **89.** 0.9 ; 90%   **91.** $\dfrac{2}{3}$; $0.\overline{6}$ **93.** $\dfrac{7}{4}$; 175%   **95.** $\dfrac{1}{2}$; 0.5

97. 0.12; 12% **99.** $\frac{1}{3}$; 33.3% **101.** $0.41\overline{6}$; $41\frac{2}{3}$% **103.** 1 ; 1 **105.** (a) 5% , (b) 4% ; investment (a) is better.

107. (a) $8\frac{1}{6}$% , (b) $9\frac{11}{25}$% ; Investment (b) is better.   **109.** (a) 6% , (b) 5%; investment (a) is better.

111. (a) 10% , (b) 10% ; Both investments are one and the same.

113. a = \$7.2 ; b = \$100 ; \$7.20 is charged annually for every \$100 borrowed.

115. a = \$.20 ; b = \$1.00 ; \$.20 in tip is left for every \$1.00 that the service costs.

117. a = \$28 ; b = \$100 ; \$28 is earned for every \$100 spent.

119. a = 6 ; b = 100 ; An increase of 6 inhabitants for every 100 existing inhabitants.

121. a = \$.30 ; b = \$1.00 ; \$.30 is subtracted for every \$1.00 spent.

123. a = \$6 ; b = \$100 ; \$6 is earned for every \$100.

125. $\frac{3}{20}$ **127.** $\frac{23}{200}$ **129.** 94.7%   **131.** 4%   **133.** Citi Bank charges higher rate.

Section 8.2

1. 37.5   **3.** 250   **5.** 243   **7.** 56   **9.** 172   **11.** 325   **13.** 70   **15.** 51   **17.** 17.1532

19. 75%   **21.** $33\frac{1}{3}$%   **23.** 50%   **25.** 156.25   **27.** 3,200   **29.** 1,000   **31.** 300   **33.** \$2,500   **35.** 40%

37. 4%   **39.** 30%   **41.** 0.5%   **43.** 33.6   **45.** 45   **47.** \$16   **49.** 37.5   **51.** 62.5   **53.** 25%

55. 11,970   **57.** \$12,075; \$10,505.25   **59.** 20%   **61.** \$89,813.95; \$89,814   **63.** 684%   **65.** \$4,000   **67.** \$14,062.40

69. \$1,850   **71.** \$625   **73.** 320   **75.** 160 g   **77.** \$10,990

Section 8.3

1. $33\frac{1}{3}$%   **3.** \$113.97   **5.** \$86.68   **7.**(a) \$127.80 (b) \$102.24   **9.** \$12   **11.** \$118.30   **13.** \$375   **15.** \$364.20

17. (a) \$5 (b) \$8.40   **19.** \$860   **21.** \$216.75   **23.** \$1,377   **25.** (a) \$640 (b) \$1,050   (c) \$1,958.75   **27.** \$5,810

29. $66\frac{2}{3}$%   **31.** 16%   **33.** \$3.36 ; 5.6%   **35.** (a) \$251.45 ; (b) \$289.17   **37.** \$48.25 ; \$7

Section 8.4

1. \$180   **3.** \$75   **5.** \$893.75   **7.** \$239.25   **9.** \$109.50   **11.** I = \$7.50 , A = \$807.50   **13.** I = \$165 , A = \$6,165   **15.** 9%

17. 5%   **19.** 4 yrs.   **21.** \$13.22   **23.** \$750   **25.** \$2,648   **27.** \$5,674.08 ; \$1,674.08   **29.** \$8,998.91   **31.** \$2,890 ; \$330

33. \$7,045.56 ; \$2,545.56   **35.** \$11,716.59 ; \$1,716.59   **37.** \$9,160.52 ; \$2,160.52   **39.** \$61   **41.** \$20

Section 8.5

1. \$3,505   **3.** \$7,425   **5.**(a) \$1,417.50 (b) \$257.25   **7.**(a) \$45,000   (b) \$105,000 (c) \$48,000   **9.** \$30,000

Review Exercise 8.7

1. 25%   **3.** $57\frac{1}{7}$%   **5.** 21%   **7.** 5%   **9.** 8%   **11.** 175%   **13.** 0.8%   **15.** .0255   **17.** 1.254   **19.** 0.0025   **21.** 37.5%

23. 475%   **25.** 26%   **27.** 166.7%   **29.** 62.5%   **31.** 3.8%   **33.** $\frac{7}{20}$ **35.** $\frac{4}{125}$ **37.** $3\frac{3}{5}$ **39.** 0.9225   **41.** 2.625 inches

43. 35   **45.** 37.5   **47.** 52%   **49.** \$4.20   **51.** (a) 37.5%   (b) 38.6% ; (b) is a better investment   **53.** \$330.00

55. (a) \$875   (b) \$700   (c) \$750.75   **57.** 2.74 yrs

Self Test 8.8

1. 5.75%   **3.** $1\frac{9}{20}$ **5.** 13.5   **7.** 25.9   **9.** 72   **11.** \$320   **13.** \$115.13   **15.** 56.8%   **17.** \$60.38, \$14.62   **19.** \$458.50

CHAPTER 9

Section 9.1

1. Mean = 67.67
Median = 65
Mode = None
Range = 40

3. Mean = 76.38
Median = 73.5
Mode = 72
Range = 15

5. Mean = 2.47
Median = 2.3
Mode = 2.3
Range = 1.8

7. Mean = 14.375 yr
Median = 14.5 yr
Mode = 15 yr
Range = 4 yr

9. Mean = $25.33
Median = $24
Mode = $24
Range = $16

11. Mean = 22.3
Median = 21
Mode = 23
Range = 19

13. Mean = 145.4 cm
Median = 145.5 cm
Mode = None
Range = 14 cm

15. Mean = 11.7
Median = 12
Mode = 12

Section 9.2

1. 2000   **3.** 30 in   **5.** 2003   **7.** 2002, 2003   **9.** 80 thousand   **11.** Line graph   **13.** 4 - 5   **15.** 8 - 9   **17.** 20%

19. $678,000   **21.** Pepperoni   **23.** 240   **25.** 2,000   **27.** 750   **29.** 75%   **31.** 150   **33.** 1,100   **35.** 22.73%

Section 9.3

1.

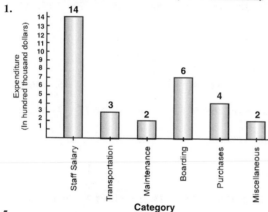

Expenditure of a School (Year 2002-2003)

3.

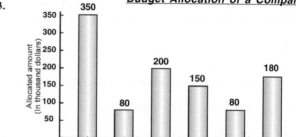

Budget Allocation of a Company

5.

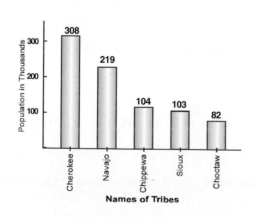

Five largest Native American Tribes : 2000

7.

Distribution of Employment by Occupational Group (Year - 2003)

9.

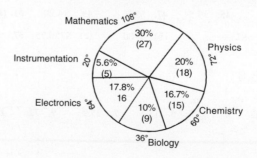

Distribution of Merit Certificates awarded for securing above 85% marks in various subjects

Section 9.4

1.
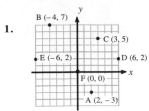
B (−4, 7), C (3, 5), E (−6, 2), D (6, 2), F (0, 0), A (2, −3)

3. (a) I (b) III (c) IV (d) II (e) IV (f) I

5. A : (2, 3), B: (0, 5), C: (− 2 , 2), D: (5, 0), E: (− 2, 0) , F: (− 4, −3), G: (− 4, 1), H: (0, − 5)

7. No **9.** Yes **11.** No **13.** Yes **15.** $\left(4, \dfrac{2}{3}\right)$

17. (8 , 2) **19.** (0, 2) **21.** (− 2, 2)

23.

x	y
−1	−2
3	0
7	2
1	−1

25.

x	y
−2	1
−1	3
−3	−1
0	5

27.

x	y
5	−1
5	0
5	−2
5	3

29.

x	y
−5	10
−5	−8
−5	5
−5	−1

31.

x	y
−1	2
2	2
0	2
8	2

33.

x	y	(x , y)
− 4	5	(− 4 ,5)
0	5	(0 ,5)
2	5	(2,5)

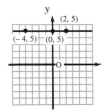

35.

x	y	(x , y)
− 3	−3	(− 3,−3)
1	−3	(1,− 3)
3	−3	(3,− 3)

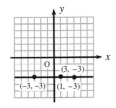

37.

x	y	(x , y)
0	0	(0 ,0)
5	3	(5 ,3)
−5	−3	(− 5,− 3)

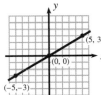

39.

x	y	(x , y)
−1	−1	(−1,−1)
3	2	(3 ,2)
−5	− 4	(−5,−4)

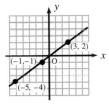

41.
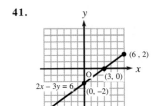
(6 , 2), (3, 0), 2x − 3y = 6, (0, −2)

43.
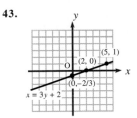
(5, 1), (2, 0), (0,−2/3), x = 3y + 2

45.
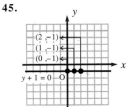
(2 ,−1), (1 ,−1), (0 ,−1), y + 1 = 0

47.
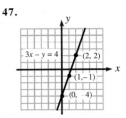
3x − y = 4, (2, 2), (1,−1), (0, − 4)

49.
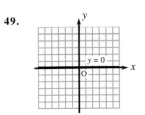
y = 0

Review Exercise 9.6

1. (a) 40 (b) 40 (c) 25 (d) 35 **3.** (a) 11.55 (b) 12 (c) 12 (d) 15 **5.** $250

7. $30 **9.** 8.00 AM **11.** Noon , 2.00 PM **13.** 27% **15.** 5,000 **17.** 37% **19.** 2003 **21.** 2002

23.
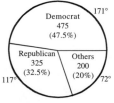
Democrat 475 (47.5%) 171°, Republican 325 (32.5%) 117°, Others 200 (20%) 72°

25.
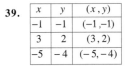
(−1, 3), (2,5), (−8, 0), (0, 0), (3, 0), (−4, −1), (0, −2), (3, −7)

27. Yes **29.** (− 4, − 5) **31.** (4, 4)

33.

x	y
−1	2
2	2
3	2
−4	2

35.

x	y
−2	−1
−2	2
−2	0
−2	1

Answers

37.

x	y
−2	−5
0	−5
3	−5

39.

x	y
−1	1
3	−2
−5	4

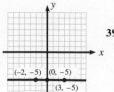

41.

x	y
−9	−2
6	8
3	6

Self Test 9.7

1. (a) 16 yrs (b) 16.5 yrs (c) None (d) 27 yrs **3.** 200 **5.** 625

7. 400 **9.** 3 hr 20 min **11.** $330 **13.** 64% **15.**

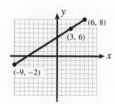

17. (2, 1), $\left(0, \frac{7}{3}\right)$, and (−1, 3)

CHAPTER 10

Section 10.1

1. 216 ounces **3.** 9 lb **5.** 210 cm **7.** 2.5 gallons **9.** 68 kg **11.** 22 g **13.** 1.08 feet **15.** 93 m **17.** 26.67 kg

19. 1.376 *l* **21.** 144 m **23.** 102 kl **25.** 41 min **27.** 51.4 ml **29.** 72.8 yd **31.** 44 ft 6 in **33.** 15 gal 1 qt

35. 55 lb 7 oz **37.** 11 kl 600 *l* **39.** 7 ft 8 in **41.** 69.82 lb **43.** 25.44 ft

Section 10.2

1. 7 **3.** 80 **5.** 90 **7.** 63,360 **9.** 21,230 **11.** 0.15 **13.** 316.5 **15.** 25 **17.** 336

19. 5.23 **21.** 60 mi/hr **23.** $4.25/min **25.** 45 gal/hr **27.** 31.25 cents/in^2 **29.** 0.1023 tons/yd^2

31. 6,000 cm **33.** 870 dm **35.** 0.000003 km **37.** 4,000 mm **39.** hg, dag, g, dg, cg, mg

41. 800 cg **43.** 23,240 dg **45.** 400 mg **47.** 0.0433 hg **49.** 2.04 hl **51.** 6,000 cl **53.** 76.8 *l* **55.** 0.0076 kl

57. 347.6 oz/cm^3 **59.** 17 m/ml **61.** Second pineapple **63.** 16

Section 10.3

1. 87.63 m **3.** 3.50 miles **5.** 1.71 m **7.** 9.60 m **9.** 5.07 km **11.** 658.37 cm/sec **13.** 48.28 km/hr

15. 43.49 kg **17.** 289.62 km/hr **19.** 5.45 kg **21.** 3 tsp **23.** 0.635 cm **25.** 0.13 cm

27. 131 **29.** 176.67 **31.** −4

Section 10.4

1. *b* **3.** *a* **5.** *c* **7.** *c* **9.** *d* **11.** *b* **13.** *b* **15.** *a* **17.** *a* **19.** *b*

21. *d* **23.** *a* **25.** *c*

Review Exercise 10.6

1. 7.85 lb **3.** 21 ton 1,444 lb **5.** 3 hr 20 min 30 sec **7.** 6 yd^2 **9.** 25 m/min **11.** 33.33 oz/in **13.** 16,820 mm

15. 15.023 km **17.** 1,056.8 gallons

Self Test 10.7

1. *c* **3.** *d* **5.** *a* **7.** *b* **9.** *b* **11.** 10.3 km **13.** 250 kg **15.** 151 *l*/min

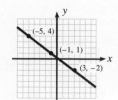

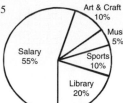

INDEX

Index